D1528599

Pharmacology *in* Exercise and Sports

Edited by
Satu M. Somani, Ph.D.
Professor of Pharmacology and Toxicology
Department of Pharmacology
School of Medicine
Southern Illinois University, Springfield

CRC Press
Boca Raton   New York   London   Tokyo

WINGATE UNIVERSITY LIBRARY

Library of Congress Cataloging-in-Publication Data

Pharmacology in exercise and sports / edited by Satu (Satyanarayan) M. Somani
    p.   cm. -- (Pharmacology and Toxicology)
  Includes bibliographical references and index.
  ISBN 0-8493-8540-7
  1. Exercise--Physiological effect. 2. Drug interactions. 3. Doping in
sports. 4. Pharmacology. I. Somani, Satu M. II. Series: Pharmacology & toxicology
(Boca Raton, Fla.).
  [DNLM: 1. Pharmacology, Clinical. 2. Exercise
physiology. 3. Pharmacokinetics.   QV 38 P5361 1995]
  QP301.P53 1995
  615'.7--dc20
  DNLM/DLC
  for Library of Congress   95-35490
                                                     CIP

This book contains information obtained from authentic and highly regarded sources. Reprinted material is quoted with permission, and sources are indicated. A wide variety of references are listed. Reasonable efforts have been made to publish reliable data and information, but the author and the publisher cannot assume responsibility for the validity of all materials or for the consequences of their use.

Neither this book nor any part may be reproduced or transmitted in any form or by any means, electronic or mechanical, including photocopying, microfilming, and recording, or by any information storage or retrieval system, without prior permission in writing from the publisher.

All rights reserved. Authorization to photocopy items for internal or personal use, or the personal or internal use of specific clients, may be granted by CRC Press, Inc., provided that $.50 per page photocopied is paid directly to Copyright Clearance Center, 27 Congress Street, Salem, MA 01970 USA. The fee code for users of the Transactional Reporting Service is ISBN 0-8493-8540-7/96/$0.00+$.50. The fee is subject to change without notice. For organizations that have been granted a photocopy license by the CCC, a separate system of payment has been arranged.

CRC Press, Inc.'s consent does not extend to copying for general distribution, for promotion, for creating new works, or for resale. Specific permission must be obtained in writing from CRC Press for such copying.

Direct all inquiries to CRC Press, Inc., 2000 Corporate Blvd., N.W., Boca Raton, Florida 33431.

© 1996 by CRC Press, Inc.

No claim to original U.S. Government works
International Standard Book Number 0-8493-8540-7
Library of Congress Card Number 95-35490
Printed in the United States of America 1 2 3 4 5 6 7 8 9 0
Printed on acid-free paper

Pharmacology and Toxicology: Basic and Clinical Aspects

Mannfred A. Hollinger, Series Editor
University of California, Davis

Published Titles

Inflammatory Cells and Mediators in Bronchial Asthma, 1990,
    Devendra K. Agrawal and Robert G. Townley
Pharmacology of the Skin, 1991, Hasan Mukhtar
In Vitro *Methods of Toxicology*, 1992, Ronald R. Watson
Basis of Toxicity Testing, 1992, Donald J. Ecobichon
Human Drug Metabolism from Molecular Biology to Man, 1992, Elizabeth Jeffreys
Platelet Activating Factor Receptor: Signal Mechanisms and Molecular Biology,
    1992, Shivendra D. Shukla
Biopharmaceutics of Ocular Drug Delivery, 1992, Peter Edman
Beneficial and Toxic Effects of Aspirin, 1993, Susan E. Feinman
Preclinical and Clinical Modulation of Anticancer Drugs, 1993, Kenneth D. Tew,
    Peter Houghton, and Janet Houghton
Peroxisome Proliferators: Unique Inducers of Drug-Metabolizing Enzymes, 1994,
    David E. Moody
*Angiotensin II Receptors, Volume I: Molecular Biology, Biochemistry,
    Pharmacology, and Clinical Perspectives,* 1994, Robert R. Ruffolo, Jr.
Angiotensin II Receptors, Volume II: Medicinal Chemistry, 1994,
    Robert R. Ruffolo, Jr.
Chemical and Structural Approaches to Rational Drug Design, 1994,
    David B. Weiner and William V. Williams
Biological Approaches to Rational Drug Design, 1994, David B. Weiner and
    William V. Williams
Direct Allosteric Control of Glutamate Receptors, 1994, M. Palfreyman,
    I. Reynolds, and P. Skolnick
Genomic and Non-Genomic Effects of Aldosterone, 1994, Martin Wehling
Human Growth Hormone Pharmacology: Basic and Clinical Aspects, 1995,
    Kathleen T. Shiverick and Arlan Rosenbloom
Placental Toxicology, 1995, B. V. Rama Sastry
Stealth Liposomes, 1995, Danilo Lasic and Frank Martin
TAXOL®: Science and Applications, 1995, Matthew Suffness
Endothelin Receptors: From the Gene to the Human, 1995, Robert R. Ruffolo, Jr.
Serotonin and Gastrointestinal Function, 1995, Timothy S. Gaginella and
    James J. Galligan
Drug Delivery Systems, 1995, Vasant V. Ranade and Mannfred A. Hollinger
*Alternative Methodologies for the Safety Evaluation of Chemicals
    in the Cosmetic Industry*, 1995, Nicola Loprieno
*Phospholipase A$_2$ in Clinical Inflammation: Molecular Approaches
    to Pathophysiology*, 1995, Keith B. Glaser and Peter Vadas
Experimental Models of Mucosal Inflammation, 1996, Timothy S. Gaginella

Pharmacology and Toxicology: Basic and Clinical Aspects

Mannfred A. Hollinger, Series Editor
University of California, Davis

Forthcoming Titles

Alcohol Consumption, Cancer and Birth Defects: Mechanisms Involved in Increased Risk Associated with Drinking, Anthony J. Garro
Antibody Therapeutics, William J. Harris and John R. Adair
Brain Mechanisms and Psychotropic Drugs, A. Baskys and G. Remington
Chemoattractant Ligands and Their Receptors, Richard Horuk
CNS Injuries: Cellular Responses and Pharmacological Strategies, Martin Berry and Ann Logan
Muscarinic Receptor Subtypes in Smooth Muscle, Richard M. Eglen
Neural Control of Airways, Peter J. Barnes
Pharmacological Effects of Ethanol on the Nervous System, Richard A. Deitrich
Pharmacological Regulation of Gene Expression in the CNS, Kalpana Merchant
Pharmacology of Intestinal Secretion, Timothy S. Gaginella
Placental Pharmacology, B. V. Rama Sastry
Receptor Characterization and Regulation, Devendra K. Agrawal
Receptor Dynamics in Neural Development, Christopher A. Shaw
Ryanodine Receptors, Vincenzo Sorrentino
Therapeutic Modulation of Cytokines, M.W. Bodmer and Brian Henderson

THE EDITOR

Satu (Satyanarayan) M. Somani, Ph.D., is a professor of pharmacology and toxicology in the Department of Pharmacology at Southern Illinois University, School of Medicine, Springfield. He received his B.Sc. from Osmania University, Hyderabad, India; B.Sc. (Hons.) (chemistry) and M.Sc. (biochemistry) from Poona University, India. He received his M.S. (pharmacy/pharmaceutical chemistry) from Duquesne University, Pittsburgh, and Ph.D. in pharmacology from Liverpool University, Liverpool, England. He was awarded an Ellis T. Davis Fellowship at Liverpool University and an NIH fellowship in clinical pharmacology, at the Department of Medicine, University of Pittsburgh. Subsequently, he became Instructor and Assistant Professor at the Department of Pharmacology, School of Medicine, University of Pittsburgh. He moved to Southern Illinois University, School of Medicine, in 1974 as an Associate Professor and was later promoted to full Professor.

Dr. Somani has been a member of the American Pharmacological Society, American Chemical Society, Society of Toxicology, American College of Sports Medicine, Indian Academy of Neurosciences, Indian Pharmacological Society, American Society of Clinical Pharmacology and Therapeutics, and American Association for the Advancement of Science.

Dr. Somani is the author of more than 100 publications in various areas of pharmacology, toxicology, and exercise pharmacology. He has edited three books. He has been interested in exercise pharmacology for more than a decade. He has been awarded over 20 grants from various agencies which include the EPA and the U.S. Army. His current research interests are: interaction of exercise and drugs with the antioxidant system in various organs of the body; anticancer agents and the antioxidant system; and also the effect of exercise on distribution, metabolism, and pharmacokinetics of drugs in animal and man.

PREFACE

Exercise is the physical training of the body in order to improve its function. Sports have existed from preliterate times when men first found some free time after they had provided their share of food and shelter for their families. Many of the benefits that exercise provides have been known from ancient times. Susruta, the father of Indian medicine, Ayurveda (600 B.C.), described how exercise provides health benefits. "Exercise is essential for good health, and it is the only way to reduce fat, and gain strength: it should be followed by massage. A man should exercise up to the onset of rapid breathing every day in all seasons; more than this may make him ill. Strong winds and hot sun must be avoided." (Translated by G. D. Singhal and T. J. S. Patterson, 1993, from *Susruta Samhita* IV.24.38.51, 75–85.) Presently, millions of people throughout the world exercise every day. Many individuals participate in organized group exercises, rehabilitation programs, or personalized fitness programs. For example, there are more than seven million athletes who participate in college sports alone each year in the U.S. Research shows that 22% of adults are active enough, 54% are somewhat active, and 24% are sedentary (*USA Today*, 2/1/95). In a sense, exercise has become a prophylactic and therapeutic panacea, particularly for the rapidly expanding aging population. It is crucial when choosing a personal exercise program for an individual to participate in an optimum exercise (intensity × frequency × duration) that will provide maximum health benefits. Many individuals exercise if they have coronary artery diseases, hypertension, or angina. Oftentimes, some of them may be taking prescribed medication or perhaps using drugs for social entertainment. As the occasions arise, drugs are taken intentionally or unintentionally by athletes and nonathletes, young and old. Few studies have been carried out with respect to pharmacology and exercise. This is the first monograph to describe how exercise affects the pharmacological aspects of drugs.

The following chapters are easily comprehensible to graduate students, researchers, and academicians in pharmacology, physiology, and physical education, those who are working in the health field, as well as physicians. This is the first book that brings together various aspects of the interactions of exercise and drugs at biochemical, molecular, cellular, and whole body levels. I welcome any comments, questions, and suggestions from students, professors, researchers, and health professionals who have an interest in exercise pharmacology.

The effects of various drugs on modes of exercise (performance) in man and animal has spurred much interest; however, there are very few research reports regarding the effects of exercise on drug pharmacokinetics and pharmacodynamics of drugs (Chapter 1). The action of a drug is dependent on its concentration in the receptor. Can exercise elevate this concentration and, thereby, enhance the action of the drug? Or conversely, can exercise decrease drug concentration and, thereby, decrease the action of the drug? These effects of exercise in combination with drugs have not yet been elucidated. When a drug is absorbed, it is distributed to various organs via systemic circulation and eventually reaches the receptor site where the action, reaction, and interaction take place. Most drugs are metabolized; metabolites are more polar compounds and they are easily excreted from the body. An individual's rate of metabolism and excretion of drugs generally determines the duration of action. The liver is the primary organ site for the metabolism of most drugs and toxicants, and they are then excreted in urine, feces, bile, sweat, saliva, tears, or breath. By exercising, the body's blood flow to the organs is altered and hepatic blood flow decreases by 18%, thereby affecting the biotransformation and elimination of some compounds. Exercise is likely to modify the processes of drug disposition which, in turn, would also affect the pharmacodynamic actions of the drug.

Since exercise has become a common activity for all ages, including patients with chronic illnesses, the interactive effects of exercise and drug disposition are important subjects and are more fully described in Chapter 1. Chapter 2 describes the basic pharmacodynamic aspects of many drugs that affect exercise performance, although there is little information on how exercise can alter pharmacodynamics. Essentially, this chapter discusses physiological or biochemical outcomes of exercise–drug interactions. It is widely recognized that free radicals, or reactive oxygen species, are the cause of many health diseases, such as cancer, cardiac problems, cataracts, arthritis, atherosclerosis, Alzheimer's, stroke, and they also cause aging.

Chapter 3 discusses how exercise causes the body to generate free radicals, or reactive oxygen species, which can activate/induce antioxidant defense mechanisms in the body. The growing interest in free radical/reactive oxygen species (oxidative stress) will revolutionize health research in the 21st century. Exercise has been known to exert numerous physiological changes in vital organ systems throughout the body. One important change is the enhanced respiration and utilization of oxygen in the body, which can generate reactive oxygen species, free radicals, in muscles, the heart, and other organs. However, cells contain several antioxidant defense mechanisms to protect themselves from the injuries associated with the presence of free radicals. Among these defenses are endogenous antioxidants (vitamin C, vitamin E, and glutathione) and antioxidant enzymes (superoxide dismutase, catalase, glutathione peroxidase, and ancillary enzyme glutathione reductase). Antioxidant enzyme activity is altered by changes in oxygen consumption (oxidative stress), and is also affected by exercise, drug use, and disease conditions. Exercise activates, or induces, antioxidant enzymes and also increases the lipid peroxidation. The activation of antioxidant enzymes may take place via the adenosine A_3 receptor. The induction of antioxidant enzymes may occur due to the transcription/translation/posttranslational processes as a result of exercise training. Studies of enzyme kinetics of antioxidant enzymes indicate that most of the organs of the body activate antioxidant enzymes due to exercise training. Certain drugs can cause severe toxicity due to metabolic conversion, which may result in reactive intermediate metabolites and reactive free radicals. Exercise can possibly ameliorate the toxicity of these drugs by the activation of antioxidant enzymes. Exercise can also maximize the free radical scavenging system by inducing/activating antioxidant enzymes.

The interaction of exercise and glutathione is explored in Chapter 4. Reduced glutathione, an essential antioxidant, scavenges free radicals and reactive oxygen species, or biologically reactive intermediate metabolites, throughout the formation of covalent binding. Glutathione is possibly converted to oxidized glutathione by exercise and needs to be reconverted back to a reduced form. It is possible that the status of the glutathione alters during exercise by enhancing the transport from cellular to intramitochondrial compartments. The various aspects of glutathione in relation to exercise are discussed in this chapter.

Chapter 5 addresses molecular aspects of antioxidant enzymes and describes how the reactive oxygen species may act as crucial intercellular messengers that regulate gene expression. Physical exercise induces oxidative stress; the state in which the reactive oxygen species are generated in excess overwhelms the tissue antioxidant defenses. Training-induced increases in antioxidant defenses in various tissues may be a genetically regulated transient adaptation process. However, because the possible mechanisms by which exercise may regulate the expression or activation of antioxidant proteins are not known, further reaseach should be conducted.

Chapter 6 deals with "exercise and heat shock proteins." Heat shock response may represent a novel defense mechanism protecting cells and whole organisms against the toxic effects of stress. Exercise-induced hyperthermia is a stimulant, provoking the heat shock response *in vivo*. It is quite possible that exhaustive exercise may promote the endogenous production of heat shock proteins which are important determinants to salutary effects of the heat shock response.

The importance of adenosine in exercise and the possibility that adenosine is involved in the activation of antioxidant enzymes via G-protein is discussed in Chapter 7. Adenosine is a product of exercise. During exercise, adenosine triphosphate (ATP) is converted initially to adenosine diphosphate (ADP), then to adenosine monophosphate (AMP), and finally to adenosine. The vital actions of adenosine are mediated in cerebral and peripheral tissues by major classes of receptors, A1, A2, and A3, during exercise. During exercise, adenosine controls coronary, cerebral, and skeletal muscle blood flow by vasodilation of blood vessels. Exercise training may provide beneficial effects by enhancing the process of angiogenesis and erythropoiesis induced by adenosine. Recent studies demonstrate the beneficial role of adenosine in augmenting the antioxidant enzyme activities and in reducing lipid peroxidation during exercise via the A_3 adenosine receptor. The interaction of exercise and selective agonists and antagonists with A_3 adenosine receptor's mediated effects on antioxidant enzymes would be an interesting study in the field of exercise research.

Chapter 8 discusses endothelium-derived nitric oxide (EDNO) and its control of blood flow during exercise, and explains whether exercise-induced dilation of the coronary and skeletal muscle vascular bed involves EDNO. Exercise training increases the endothelium-induced dilation of vessels from both of these vascular beds. EDNO plays an important role in the control of blood flow during exercise. There are large increases in blood flow to cardiac and active skeletal muscles during the adjustment from rest to exercise.

Chapter 9 explains the role of platelet function in exercise. Exercise seems to induce the activation of the platelet in untrained as well as endurance-trained individuals. The availability of proaggregatory compounds such as catechol amine, adenosine diphosphate, and platelet activating factor (PAF) may serve as contributing factors for increasing blood pressure from enhanced heart rate; sensitivity of platelets to these metabolites will also determine the extent of activation that occurs during exercise. β-Blockers, calcium antagonists, ticlopudine, and thromboxane synthetase inhibitors have been tested for their ability to prevent exercise-mediated platelet activation.

Chapter 10 discusses the benefits of exercise and regular physical activity to the heart. Definitive studies demonstrating decreased coronary heart disease, sudden death, lower mortality, incidence of infarction and re-infarction, and primary and secondary prevention of coronary heart disease are not available. This chapter elaborates on the interaction of exercise and specific cardiovascular drugs, as well as serotonin and catecholamines in relation to the pharmacodynamic effects of these drugs. Alterations in the cholinergic system, due to physical exercise and/or drug, pesticides, or chemical stressors have not received much attention. Chapter 11 discusses whether these compounds, and exercise, or the combination of these two factors, elicit changes in the synthetic choline acetyl transferase and degradative acetylcholinesterase enzymes of acetyl choline (neurotransmitter) and cholinergic receptors in the central brain regions and peripheral systems.

Chapter 12 reveals that exercise clearly has intensity-dependent effects on the neuroendocrine systems that are reproducible. Exercise appears to alter the immune system in an intensity-dependent manner. Neuroendocrine responses may be a connecting link to the immunological changes triggered by exercise. Pharmacological manipulations provide strategies that may enable some of these mechanistic issues to be solved, and drugs remain a powerful tool for investigating the mechanisms involved in physiological responses to exercise.

Chapter 13 is unique in that it is related to the sedentary vs. ambulatory status of pharmacokinetics and pharmacodynamics. Ambulatory activity usually enhances the absorption of drugs administered intramuscularly. However, the elimination of drugs appears to increase during the sedentary state which, in turn, decreases the drug's plasma concentration. This will have the same effect on the pharmacodynamics of drugs.

Yoga is an ancient health art developed around 800 B.C. and it increases health, vitality, and self-awareness. Yoga seems to provide benefits in prevention or correction of the disease processes such as hypertension, asthma, diabetes, cognitive and motor deficits, visual and auditory function and psychiatric disorders. Yoga helps to release the stress and most common stress-reduction techniques are derived from yoga. Numerous scientific studies on yoga control subjects have been carried out to prove the usefulness of yoga in conjunction with or without the use of drugs and medication. Yoga helps to reduce the drug dosages. Chapter 14 evaluates the physiological, pharmacological, and clinical findings to deduce whether yoga indeed contributes to better health.

All the chapters were thoroughly reviewed by no fewer than four reviewers, and their valuable comments were helpful in revising the manuscript. I take this opportunity to express my personal and deep gratitude to many experts in the field who have helped to critically review the chapters, especially Gregory J. Brewer, Ph.D., Springfield, IL; Philip J. Buckenmeyer, Ph.D., Syracuse, NY; Donald M. Caspary, Ph.D., Springfield, IL; Clinton N. Corder, M.D., Ph.D., Oklahoma City, OK; George A. Dunaway, Ph.D., Springfield, IL.; Natalie Eddington, Ph.D., Baltimore, MD; Carl L. Faingold, Ph.D., Springfield, IL.; Thomas G. Ferry, M.D., Indianapolis, IN; Stuart Frank, M.D. Springfield, IL; Ezio Giacobini, M.D., Ph.D., Springfield, IL.; Thomas H. Hintze, Ph.D., Valhalla, NY; Mannfred A. Hollinger, Ph.D., Davis, CA: Kazim Husain, Ph.D., Springfield, IL; Li Li Ji, Ph.D., Madison, WI; Chen-Ching Lai, Ph.D., Springfield, IL; Henry Lardy, Ph.D., Madison, WI; Tony Jer-Fu Lee, Ph.D., Springfield, IL; Mo Malafa, M.D., Springfield, IL; Bala Manyam, M.D., Springfield, IL; Sameer Mathur, M.D., Ph.D. Program, Evanston, IL; Richard M. McAllister, Ph.D., Columbia, MO; Edward J. Moticka, Ph.D., Springfield, IL; Timothy I. Musch, Ph.D., Kansas, MO; Scot Powers, Ph.D., Gainesville, FL; Vickram Ramkumar, Ph.D., Springfield, IL; Chandan K. Sen, Ph.D., Berkeley, CA; John A. Smith, Ph.D., Australia; Shipra S. Somani, MSW, Springfield, IL; Ching-Yuan Su, Ph.D., Springfield, IL.

I sincerely thank all contributors for submitting their chapters in a timely fashion and for making necessary modifications in light of the reviewers' comments. The contributors have suggested a number of future perspectives and possibilities for research direction. I thank Dr. Carl J. Getto, Dean and provost, for his encouragement to publish this volume. I greatly appreciate the support provided by Dr. Edward J. Moticka, Associate Dean for Academic Affairs, Southern Illinois University, School of Medicine, for this book. I would like to express my gratitude to Michelle Ernst for her zeal in assisting me, from the inception of this project, with correspondence and typing manuscripts. She was there whenever I needed her help. My thanks are due to Shelli Drummond for her editorial assistance and Jack R. Reynolds, Jr., for designing the front cover of this book. Thanks are also due to Charlene Meents for her secretarial assistance. Finally I would like to thank my family, my wife Shipra and daughters, Indira and Sheila, whose constant patience, love, and support underlie all that I do.

Satu (Satyanarayan) M. Somani

CONTRIBUTORS

T. K. Bera, Ph.D.
"Kaivalyadham", Scientific Research
  Department
Pune, Maharashtra
India

Satyanarayan G. Bhat, Ph.D.
"Kaivalyadham", Scientific Research
  Department
Pune, Maharashtra
India

Philip J. Buckenmeyer, Ph.D.
Department of Health and Physical
  Education
Syracuse University
Syracuse, New York

Chawnshang Chang
Department of Human Oncology
University of Wisconsin at Madison
Madison, Wisconsin

Clinton N. Corder, M.D., Ph.D.
Oklahoma Foundation for Cardiovas-
  cular Reseach Inc.
Oklahoma City, Oklahoma

Michael D. Delp, Ph.D.
Department of Health and
  Kinesiology and Medical
  Physiology
Texas A & M University
College Station, Texas

Stuart Frank, M.D.
Department of Medicine
Southern Illinois University
School of Medicine
Springfield, Illinois

Mannfred A. Hollinger, Ph.D.
Department of Medical Pharmacology
  and Toxicology
School of Medicine
University of California
Davis, California

Kazim Husain, Ph.D.
Department of Pharmacology
School of Medicine
Southern Illinois University
Springfield, Illinois

Li Li Ji, Ph.D.
Department of Kinesiology
University of Wisconsin–Madison
Biodynamics Lab
Madison, Wisconsin

Gary H. Kamimori, Ph.D.
Division of Neuropsychiatry
Department of Behavioral Biology
Walter Reed Army Institute of
  Research
Washington, D.C.

Chen-Ching Lai, Ph.D.
Department of Pharmacology
School of Medicine
Southern Illinois University
Springfield, Illinois

M. Harold Laughlin, Ph.D.
Department of Biomedical Sciences
College of Veterinary Medicine
University of Missouri
Columbia, Missouri

Christiaan Leeuwenburgh, Ph.D.
Department of Kinesiology
Biodynamics Lab
University of Wisconsin–Madison
Madison, Wisconsin

Richard M. McAllister, Ph.D.
Department of Biomedical Sciences
College of Veterinary Medicine
University of Missouri
Columbia, Missouri

Wallace R. Pratt, M.D., Ph.D.
Oklahoma Medical Research
  Foundation
Oklahoma City, Oklahoma

Gundu H.R. Rao, Ph.D.
Laboratory of Medicine and
  Pathology
University of Minnesota Medical
  School
Minneapolis, Minnesota

Chandan K. Sen, Ph.D.
Department of Physiology
Faculty of Medicine
University of Kuopio
Kuopio, Finland, and
Department of Molecular and Cell
  Biology
University of California, Berkeley
Berkeley, California

John. A. Smith, Ph.D.
Department of Physiology and
  Applied Nutrition
Australian Institute of Sport
Sports Science and Sports Medicine
  Centre
Belconen, Australia

Satu M. Somani, Ph.D.
Department of Pharmacology
School of Medicine
Southern Illinois University
Springfield, Illinois

Ching-Yuan Su, Ph.D.
Department of Medicine
Southern Illinois University
School of Medicine
Springfield, Illinois

TABLE OF CONTENTS

Chapter 1

THE EFFECTS OF EXERCISE ON ABSORPTION, DISTRIBUTION, METABOLISM, EXCRETION, AND PHARMACOKINETICS OF DRUGS

Satu M. Somani and Gary H. Kamimori

CONTENTS

0-8493-8540-1/96/$0.00+$.50
© 1996 by CRC Press, Inc.

1. INTRODUCTION

Drugs are administered by various routes and in most cases need to be absorbed into the systemic circulation in order to be transported and distributed to various organs and to the receptors sites where the action, reaction, and interaction of the drugs occur (Figure 1). Drugs may be bound to plasma proteins, and only the unbound drug is pharmacologically active.[1] Most drugs are metabolized to more polar compounds to facilitate their excretion from the body. The metabolites or drugs may be excreted in the urine, feces, bile, sweat, saliva, tears, milk, or breath.[1] The rate of metabolism and excretion of drugs generally determines their duration of action. The predominant rate-limiting factors for drug metabolism and elimination are delivery of the drug to the site of metabolism, or elimination, and/or the ability of the enzyme systems to handle drug metabolism. As a result, tissue blood flow and enzyme activity are significant factors in drug pharmacokinetics and, concomitantly, their pharmacodynamics. The pharmacokinetics and pharmacodynamics of many drugs can be influenced by exercise. The effects of exercise need to be considered, not only in the large exercise-oriented segment of the population but, particularly in the geriatric population which is increasing in number rapidly. The effect of exercise on drug disposition and pharmacokinetics have been reviewed by Somani et al.,[2] van Baak,[3] and Ylitalo.[4] Somani et al.[5] have extensively studied the effect of exercise on the pharmacokinetics and pharmacodynamics of physostigmine in the rat.

Investigators have suggested that modifications in tissue blood flow, resulting from acute exercise, should have the capacity to modify the pharmacokinetics of certain drugs.[2,3] However, little effort was focused on this issue prior to the "fitness boom" of the early 80s, when exercise became an important activity for individuals of all ages and physical condition, including patients on multiple drug therapy. With the increasing interest in health and fitness, the field of "exercise pharmacology" has become an area of some interest. Over the last decade, several studies have investigated the effects of acute physical exercise and physical fitness on the pharmacokinetics of various drugs.

Previous reviews, relevant to exercise, have dealt with issues that are related to drug-temperature interactions,[6] renal function and exercise,[7-9] liver function and exercise,[10] blood flow and energetics during exercise,[11] drug binding,[12] pharmacodynamics and exercise,[13] and blood flow and drug pharmacokinetics.[14,15] Dossing[16] reviewed the effects of acute and chronic exercise on hepatic drug metabolism while Rosenbloom and Sutton[17] have reviewed some aspects

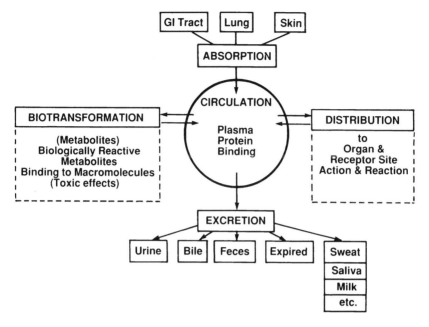

FIGURE 1. General scheme for the absorption, distribution, metabolism and excretion of a drug from the body. (From Somani, S. M., Gupta, S. K., Frank, S., and Corder, C. N., *Drug Dev. Res.*, 20, 251, 1990. With permission.)

of the effects of exercise on drug absorption and hepatic and renal elimination. This chapter summarizes the literature on the effects of exercise on absorption, distribution, metabolism, and excretion of drugs in the body, and how these processes alter the pharmacokinetics of drugs during exercise.

2. HOW EXERCISE CAN AFFECT DRUG PHARMACOKINETICS

2.1. BASICS OF PHARMACOKINETICS

Pharmacokinetics involves the kinetics of drug absorption, distribution, and elimination (i.e., excretion and metabolism). The description of drug distribution and elimination is often termed "drug disposition." The study of pharmacokinetics involves the investigation of factors which influence the rate and amount of drug that reaches the systemic circulation. Therefore, the pharmacokinetics of drugs are useful in understanding the relationship between the physiochemical properties of the drug and pharmacologic or clinical effects of the drug. Individual variations in the pharmacokinetics of drugs are quite common. Monitoring the concentration of drugs in the blood or plasma insures that the calculated dose actually delivers the plasma level required for therapeutic effect. Moreover, the patients' physiologic functions may be affected by disease, nutrition, environment, concurrent drug therapy, and other factors such as exercise. Pharmacokinetic models allow for a more accurate

interpretation of the relationship between plasma drug levels and pharmacological responses.

The most simple model is the one compartment model in which the drug is
assumed to be distributed instantaneously and uniformly throughout the system. Elimination of a drug from the system is proportional to its concentration
in the system. The following equation represents a one-compartment model
after an intravenous bolus administration.

$$C = C_o e^{-K_{el}t}$$

C is the concentration at any time t, C_o is the concentration at time zero, and
K_{el} is the elimination rate constant. A semilog plot of C vs. time yields a straight
line with ordinate intercept C_o and slope $-K_{el}$. The elimination rate (K_{el}) is the
summation of both renal (K_{re}) and metabolic (K_{me}) rates.

A good number of drugs are eliminated by first-order kinetics. The time
required for elimination to half of its original amount is known as half-life ($t_{1/2}$).
The relation of $t_{1/2}$ to K_{el} is given by the following equation:

$$t_{1/2} = \frac{0.693}{K_{el}}$$

The half-life has more physical significance than K_{el} in that the percent
remaining in the body, as per unit time, can be calculated easily. However,
when a drug is administered to a man or an animal, its monoexponential decline
or elimination is rarely seen. Instead, a drug usually exhibits biexponential
decline (Figure 2). The first rapid decline is called the distribution phase (α),
and the slow decline is the elimination phase (β). This biexponential elimination represents the two-compartment model (Figure 2).

The apparent volume of distribution (V_d) of a drug is the proportionality
between the amount of a drug administered and its plasma concentration. The
ordinate intercept of semilog concentration vs. time plot is used to estimate the
volume of distribution when the intravenous bolus dose "D" is known.

$$V_d = \frac{D}{C_o}$$

C_o is the concentration of a drug at time t_o, obtained from the intercept on
the semilog graph. If the V_d is found to be a very large number, i.e., >100% of
body weight, then it may be assumed that the drug is concentrated in the tissue
compartment. If V_d represents a percentage of body weight, such value may
represent the true anatomic value, for example, 25% of body weight for
gentamicin represents the extracellular volume of the body.

The total amount of drug cleared from the body at a given time is calculated
by multiplying V_d with K_{el} of a drug at that time, and is called "clearance."

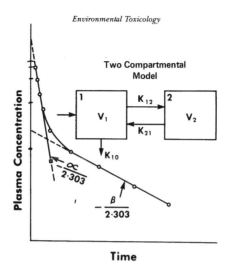

FIGURE 2.   The plasma concentration vs. time is plotted on semilogarithic graph. Biexponential decline or elimination of a drug is shown using a two compartment model, which most of the drugs follow. (From Somani, S. M., *Environmental Toxicology: Principles and Policies,* Charles C Thomas, Springfield, IL, 1981, 11–28. With permission.)

Clearance (Cl) can be defined as the volume of plasma that is cleared of the drug per unit time. Clearance by the kidney is called "renal clearance." Clearance by any other route is considered nonrenal clearance. Clearance is mathematically defined as follows:

$$\text{Cl} = \frac{\text{Excretion Rate}}{\text{Plasma Concentration}} = \text{ml} * \text{min}^{-1}$$

$$\text{Cl} = K_{el} \times V_d$$

When clearance of a drug is known, one can develop the dosage regimen for that drug. Another important term in pharmacokinetics is bioavailability. The amount of administered drug required to reach the systemic circulation and the rate on which it occurs is called bioavailability and is denoted by F.

$$F = \frac{\text{Dose}_{iv} \times \text{AUC}_{po}}{\text{Dose}_{po} \times \text{AUC}_{iv}}$$

where AUC is the area under the curve. Bioavailability is also expressed by

$$F = 1 - \text{Extraction Ratio}$$

TABLE 1
Distribution of Cardiac Output (ml*min⁻¹) by Volume and Percent at Rest and During Light, Moderate, and Strenuous Exercise

Tissue	Rest		Light		Moderate		Strenuous	
					Exercise			
Splanchnic	1,350	(27%)	1,100	(12%)	600	(3%)	300	(1%)
Renal	1,100	(22%)	900	(10%)	600	(3%)	250	(1%)
Cerebral	700	(14%)	750	(8%)	750	(4%)	750	(3%)
Coronary	200	(4%)	350	(4%)	750	(4%)	1,000	(4%)
Muscle	1,000	(20%)	4,500	(47%)	12,500	(71%)	22,000	(88%)
Skin	300	(6%)	1,500	(15%)	1,900	(12%)	600	(2%)
Other	350	(7%)	400	(4%)	400	(3%)	100	(1%)
	5000		9500		17,500		25,000	

Modified from Anderson, K. L., *Exercise Physiology,* Falls, H. B., Ed., Academic Press, New York, 1968. With permission.

2.2. EFFECT OF EXERCISE ON PHARMACOKINETICS

Changes in tissue blood flow have been identified as one of the most important factors affecting drug pharmacokinetics. During exercise, profound hemodynamic changes occur: cardiac output is increased and blood flow is redistributed away from the splanchnic area and kidneys towards the active skeletal muscle and skin. Drug pharmacokinetics can also be modified by a variety of internal (intrinsic) and external (extrinsic) factors which have the capacity to affect drug absorption, distribution, metabolism, and elimination. Internal factors include: plasma protein binding,[12] pH,[18] metabolic disease,[19] and drug-drug interactions.[16] Examples of external factors include: temperature,[6,20,31] humidity,[21] altitude,[23,24] hypoxia,[24] posture,[25] and age.[26] In the majority of the aforementioned cases, the reported changes in pharmacokinetics have been attributed to modifications in either tissue blood flow or to changes in the enzyme systems. This section will present an overview of the changes in tissue blood flow and other physiological factors associated with exercise, which have the capacity to modify drug pharmacokinetics.

2.3. EFFECT OF EXERCISE ON TISSUE BLOOD FLOW

The redistribution of blood during exercise is accomplished through a number of neural and hormonal vascular pathways, as well as by the local metabolic conditions of the muscles themselves. At rest, approximately 15 to 20% of the total systemic blood flow is distributed to the muscles while the majority flows to the viscera, heart, and brain. During exercise, blood flow is redistributed so that the active muscle tissue, including the heart, receives a greater proportion of the cardiac output. During maximal exercise, as much as 85 to 90% of total cardiac output may be redistributed to the working muscle tissue. Data on tissue blood flow at rest and during light, moderate, and strenuous exercise is presented in Table 1. The redistribution of blood flow during exercise under "normal" (no extreme of temperature or humidity) conditions is a result of several reflex responses. Initially, there is a reflex vasodilation of the arterioles, supplying blood to the active skeletal muscle. This response will occur immediately prior to, and at the very beginning of exercise. In the early period of exercise, a reflex vasoconstriction of the arterioles, which supply blood to the inactive areas of the body, will occur. This results in a decreased flow to the visceral organs and skin. As exercise continues, vasodilation in the active muscles results from increases in local temperature, CO_2, and lactic acid, and from a decrease in O_2. In addition, if body temperature increases as a result of exercise or environmental heat, skin blood flow (vasodilation) increases in order to facilitate heat loss.

At rest, the kidneys and splanchnic tissue only utilize 10 to 25% of the oxygen available in their blood supply. Consequently, they can tolerate a considerable decrease in blood flow before their oxygen demand exceeds supply and compromises function.[27] As blood flow is decreased, oxygen extraction from the available blood supply increases in order to meet the energy requirements of the tissue. A substantial reduction in splanchnic and renal blood flow can be sustained for more than an hour during heavy exercise. However, it is possible that a prolonged reduction in blood flow to the liver and kidneys may have substantial consequences.

2.4. EFFECT OF EXERCISE ON PHYSIOLOGICAL FACTORS WHICH INFLUENCE DRUG PHARMACOKINETICS

Exercise influences a large number of physiological factors including hemodynamics,[28] pH,[18] hypoxia,[24] temperature,[29] urinary flow,[30] and gastrointestinal function[31] that influences the pharmacokinetics of drugs. Previous studies have clearly demonstrated that exercise can influence the pharmacokinetics of certain drugs. However, the magnitude and duration of the effects may vary. This is not surprising in view of the widely differing physiochemical properties of drugs, the many possible and, oftentimes opposing effects of exercise on the parameters affecting drug pharmacokinetics, and the different types of exercise performed.[3]

Physical exercise leads to changes in thyroid function, sex hormones, cortisol metabolism, and lipoprotein metabolism.[16] Lipoproteins, thyroxine, sex hormones, and cortisol are all biotransformed by the hepatic microsomal enzyme system and are affected by exposure to inducers of hepatic microsomal enzyme activity in a manner similar to that observed in physically fit individuals.[31] Accordingly, it is possible that the changes in hepatic microsomal enzyme activity, associated with changes in physical fitness and the changes in concentration of hormones and lipoproteins, are somehow related.

Exercise may influence the plasma protein binding of certain drugs and the diffusion across membranes. Changes in these factors could affect the hepatic clearance of drugs with a low hepatic extraction ratio, in which these factors are rate-limiting.[6] Enzymatic reactions are temperature-dependent, suggesting that the increase in body temperature during exercise might increase the enzyme activity and thus the metabolic clearance of low extraction drugs in which the enzymatic capacity of the liver is rate-limiting.[6] Exercise has also been shown to increase bile flow and excretion,[33] thus increasing the hepatic clearance of a drug whose clearance is biliary excretion-dependent.

2.5. CLINICAL RELEVANCE OF ALTERED DRUG PHARMACOKINETICS

Changes in drug pharmacokinetics can alter the pharmacodynamics and/or toxicity of a variety of drugs. If a drug is removed more rapidly from the body, normal dosing schedules may prove inadequate due to either a reduction in drug residence time or an inadequate drug concentration. Conversely, a decrease in drug clearance with no modification in the administration schedule may result in an undesirable increase in drug concentration and a greater potential for a toxic reaction. In addition, a variety of drugs (e.g., digoxin, oxprenolol) require the maintenance of a "therapeutic" concentration range. Jogestrand and Andersson[34] and Koopmans et al.[35] have demonstrated that the timing of exercise, relative to the administration of a drug, can significantly modify its pharmacokinetics. This finding increases the difficulty in determining the clinically relevant therapeutic interval for proper maintenance of the drug's concentration.

The chance of a clinically relevant effect of exercise on the pharmacokinetics of a particular drug is largest in those with a steep dose-response curve, a narrow therapeutic range, a need for continuity of therapeutic effectiveness, and a relatively short half-life, in combination with intensive exercise of long duration.[3] The effects of strenuous exercise on drugs that have specific and well-defined characteristics (e.g., first pass elimination) can be predicted and could be significant for drugs meeting defined criteria. These drugs must be handled by the liver or kidney in a flow-limited fashion and have a short half-life than compared with the total duration of exercise. In addition, exercise intensity should reach a minimum of 50% VO_2max.[36]

With these theoretical considerations in mind, exercise might be expected to impair the hepatic clearance of drugs with a high hepatic extraction ratio. The influence of exercise on the hepatic clearance of drugs with a low hepatic extraction ratio depends on the physiochemical properties of the drug, the factor which is rate-limiting in the process of hepatic clearance, and the type of exercise that is being performed.

3. EFFECT OF EXERCISE ON DRUG ABSORPTION

3.1. EFFECT OF EXERCISE ON DRUG ABSORPTION AFTER INTRAMUSCULAR, TRANSDERMAL, AND SUBCUTANEOUS ADMINISTRATION

The main factor affecting drug absorption following intramuscular (i.m.), transdermal (t.d.), or subcutaneous (s.c.) administration is a modification in tissue blood flow.[37] Several studies have demonstrated the relationship

TABLE 2
Effect of Exercise on Drug Absorption

Drug	Route of Administration	Change[a]	Ref.
Ampicillin	Intramuscular	I	Cadorniga et al. (84)
Atenolol	Oral	NC	van Baak et al. (57)
Atenolol	Oral	I	Mason et al. (53)
Atropine	Intramuscular	I	Kamimori et al. (39)
Bisoprolol	Oral	NC	Le Coz et al. (118)
Caffeine	Oral	I	Collomp et al. (130)
Digoxin	Oral	I	Jogestrand and Andersson (34)
Glyceryl Trinitrate	Transdermal	I	Barkve et al. (21)
Glyceryl Trinitrate	Transdermal	I	Gjesdal et al. (41)
Methyl Salicylate	Subcutaneous	I	Danon et al. (20)
Nedocromil Sodium	Inhaled	I	Ghosh et al. (44)
Quinidine	Oral	D	Aslaksen and Aanderud (131)
Salicylate	Oral	D	Aslaksen and Aanderud (131)
Sulfadimidine	Oral	D	Aslaksen and Aanderud (131)
Propranolol	Oral	I	van Baak et al. (57)
Verapamil	Oral	I	van Baak et al. (57)

[a] I = increase, D = decrease, NC = no change.

between blood flow and exercise.[6,11,28] Kamimori et al.[39] examined the effects of low intensity (40% VO_2max) cycle exercise on the pharmacokinetics of (anterolateral aspect of the quadriceps) atropine after intramuscular administration. They observed an increase in the absorption rate constant and the peak serum concentration, and a decrease in the time to peak as compared to rest. These results illustrate the effects of increased muscle blood flow resulting from prior exercise, on drug absorption. In the same study, they also examined the effects of 90 min of intermittent (25 min cycle, 5 min rest) low intensity cycle exercise immediately following atropine administration. They observed no change in the absorption rate constant, but did observe a significant decrease in the volume of distribution as well as an increase in the peak serum concentration and the area under the curve. These results suggest that prior administration of the drug had only a minimal effect on the absorption rate, but a much more profound effect on drug distribution. Additional studies have also shown that as muscle blood flow increases with exercise, the absorption of intramuscularly injected drugs also increases.[2,40] Table 2 includes examples of the effect of exercise on the absorption of select drugs following oral or i.m. or s.c. administration. The changes in blood flow are probably responsible for the corresponding changes in absorption.

Barkve et al.[21] examined the effects of low intensity exercise or low humidity 90°C sauna on the absorption of transdermal glyceryl trinitrate (GTN). Low

SPLANCHNIC VASCULAR BED

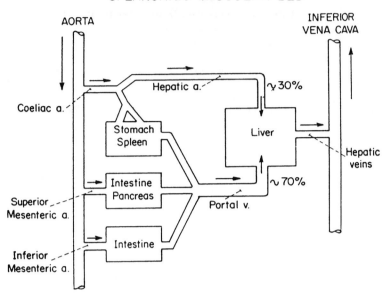

FIGURE 3. Schematic representation of the splanchnic circulation showing series-parallel arrangement of various splanchnic organs that drain into the portal vein and supply the liver with approximately 70% of its flow. The remaining 30% of liver blood flow is supplied by the hepatic artery. (Modified from Rowell, L. B., *Human Circulation,* Oxford University Press, New York, 1986, chaps. 4 and 9. With permission.)

intensity exercise increased mean plasma GTN twofold while heat exposure increased mean plasma GTN by fivefold. In a similar follow up study, Gjesdal et al.[41] used the same exercise protocol and examined the relationship between the time of patch change and mean plasma GTN levels. They found a 19% increase in GTN concentration following exercise with a patch in place for 24 h and a 56% increase with a patch which had been in place for 2 h. Thus, changing the patch augmented nitrate availability during exercise. The pharmacodynamic consequence of this increased absorption and availability could translate into a pharmacodynamic (albeit transient) improvement in exercise capacity with a change in patch.

3.2. EFFECT OF EXERCISE ON DRUG ABSORPTION AFTER ORAL OR INHALATION ADMINISTRATION

Most drugs ingested orally are absorbed through the intestine via splanchnic blood flow. During exercise, the decrease in splanchnic blood flow[11] results in decreased drug absorption. Ochsenfahrt and Winne[42] determined that the intestinal absorption of aniline, amidopyrine, antipyrine, benzoic, and salicylic acid was dependent on splanchnic blood flow (Figure 3). Schulz and Winne[43] showed that blood flow and antipyrine intestinal absorption were related. The effect of exercise has not been as comprehensively studied as the effect of altered blood flow. In limited studies (Table 2), the results were as expected because of the decreased splanchnic blood flow due to exercise.

Drugs like nedocromil sodium may also be orally administered through inhalation. In these cases, the drug is often administered as a nebulized solution which is rapidly absorbed through the bronchial mucosa. Ghosh et al.[44] examined the effects of a variety of physiological maneuvers on the absorption of inhaled nedocromil sodium. They found a significant increase in the plasma drug concentration following 8 min of steady-state exercise, a series of forced vital capacity measurements (FEV_1), and exercise in combination with FEV_1. They concluded that the increases in drug absorption were probably a consequence of an increase in lung volume. Acute exercise decreases the blood flow to liver; hence, it will increase the plasma concentration of those drugs which have first pass effect and high clearance (high extraction ratio, high intrinsic clearance).

3.3. ROLE OF EXERCISE ON FACTORS AFFECTING DRUG ABSORPTION

The physicochemical properties of a drug play an important role in determining how well a drug is absorbed during altered blood flow. Drugs are transported across lipid membranes by four mechanisms: (1) diffusion; (2) filtration; (3) active transport; and (4) pinocytosis. The most common of these is diffusion. Wilkinson suggested that the absorption of lipophilic drugs, which are limited by blood and must diffuse across less permeable barriers, seems to be more independent of blood flow.[15] Drugs which diffuse across permeable barriers are more dependent on splanchnic blood flow, because diffusion across the epithelial cells is not the rate-limiting step.

Tsujimoto et al.[45] showed that "the product formulation of the drug (i.e., tablet, capsule, ointment, powder, etc.) and certain physicochemical properties of the drug (i.e., molecular size, lipophilicity, acid/base characteristics, etc.) were the main determinants of the rate and extent of drug entry into the body." Figure 3 shows the varying relationship between absorption rate and splanchnic blood flow for different substances.[42] It is difficult to experimentally test the effect of blood flow on drug permeability because muscle blood flow can vary as much as 19% in different muscle tissues,[40] and there are large intraindividual variations with drug absorption. Winne[46] described the absorption rate of a drug in a simple equation using blood flow dependence and membrane permeability dependence. However, current models provide an incomplete description of drug absorption.[46,47]

Another possible effect of exercise on the alteration of drug absorption may be attributed to changes in pH.[18] During physical activity, lactic acid is produced, slightly decreasing the pH of blood and muscle. This change in pH may alter drug ionization and polarity.[48,49] Drug absorption is either enhanced or decreased, depending on the nature of the drug molecule and its pKa.

Even though changes in drug absorption, resulting from exercise-induced changes in blood flow have been noted, there is very little data about the rate of drug absorption and thus the bioavailability of drugs during exercise. Drug absorption from skin and muscle is increased by exercise because of the increase in blood flow in these organs during exercise, as previously discussed. In contrast, intestinal absorption decreases with decreased splanchnic blood flow during exercise. The membrane permeability determines the extent to which the absorption of the drug is affected by different levels of exercise. The effect of exercise on drug absorption with a wide range of membrane permeabilities and with differing routes of administration has not been comprehensively studied.

4. EFFECT OF EXERCISE ON DRUG DISTRIBUTION

The volume of distribution (V_d) is not a "real" volume but an artifact, a hypothetical volume of body fluid that would be required to dissolve the total amount of drug. It is a proportionality constant relating the amount of drug in the body to the measured concentration in biological fluid (blood, plasma, or serum). The volume of distribution is dependent on three major variables: (1) blood flow, (2) protein and tissue binding, and (3) body composition.

The rate of blood flow in the tissues controls the equilibrium between the concentration of drug in plasma and tissues. Generally, this rate of equilibrium is more rapid between plasma and tissue with high blood flow rather than plasma and tissue with low blood flow. Whenever there is a change in plasma concentration, changes will immediately appear in tissues with high blood flow.

Once the drug reaches systemic circulation, it circulates in the blood and binds to plasma proteins. Albumin concentration makes up about 70% of the composition of the plasma proteins; it is the major site of drug binding. Different sites on the albumin have different affinities for different drugs. Drug molecules are transported in either bound or unbound form to organs and tissues, and the ability of the organ to extract the drug is dependent upon the characteristics of the drug and the organ in question. Binding of drugs to albumin is important for a number of reasons, but most importantly, the drug's toxicity may be affected. The fraction of the bound drug is considered pharmacologically inactive and nontoxic. A strongly bound drug may displace a weak drug, thereby increasing the free concentration of the latter. This can make it excessively more available for extraction into the tissues. Albumin binding may decrease the availability of the free drug, but it may also increase the duration of the drug's pharmacological effect in the body. This is important when strongly bound drugs are being displaced because there is a relative change in blood concentration compared to the changes with weakly bound drugs. Changes in these parameters, concomitant with exercise, will result in changes in drug distribution.

4.1. EFFECT OF EXERCISE ON THE VOLUME OF DISTRIBUTION

Considering the apparent volume of distribution of a drug and its relationship to plasma and tissue distribution, the V_d can be characterized as:

$$V_d = V_p + V_T * (fu/f_T)$$

where V_p is the volume of plasma, V_T is the volume of tissue, fu is the free fraction of drug in plasma , and f_T is the free fraction of drug in tissue.

Exercise has been shown to increase serum albumin concentration. This may be due to the decrease in plasma volume and concomitant increase in plasma protein concentration that occurs with exercise.[63] Such an increase would lead to a lower free fraction of drugs, and a higher bound fraction. As illustrated in the aforementioned equation, this would result in a smaller V_d, at least for a capacity-limited drug.[14]

4.2. EFFECT OF EXERCISE ON DISTRIBUTION OF CAPACITY- AND FLOW-LIMITED DRUGS

Drugs strongly bound and poorly extracted are considered capacity-limited drugs, while drugs which are not limited by binding, but by blood flow, are classified as flow-limited. A variety of terms have been used to describe these two classes. For all intensive purposes, the term capacity-limited is equivalent to low clearance, low extraction ratio, and low intrinsic clearance, while flow-limited is synonymous with high clearance, high extraction ratio, and high intrinsic clearance.

For capacity-limited drugs, a high percentage of the dose will be found bound to plasma proteins after administration. In the rat for example, warfarin is extracted by the liver depending on the fraction of unbound drug that exists in the blood. The drug is capacity-limited because of this dependency of extraction and plasma protein binding.[2]

In contrast, propranolol is a flow-limited drug which has a hepatic extraction ratio in man that is larger than the free fraction because much of the drug is extracted before being bound. Extraction is then less dependent on plasma protein binding. With some drugs, such as propranolol,[64] bromosulfophthalein,[65] and nortriptyline,[66] the data suggest that more drug is extracted from the blood than from the fraction unbound, and that even if binding is changed, extraction and metabolism may not change.

Tables 3 and 4 show the tabulation of common drugs which are flow-limited and capacity-limited based on pharmacokinetic parameters such as bioavailability, extraction ratio, and the fraction bound or unbound.[45] The extraction ratio may be calculated as

$$ER = 1 - F$$

where F is bioavailability. Drugs that are bound less than 90%, and which have an extraction ratio of 0.5 or greater, are classified as flow-limited. Exercise has a different effect on the disposition of a drug, depending on whether the drug is flow-limited or capacity-limited.

Drugs in the body have a characteristic V_d which can be defined as: $V_d =$ Dose/Plasma concentration. This equation illustrates the relationship between V_d, the amount of drug administered, and its resultant plasma concentration.

TABLE 3
List of Flow-Limited Drugs

Acebutolol	Cyclophosphamide	Minocycline
Acetaminophen	Cyclosporine	Morphine
Acetylprocainamide	Cytarabine	Moxalactam
Acetylsalicylic acid	Dapsone	Nadolol
Acyclovir	Desipramine	Nafcillin
Alprazolam	Desmethyldiazepam	Naloxone
Alprenolol	Dexamethasone	Neostigmine
Amikacin	Dextropropoxyphene	Netilmicin
Amiodarone	Digoxin	Nicotine
Amitriptyline	Diltiazem	Nifedipine
Amoxicillin	Diphenhydramine	Nitroglycerine
Ampicillin	Doxepin	Nortriptyline
Amrinone	Doxorubicin	Oxacillin
Amylobarbitone	Doxycycline	Pancuronium
Antipyrine	Erythromycine	Pentazocine
Atenolol	Ethambutol	Phenobarbital
Azlocillin	Ethosuximide	Physostigmine
Betamethasone	Fentanyl	Pindolol
Bretylium	Flucytosine	Piperacillin
Bromosulfophthalein	Flunitrazepam	Prednisone
Caffeine	Fluorouracil	Primidone
Captopril	Gentamicin	Procainamide
Carbamazepine	Hexobarbitol	Propranolol
Carbenicillin	Hydralazine	Pyridostigmine
Cefamandole	Hydrochlorothiazide	Quinine
Cefazolin	Imipramine	Ranitidine
Ceforanide	Indocyanine green	Sotalol
Cefotaxime	Isoniazid	Streptomycin
Cefoxitin	Isosorbide dinitrate	Sulfadiazine
Ceftazidime	Labetalol	Sulfamethoxazole
Ceftizoxime	Lidocaine	Terbutaline
Cefuroxime	Lithium	Tetracycline
Cephalexin	Melphalan	Theophylline
Cephapirin	Meperidine	Thiopental
Cephradine	Mercaptopurine	Ticarillin
Chloramphenicol	Methicillin	Timolol
Chlormethiazole	Methotrexate	Tobramycin
Chloroquine	Methyldopa	Tocainide
Chlorothiazide	Methylprednisolone	Triamterene
Chlorthalidone	Metoprolol	Trimethoprim
Cimetidine	Metronidazole	Tubocurarine
Cloxacillin	Mexiletine	Vancomycin
Cocaine	Mezlocillin	Verapamil

Note: Flow-limited drugs are those which are bound less than 90% and the extraction ratio (ER) is 0.5 or greater, (ER = 1–F), F is bioavailability.

Modified from Somani, S. M., Gupta, S. K., Frank, S., and Corder, C. N., *Drug Dev. Res.,* 20, 251, 1990. With permission.

TABLE 4
List of Capacity-Limited Drugs

Chlordiazepoxide	Ibuprofen	Probenecid
Chlorpromazine	Indomethacin	Protriptyline
Clindamycin	Ketoprofen	Quinidine
Clofibrate	Lorazepam	Sulfisoxazole
Clonazepam	Methadone	Temazepam
Diazepam	Naproxen	Tolbutamide
Diazoxide	Oxazepam	Tolmetin
Dicloxacillin	Phenylbutazone	Triazolam
Digitoxin	Phenytoin	Valproic acid
Furosemide	Prazosin	Warfarin
Haloperidol	Prednisolone	

Note: Capacity-limited drugs are those which are bound more than 90% and extraction ratio (ER) is less than 0.5, (ER = 1–F), F is bioavailability.

From Somani, S. M., Gupta, S. K., Frank, S., and Corder, C. N., *Drug Dev. Res.,* 20, 251, 1990. With permission.

The binding characteristics of the drug have a large effect on the drug's V_d. The V_d for indocyanine green (ICG), a capacity-limited drug, is almost equal to the plasma volume, indicating that most of the drug remains in bound form.[36,67,68] Digoxin, a flow-limited drug, distributes itself in the body and has a plasma concentration of about 1 µg/l, or a V_d of about 14.3 l/kg.[36]

Recently, Somani et al.[69] have reported how exercise alters the time course of distribution of radioactivity in various tissues of rat after intramuscular administration of ^{3}H-physostigmine (^{3}H-Phy), a flow-limited drug that is poorly bound and highly extractable. Rats were endurance trained for 6 weeks on a treadmill and were subjected to an acute bout of exercise (80% VO_2 max). Immediately after exercise, ^{3}H-Phy was administered and the rats were sacrificed at various times; plasma and tissues were collected and analyzed. At 2 min, the radioactivity in the brain, heart, lung, kidney, liver, and muscle was increased 337, 191, 106, 385, 126, and 80% over control, respectively. Radioactivity concentration in kidney, liver, and muscle remained higher up to 10 min after exercise, whereas the concentration in the brain and heart decreased below control within 5 min. The half-life of radioactivity in trained vs. control rats was brain (18 vs. 20 min), liver (25 vs. 30 min), heart (31 vs. 26 min), kidney (30 vs. 28 min), and muscle (45 vs. 31 min). There were no significant differences, in $t_{1/2}$ except in muscle. These authors indicated that exercise affects the distribution and kinetics of radioactivity (drug and its metabolites) depending on the blood flow to the organs. Pharmacokinetics parameters were determined for physostigmine using a PC-Nonlin program of statistical consultants. Table 5 clearly shows that the absorption phase, time to reach for maximum drug concentration (t_{max}) and maximum drug concentration (C_{max})

TABLE 5
Effect of Training on Physostigmine Pharmacokinetics in the Rat after Intramuscular Administration

	Control	Trained
AUC (ng*min/ml)	578.8 ± 88.7	834.2 ± 45.8
$t_{1/2}$ (min)	8.8 ± 2.9	5.7 ± 1.6
K_{el} (min^{-1})	0.08 ± 0.03	0.04 ± 0.005
Cl (ml/min/kg)	120.9 ± 18.5	83.9 ± 4.6
V_d (ml/kg)	1511	2097
C_{max} (ng/ml)	31.3	
t_{max} (min)	4.9	

has essentially disappeared in endurance-trained rats, resulting from increased blood flow due to exercise. The area under the curve and half-life have also increased as a result of endurance training.

For drugs that are flow-limited (Table 3), however, there probably is a lower dependence on albumin concentration. Ylitalo and Hinkka[70] showed that sulfadimidine, a weakly-binding drug, did not show significant change in serum level with exercise. Although altered protein binding may be significant, it is an important factor in the effect of exercise on drug distribution of many drugs due to altered blood flow.[71] If blood flow to an organ or tissue is increased, the amount of unbound drug in the organ per unit time is increased. This should increase extraction of the drug from the blood. Many drugs are extracted and metabolized in the liver, where blood flow during exercise is reduced to as little as half the regular flow.[6,68,72,73] Therefore, the hepatic distribution of most drugs should decrease during exercise.

The effect of exercise on V_d has been tested with a variety of drugs (Table 6). Ylitalo et al.[74] found that serum concentrations of orally ingested sulfamethizole, tetracycline, and doxycycline increased with exercise, thereby indicating that hepatic extraction was reduced. These results are consistent with the above proposition because as hepatic blood flow decreases, the hepatic extraction ratio should also decrease. This means that a higher plasma concentration and a lower volume of distribution would result. However, changes in absorption and elimination rates during exercise may also have contributed to these results. Similarly, the serum level of some drugs, such as acebutolol,[13,50] amitriptyline,[51] antipyrine,[52] atenolol,[53] desipramine,[51] indocyanine green,[54] nitroglycerine,[55] penicillin,[55] propranolol,[50,57-60] and sotalol[61] has been increased with physical stress and exercise, although verapamil remains unchanged.[62] This phenomenon, however, is only characteristic of flow-limited drugs.

For capacity-limited drugs, altered blood flow may have another type of effect on the ability of bodily tissues to extract drugs. In some cases, a decreased blood flow to specific tissues can result in increased extraction ratios by those tissues. This would only be true for drugs that are capacity-limited, because the removal process of such drugs from the plasma takes some time

TABLE 6
Effect of Exercise on Volume of Distribution

Type and Drug Name	% change in V_d[a]	Intensity of Exercise	Ref.
Flow-limited			
Acebutolol	−8.9	Light	Henry et al. (50)
Antipyrine	−74.7	Heavy	Swartz et al. (52)
Atropine	−28.8	Moderate	Kamimori et al. (39)
Benzylpenicillin	−35.5	Moderate	Schmidt and Roholt (56)
Caffeine	−36.4	Light	Collomp et al. (130)
Diazepam	+25.0	Heavy	Klotz and Lucke (76)
Doxycycline	−26.2	Heavy	Ylitalo et al. (74)
Indocyanine Green	−23.3	Moderate	Daneshmend et al. (54)
Nitroglycerine	−38.8	Heavy	Weber et al. (55)
Physostigmine	+38.8	Trained	Somani et al. (2)
Propranolol	−6.0	Moderate	Arends et al. (87)
Propranolol	n.s.[a]	Moderate	Frank et al. (58)
Propranolol	−14.1	Light	Henry et al. (50)
Propranolol	−50.0	Heavy	Powis and Snow (60)
Propranolol	−sig.	Heavy	van Baak et al. (57)
Sulfamethizole	−38.4	Heavy	Ylitalo et al. (74)
Tetracycline	−9.6	Heavy	Ylitalo et al. (74)
Theophylline	−sig.	Moderate	Schlaeffer et al. (90)
Verapamil	−sig.	Moderate	van Baak et al. (57)
Capacity-limited			
Valproic Acid	n.s.[a]	Heavy	Marsh et al. (75)

[a]   n.s. = No significant change.
[b]   Calculated from % change in serum concentration if necessary.

Modified from Somani, S. M., Gupta, S. K., Frank, S., and Corder, C. N., *Drug Dev. Res.,* 20, 251, 1990. With permission.

to complete. When blood flow is decreased, drugs stay in contact with tissue sinusoids for a longer amount of time, and it is then possible to extract more of the drug from the plasma.[52] This effect would counteract the effect that would occur as a result of increased albumin binding. Unfortunately, only limited data is available in this area. Valproic acid, a capacity-limited drug, showed an unchanged V_d with exercise,[75] and the V_d of diazepam, a capacity-limited drug, increased significantly.[76]

4.3. ROLE OF TEMPERATURE AND pH IN EXERCISE ALTERATIONS OF DRUG DISTRIBUTION

Another factor considered in the effect of exercise on drug distribution is the increase in body temperature that results from exercise.[11] There is a definite relationship between temperature and the ability of a drug to bind to plasma proteins.[6] As the body's temperature rises, the free fraction of drug in the blood also rises. This has been shown for a variety of drugs including phenytoin (diphenylhydantoin),[77] and warfarin.[78] Somani and McDonald[79] reported the effect of temperature on binding of salicylate and warfarin. Warfarin was bound twofold more tightly at 0°C and fourfold at 37°C than salicylate. This demonstrates that an increase in temperature decreases the binding ability of salicylate while the binding ability of warfarin, which is bound tightly, is relatively unchanged. Experiments testing the interrelationship of exercise, temperature, and plasma protein binding must consider many other variables. Presently, the studies addressing this issue appear to be inconsistent.

Another factor considered when evaluating the effect of exercise on drug distribution is pH. Muscle and blood will have a lower pH during exercise because of the production of lactic acid. The differences in pH between muscle, or other tissue, and the blood will also change. These variances may affect the amount of drug sequestered in a certain tissue during exercise. Experiments by Henry et al.[50] with two basic drugs, propranolol and acebutolol, showed that exercise increased the plasma concentration of these drugs. This can be attributed to a change in the blood pH-dependent partition during exercise.

The distribution and binding of a drug to skeletal muscle is especially important for drugs like digoxin. Joreteg and Jogestrand[80] reported that digoxin uptake was significantly increased, and serum digoxin decreased, at different intensities of exercise in man. Furthermore, the magnitude of the increase in the binding to skeletal muscle was greater at the higher workload. In another study, Joreteg and Jogestrand[81] evaluated the profound effects that exercise can have on the binding of a drug to skeletal muscle. Additionally, as arterioles dilate during exercise to permit more blood perfusion to skeletal muscle, more of the drug can be sequestered in muscle and adipose tissue. However, when exercise ceases, the arterioles close, circulation to the organ system is reduced, and the drug may not re-enter the circulatory system as readily.[58]

5. EFFECT OF EXERCISE ON DRUG METABOLISM

Drug metabolism takes place in many parts of the body. It can occur in the bloodstream, brain, spleen, kidneys, muscle tissue, the gastrointestinal tract, and many other tissues. However, the major organ in which drug metabolism occurs is the liver. The liver is the primary organ of waste disposal and works in close collaboration with the kidneys to eliminate unwanted substances from the body.

The majority of hepatic drug metabolism occurs within the endoplasmic reticulum of the liver parenchymal cells. Microsomes are artifacts produced by the breakdown of endoplasmic reticulum and are obtained by sequential centrifugation of the homogenized liver. The hepatic drug metabolizing capacity of an individual depends on a complex interaction between genetic and environmental factors, and differences in these factors are responsible for the well-established and extensive intraindividual differences in drug biotransformation.

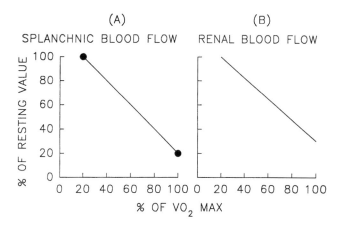

FIGURE 4. In strenuous exercise, visceral blood flow is decreased, and for both to the gastrointestinal tract and spleen (A), or kidney (B), an approximately linear relationship exists between the decrease in blood flow (as a percentage of the resting value) and the percentage of maximal oxygen uptake achieved during exercises. (Modified from Rowell, L. B., *Physiol. Dev.*, 54, 75, 1974. With permission.)

5.1. THE LIVER

The liver is the largest gland in the body weighing about 1.2 to 1.6 kg in normal adults. Figure 3 illustrates how blood is supplied to the liver. The liver receives 80% of its blood from the portal vein, which is connected to the region of the gall bladder, gastrointestinal tract, and spleen. The rest of its blood is supplied from the aorta via the hepatic artery, whose primary responsibility is for the oxygenation of the liver. Although this artery supplies only 20% of total hepatic flow, it provides a major share of the oxygen required by the liver.[28]

As previously discussed (see Table 1), hepatic blood flow is significantly decreased during exercise. The degree to which blood flow decreases is illustrated in Figure 4A which shows the relationship between the increasing oxygen requirements of exercise and hepatic blood flow.

5.2. HEPATIC CLEARANCE AND THE EXTRACTION RATIO

Hepatic clearance, the most direct quantitative measure of the liver's ability to eliminate a drug, includes biliary excretory clearance and hepatic metabolic clearance. Hepatic clearance can be defined by the following equation of Wilkinson:[15]

$$\text{Hepatic clearance} = QH \frac{f_{ub} \times Cl_{int}}{QH + f_{ub} \times Cl_{int}}$$

where QH = hepatic blood flow, f_{ub} = fraction of unbound drug, and Cl_{int} = intrinsic clearance of the unbound drug. As illustrated in this equation, hepatic clearance and extraction are influenced by two independent variables, intrinsic hepatic clearance and hepatic blood flow. Intrinsic hepatic clearance is defined by the liver's ability to irreversibly remove drugs from the circulation in the absence of any flow limitation. For example, if the liver's ability to metabolize a drug was increased twofold, as might occur with enzyme induction, then the extraction efficiency would also increase, but the magnitude of the change would be dependent upon the initial value of intrinsic clearance. If this value is small, then extraction would also be small and the increase in intrinsic clearance would result in a proportional change in the extraction and thus clearance of the drug. Conversely, if the intrinsic clearance and extraction are already high, then a doubling of the intrinsic clearance would have little effect on either the extraction ratio or drug clearance.

Another important factor in the clearance of a drug is its extraction ratio (ER), which can be expressed as:

$$ ER = \frac{f_{ub} * Cl_{int}}{QH + f_{ub} * Cl_{int}} $$

where QH = hepatic blood flow, f_{ub} = fraction of unbound drug, and Cl_{int} = intrinsic clearance of the unbound drug. The metabolism and elimination characteristics of each drug can be expressed on the basis of their extraction ratio. The drug extraction ratio is dependent upon three fundamental biological determinants: (1) the blood flow to the organ of elimination, (2) the inherent ability of the organ of drug removal to irreversibly clear the drug from circulation, and (3) the binding of drug to plasma proteins and cellular components of blood. Three important limiting cases for this equation can be identified:

Case 1. If the drug has a high ER (ER > 0.7) when $f_{ub}*Cl_{int} >>> QH$, the equation reduces to:

$$ \text{Hepatic clearance} = QH $$

This means that hepatic clearance of high ER drugs is only dependent on blood flow, not on protein binding or the metabolizing capabilities of the liver.

Case 2. If the drug has a low ER (ER < 0.3) when $f_{ub}*Cl_{int} <<<<< QH$, the equation reduces to:

$$ \text{Hepatic clearance} = f_{ub}*Cl_{int} $$

This means that the clearance of low ER drugs is only dependent on protein binding and metabolizing enzymes. Changes in either one of these will cause direct changes in hepatic clearance while changes in blood flow will have no effect.

Case 3. The hepatic clearance of moderate ER (ER 0.31 to 0.69) drugs is dependent on protein binding, hepatic blood flow, and intrinsic clearance.

Blood flow is another important factor in determining drug metabolism, as well as absorption and distribution. For some drugs, it is possible that blood flow may be a limiting factor in drug metabolism, when, for example, the supply rate of the drug is slower than the metabolic rate.[15] In this case, metabolic rate depends on blood flow. A high blood flow does not necessarily lead to a higher rate of supply of a drug. However, protein binding can limit extraction, which in turn, may limit metabolism. Figure 5 serves to further illustrate the relationship between hepatic blood flow as a function of the hepatic extraction ratio.

A number of studies have shown that clearance is a function of hepatic blood flow for many flow-limited drugs, including bromosulfophthalein[82] and hydrocortisone.[83] Experiments studying the effect of exercise on drug elimination for flow-limited drugs have generally agreed with the blood flow dependency argument. As Table 7 illustrates, clearance was decreased during exercise for some flow-limited drugs, such as ampicillin,[84] caffeine,[85,86] indocyanine green,[52] pralidoxime,[38] riboflavin,[88] sulfadimidine, acetylsulfadimidine, procainamide,[70] testosterone,[89] and theophylline,[90] although the clearance of antipyrine was not significantly changed.[52]

Propranolol, which is flow-limited,[58] should also have a decreased clearance. A study by Arends et al.[87] showed a decreased half-life after oral administration of propranolol; however, a later study by Arends et al.[87] showed that propranolol clearance is increased with oral administration during exercise, but is unchanged with i.v. administration. Somani et al.[69] and Frank et al.[58] studied the effect of exercise on propranolol clearance in volunteers who were given i.v. injection. This study revealed variable decreases and increases in propranolol clearance due to exercise. The interindividual variations were evident.

For capacity-limited drugs, extraction is increased[91] because the mechanism of drug removal from the binding protein has more time to operate with the decreased blood flow. Because of the increased metabolism and increased drug removal, the total extraction ratio should increase. Moreover, the increased bile flow should have a more important effect in the case of flow-limited drugs. In the same way that decreased blood flow is important for flow-limited drugs, the increased extraction ratio is important for capacity-limited drugs.

Data on the effect of exercise on capacity-limited drug elimination is very limited. Valproic acid[92] and diazepam are the only two capacity-limited drugs which have been evaluated by testing the effect of exercise on drug elimination. Valproic acid clearance[75] showed no significant change in clearance with exercise, while diazepam clearance[76] increased significantly. It is not known why valproic acid clearance does not seem to increase with exercise, but diazepam, at least, does show the expected change in clearance with exercise.

As hepatic elimination depends on blood flow, another factor that may affect the extraction ratio is altered bile flow, although its effect on exercise is not well understood. Reed et al.[93] showed that changes in blood flow did not

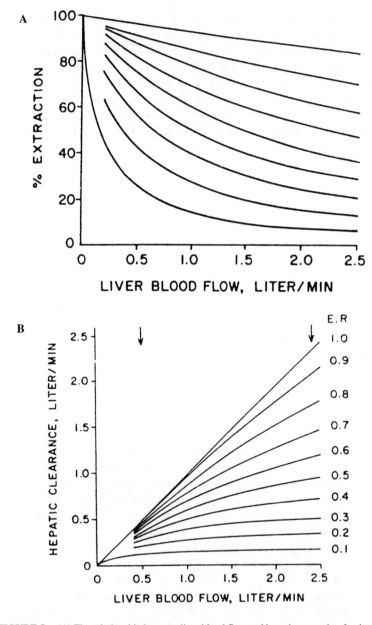

FIGURE 5. (A) The relationship between liver blood flow and hepatic extraction for drugs with varying extraction ratios. The individual curves reflect a 10% stepwise change in extraction at a normal flow of 1.5 l/min, and therefore each is complementary to the equivalent curve in (B). (B) The relationship between liver blood flow and total hepatic clearance for drugs with varying extraction ratios (ER). The arrows indicate the normal physiological range of liver blood flow and the extraction values refer to a normal flow of 1.5 l/min. (Modified from Shand, D. G., Kornhauser, D. M., and Wilkinson, G. R., *J. Pharmacol. Exp. Ther.,* 195, 424, 1975. With permission.)

TABLE 7
Effect of Exercise on Drug Clearance

Type of Elimination, Drug Type, and Drug Name	% Change in Clearance	Intensity of Exercise	Ref.
Hepatic and/or renal elimination			
Flow-limited			
Acetylsulfadimidine	−52.0	Heavy	Ylitalo and Hinkka (70)
Ampicillin	−11.8	Moderate	Cadorniga et al. (84)
Antipyrine	n.s.[a]	Heavy	Swartz et al. (52)
Atenolol	−8.0	Stress test	Mason et al. (53)
Atropine	−16.1	Moderate	Kamimori et al. (39)
Bisiprolol	+7.1	Stress test	Le Coz et al. (118)
Caffeine	−24.5	Moderate	Kamimori et al. (86)
Caffeine	n.s.[a]	Light	Collomp et al. (130)
Diazepam	+22.0	Heavy	Klotz and Lucke (76)
Digoxin	−13.6	Low	Jogestrand and Andersson (34)
Indocyanine green	−51.7	Moderate	Daneshmend et al. (54)
Indocyanine green	−33.0	Heavy	Shand et al. (64)
Indocyanine green	−36.0	Heavy	Swartz et al. (52)
Indocyanine green	−50.6	Heavy	Arends et al. (87)
Physostigmine	+37.0	Trained	Somani et al. (2)
Pralidoxime	−18.8	Heavy	Swartz and Sidell (38)
Procainamide	−84.0	Heavy	Ylitalo and Hinkka (70)
Propranolol	+15.0	Moderate	Arends et al. (87)
Propranolol	n.s.[a]	Moderate	Frank et al. (58)
Sulfadimidine	−11.0	Heavy	Ylitalo and Hinkka (70)
Testosterone	−29.0	Heavy	Cadoux-Hudson et al. (89)
Theophylline	−24.2	Moderate	Schlaeffer et al. (90)
Capacity-limited			
Valproic acid	n.s.[a]	Heavy	Marsh et al. (75)
Lung elimination			
Aminopyrine	+13.0	Heavy	Boel et al. (103)
Technetium-99mDTPA	+86.8	Moderate	Meignan et al. (125)

[a] n.s. = No significant difference.

Modified from Somani, S. M., Gupta, S. K., Frank, S., and Corder, C. M., *Drug Dev. Res.,* 20, 251, 1990. With permission.

alter the bile flow. Despite this finding, exercise does seem to have some stimulatory effect on bile flow. Ardies et al.[31] and Simko and Kelley[33] both reported a 15 to 20% increase in bile flow with mild exercise. Another experiment by Simko and Kelley[94] shows no significant increase with mild exercise. Therefore, the effect of exercise and bile flow on drug disposition is still uncertain. Because bile flow is very slow[31] compared to hepatic blood flow, it is probable in most cases that any effect of altered bile flow will be overshadowed by the effect of altered hepatic blood flow. Additional studies are needed to evaluate this aspect of drug elimination.

In our laboratory, we have studied the effect of exercise on the pharmaco-kinetics and metabolism of caffeine after oral[86,95] and i.v.[85] administration. We have shown that the effect of exercise on the pharmacokinetics of caffeine is marked but variable. In addition, exercise affected the appearance rate of paraxanthine (major metabolite of caffeine); the paraxanthine to caffeine ratio was different for normal weight as compared to obese volunteers.[86] These two populations metabolize caffeine differently during exercise.

5.3. EFFECT OF EXERCISE ON CYTOCHROME P-450 AND DRUG METABOLISM

When a drug is metabolized, the intermediate and final products are usually more polar or more ionized than the original drug. These compounds are less able to bind to plasma and tissue proteins, less likely to be stored in fat, and less able to penetrate cell membranes. Most drugs are metabolized by a system of enzymes of low substrate specificity, known as mixed function oxygenases or microsomal hydroxylases. They are mainly present in the liver, but are also found, to some extent, in the intestine, skin, kidney, lung, and other tissues. This enzyme system requires nicotinamide adenine dinucleotide phosphate (reduced) (NADPH) and molecular oxygen for activity. Molecular oxygen is an essential component of the hepatic microsomal mixed-function oxidase system; this system is involved in the metabolism of drugs and foreign com-pounds. The amount of oxygen available for biotransformation is an important determinant of metabolic capacity in animals.[96] A decrease in hepatic blood flow would also result in a decrease in the supply of molecular oxygen, which might affect the rate of biotransformation. The rate at which various drugs are metabolized by this enzyme system varies widely. The activity of a drug in optimal doses is thus dependent on the rate of metabolism and on the relative extent of the different metabolic pathways. The mechanism of these enzyme systems involves an electron transport chain, and the rate-limiting step in the overall reaction is a heme-containing protein called cytochrome P-450. Cyto-chrome P-450 (cyt P-450) is a conglomerate of enzymes that are products of a gene superfamily that has been fractionated into 18 separate, but related (8 mammalian, 10 plant), gene families.[97-99] These enzymes are located in the smooth endoplasmic reticulum[99] and provide many vital functions, including the metabolism of foreign compounds such as drugs, chemicals, insecticides, pesticides, and environmental contaminants. The function of these enzymes is to convert a lipid-soluble compound to less lipid soluble compound or more polar form, usually by oxidation, which can then be easily excreted from the body. These enzymes also metabolize endogenous compounds such as ste-roids, protaglandins, biogenic amines, and fatty acids.[31,98,99] Such compounds are metabolized by different families of cyt P-450s, where the concentration and specific activity of the different isozymes within each family determines the liver's ability to deactivate, biotransform, or metabolize specific drugs or compounds.[98,100]

Changes in microsomal enzyme levels, microsomal enzyme activities, or in the specific activity of various cytochrome P-450 levels, can also modify the metabolic activity of a drug. Drugs and chemicals are known to induce the cyt P-450s; for example, ethanol specifically induces cyt P-450 II E1 (E-subfamily).[31,101] In human subjects, the rate of spironolactone and antipyrine clearance increased with exercise.[103] In addition, Shand et al.[14] have demonstrated that maximal oxygen consumption and the metabolism of aminopyrine and antipyrine increased following 3 and 6 months of physical training. This suggests that exercise training has the potential to modify drug metabolism by affecting cyt P-450-dependent activities. However, to date, conflicting results have yet to confirm whether exercise induces or inhibits the cyt P-450s. Controversy exists regarding the mode of exercise used in research (running vs. swimming), duration and intensity of exercise, age, and strain of rat studied.

Day and Weiner[104] examined the effects of 8 weeks of treadmill running in 10-month old male Fisher-344 rats. They reported a 30% decrease in cyt P-450 levels and a decrease in the microsomal metabolism of *p*-nitroanisole (PNA) and aniline, with no change in the metabolism of ethoxyresorufin. In addition, they concluded that chronic treadmill exercise appeared to provide protection from carbon tetrachloride toxicity in hepatocytes incubated with this solvent. Yiamouyiannis et al.[105] examined the activity of biotransformation enzymes in chronically exercised rats using a running wheel. These authors showed a significant increase in liver weight (11%), styrene oxide hydroxylase activity (175%), *N*-demethylase to benzphetamine (160%), glutathione-s-transferase to ethacrynic acid (125%), 2-naphthol to sulfa transferase (114%), and uridine diphosphate (UDP) glucuronosyl transferase to morphine in isolated hepatic microsomes from exercised rats compared to sedentary controls. These authors indicated that chronic exercise may increase the capacity of the liver to metabolize xenobiotics.

A similar decrease in cyt P-450 following treadmill training has been reported by Ramos et al.[106] They observed a decrease in cyt P-450 (30% of control), *p*-nitroanisole-o-demethylase activity (25% of control), and UDP-glucuronyl-transferase activity (25% of control) following treadmill exercise. These results suggest that trained treadmill exercise diminishes Phase I metabolism and glucuronidation. In another study, Day et al.[107] examined the effects of swimming and running on metabolism and reported a decrease in cyt P-450 in the treadmill-exercised group and an increase in cyt P-450 in the swim-exercised group. UDP-glucuronyl-transferase activity was not affected. These investigators suggested that the results of the swimming study appeared to be influenced by stress or some unknown component associated with exposure to water. In contrast, Ardies et al.[31] examined the effects of swimming exercise and ethanol consumption on hepatic cyt P-450-dependent monooxygenases in male rats. They found no change in cyt P-450 due to swimming alone. They reported that repeated swim exercise in conjunction with ethanol consumption produced a synergistic increase in ethanol-inducible cyt P-450 II E1. Michaud et al.[108] examined the effects of 11 weeks of endurance training on total hepatic cyt P-450 content and cyt P-450-mediated (CYP1A and CYP2B) hepatic microsomal mixed-function oxidase metabolism in male Sprague-Dawley rats. Total liver cyt P-450 content was not significantly different between trained and control groups. In addition, plasma clearance of theophylline and antipyrine was also not significantly modified. They concluded that strenuous endurance training did not alter total hepatic cyt P-450 content or CYP1A or CYP2B activity. In a study using isolated renal microsomes, Piatkowski et al.[109] reported that exercise significantly increased renal microsomal cyt P-450 (60% in young, 34% in middle-aged) as compared to age-matched sedentary controls. In another interesting variation, Merrill et al.[110] reported a decrease in the amount of microsomal cyt P-450 and the activities of aniline hydroxylase and ethylmorphine-N-demethylase in rat livers that had flown aboard Cosmos 1887 space flight. These results indicate the possible effects of prolonged weightlessness on altered liver function, and this may be related to the change in the distribution of blood flow.

In summary, a great deal of conflicting data exist regarding the effects (induction vs. inhibition) of exercise on cyt P-450 in the rat model of drug metabolism. Many of the reported differences and inconsistencies may be related to the variations in exercise mode, intensity, duration, time of sacrifice relative to exercise, animal strain, and class of drug metabolism examined. In addition, a variety of additional variables which could either induce or inhibit cyt P-450 probably exist. An example of this has been reported by Serbinova et al.[111] who compared the effect of iron (Fe) loading combined with additional oxidative stressors. They reported that the loading of Fe significantly decreased cyt P-450 and that the addition of exercise further depleted this enzyme. A great deal of additional research in this area will be required before definitive answers to the aforementioned questions can be identified.

5.4. EFFECT OF EXERCISE ON GLUTATHIONE AND DRUG METABOLISM

The effect of exercise on glutathione (GSH) and oxidized glutathione (GSSG) in various tissues and plasma is reported in Chapter 3 by Somani and extensively described in Chapter 4 by Ji. Exercise seems to deplete GSH or to convert it to GSSG. The compartmentalization of GSH exists at the tissue level, subcellular level, and different organ levels. Exercise enhances or depletes blood flow to various organs which will, in turn, influence the compartmentalization of GSH. Exercise may alter the intra- and extracellular transport of GSH, its synthesis, and degradation as related to an increase in oxygen uptake, or a decrease in the conjugation of GSH with exogenous or endogenous compounds. Reduced glutathione forms the conjugate with the biologically reactive intermediate metabolites of drugs or chemicals. If GSH is depleted as a result of exercise, there will be insufficient quantities available for conjugation reactions, resulting in an increased possibility of cellular injury.

Recently, Somani et al.[112] reported that the ratio of GSH/GSSG significantly increased from 6.8 to 8.3 in the cerebral cortex, and from 9.4 to 13.5 in the brain stem as a result of exercise training (7.5 weeks) in rats. Different brain regions contained different activities of antioxidant enzymes, as well as GSH and GSSG levels, which were preferentially altered as a result of exercise training to cope with oxidative stress. Somani et al.[113] also reported the effect of acute exercise and exercise training on GSH and GSSG in the cytosolic fraction of the rat heart. The ratio of GSH/GSSG did not alter significantly in this fraction.

5.5.   EFFECT OF CHRONIC EXERCISE ON LIVER FUNCTION

There are more data on the effect of chronic exercise and physical fitness on hepatic drug metabolism than on the effect of acute exercise. Biological changes that occur with physical fitness, may be due to changes in the microsomal enzyme system. Boel et al.[103] studied 14 students prior to and following 3 and 6 months of physical training. Salivary clearance of antipyrine and the aminopyrine breath test were used as indices of hepatic drug metabolism. Following 3 months of training, the average VO_2max was increased by 6% with a corresponding increase in the rate of metabolism of antipyrine (12%) and aminopyrine (13%). In spite of the large interindividual variation, there was a significant correlation between the extent of change in the maximal oxygen uptake and the corresponding change in antipyrine clearance, but not in aminopyrine metabolism. Vesell[115] reported that the disappearance rate constant, as measured by the aminopyrine breath test, was 40% greater in 8 athletes as compared to values obtained in normal men. In an additional 8 long distance runners, whose average VO_2max was 44% higher than the controls, they reported no difference in aminopyrine metabolism, galactose elimination capacity, or indocyanine green clearance between the two groups. The phenomenon of an elevation in the rate of drug metabolism in young and physically fit people, as compared to untrained people, has been termed "endogenous enzyme induction." The effect of physical fitness on drug metabolism has generally not been included in studies regarding the factors which influence human drug metabolism.[116]

The decrease in hepatic blood flow that occurs with exercise would, of course, decrease the amount of drug supplied to liver, and, thus, the metabolism of the drug should decrease. The "hepatic arterial buffer response," first discussed by Brauer[82] and later by Lautt,[117] suggests that "the main intrinsic control of hepatic blood flow is designed to hold total hepatic blood flow steady." It is a mechanism functioning to keep overall metabolism relatively steady. This mechanism may in part explain why alterations in metabolism were only found when subjects were severely exercised.

Although much more research needs to be done in this field, it appears that acute exercise does increase metabolic activity. This would indicate that contributions from the factors of decreased blood flow and increased binding are usually overshadowed by the limiting effect of the microsomal enzyme system function or by the hepatic arterial buffer response. The evidence is much more conclusive that chronic exercise enhances metabolic efficiency and activity. In this case, blood flow and the extent of binding would not be factors of importance affecting the rate of metabolism. Work needs to be done in studying the effect of both acute and chronic exercise on isozymes of cyt P-450 levels and the specificity and alterations in the types of cyt P-450, as well as the hepatic metabolism of drugs.

6. EFFECT OF EXERCISE ON RENAL ELIMINATION

Drugs are eliminated from the body either by metabolism or by excretion in urine, bile, feces, milk, saliva, sweat, tears, or breath. The kidney is a very efficient organ for drug excretion. The unbound drugs are filtered at the glomerulus, but bound drugs are not filtered, due to the size of the capillary pores. These bound drugs return to circulation. Drugs that are less ionized will be reabsorbed into the blood. The liver excretes drugs in the bile, from which drugs may be excreted in the feces or be reabsorbed from the intestine. Sweating is a relatively minor pathway at rest, but may become a major pathway for drug elimination during exercise because of the large surface area of the skin.

Clearance is the most important parameter for describing drug elimination. It represents the blood volume from which a drug is removed per unit of time. Clearance depends only on blood flow and on the extraction ratio. Each eliminating organ (usually the kidney and liver) has its own clearance; and the total clearance is the sum of the clearances for the eliminating organs. In some cases a drug may be eliminated by both hepatic and renal mechanisms. However, few studies have examined the effects of exercise on drugs that are removed by both pathways due not only to the increased complexity of the design, but also, the interpretation of the results. However, by simplifying the study to an examination of the drug pharmacokinetics, it is possible to evaluate these types of drugs. Le Coz et al.[118] examined the effects of a stress test (Bailey's) on the pharmacokinetics of bisoprolol. The area under the curve was significantly decreased by exercise, resulting in an increase in the apparent clearance of the drug.

6.1. THE KIDNEYS

The kidneys are the pair of bean-shaped organs about 11 cm long, 5 cm wide, and 3 cm thick, located on either side of the spinal column, posterior to the peritoneum, just opposite the 12th thoracic and the first 3 lumbar vertebrae. In a supine resting human, the 2 kidneys will normally receive about 22% (1.1 l* min^{-1}) of the cardiac output, making this the second largest pathway of regional circulation at rest (Table 1). As with the splanchnic circulation, renal circulation also dramatically decreases in direct proportion to the intensity of exercise (Table 1). When related to the total renal mass of 300 g, renal blood flow is extremely high; the kidney extracts only 6% of the oxygen from blood (Figure 4A). As a result, when oxygen requirements increase during exercise, the kidney can easily meet its oxygen requirements even with the major reduction in blood flow.

The kidneys are responsible for the regulation of body fluid levels, electrolyte balance and metabolic waste, and drug removal from the body. Disturbances in the electrolyte and fluid balance in the body, resulting from exercise, may result in a change in the volume of distribution. Likewise, a change in renal blood flow, and consequently drug delivery to the kidneys, could affect the pharmacokinetics of a variety of drugs.

6.2. EFFECT OF EXERCISE ON RENAL ELIMINATION

Renal clearance depends on blood flow and the extraction ratio. Previous studies have demonstrated that exercise reduces renal blood flow, and the glomerular filtration rate,[7-9,38] in an intensity-dependent manner (Table 1). As a result, the filtration rate of drugs will be reduced during exercise. Similarly, the secretion of drugs with a high renal extraction ratio, that exhibit blood flow-dependent excretion, will be impaired during exercise. It has also been shown that the kidney has an autoregulatory mechanism which stabilizes blood flow during mild exertion.[15] A study by Ylitalo et al.[74] revealed that exercise inhibited the renal excretion of tetracycline and doxycycline. In addition, Ghione et al.[9] showed that isometric exercise reduced the uptake rate of technetium-99m dimercapturic succinic acid (DMSA) by the kidney. Both of these decreases can be attributed to the decrease in renal blood flow that occurs with exercise. Virvidakis et al.[119] also found that altered renal responses are generally due to altered renal blood flow. These experiments demonstrate a distinct relationship between blood flow and drug clearance.

The amount of drug extracted by the kidney depends on glomerular filtration rate (GFR), tubular secretion, and tubular reabsorption. Because of autoregulatory mechanisms, GFR is held relatively constant when renal blood flow is increased.[15,120] Exercise results in an increased percentage of damaged glomeruli,[29,121-123] but it also decreases the GFR.[7,30,70,124] Since clearance is affected by both GFR and blood flow, a fall in GFR and reduced blood flow substantially decreases clearance. Altered renal blood flow is the more important factor since GFR decreases less than renal blood flow with exercise.[8] No studies exist that test the effect of exercise on drug elimination as a function of GFR because it is difficult to control the blood flow.

Another important factor is the tubular reabsorption process, which is passive for the vast majority of drugs. The degree of reabsorption depends on the polarity of the drug, the state of ionization, and urine flow. The urinary pH may decrease during exercise,[74] and therefore, the reabsorption of nonpolar weak acids is increased while that of nonpolar weak bases decreased. The reduction in urine flow during exercise, which is related not only to the degree of exertion but also to the hydration state of the subject,[8] may lead to an increase in the reabsorption of nonpolar unionized drugs.

Passive and active diffusion are temperature-dependent processes. Theoretically then, as body temperature increases during exercise,[6] the diffusion processes involved in the renal excretion of drugs should also increase in speed. In addition, changes in plasma protein binding can affect the filtration rate of certain drugs, as well as the secretion of drugs with a low renal extraction ratio.

6.3. EFFECT OF EXERCISE ON OTHER FORMS OF ELIMINATION

6.3.1. Lungs

Exercise increases cardiac output almost fivefold, with an equivalent increase in pulmonary blood flow. During exercise, the clearance of drugs that are eliminated by the lung should increase. Few drugs have significant pulmonary elimination and fewer studies have been conducted that evaluate the effect of exercise on pulmonary excretion. One study by Meignan et al.[125] showed that apical lung clearance of inhaled technetium-99m DTPA was increased almost twofold with increased apical blood flow, while basal lung clearance was unchanged with slight changes in basal blood flow. Another study done by Boel et al.[103] showed that lung clearance of aminopyrine increased with exercise, further supporting the blood flow-limited proposition. Similar increases in lung clearance of trichloroethylene with exercise were shown in a study by Monster et al.[126] These studies demonstrate a definite increase in lung clearance with exercise.

6.3.2. Effect of Exercise on Sweat or Skin Drug Elimination

The elimination of drugs through sweat during exercise has not been studied in detail, partly due to the quantitative difficulties of collecting sweat; however, new methods are being developed.[127] It is known that many drugs are eliminated through sweat, such as salicylate, antipyrine, methylene blue, sulfonmethane, quinine, fluorescein, sulfanilamide, dehydroascorbic acid, nicotinamide, sulfapyridine, sulfathiazole, sulfadiazine, and *p*-amino-hippuric acid.[128] Fukomoto et al.[129] analyzed sweat composition from exercise-induced sweat as compared to heat-induced sweat and found higher sodium and chloride concentrations, and lower urea nitrogen and creatinine concentrations in the exercise-induced sweat. There was an increase in blood flow to the skin and an increase in sweat during exercise due to the need for thermoregulation.[11] This resulted in an increased clearance for drugs that can penetrate the skin.

To summarize the elimination aspect, exercise affects drug elimination in many different ways. The changes in clearance are due to the sum total changes in clearance of the extracting organs, usually the kidney and liver. Because of decreased blood flow to both organs and decreased GFR due to exercise, the clearance of flow-limited drugs decreases, while the clearance of capacity-

ABSORPTION	Route of administration	Intramuscular or Subcutaneous		Oral or Rectal	
	Permeability	Low	High	Low	High
	Change in absorption	↑	↑↑	↓	↓↓

DISTRIBUTION	Type of drug	Flow-limited	Capacity-limited
	Change in V_d	↓↓	↑↑

METABOLISM	Extent of metabolism	↓ ↑ (substrate dependent)

ELIMINATION	Eliminating organ	Hepatic and/or Renal		Lung	Sweat
	Type of drug	Capacity-limited	Flow-limited		
	Change in Cl	↑	↓	↑	↑*

*↑ most probably increases, but not suffcient data available

V_d Volume of distribution, Cl Clearance

↑ Increase, ↑↑ Marked increase, ↓ Decrease, ↓↓ Marked decrease

FIGURE 6. Summary of the effect of exercise on the absorption, distribution, metabolism, and elimination of the drug in the body. (From Somani, S. M., Gupta, S. K., Frank, S., and Corder, C. N., *Drug Dev. Res.,* 20, 251, 1990. With permission.)

limited drugs increases. For capacity-limited drugs, the factors of enhanced bile flow, enhanced metabolism and enhanced drug removal from the binding proteins are more important than altered blood flow. Lung drug clearance, which does not seem to be very important for most drugs, increases with the increased blood flow with exercise. Sweat, or perhaps what can be called skin clearance, has not been studied sufficiently to arrive at any conclusions. More work needs to be done in calculating how exercise contributes to elimination of capacity-limited drugs before any more definite conclusions can be made.

This chapter has discussed the effect of exercise on drug absorption,[131] taking into account altered permeability,[46,47] distribution, elimination,[130] and pharmacokinetics.[1,2] This chapter provides many interesting theories for the differential effects of blood flow on the pharmacokinetics of flow- vs. capacity-limited drugs, one- vs. two-compartmental models, or permeable vs. impermeable drugs. The effect of exercise on pharmacokinetics can best be described by the concentration-time curves of drugs at rest and in exercise with different permeabilities, extraction levels, or routes of administration.

7. SUMMARY

The effect of exercise on the disposition and pharmacokinetics of drugs is evaluated in this chapter and is summarized in Figure 6 . The data seem to form a coherent picture of the effect of exercise on drug disposition. Exercise in general decreases the absorption after oral administration and increases the absorption after intramuscular and subcutaneous administration due to the increased blood flow in muscle mass. Exercise increases the volume of distribution of flow-limited drugs. Exercise will affect the plasma concentration of high protein binding drugs more than the low protein binding drugs. Hence, highly bound drugs will elicit more of a clinically significant impact in the exercising population. Acute exercise decreases the blood flow to liver; hence it will increase the plasma concentrations of those drugs which have first-pass effect and high clearance (high extraction ratio and high intrinsic clearance). Treadmill exercise or running wheel, but not swimming diminishes, or elevates, the Phase I metabolism and glucuronidation. The effect of exercise on drug metabolism may be substrate-specific, suggesting alterations in isozymes of cyt P-450. Exercise seems to decrease glutathione concentration. However, exercise training appears to ameliorate the toxic effects of drugs by enhancing antioxidant enzymes (Chapter 3). Exercise increases the hepatic and renal elimination of capacity-limited drugs, but decreases elimination of flow-limited drugs. The effect of exercise on drug disposition is also related to other factors including temperature, pH, drug permeability, and barometric pressure; the most critical factor, however, appears to be altered blood flow concomitant with exercise. There is a wide inter- and intraindividual variation in the metabolism and pharmacokinetics of drugs due to exercise. In light of these results, however, much more research needs to be done on a wide range of pharmacokinetic variables, including the concentration time curve of a drug and its metabolites, and different types of drugs given via different routes of administration. It remains to be determined what factors play a major role in drug disposition as a consequence of exercise. Exercise influences the amount of drug reaching the receptor site, which significantly affects pharmacodynamic activity. This aspect of pharmacology has vast implications in therapeutics, particularly for drugs that have a low margin of safety.

REFERENCES

1. **Somani, S. M.,** Metabolism and disposition of chemicals in relation to toxicity, in *Environmental Toxicology: Principles and Policies*, Somani, S. M. and Cavender, F. L., Eds., Charles C Thomas, Springfield, IL., 1981, 11–28.
2. **Somani, S. M., Gupta S. K., Frank S., and Corder, C. N.,** Effect of exercise on disposition and pharmacokinetics of drugs, *Drug Dev. Res.,* 20, 251, 1990.
3. **van Baak, M. A.,** Influence of exercise on the pharmacokinetics of drugs, *Clin. Pharmacokinet.,* 19, 32, 1990.
4. **Ylitalo, P.,** Effect of exercise on pharmacokinetics, *Ann. Med.,* 23, 289, 1991.
5. **Somani, S. M., Babu, S. R., Buckenmeyer, P., DaSilva, M., Dube, S. N., Fitzpatrick, L., Garcia, V., Klingler, K., Knowlton, R., McCoy, J., Rashid, A., Rbak, M., and Sunderam, S.,** Effect of exercise on pharmacokinetics and pharmacodynamics of physostigmine in rats, Report submitted to U.S. Army Medical Research and Development Command, Fort Detrick, Frederick, MD, 1991.
6. **Ballard, B. E.,** Pharmacokinetics and temperature, *J. Pharm. Sci.,* 63, 1345, 1974.

7. **Castenfors, J.,** Renal function during prolonged exercise, *Ann. N.Y. Acad. Sci.,* 301, 151, 1977.
8. **Poortmans, J. R.,** Exercise and renal function, *Sports Med.,* 1, 125, 1984.
9. **Ghione, S., Fommei, E., Palla, L., Rosa, C., Palombo, C., Ragazzini, A., Marabotti, C., and Genovesi-Ebert, A.,** Changes in renal function during physical and mental effort, *Clin. Exp. Hyper. Pt A, Theory Pract.,* 9, 89, 1987.
10. **Ducry, J. J., Howald, H., Zysset, T., and Bircher, J.,** Liver function in physically trained subjects, *Dig. Dis. Sci.,* 24, 192, 1979.
11. **Horvath, S.,** Review of energetics and blood flow in exercise, *Diabetes,* 28, 33, 1979.
12. **Oie, S.,** Drug distribution and binding, *J. Clin. Pharmacol.,* 26, 583, 1986.
13. **Lowenthal, D. T. and Kendrick, Z. V.,** Drug-exercise interactions, *Ann. Rev. Pharmacol. Toxicol.,* 25, 275, 1988.
14. **Shand, D. G., Cotham, R. H., and Wilkinson, G. R.,** Perfusion-limited effects of plasma drug binding on hepatic drug extraction, *Life Sci.,* 19, 125, 1976.
15. **Wilkinson, G. R.,** Pharmacokinetics of drug disposition: hemodynamic considerations, *Ann. Rev. Pharmacol.,* 15, 11, 1975.
16. **Dossing, M.,** Effect of acute and chronic exercise on hepatic drug metabolism, *Clin. Pharmacokin.,* 10, 426, 1985.
17. **Rosenbloom, D. and Sutton, J. R.,** Drugs and exercise, *Med. Clin. North Am.,* 69, 177, 1985.
18. **Levine, R. R.,** Factors affecting gastrointestinal absorption of drugs, *Am. J. Dig. Dis.,* 15, 171, 1970.
19. **Boucher, B. A., Kuhl, D. A., Fabian, T. C., and Robertson, J. T.,** Effect of neurotrauma on hepatic drug clearance, *Clin. Pharmacol. Ther.,* 50, 487, 1991.
20. **Danon, A., Ben-Shimon, S., and Ben-Zvi, Z.,** Effect of exercise and heat exposure on percutaneous absorption of methyl salicylate, *Eur. J. Clin. Pharmacol.,* 31, 49, 1986.
21. **Barkve, T. F., Langseth-Manriqu, K., Bedesen, J. E., and Gjesdal, K.,** Increased uptake of transdermal glycryl trinitrate during physical exercise and during high ambient temperature, *Am. Heart J.,* 112, 537, 1986.
22. **Kamimori, G. H., Eddington, N. A., Hoyt, R. W., Fulco, C. S., Lugo, S., Durkot, M., Brunhart, A. E., and Cymerman, A.,** Effects of altitude (4300 m) on the pharmacokinetics of caffeine and cardio-green in humans, *Eur. J. Clin. Pharmacol.,* 48, 167, 1995.
23. **Kamimori, G. H., Hoyt, R. W., Eddington, N. D., Young, P. M., Durkot, M. A., Forte, V. A., Brunhart, A. E., Lugo, S., and Cymerman, A.,** Effects of chronic hypoxia (4600 m) on the pharmacokinetics of caffeine and cardio-green in micro swine, *Aviat. Space Environ. Med.,* 66, 247, 1995.
24. **Jones, D. P., Aw, T. Y., and Shan, X.,** Drug metabolism and toxicity during hypoxia, *Drug Metab. Rev.,* 20, 247, 1989.
25. **Woodruff Modi, M., Hassett, J. M., and Lalka, D.,** Influence of posture on hepatic perfusion and the presystemic biotransformation of propranolol: simulation of the food effect, *Clin. Pharmacol. Ther.,* 44, 268, 1988.
26. **Woodhouse, K. W. and Wynne, H. A.,** Age-related changes in liver size and hepatic blood flow: the influence of drug metabolism in the elderly, *Clin. Pharmacokinet.,* 15, 287, 1988.
27. **Rowell, L. B.,** Human cardiovascular adjustments to exercise and thermal stress, *Physiol. Rev.,* 54, 75, 1974.
28. **Rowell, L. B.,** *Human Circulation,* Oxford University Press, New York, 1986, chaps. 4 and 9.
29. **Knochel, J. P., Dotin, L. N., and Hamburger, R. J.,** Heat stress, exercise, and muscle injury: effects on urate metabolism and renal function, *Ann. Int. Med.,* 81, 321, 1974.
30. **Refsum, H. E. and Stromme, S. B.,** Relationship between urine flow, glomerular filtration, and urine solute concentrations during prolonged heavy exercise, *Scand. J. Clin. Lab. Invest.,* 35, 775, 1975.

31. **Ardies, C. M., Zachman, E. K., and Koehn, B. J.,** Effect of swimming exercise on rat liver P450-dependent monooxygenases, *Med. Sci. Sports Exerc.,* 26, 1453, 1994.
32. **Rowland, M.,** Protein binding and drug clearance, *Clin. Pharmacokin.,* 9, 10, 1984.
33. **Simko, V. and Kelley, R. E.,** Effect of physical exercise on bile and red blood cell lipids in humans, *Atherosclerosis,* 32, 423, 1979.
34. **Jogestrand, T. and Andersson, K.,** Effects of physical exercise on the pharmacokinetics of digoxin during maintenance treatment, *J. Cardiovasc. Pharmacol.,* 14, 73, 1989.
35. **Koopmans, R., Oosterhuis, B., Karemaker, J. M., Wemer, J., and van Boxtel, C. J.,** The effect of oxprenolol dosage time on its pharmacokinetics and hemodynamic effects during ex in man, *Eur. J. Clin. Pharmacol.,* 44, 171, 1993.
36. **Sweeney, G. D.,** Drugs — some basic concepts, *Med. Sci. Sports Exerc.,* 13, 247, 1981.
37. **Hayton, W. L.,** Rate-limiting barriers to intestinal drug absorption: a review, *J. Pharmacokin. Biopharmaceut.,* 8, 321, 1980.
38. **Swartz, R. D. and Sidell, F. R.,** Effects of heat and exercise on the elimination of pralidoxime in man, *Clin. Pharmacol. Ther.,* 14, 83, 1973.
39. **Kamimori, G. H., Smallridge, R. C., Redmond, D. P., Belenky, G. L., and Fein, H. G.,** The effects of exercise on atropine pharmacokinetics, *Eur. J. Clin. Pharmacol.,* 39, 395, 1990.
40. **Evans, E. F., Proctor, J. D., Fratkin, M. J., Velandia, J., and Wasserman, A.J.,** Blood flow in muscle groups and drug absorption, *Clin. Pharmacol. Ther.,* 17, 44, 1975.
41. **Gjesdal, K., Klemsdal, T. O., Rykke, E. O., and Bredesen, J. E.,** Transdermal nitrate therapy: bioavailability during exercise increases transiently after the daily change of patch, *Br. J. Clin. Pharmacol.,* 31, 560, 1991.
42. **Ochsenfahrt, H. and Winne, D.,** The influence of blood flow on the absorption of drugs from the jejunum of rat, *Naunyn-Schmiedebergs Arch. Pharmacol.,* 264, 55, 1969.
43. **Schulz, R. and Winne, D.,** Relationship between antipyrine absorption and blood flow rate in rat jejunum, ileum, and colon, *Naunyn-Schmiedebergs Arch. Pharmacol.,* 335, 97, 1987.
44. **Ghosh, S. K., Neale, M. G., and Patel, K. R.,** The effect of physiological manoeuvres on the absorption of inhaled nedocromil sodium, *Br. J. Pharmacol.,* 37, 305, 1994.
45. **Tsujimoto, G., Hashimoto, K., and Hoffman, B. B.,** Pharmacokinetic and pharmacodynamic principles of drug therapy in old age. Part 1, *Int. J. Clin. Pharm. Ther. Toxicol.,* 27, 13, 1989.
46. **Winne, D.,** Blood flow in intestinal absorption models, *J. Pharmacokin. Biopharm.,* 6, 55, 1978.
47. **Winne, D.,** Influence of blood flow on intestinal absorption of xenobiotics, *Pharmacology,* 21, 1, 1980.
48. **Babu, S. R. , Buckenmeyer, P., Knowlton, R. G., and Somani, S. M.,** Effect of physostigmine on plasma lactate and pyruvate in untrained/trained rats, *Pharmacol. Biochem. Behav.,* 42, 67, 1993.
49. **Buckenmeyer, P. J., Babu, S. R., Knowlton, R. G., and Somani, S. M.,** Effect of concurrent exercise and physostigmine on lactate and pyruvate in plasma, muscle, and brain tissue of rats, *Pharmacol. Biochem. Behav.,* 47, 779, 1994.
50. **Henry, J. A., Iliopoulou, A., Kaye, C. M., Sankey, M. G., and Turner, P.,** Changes in plasma concentrations of acebutolol, propranolol and indomethacin during physical exercise, *Life Sci.,* 28, 1925, 1981.
51. **Zwaan, M. de,** Exercise and antidepressant serum levels, *Biol. Psychiatry,* 32, 210, 1992.
52. **Swartz, R. D., Sidell, F. R., and Cucinell, S. A.,** Effects of physical stress on the disposition of drugs eliminated by the liver in man, *J. Pharmacol. Exp. Ther.,* 188, 1, 1974.
53. **Mason, W. D., Kochak, G., Winer, N., and Cohen, I.,** Effect of exercise on renal clearance of atenolol, *J. Pharm. Sci.,* 69, 344, 1980.
54. **Daneshmend, T. K., Jackson, L., and Roberts, C. J. C.,** Physiological and pharmacological variability in estimated hepatic blood flow in man, *Br. J. Clin. Pharmacol.,* 11, 491, 1981.

55. **Weber, S., de Lauture, D., Rey, E., Darragon, T., Severins, J. P., Ditisheim, A., Olive, G., and DeGeorges, M.,** The effects of moderate sustained exercise on the pharmacokinetics of nitroglycerine, *Br. J. Clin. Pharm.,* 23, 103, 1987.

56. **Schmidt, H. and Roholt, K.,** Penicillin serum concentrations in relation to exercise, *Acta Pathol. Microbiol. Scand.,* 68, 396, 1966.

57. **van Baak, M. A. van, Mooij, J. M. V., and Schiffers, P. M. H.,** Exercise and the pharmacokinetics of propranolol, verapamil and atenolol, *Eur. J. Clin. Pharmacol.,* 43, 547, 1992.

58. **Frank, S., Somani, S. M., and Kohnle, M.,** Effect of exercise on propanolol pharmacokinetics, *Eur. J. Clin. Pharmacol.,* 39, 391, 1990.

59. **Hurwitz, G. A., Webb, J. G., Walle, T., Bai, S. A., and Daniel, H. B.,** Exercise-induced increments in plasma levels of propranolol and noradrenaline, *Br. J. Clin. Pharmacol.,* 16, 599, 1983.

60. **Powis, G. and Snow, D. H.,** The effects of exercise and adrenaline infusion upon the blood levels of propranolol and antipyrine in the horse, *J. Pharmacol. Exp. Ther.,* 205, 725, 1977.

61. **Pirttiaho, H. I., Sotaniemi, E. A., Pelkonen, R. O., Pitkanen, U., Anttila, M., and Sundqvist, H.,** Roles of hepatic blood flow and enzyme activity in the kinetics of propranolol and sotalol, *Br. J. Clin. Pharmacol.,* 9, 399, 1980.

62. **Mooy, J., Arends, B., van Kemenade, J., Boehm, R., Rahn, K. H., and van Baak, M.,** Influence of prolonged submaximal exercise on the pharmacokinetics of verapamil in humans, *J. Cardiovasc. Pharm.,* 8, 940, 1986.

63. **Novosadova, J.,** The changes in hematocrit, hemoglobin, plasma volume and proteins during and after different types of exercise, *Eur. J. Appl. Physiol. Occup. Physiol.,* 36, 223, 1977.

64. **Shand, D. G., Kornhauser, D. M., and Wilkonson, G. R.,** Effects of route of administration and blood flow on hepatic elimination, *J. Pharmacol. Exp. Ther.,* 195, 424, 1975.

65. **Bradley, S. E., Ingelfinger, F. J., and Bradley, G. P.,** Hepatic circulation in cirrhosis of the liver, *Circulation,* 5, 419, 1952.

66. **Von Bahr, C., Alexanderson, B., Azarnoff, D. L., Sjoqvist, F., and Orrenius, S.,** A comparative study of drug metabolism in the isolated perfused liver and in vivo in rats, *Eur. J. Pharmacol.,* 9, 99, 1970.

67. **Cherrick, G. R., Stein, S. W., Leevy, C. M., and Davidson, C. S.,** Indocyanine green: observations on its physical properties, plasma decay, and hepatic extraction, *J. Clin. Invest.,* 39, 592, 1960.

68. **Nies, A. S., Shand, D. G., and Wilkinson, G. R.,** Altered hepatic blood flow and drug disposition, *Clin. Pharmacokin.,* 1, 135, 1976.

69. **Somani, S. M., Babu, S. R., and Rashid, A.,** Effect of endurance training on pharmacokinetics distribution of ^{3}H-physostigmine in rats, 11th Int. Congr. Pharmacol. (IUPHAR), Amsterdam, The Netherlands, 1990.

70. **Ylitalo, P. and Hinkka, H.,** Effect of exercise on plasma levels and urinary excretion of sulphadimidine and procainamide, *Int. J. Clin. Pharm. Toxicol.,* 23, 548, 1985.

71. **Benet, L. Z.,** Effect of route of administration and distribution on drug action, *J. Pharmacokin. Biopharm.,* 6, 559, 1978.

72. **Imai, N., Stone, C. K., Woolf, P. D., and Liang, C. S.,** Effects of naloxone on systemic and regional hemodynamic responses to exercise in dogs, *J. Appl. Physiol.,* 64, 1493, 1988.

73. **McDonald, R. B., Hamilton, J. S., Stern, J. S., and Horwitz, B. A.,** Regional blood flow of exercise-trained younger and older cold-exposed rats, *Am. J. Physiol.,* 256, R1069, 1989.

74. **Ylitalo, P., Hinkka, H., and Neuvonen, P. J.,** Effects of exercise on the serum level and urinary excretion of tetracycline, doxycycline and sulphamethizole, *Eur. J. Clin. Pharm.,* 12, 367, 1977.

75. **Marsh, T. D., Garnett, W. R., Poynor, W. J., and Pellock, J. M.,** Effects of exercise on valproic acid pharmacokinetics, *Clin. Pharmacol.,* 2, 62, 1983.

76. **Klotz, U. and Lucke, C.,** Physical exercise and disposition of diazepam, *Br. J. Clin. Pharm.,* 5, 349, 1978.

77. **Lunde, P. K. M., Rane, A., Yaffe, S. J., Lund, L., and Sjoqvist, F.,** Plasma protein binding of diphenylhydantoin in man, *Clin. Pharmacol. Exp. Ther.,* 11, 846, 1970.

78. **O'Reilly, R. A.,** The binding of sodium warfarin to plasma albumin and its displacement by phenylbutazone, *Ann. N.Y. Acad. Sci.,* 226, 293, 1973.

79. **Somani, S. M. and McDonald, R. H., Jr.,** Cross competition for protein binding sites by warfarin and salicylates, *Pharmacologist,* 12, 244, 1970.

80. **Joreteg, T. and Jogestrand, T.,** Physical exercise and digoxin binding to skeletal muscle: relation to exercise intensity, *Eur. J. Clin. Pharmacol.,* 25, 585, 1983.

81. **Joreteg, T. and Jogestrand, T.,** Physical exercise and binding of digoxin to skeletal muscle — effect of muscle activation frequency, *Eur. J. Clin. Pharmacol.,* 27, 567, 1984.

82. **Brauer, R. W.,** Liver circulation and function, *Physiol. Rev.,* 43, 115, 1963.

83. **Paterson, J. Y. F. and Harrison, F. A.,** The splanchnic and hepatic uptake of cortisol in conscious and anaesthetized sheep, *J. Endocrin.,* 55, 335, 1972.

84. **Cadorniga, R., Arias, I., and Migoya, I.,** Variation of the pharmco-kinetics of sodium ampicillin as a function of physical exercise, *Farmaco Edizione Practica,* 29, 386, 1974.

85. **Hetzler, R. K.,** The effect of prolonged walking on the pharmaco-kinetics and metabolism of caffeine, Ph.D. thesis, Southern Illinois University, Carbondale, IL, 1988, 76.

86. **Kamimori, G. H., Somani, S. M., Knowlton, R. G., and Perkins, R. M.,** The effects of obesity and exercise on the pharmacokinetics of caffeine in lean and obese volunteers, *Eur. J. Clin. Pharmacol.,* 31, 595, 1986.

87. **Arends, B. G., Bohm, R. O. B., van Kemenade, J. E., Rahn, K. H., and van Baak, M. A.,** Influence of physical exercise on the pharmacokinetics of propanolol, *Eur. J. Clin. Pharmacol.,* 31, 375, 1986.

88. **Belko, A. Z.,** Vitamins and exercise — an update, *Med. Sci. Sports Exerc.,* 19, S191, 1987.

89. **Cadoux-Hudson, T. A., Few, J. D., and Imms, F. J.,** The effect of exercise on the production and clearance of testosterone in well-trained young men, *Eur J. Appl. Physiol.,* 54, 321, 1985.

90. **Schlaeffer, F., Engelberg, I., Kaplanski, J., and Danon, A.,** Effect of exercise and environmental heat on theophylline kinetics, *Respiration,* 45, 438, 1984.

91. **Gibaldi, M. and Koup, J. R.,** Pharmacokinetic concepts — drug binding, apparent volume of distribution and clearance, *Eur. J. Pharmacol.,* 20, 299, 1981.

92. **Gugler, R. and von Uhruh, G. E.,** Clinical pharmacokinetics of valproic acid, *Clin. Pharmacokin.,* 5, 67, 1980.

93. **Reed, J. S., Smith, N. D., and Boyer, J. L.,** Hemodynamic effects on oxygen consumption and bile flow in isolated skate liver, *Am. J. Physiol.,* 242, G313, 1982.

94. **Simko, V. and Kelley, R. E.,** Effect of chronic intermittent exercise on biliary lipids, plasma lecithin cholesterol acyltransferase, and red blood cell lipids in rats, *Am. J. Clin. Nutr.,* 32, 1376, 1979.

95. **Kamimori, G. H.,** The effect of pre-exercise caffeine ingestion on free fatty acid metabolism and metabolism at rest, during and following prolonged sub-maximal exercise in lean and obese volunteers, Ph.D. thesis, Southern Illinois University, Carbondale IL, 1985.

96. **Jones, D. P. and Mason, H. S.,** Gradients of O_2 concentration in hepatocytes, *J. Biol. Chem.,* 253, 4874, 1987.

97. **Gonzalez, F. J.,** Human cytochromes P450: problems and prospects, *Trends Pharmacol. Sci.,* 13, 346, 1992.

98. **Lu, A. Y. H. and West, S. B.,** Multiplicity of mammalian microsomal cytochromes P-450, *Pharmacol. Rev.,* 31, 277, 1980.

99. **Nebert, D. W. and Gonzalez, F. J.,** P450 genes: structure, evolution, and regulation, *Annu. Rev. Biochem.,* 56, 945, 1987.

100. **Yang, C. S., Yoo, J. H., Ishizaki, H., and Hong, J.,** P450IIE1: roles in nitrosamine metabolism and mechanisms of regulation, *Drug Metab. Rev.,* 22, 147, 1990.

101. **Ardies, C. M., Morris, G. S., Erickson, C. K., and Farrar, R. P.,** Both acute and chronic exercise enhance in vivo ethanol clearance in rats, *J. Appl. Physiol.,* 66, 555, 1989.

102. **Frenkl, R., Gyore, A., Meszaros, J., and Szeberenyi, S. Z.,** A study of the enzyme inducing effect of physical exercise in man. The trained liver, *J. Sports Med.,* 20, 371, 1980.
103. **Boel, J., Andersen, L. B., Rasmussen, B., Hansen, S. H., and Dossing, M.,** Hepatic drug metabolism and physical fitness, *Clin. Pharm. Ther.,* 36, 121, 1984.
104. **Day, W. W. and Weiner, M.,** Inhibition of hepatic drug metabolism and carbon tetrachloride toxicity in Fisher-344 rats by exercise, *Biochem. Pharmacol.,* 42, 181, 1991.
105. **Yiamouyiannis, C. A., Sanders, R. A., Walkins, J. B., III, and Martin, B. J.,** Chronic physical exercise alters xenobiotic biotransformation, *FASEB J.,* 4, 3461, 1990.
106. **Ramos, C. L., Day, W. W., Piatkowski, T. S., Mei, J., Chesky, J. A., and Weiner, M.,** Differential effects of treadmill running and swimming on hematic microsomal metabolism in middle-aged and aged Fisher-344 rats, *FASEB J.,* 4, 3462, 1990.
107. **Day, W. W., Chesky, J. A., and Weiner, M.,** Differential effects of swimming and running on microsomal metabolism in middle-aged and aged Fisher 344 rats, *Mech. Ageing Dev.,* 63, 275, 1992.
108. **Michaud, T. J., Bachmann, K. A., Andres, F. F., Flynn, M. G., Sherman, G. P., and Rodriguez-Zayas, J.,** Exercise training does not alter cytochrome P450 content and microsomal metabolism, *Med. Sci. Sports Exerc.,* 26, 978, 1994.
109. **Piatkowski, T. S., Day, W. W., and Weiner, M.,** Increased renal drug metabolism in treadmill-exercised Fisher-344 male rats, *Drug Met. Disp.,* 21, 474, 1993.
110. **Merrill, A. H., Jr., Hoel, M., Wang, E., Mullins, R. E., Hargrove, J. L., Jones, D. P., and Popova, I. A.,** Altered carbohydrate, lipid and xenobiotic metabolism by liver from rats flown on Cosmos 1887, *FASEB J.,* 4, 95, 1990.
111. **Serbinova, B. A., Kadiiska, M. B., Bakalova, R. A., Koynova, G. M., Stoyanovsky, D. A., Karakasbev, P. C., Stoytchev, T. S., Wolinsky, I., and Kagan, V.,** Lipid peroxidation activation and cytochrome P-450 decrease in rat liver endoplasmic reticulum under oxidative stress, *Toxicol. Lett.,* 47, 119, 1989.
112. **Somani, S. M., Ravi, R., and Rybak, L. P.,** Effect of exercise training on antioxidant system in brain regions of rat, *Biochem. Behav.,* 50, 635, 1995.
113. **Somani, S. M., Frank, S., and Rybak, L. P.,** Responses of antioxidant system to acute and trained exercise in rat heart subcellular fractions, *Biochem. Behav.,* 51, 627, 1995.
114. **Sudo, A.,** Changes of adrenaline concentration in various organs of the rat during and following four hours' swimming, *Industr. Health,* 24, 191, 1986.
115. **Vesell, E. S.,** Complex effects of diet on drug disposition, *Clin. Pharmacol. Ther.,* 36, 285, 1984.
116. **Breimer, D. D.,** Variability in human drug metabolism and its implications, *Int. J. Clin. Pharm. Res.,* 3 , 399, 1983.
117. **Lautt, W. W.,** Relationship between hepatic blood flow and overall metabolism: the hepatic arterial buffer response, *Fed. Proc.,* 42, 1662, 1983.
118. **Le Coz, F., Sauleman, P., Poirier, J. M., Cuche, J. L., Midavaine, M., Rames, A., Lecocq, B., and Jaillon, P.,** Oral pharmacokinetics of bisiprolol in resting and exercising healthy volunteers, *J. Cardiovasc. Pharmacol.,* 18, 28, 1991.
119. **Virvidakis, C., Loukas, A., Mayopoulou-Symvoulidou, D., and Mountokalakis, T.,** Renal responses to bicycle exercise in trained athletes: influence of exercise intensity, *Int. J. Sports Med.,* 7, 86, 1986.
120. **Joles, J. A., den Hertog, J. M., Velthuizen, J., and Boshouwers, F. M.,** Glomerular filtration rate in intact and splenectomized running and swimming dogs, *Int. J. Sports Med.,* 6, 20, 1985.
121. **Cornacoff, J. B., Hebert, L. A., Sharma, H. M., Bay, W. H., and Young, D. C.,** Adverse effect of exercise on immune complex-mediated glomerulonephritis, *Nephron,* 40, 292, 1985.
122. **Jackson, R. C.,** Exercise-induced renal failure and muscle damage, *Proc. R. Soc. Med.,* 63, 566, 1970.
123. **Lichtig, C., Levy, J., Gershon, D., and Reznick, A. Z.,** Effect of aging and exercise on the kidney. Anatomical and morphological studies, *Gerontology,* 33, 40, 1987.

124. **Sadowski, J., Gellert, R., Kurkus, J., and Portalaska, E.,** Denervated and intact kidney responses to exercise in the dog, *J. Appl. Physiol.,* 51, 1618, 1981.
125. **Meignan, M., Rosso, J., Leveau, J., Katz, A., Cinotti, L., Madelaine, G., and Galle, P.,** Exercise increases the lung clearance of inhaled technetium-99m DTPA, *J. Nucl. Med.,* 27, 274, 1986.
126. **Monster, A. C., Boersma, G., and Duba, W. C.,** Pharmacokinetics of trichloroethylene in volunteers, influence of workload and exposure concentration, *Int. Arch. Occup. Environ. Health,* 38, 87, 1976.
127. **Pilardeau, P. A., Harichaux, P., Chalumeau, M. T., Vasseur, B., Vaysse, J., and Garnier, M.,** Sweat collection from athletes, *Br. J. Sports Med.,* 19, 197, 1985.
128. **Stowe, C. M. and Plaa, G. L.,** Extrarenal excretion of drugs and chemicals, *Ann. Rev. Pharmacol.,* 8, 337, 1968.
129. **Fukomoto, T., Tanaka, T., Fujioka, H., Yoshihara, S., Ochi, T., and Kuroiwa, A.,** Differences in composition of sweat induced by thermal exposure and by running exercise, *Clin. Cardiol.,* 11, 707, 1988.
130. **Collomp, K., Anselme, F., Audran, M., Gay, J. P., Chanal, J. L., and Prefaut, C.,** Effects of moderate exercise on the pharmacokinetics of caffeine, *Eur. J. Clin. Pharmacol.,* 40, 279, 1991.
131. **Aslaksen, A. and Aanderud, L.,** Drug absorption during physical exercise, *Br. J. Clin. Pharmacol.,* 10, 383, 1980.

Chapter 2

EXERCISE AND PHARMACODYNAMICS OF DRUGS

Philip J. Buckenmeyer and Satu M. Somani

CONTENTS

1. INTRODUCTION

The importance of exercise for the overall health of human beings has gained significant recognition during the last decade. Epidemiological studies,[1,2] in part, have given impetus to this exercise phenomenon. In a sense, exercise has become a prophylactic and therapeutic panacea. However, it cannot stand alone for our many health needs and ailments. We, as fallible beings, still need to rely on other factors such as proper nutrition, avoidance of

0-8493-8540-1/96/$0.00+$.50
© 1996 by CRC Press, Inc.

unhealthful acts, such as excessive alcohol intake and smoking, and use of stress releasers such as meditation and recreational activities to maintain a healthy quality of life.

Despite the shift in the nature of illnesses, from infectious diseases of the early 1900s to a greater predominance of degenerative conditions in the latter stages of this century, we still find that certain medications/drugs are necessary to allay various ailing conditions. Various drugs are prescribed to lessen the stress of debilitating conditions such as psychosomatic, cardiovascular, and pulmonary disorders. Yet, as we pursue healthy activities such as athletic competition, we often attempt to better our odds in using drugs to gain an advantage over our peers. On a short-term basis, drugs would appear to be the answer to our medical ills, and paradoxically, our answer to maximizing our athletic skills. In terms of one's medical condition, exercise is often an adjunct therapy. In athletic competition, drugs often become an additive therapy to exercise. Regardless of the scenario, we must have an understanding of the exercise-drug interaction on the body as we seek to attain an optimal outcome.

Much has been written about the physiological processes associated with drug-body interactions. These interactions have been coined as "pharmacodynamic" and "pharmacokinetic." Pharmacodynamic interactions refer to the effects of a drug on the body; more specifically, drug-receptor binding characteristics and dose-response relationships. Pharmacokinetic refers to the manner in which the body handles the drug once it enters the body, or how the drug is absorbed, distributed, metabolized, and eliminated. The primary focus of this chapter will be on the pharmacodynamic aspects of various drugs and how they interact with exercise. We will define a "drug" as any substance with a small molecular nature that, when introduced into the body, alters the body's function by interactions at the subcellular level.

Most drugs act on a subcellular level through tissue macromolecules such as proteins, carbohydrate-protein structures, lipid-protein structures, and nucleic acids. Drug interactions usually occur through membrane-bound receptors or structures within the targeted cells. The binding of a drug to a receptor, or "second messenger" molecule, is most often a reversible phenomenon. For example, cardiac patients who must control their epinephrine-stimulated heart rate response may be prescribed to take indural, which serves as a competitive antagonist for the B-receptor-bound epinephrine. Dependent upon the dosage and specificity of the drug, either an appropriate action, a toxemic outcome, or nonevident response will occur. Other drugs may not interact directly with receptors, but change subcellular mechanisms through a change in the extracellular millieu. For example, sodium bicarbonate, when ingested through various routes, can change the pH of the blood and, hence, indirectly influence cellular mechanisms that are affected by acid-base changes.

Most "exercise-drug interaction" literature does not address the biochemical parameters in significant detail. This chapter will address this area, which is lacking in sufficient information, as well as current exercise-drug interactions on a physiological level. The chapter is divided into three general categories: (1) medicinal drugs and exercise; (2) ergogenic drugs and exercise; and (3) ergolytic drugs and exercise.

2. MEDICINAL DRUGS AND EXERCISE

This section will focus on common drugs which are usually presribed to enhance the quality of life for an individual who has an underlying disease or medical condition. In this sense, we are dealing with drugs administered to people with cardiovascular, pulmonary, metabolic, or acute inflammatory conditions. Exercise enters the scenario when it is used as an adjunct to provide an external stressor, as in stress testing or when exercise is used to enhance the functional level of the damaged anatomical system. In fewer cases, these drugs may be used to improve performance of the highly skilled athlete. Since cardiovascular drugs and exercise are discussed in another chapter of this book, this important category will not be treated here.

2.1. PULMONARY DISEASE DRUGS
2.1.1. Bronchodilators and Related Agents
Pharmacologic Aspect. There are various bronchodilators that are utilized to prevent and reverse acute bronchospasm, as well as reduce the level of responsiveness of pulmonary airways to foreign allergens. Cromolyn sodium prevents the antigen-induced release of histamine from sensitized mast cells by inhibiting the transmembrane influx of calcium provoked by IgE antibody-antigen interactions. Methylxanthines appear to inhibit phosphodiesterase or block cell surface receptors for adenosine such that the rate of cAMP degradation is slowed, and the rate of adenyl cyclase synthesis is increased, respectively. These factors increase the intracellular levels of cAMP which signals smooth muscle relaxation of the airways. Sympathomimetic agents stimulate B_2 receptors to relax the airway smooth musculature. Muscarinic antagonists act by competitively inhibiting the effects of acetylcholine released from mucarinic receptors. The exact mechanism of corticosteroids remains unanswered; however they appear to potentiate the action of β-receptor agonists and/or modify the inflammatory response of the airways.

Exercise-Drug Interaction. Exercise and pulmonary disease drugs interactions are summarized in Table 1.

These drugs, primarily used by asthmatics, allow patients to engage in physical activity more easily and for longer durations. The beta-sympathomimetic agents are administered, usually as aerosols, prior to exercise work, in 90% of asthmatic patients who are subjected to exercise-induced asthma (EIA). Cromolyn sodium prevents EIA in 60 to 70% of patients.[3] These individuals should be cautioned in that these drugs can induce higher heart rates, hypertension, and some ventricular dysrhythmias.[4] These drugs do not give the asthmatic any

TABLE 1
Interaction of Pulmonary Disease Drugs and Exercise

Drug Classification		Biochemical Effects During Exercise
Bronchodilators	1.	Through their inhibition of phosphodiesterase, resulting in higher levels of cAMP and subsequent calcium influx, these drugs have the potential of improving contractility and reducing fatigue of diaphragm muscles during exercise in individuals with chronic obstructive lung disease.
	2.	Through their inhibitory effect on activity of presynaptic adenosine receptors, resulting in a greater catecholamine release, these drugs have the potential of increasing heart rate and contractility of cardiac muscle during exercise.

advantage over the healthy individual in exercise performance, but they do remove the respiratory disadvantage.[5] In cystic fibrosis patients, bronchodilators can impair lung function during exercise.[6] Therefore, one must be cautious of the use of these drugs for different degrees of pulmonary restriction during exercise.

2.2. METABOLIC DISEASE/THERAPEUTIC DRUGS
2.2.1. Insulin
Pharmacologic Aspect. Insulin acts by binding to receptors that are located on various organs, in particular the liver, muscle, and adipose tissue. These receptors have both an alpha and beta subunit. When the alpha subunit interacts with insulin, tyrosine kinase is activated in the adjacent beta subunit. Subsequently, this enzyme initiates the sequential phosphorylation of proteins within the target organ cell. This process results in the translocation of certain proteins like the glucose transporters, and hence, the transport of glucose from the blood to the intracellular space of the target cell.

Exercise-Insulin Interaction. Exercise and insulin interactions are summarized in Table 2.

Insulin is primarily used in the treatment of Type I (insulin-dependent diabetes) and sometimes with Type II (noninsulin-dependent diabetes) diabetes mellitus. In Type I diabetics, exercise can be used successfully in improving and maintaining glycemic control. With an appropriate amount of insulin in the blood, exercise increases the uptake of glucose into the target cells. Without proper monitoring, Type I diabetics are susceptible to hypoglycemia during and immediately after exercise, since the liver cannot keep pace with the rate of glucose uptake. Appropriate monitoring techniques of blood glucose levels are essential in reducing the health risks associated with diabetes. In addition, it has been shown that aerobic exercise and training can be effective means of enhancing glycemic control.[7] In Type II diabetics, exercise plays a significant role in maintaining glycemic control. Muscle contraction provides an "insulin-like" effect whereby membrane permeability is increased, most likely due to

TABLE 2
Interaction of Metabolic Disease Drugs and Exercise

Drug	Biochemical Effects
Insulin	Through its binding to insulin receptors, glucose uptake is significantly enhanced with exercise.
Thyroid drugs	1. Through binding to T_3 receptors on cell membrane, there is a potential for an increase in glucose and amino acid uptake in skeletal muscle with exercise.
	2. Through binding to T_3 receptors on mitochondrial membrane, there is a potential for an increase in energy metabolism and oxygen utilization with exercise.
	3. Through binding to T_3 receptors in the nucleus, there is a potential for increased RNA polymerase activity and transcription of DNA into RNA resulting in enhanced protein synthesis with exercise.
Carbamates	The inhibitory action on acetylcholinesterase and choline-acetyltransferase creates a greater demand on glycolysis in skeletal muscle. This results in greater lactate accumulation. With acute exercise and aerobic training, there appears to be a shift toward a greater pyruvate/lactate ratio resulting in a lessened fatigue response in skeletal muscle during exercise while on these drugs.

the increased availability of glucose transporters.[8] As the result of a brief bout of exercise, there is a decrease in insulin resistance and an increase in insulin sensitivity. Thus, a regular exercise routine can help reduce the cardiovascular risks associated with Type II diabetes.

2.2.2. Thyroid Drugs

Pharmacologic Aspect. The exact mechanism of these drugs remains elusive; however, their effects appear to occur via receptor mechanisms in the nucleus, mitochondria, and plasma membrane. The most sensitive organs are the pituitary, liver, kidney, heart, skeletal muscle, lung, and intestine. Upon binding to the nuclear receptor, there is an increase in RNA polymerase activity and transcription of DNA into RNA, resulting in increased mRNA and subsequently an increase in protein synthesis. Binding to the mitochondrial receptor appears to enhance energy metabolism via an increase in oxygen utilization. Interaction with plasma membrane receptors stimulates Na-K$^+$ ATPase activity, thus resulting in increase Na$^+$ and K$^+$ transport across the membrane.

Exercise-Drug Interaction. The interaction of exercise and thyroid drugs are summarized in Table 2.

These drugs are important for optimal growth, development, and function of all body tissues, particularly in the hypothyroid patient. Little information is available to address the interaction between thyroid drugs and exercise; however, it would be likely that without the drug, hypothyroid patients would experience significant muscle fatigue and stiffness in attempt to perform endurance exercises.

2.2.3. Carbamates

Pharmacologic Aspect. Carbamates are indirect-acting cholinomimetic drugs that act as acetylcholinesterase inhibitors. By inhibiting this enzyme's action (hydrolyzing acetylcholine in the synaptic cleft), the concentration of acetylcholine is increased. The carbamates are extensively discussed in Chapter 7 on exercise and the cholinergic system.

Exercise-Drug Interaction. The interactions of exercise and carbamates are summarized in Table 2.

These drugs can be utilized for therapeutic intervention such as myasthenia gravis and glaucoma. Of primary interest to the exercise field is the use of these drugs to enhance the strength of skeletal muscles which have been weakened by myasthenia gravis, a disease of the neuromuscular junction. This disease resembles the neuromuscular paralysis which can occur from exposure to neuromuscular blocking drugs, such as those used in chemical warfare. In this arena, recent interest has risen in the effect of carbamates on exercise performance. Thermoregulatory studies with pyridostigmine ingestion have revealed no decrement in aerobic performance when compared to control settings.[9-11] However, one investigation noted a minimal decrease in handgrip strength.[9] Another of the carbamates which has been addressed in terms of its interaction with exercise is physostigmine. Under thermal stress conditions, this drug has been correlated to a serial decrement in endurance performance as drug dosage and core temperature increases.[12] Nonthermal exercise studies have revealed a prolonged inhibitory effect of physostigmine on acetylcholinesterase and choline-acetyltransferase activities in skeletal muscle,[13] resulting in a greater accumulation of metabolic lactate.[14] The fact that endurance time has been found to increase with physostigmine administration[15] supports the potential for greater lactate accumulation. A higher level of aerobic training may enhance the benefit of this drug.[16,17] These studies suggest that an advantage can be gained in using pyridostigmine and physostigmine as counters to neuromuscular disease and blocking drugs, respectively.

2.3. ACUTE ANTI-INFLAMMATORY DRUGS
2.3.1. Nonsteroidal Anti-Inflammatory Drugs (NSAIDs)

Pharmacologic Aspect. NSAIDs produce anti-inflammatory, analgesic, and antipyretic responses. The most notable of these drugs are the salicylates. Salicylates effectively inhibit prostaglandin biosynthesis by irreversibly blocking the enzyme cyclooxygenase, which catalyzes the conversion of arachidonic acid to endoperoxide compounds. It also interferes with chemical compounds associated with the kallikrein system by inhibiting granulocyte attachment to damaged vasculature, stabilizing lysosomes, and preventing the migration of leukocytes to the site of tissue injury.

TABLE 3
Interaction of Acute Anti-Inflammatory Drugs and Exercise

Drug	Biochemical Effects
NSAIDs	It is unclear if the interaction of NSAIDs with exercise would alter the capacity to inhibit prostaglandin biosynthesis.
Corticosteroids	In terms of their anti-inflammatory action, it is unclear if exercise would enhance or detract from the inhibition of phospholipase A_2 and blockage of the synthesis of prostaglandins.

Exercise-Drug Interaction. The interactions of antiinflammatory drugs and exercise are summarized in Table 3.

These drugs are used primarily to treat rheumatic conditions, as well as soft tissue injuries in athletes. NSAIDS do not directly enhance exercise performance. However, their "pain-killing" property may indirectly assist the athlete when participating in a "pain-limited" activity. These drugs often hasten pain relief in conjuction with rest, ice, compression, and elevation of acute injuries.[18] These drugs are not currently banned by the International Olympic Committee (IOC) or the NCAA.

2.3.2. Corticosteroids

Pharmacologic Aspect. Corticosteroids, e.g., glucocorticoids and minercorticoids, appear to bind to either cell surface or cytoplasmic receptors (after diffusion through the cell membrane). This drug-receptor interaction sets off various metabolic reactions. In terms of its antiinflammatory action, phospholipase A_2 activity is inhibited and the synthesis of prostaglandins is blocked. A significant increase in neutrophils occurs; however, the number of B- and T-lymphocytes, monocytes, eosinophils, and basophils in the circulation decreases.

Exercise-Drug Interaction. See Table 3 for a summary of the interactions of antiinflammatory drugs and exercise.

Although the analgesic effect from an athletic injury is reduced by the administration of corticosteroids, the ability of leukocytes and macrophages to respond to the inflammatory process can be significantly reduced. These drugs also inhibit collagen formation and slow wound healing.[19] Therefore, one must weigh the advantages and disadvantages of utilizing these drugs; their analgesic properties for athletic performance may be countered by further damage to the internal tissue structures.

3. ERGOGENIC DRUGS AND EXERCISE

This section will focus on common drugs that are usually utilized to enhance the performance of a physical activity. These drugs might sometimes be referred to as "stimulants" to the body. Hence, their use should carry a level of caution.

TABLE 4
Interaction of Ergogenic Drugs and Exercise

Drug	Biochemical Effects
Amphetamines	Since both amphetamines and exercise increase catecholamine release, it would seem that a greater systemic metabolic effect would be created.
Caffeine	1. With exercise there is an increased potential for an elevation of oxygenase activities.
	2. With exercise, there would appear to be a greater calcium flux into the muscle.
	3. With exercise, there is the likelihood of increased cellular cyclic AMP levels due to an increase in adenyl cyclase activity and/or inhibition of phosphodiesterase. These mechanisms have been associated with an increase in lipase activity in adipose tissue.
	4. It is unclear if exercise would alter the blocking of adenosine receptors by caffeine or its derivatives.
Erythropoietin	In conjunction with exercise, there is a greater potential for stimulation of new erythroid precursor cells in the bone marrow, which can subsequently lead to increased red blood cell formation.
Sodium bicarbonate	This drug counterbalances the efflux of hydrogen ions from the exercising muscle, thereby delaying the decrease in intracellular pH and offsetting the rate of fatigue.
Sodium phosphate	1. In conjunction with exercise, it would tend to promote phosphate-stimulated glycolysis.
	2. In conjunction with exercise, there may be a greater potential for oxidative phosphorylation and creatine phosphate synthesis.
	3. In conjunction with exercise, there may be an alteration in oxyhemoglobin affinity.
	4. In conjuction with exercise, there is a potential for increased red cell anaerobic glycolysis and efficiency.
	5. In conjunction with exercise, there may be a delay in the elevation of lactate in the muscle and its efflux into the blood.

3.1. AMPHETAMINES

Pharmacologic Aspect. Amphetamines have several mechanisms by which their "stimulant" actions are believed to occur. They have both central and peripheral effects, which include enhanced release of endogenous catecholamines, inhibition of monoamine oxidase (responsible for metabolic degradation of endogenous catecholamines), displacement of catecholamines from their specific alpha- and beta-adrenergic binding sites, and prevention of synaptic catecholamine reuptake.

Exercise-Drug Interaction: The interactions of amphetamines and exercise are summarized in Table 4.

These drugs have certain therapeutic uses such as an appetite suppression for obese patients, prevention of normal sleep lapses during periods of inactivity, treatment for various brain dysfunctions, reduction of periods of depression, and attenuation of severe menstrual cramps. Their interaction with exercise has revealed such effects as reduction of muscular fatigue,[20] improvement of forearm and handgrip strength,[21] and increased exercise performance in running, swimming, and weight throwing events.[22] Other researchers have not found any enhancement of exercise performance from these drugs.[23,24] In general, amphetamines will exhibit increased alertness but appear to vary in their potential for exercise performance benefit.

3.2. CAFFEINE

Pharmacologic Aspect. Caffeine is one of the most widely used and studied ergogenic drugs in sports. Its effects are believed to occur from its breakdown by-products. The demethylation of caffeine by hepatic cytochrome P-450 oxygenases occurs within minutes of ingestion, resulting in dimethylxanthines (e.g., paraxanthine).[25] Exercise appears to increase the activities of oxygenases similar to a magnitude corresponding to heavy smoking.[26] The breakdown products from caffeine are responsible for three possible mechanisms of action: (1) increased myofilament affinity for calcium and permeability of the sarcoplasmic reticulum to calcium allowing for a greater availability of calcium for muscular contraction; (2) increase of cellular $3'5'$-cyclic adenosine monophosphate (AMP) by either increasing circulating catecholamines which subsequently increase adenyl cyclase activity or by inhibiting phosphodiesterase (catalyzes the conversion of cyclic AMP to $5'$-AMP); and (3) blocking of adenosine receptors that are responsible for the initiation of central nervous system "sedation" effects via binding of adenosine.[27] Caffeine is found in many notable preparations including coffee, tea, cola drinks, cocoa, milk chocolate, and medications such as Anacin®, Excedrin®, Midol®, No Doz®, and Vivarin®. It is the most addictive drug known to humankind.

Exercise-Drug Interaction. The interactions of exercise and caffeine are summarized in Table 4 and are also discussed in Chapter 1.

Caffeine is used in various "over-the-counter" analgesic medications and has been shown to be useful in atopic dermatitis. Its close relative, theophylline, is utilized as a bronchodilator for asthmatics. However, it has received considerable attention in sports, particularly in endurance activities. This is due to its purported "glycogen-sparing" effect, and subsequent increase of fat metabolism. Conflicting reports suggest that it either enhances endurance performance[28,29] or it has no ergogenic effect at all.[30,31] Under environmental conditions, caffeine has been shown to enhance cycling performance at altitude,[32] and elevate plasma epinephrine levels in conjunction with an increase in fat metabolism and serum free fatty acids during cycling in a cold environment

(5°C, 70% relative humidity).[33] Metabolically, caffeine users have been shown to elicit greater plasma theophylline concentrations vs. greater levels of paraxanthine in nonusers during submaximal exercise.[34] Plasma free fatty acids, glycerol, and respiratory exchange ratio did not differ between these caffeine users and nonusers. Caffeine not only appears to affect aerobic exercise, but it has been shown to increase maximal anaerobic power/performance and blood lactate concentrations.[35] In summary, caffeine's effect on exercise performance is still debatable, but it does appear to increase catecholamine levels in most exercise investigations. The equivocal findings in research literature are most likely due to methodological variances which need to be resolved.

3.3. ERYTHROPOIETIN
Pharmacologic Aspect. Erythropoietin is a drug that stimulates the proliferation and differentiation of certain erythroid precursor cells in the bone marrow, and subsequently leads to increased red blood cell formation and improvement in anemic patients.

Exercise-Drug Interaction. The interactions of exercise and erythropoietin are summarized in Table 4.

    This drug is primarily utilized in renal failure patients in order to improve hematocrit and hemoglobin levels, thus lessening the need for blood transfusions on a regular basis. In end-stage renal diseased/hemodialysis patients, administration of this drug has been shown to increase exercise capacity.[36] This drug is of interest to exercise researchers because it could mimic conventional blood doping outcomes. Research suggests that endurance performance, following several weeks of erythropoietin injections, may be improved from 10 to 24%.[37-39] However, athletes should be cautioned in its use since it has been shown to significantly increase systolic blood pressure,[40] and its blood thickening property could lead to cardiovascular risks.[41] It has recently been banned by the IOC.

3.4. SODIUM BICARBONATE
Pharmacologic Aspect. Sodium bicarbonate is a drug utilized to buffer the blood against a change in pH. Its mechanism of action is to simply increase blood pH such that there is a facilitated efflux of hydrogen ions from the exercising muscle, thereby delaying the decrease in intracellular pH and offsetting the rate of fatigue. Lactic acid accumulation and its associated "acidic" effects are believed to impair muscle performance by reducing aerobic glycolysis and/or fatty acid oxidation.

Exercise-Drug Interaction. The interactions of exercise and sodium bicarbonate are summarized in Table 4. Sodium bicarbonate loading has been shown to be an effective ergogenic aid in both endurance events[42] and anaerobic activities.[43] Yet, other studies have not shown significant changes in exercise performance with bicarbonate loading.[44,45] Therefore, this drug deserves further investigation.

3.5. SODIUM PHOSPHATE

Pharmacologic Aspect. Sodium phosphate has been utilized as an ergogenic drug. According to Kreider et al.,[46] it is believed to have six various mechanisms of action which may affect athletic performance. These mechanisms include: (1) elevation in serum and intracellular phosphate subsequently enhancing phosphate-stimulated glycolysis; (2) increased availability of phosphate for oxidative phosphorylation and creatine phosphate synthesis; (3) elevation in red cell 2,3-diphosphoglycerate (2,3-DPG) which leads to a reduced oxyhemoglobin affinity at a given oxygen tension; (4) increased red cell anaerobic glycolysis and efficiency; (5) enhanced myocardial and cardiovascular efficiency; and (6) increase in anaerobic threshold. The interactions of exercise and sodium phosphate are summarized in Table 4.

Sodium phosphate is ingested in an attempt to improve oxidative metabolism. Its effectiveness is debatable. Some investigators have reported increases in aerobic capacity and anaerobic thresholds of trained athletes.[47,48] Other research studies show no advantage in phosphate loading, particularly in running,[46] bicycling,[46,49] and isokinetic leg extension.[50] This drug is also open to further research consideration.

4. ERGOLYTIC DRUGS AND EXERCISE

This section will focus on common drugs that are usually associated with poor outcomes during physical activity. These drugs might sometimes be referred to as "depressants" to the body. Hence, they carry a significant level of caution in their use. In many cases, these drugs will lead to impairment of exercise performance or medical complications.

4.1. ALCOHOL

Pharmacologic Aspect. The exact mechanism of alcohol remains elusive; however, it appears to increase the fluidity of most biological membranes. This action results in several alterations in membrane function including effects on neurotransmitter receptors for dopamine, glutamate, norepinephrine, and opioids; change in function of the Na^+-K^+ ATPase mechanism (i.e., reduction in the sodium current); disruption of normal enzyme activities of 5′-nucleotidase, acetylcholinesterase, and adenyl cyclase; hampering of mitochondrial electron transport function; and change in the operation of ion channels such as for Ca^{++}.

Exercise-Drug Interaction. Alcohol (ethanol) is not a drug of choice for sport competition; however, individuals have used it in an attempt to improve self-confidence and relax before stressful events.[51] It is known to adversely affect reaction time and hand-eye coordination,[52] as well as accuracy,[53] balance,[54] and complex gross motor tasks.[55] The literature is in general agreement that alcohol does not aid in muscular strength tasks. It either has no effect[56] or actually hampers anaerobic muscular performance.[57] In terms of cardiovascular endurance, alcohol appears to decrease performance,[58,59] although some studies show no significant detrimental effect.[60,61] Overall, it does not appear that alcohol provides any significant benefits for athletic competition, and it can put the individual at a higher risk for injury if alcohol is used. In fact, the American College of Sports Medicine has taken a stand against its use in athletics.[62]

4.2. COCAINE

Pharmacologic Aspect. Cocaine might best be considered a highly potent amphetamine since outcomes are similar but magnified. Its action is to block the reuptake of dopamine and norepinephrine at the synaptic cleft of the neuronal junction.[113] This results in a significant increase and potentiation of these transmitters. The primary effects of this drug are local anesthesia, stimulation of the central nervous system, and an enhanced cardiovascular response.

Exercise-Drug Interaction. Medicinally, this drug has been used in conjunction with epinephrine as a topical anesthetic for nasal surgical procedures. Since cocaine elicits a sensation of euphoria, it has been used by athletes in sports competition in an effort to gain an edge. No current human research is available relative to the effects of cocaine on athletic performance. However, within the context of animal (rat) studies dealing with this topic,[63-68] it has proven to be ineffective and detrimental to exercise performance. It seems that cocaine use during endurance exercise results in premature fatigue, subsequent to its augmentation of catecholamine levels.[65] One causative factor of this fatigue may be a lack of oxygen availability to the working cells due to catecholamine-induced vasoconstriction of vessels near the muscle, thus resulting in a greater breakdown of stored carbohydrates,[64,66] a limiting factor to endurance capability. Cocaine also appears to enhance the increase in core temperature during exercise,[68] suggesting that the increase in catecholamines has an effect on the temperature regulation center of the brain. Fat metabolism during exercise does not appear to be altered as a result of cocaine ingestion.[67] In terms of exercise performance, cocaine should not be used since there are many risks and no obvious benefits.

4.3. NICOTINE

Pharmacologic Aspect. Nicotine elicits both sympathetic (stimulatory) and parasympathetic (depressive) actions on both central and peripheral sites of the body. Its actions are accomplished through binding to nicotinic receptors which subsequently cause a conformational change in ion channels of the cell membrane. This alteration allows sodium and potassium to diffuse more readily into the cell, resulting in a more rapid depolarization process. Two of its most obvious outcomes are increased heart rate and blood pressure.

Exercise-Drug Interaction. Nicotine, generally attained through smoking or smokeless tobacco, does not appear to have a significant role in medicine. It has been used by athletes in an attempt to attain a calming effect. In two different rat studies, contradictory results showed both an improvement in swimming tasks[69] and a decrease in swimming endurance.[70] In human studies, either a decrease in aerobic capacity,[71] or no effect on work capability,[72] has been observed with nicotine administration. It would appear, therefore, that nicotine presents athletes with a greater cardiovascular health risk than an exercise performance benefit.

4.4. MARIJUANA

Pharmacologic Aspect. Marijuana takes the form of chemical entities known as cannabinoids. Certain cannabinoids advance through the blood-brain barrier and bind to highly specific receptors in the brain, resulting in various neurochemical changes. Some of these changes include an increase in catecholamine synthesis,[73] an alteration in neurotransmitter (norepinephrine, dopamine, serotonin, and GABA) uptake,[74] and a dose-related decrease in acetylcholine synthesis and release.[75] These mechanisms ultimately lead to attenuated behavioral responses such as decreased levels of concentration and excitement, and subsequently, a "relaxed" state of consciousness.

Exercise-Drug Interaction. Marijuana is sometimes used as a medicinal drug to act as a bronchodilator, decrease intraocular pressure, relieve muscle spasms, and reduce nausea (particularly in chemotherapy patients). An attempt by the athlete to achieve a relaxed sensation for competition is readily counterbalanced by detrimental effects on exercise performance. Marijuana use has been shown to impair psychomotor skills,[76] decrease muscle strength,[77] and diminish aerobic performance.[78] These studies clearly show that this drug is appropriately named an "ergolytic" and should not be considered for athletic performance.

5. SUMMARY

Several interactions occur when certain drugs are ingested before, during, or after an acute exercise bout. Chronic drug usage may either enhance, desensitize, or have no effect on the body's physiological responses to exercise. The level of exercise training may also affect how the body will respond to certain drugs. This chapter has covered some of these issues through a brief account of the basic pharmacodynamic aspects of common drugs often used by individuals who are physically active. General and specific physiological/biochemical outcomes were reported to give the reader some insight into the exercise-drug interaction for both acute exercise sessions and physical training regimens. The research literature provides us with significant information on systemic effects of this interaction, but information is still lacking on many subcellular and metabolic responses. Several questions remain as to the exercise-drug interaction, and pharmacologists and exercise physiologists should continue to collaborate on research efforts.

REFERENCES

1. **Blair, S. N., Kohl, H. W., Paffenbarger, R. S., Clark, D. G., Cooper, K. H., and Gibbons, L. W.,** Physical fitness and all-cause mortality. A prospective study of healthy men and women, *JAMA,* 262, 2395, 1989.

2. **Paffenbarger, R. S., Hyde, R. T., Wing, A. L., and Steinmetz, C. H.,** A natural history of athleticism and cardiovascular health, *JAMA,* 252, 491, 1984.

3. **Anderson, S. D.,** Drugs affecting the respiratory system with particular reference to asthma, *Med. Sci. Sports Exerc.,* 13(4), 259, 1981.

4. American College of Sports Medicine, *Guidelines for Exercise Testing and Prescription,* Lea & Febiger, Philadephia, 1991, 153.

5. **Morton, A. R. and Fitch, K. D.,** Asthmatic drugs and competitive sport. An update, *Sports Med.,* 14(4), 228, 1992.

6. **Kusenbach, G., Friedrichs, F., Skopnik, H., and Heimann, G.,** Increased physiological dead space during exercise after bronchodilation in cystic fibrosis, *Ped. Pulmonol.,* 15(5), 273, 1993.

7. **Vitug, A., Schneider, S. H., and Ruderman, N. B.,** Exercise and Type I diabetes mellitus, *Exerc. Sport Sci. Rev.,* 16, 285, 1988.

8. **Ivy, J. L.,** The insulin-like effect of muscle contraction, *Exerc. Sport Sci. Rev.,* 15, 29, 1987.

9. **Cook, J. E., Kolka, M. A., and Wenger, C. B.,** Chronic pyridostigmine bromide administration: side effects among soldiers working in a desert environment, *Mil. Med.,* 157(5), 250, 1992.

10. **Epstein, Y., Arnon, R., Moran, D., Seidman, D. S., and Danon, Y.,** Effect of pyridostigmine on the exercise-heat response of man, *Eur. J. Appl. Physiol. Occup. Physiol.,* 61(1–2), 128, 1990.

11. **Wenger, B. and Latzka, W. A.,** Effects of pyridostigmine bromide on physiological responses to heat, exercise, and hypohydration, *Aviat. Space Environ. Med.,* 63(1), 37, 1992.

12. **Matthew, C. B., Francesconi, R. P., and Hubbard, R. W.,** Physostigmine: dose-response effects on endurance and thermoregulation during exercise, *Life Sci.,* 50(1), 39, 1992.

13. **Babu, S. R., Somani, S. M., and Dube, S. N.,** Effect of physostigmine and exercise on choline acetyltransferase and acetylcholinesterase activities in fast and slow muscles of rat, *Pharmacol. Biochem. Behav.,* 45(3), 713, 1993.

14. **Buckenmeyer, P. J., Babu, S. R., Knowlton, R. G., and Somani, S. M.,** Effect of concurrent exercise and physostigmine on lactate and pyruvate in plasma, muscle, and brain tissue of rats, *Pharmacol. Biochem. Behav.,* 47(4), 779, 1994.

15. **Dube, S. N., Somani, S. M., and Colliver, J. A.,** Interactive effects of physostigmine and exercise on cholinesterase activity in red blood cells and tissues of rat, *Arch. Int. Pharm. Ther.,* 307, 71, 1990.

16. **Babu, S. R., Buckenmeyer, P. J., Knowlton, R. G., and Somani, S. M.,** Effect of physostigmine on plasma lactate and pyruvate in untrained/trained rats, *Pharmacol. Biochem. Behav.,* 42(1), 67, 1992.

17. **Somani, S. M. and Dube, S. N.,** Endurance training changes central and peripheral responses to physostigmine, *Pharmacol. Biochem. Behav.,* 41(4), 773, 1992.
18. **Santelli, H., Tuccimei, V., and Cannestra, F. M.,** Comparative study with piroxicam and ibuprofen versus placebo in the supportive treatment of minor sports injuries, *J. Int. Med. Res.,* 8, 265, 1980.
19. **Noyes, F. R., Grouw, E. S., Nussbaum, N. S., and Cooper, S. M.,** Effect of intra-articular corticosteriods on ligament properties, *Clin. Orthop.,* 123, 197, 1977.
20. **Alles, G. A. and Feigen, G. A.,** The influence of benzedrine on work decrement and patellar reflex, *Am. J. Physiol.,* 136, 392, 1942.
21. **Hurst, P. M., Radlow, R., and Bagley, S. K.,** The effects of D-amphetamine and chlordiazepoxide upon strength and estimated strength. *Ergonomics,* 11, 47, 1968.
22. **Smith, G. M. and Beecher, H. K.,** Amphetamine sulfate and athletic performance, *JAMA,* 170, 542, 1959.
23. **Chandler, J. V. and Blair, S. N.,** The effect of amphetamines on selected physiological components related to athletic success, *Med. Sci. Sports Exerc.,* 12, 65, 1980.
24. **Williams, M. H. and Thompson, J.,** Effect of variant dosages of amphetamine upon endurance, *Res. Q.,* 44, 417, 1973.
25. **Graham, T. E., Rush, J. W., and van Soeren, M. H.,** Caffeine and exercise: metabolism and performance, *Can. J. Appl. Physiol.,* 19(2), 111, 1994.
26. **Vistisen, K., Poulsen, H. E., and Loft, S.,** Foreign compound metabolism capacity in man measured form metabolites of dietary caffeine, *Carcinogenesis,* 13(9), 1561, 1992.
27. **Dodd, S. L., Herb, R. A., and Powers, S. K.,** Caffeine and exercise performance. An update, *Sports Med.,* 15(1), 14, 1993.
28. **Graham, T. E. and Spriet, L. L.,** Performance and metabolic responses to a high caffeine dose during prolonged exercise, *J. Appl. Physiol.,* 71(6), 2292, 1991.
29. **Spriet, L. L., MacLean, D. A., Dyck, D. J., Hultman, E., Cederblad, G., and Graham, T. E.,** Caffeine ingestion and muscle metabolism during prolonged exercise in humans, *Am. J. Physiol.,* 262(6 Pt 1), E891, 1992.
30. **Butts, N. K. and Crowell, D.,** Effect of caffeine ingestion on cardiorespiratory endurance in men and women, *Res. Q. Exerc. Sport,* 56, 301, 1985.
31. **Rodrigues, L. O., Russo, A. K., Silva, A. C., Picarro, I. C., Silva, F. R., Zogaib, P. S., and Soares, D. D.,** Effects of caffeine on the rate of perceived exertion, *Brazil. J. Med. Biol. Res.,* 23(10), 965, 1990.
32. **Fulco, C. S., Rock, P. B., Trad, L. A., Rose, M. S., Forte, V. A., Jr., Young, P. M., and Cymerman, A.,** Effect of caffeine on submaximal exercise performance at altitude, *Aviat. Space Environ. Med.,* 65(6), 539, 1994.
33. **Anderson, D. E. and Hickey, M. S.,** Effects of caffeine on the metabolic and catecholamine responses to exercise in 5 and 28 degrees C, *Med. Sci. Sports Exerc.,* 26(4), 453, 1994.
34. **Van Soeren, M. H., Sathasivam, P., Spriet, L. L., and Graham, T. E.,** Caffeine metabolism and epinephrine responses during exercise in users and nonusers, *J. Appl. Physiol.,* 75(2), 805, 1993.
35. **Anselme, F., Collomp, K., Mercier, B., Ahmaidi, S., and Prefaut, C.,** Caffeine increases maximal anaerobic power and blood lactate concentration, *Eur. J. Appl. Physiol. Occup. Physiol.,* 65(2), 188, 1992.
36. **Barany, P., Freyschuss, U., Pettersson, E., and Bergstrom, J.,** Treatment of anaemia in haemodialysis patients with erythropoietin: long-term effects on exercise capacity, *Clin. Sci.,* 84(4), 441, 1993.
37. **Burke, E., Coyle, E. F., Eichner, E. R., Nadel, E. R., and Williams, M. H.,** Blood doping and plasma volume expansion: benefits and dangers, *Gatorade Sports Sci. Exch.* (Roundtable), Spring 1991.
38. **Ekblom, B.,** Effects of iron deficiency, variations in hemoglobin concentration and erythropoietin injections on physical performance and relevent physiological parameters, *Proc. 1st I.O.C. World Cong. Sports Sci.,* 1989, 9.

39. **Schena, F., Cevese, A., Guidi, G. G., Mosconi, C., and Pattini, A.,** Serum erythropoietin changes in runners and mountain-bikers after a 42 km race, *Med. Sci. Sports Exerc.,* 22(2), S135, 1990.

40. **Berglund, B. and Ekblom, B.,** Effect of recombinant human erythropoietin treatment on blood pressure and some haematological parameters in healthy men, *J. Intern. Med.,* 229(2), 125, 1991.

41. **Cowart, V. S.,** Erythropoietin: a dangerous new form of blood doping?, *Phys. Sportsmed.,* 17, 115, 1989.

42. **Kayser, B., Ferretti, G., Grassi, B., Binzoni, T., and Cerretelli, P.,** Maximal lactic capacity at altitude: effect of bicarbonate loading, *J. Appl. Physiol.,* 75(3), 1070, 1993.

43. **McNaughton, L., Curtin, R., Goodman, G., Perry D., Turner, B., and Showell, C.,** Anaerobic work and power output during cycle ergometer exercises: effects of bicarbonate loading, *J. Sports Sci.,* 9(2), 151, 1991.

44. **Kozak-Collins, K., Burke, E. R., and Schoene, R. B.,** Sodium bicarbonate ingestion does not improve performance in women cyclists, *Med. Sci. Sports Exerc.,* 26(12), 1510, 1994.

45. **McCartney, N., Heigenhauser, G. J. F., and Jones, N. L.,** Effects of pH on maximal power output and fatigue during short-term dynamic exercise, *J. Appl. Physiol.,* 55, 225, 1983.

46. **Kreider, R. B., Miller, G. W., Williams, M. H., Somma, C. T., and Nasser, T. A.,** Effects of phosphate loading on oxygen uptake, ventilatory anaerobic threshold, and run performance, *Med. Sci. Sports Exerc.,* 22, 250, 1990.

47. **Kreider, R. B., Miller, G. W., Schenck, D., Cortes, C. W., Miriel, V., Somma, C. T., Rowland, P., Turner, C., and Hill, D.,** Effects of phosphate loading on metabolic and myocardial responses to maximal and endurance exercise, *Int. J. Sports Nutr.,* 2(1), 20, 1992.

48. **Stewart, I., McNaughton, L., Davies, P., and Tristram, S.,** Phosphate loading and the effects on VO_2 max in trained cyclists, *Res. Q. Exerc. Sport,* 61, 80, 1990.

49. **Duffy, D. J. and Conlee, R. K.,** Effects of phosphate loading on leg power and high intensity treadmill exercise, *Med. Sci. Sports Exerc.,* 18, 674, 1986.

50. **Weathermax, R. S., Ahlberg, A., Deady, M., Otto, R. M., Perez, H. R., Cooperstein, D., and Wygand, J.,** Effects of phosphate loading on bicycle time trial performance, *Med. Sci. Sports Exerc.,* 18(Suppl.), S11, 1986.

51. **Carpenter, J.,** Effects of alcohol on some psychological processes, *Q. J. Stud. Alcohol,* 23, 274, 1962.

52. **Coopersmith, S.,** The effect of alcohol on reaction to affective stimuli, *Q. J. Stud. Alcohol,* 25, 459, 1964.

53. **Rundell, O. and Williams, H.,** Alcohol and speed accuracy trade-off, *Hum. Factors,* 21, 433, 1979.

54. **Begbie, G.,** The effects of alcohol and of varying amounts of visual information on a balancing test, *Ergonomics,* 9, 325, 1966.

55. **Nelson, D.,** Effects of ethyl alcohol on the performance of selected gross motor tests, *Res. Q.,* 30, 312, 1959.

56. **Williams, M. H.,** Effect of selected doses of alcohol on fatigue parameters of the forearm flexor muscles, *Res. Q.,* 40, 832, 1969.

57. **Hebbellinck, M.,** The effects of a small dose of ethyl alcohol on certain basic components of human physical performance, *Arch. Int. Pharmacodyn. Ther.,* 143, 247, 1963.

58. **Houmard, J. A., Langenfeld, M. E., Wiley, R. L., and Seifert, J.,** Effects of the acute ingestion of small amounts of alcohol on 5-mile run times, *J. Sports Med.,* 27, 253, 1987.

59. **Kendrick, Z. V., Affrime, M. B., and Lowenthal, D. T.,** Effect of ethanol on metabolic responses to treadmill running in well-trained men, *J. Clin. Pharmacol.,* 33, 136, 1993.

60. **Bond, V., Franks, B. D., and Hawley, E. T.,** Effects of small and moderate doses of alcohol on submaximal cardiorespiratory function, perceived exertion and endurance performance in abstainers and moderate drinkers, *J. Sports Med.,* 23, 221, 1983.

61. **Blonqvist, G., Saltin, B., and Mitchell, J.,** Acute effects of ethanol ingestion on the response to submaximal and maximal exercise in man, *Circulation,* 42, 463, 1970.
62. American College of Sports Medicine, The use of alcohol in sports, *Med. Sci. Sports Exerc.,* 14, 481, 1982.
63. **Bracken, M. E., Bracken, D. R., Winder, W. W., and Conlee, R. K.,** Effect of various doses of cocaine on endurance capacity in rats, *J. Appl. Physiol.,* 66, 377, 1989.
64. **Braiden, R. W., Fellingham, G. W., and Conlee, R. K.,** Effects of cocaine on glycogen metabolism and endurance during high intensity exercise, *Med. Sci. Sports Exerc.,* 26(6), 695, 1994.
65. **Conlee, R. K., Barnett, D. W., Kelly, K. P., and Han, D. H.,** Effects of cocaine, exercise, and resting conditions on plasma corticosterone and catecholamine concentrations in the rat, *Metab. Clin. Exp.,* 40(10), 1043, 1991.
66. **Conlee, R. K., Barnett, D. W., Kelly, K. P., and Han, D. H.,** Effects of cocaine on plasma catecholamines and muscle glycogen concentrations during exercise in the rat, *J. Appl. Physiol.,* 70(3), 1323, 1991.
67. **Morris, G. S., Fiore, P. V., Hamlin, R. L., and Sherman, W. M.,** Effects of long-term cocaine administration and exercise on cardiac metabolism and isomyosin expression, *Can. J. Physiol. Pharmacol.,* 72(1), 1, 1994.
68. **Lomax, P. and Daniel, K. A.,** Cocaine and body temperature in the rat: effect of exercise, *Pharmacol. Biochem. Behav.,* 36(4), 889, 1990.
69. **Battig, K. von,** Differential effect of nicotine and tobacco smoking alkaloids on swimming endurance in the rat, *Psychopharmacology,* 18, 330, 1970.
70. **Bhagat, B. and Wheeler, W.,** Effect of nicotine on the swimming endurance of rats, *Neuropharmacology,* 12, 1161, 1973.
71. **Klausen, K., Andersen, S., and Nandrup, S.,** Acute effects of cigarette smoking and inhalation of carbon monoxide during maximal exercise, *Eur. J. Appl. Physiol.,* 51, 371, 1983.
72. **Edwards, S. W., Glover, E. D., and Schroeder, K. L.,** The effects of smokeless tobacco on heart rate and neuromuscular reactivity in athletes and nonathletes, *Phys. Sportsmed.,* 15(7), 141, 1987.
73. **Bloom, A., Johnson, K., and Dewey, W.,** The effects of cannabinoids on body temperature and brain catecholamine synthesis, *Res. Commun. Chem. Path. Pharmacol.,* 20, 51, 1978.
74. **Banerjee, S., Snyder, S., and Mechoulam, R.,** Cannabinoids: influence on neurotransmitter uptake in rat brain synaptosomes, *Pharm. Exp. Ther.,* 194, 74, 1975.
75. **Tripathi, H., Vocci, F., and Dewey, W.,** Effect of cannabinoids on cholinergic systems in various regions of the mouse brain, *Fed. Proc.,* 38, 590, 1979.
76. **Bird, K. D., Boleyn, T., Chesher, G. B., Jackson, D. M., Starmer, G. A., and Teo, R. K. C.,** Intercannabinoid and cannabinoid-ethanol interactions and their effects on human performance, *Psychopharmacology,* 71, 181, 1980.
77. **Hollister, L.,** Health aspects of cannabis, *Pharmacol. Rev.,* 38, 1, 1986.
78. **Renaud, A. M. and Cormier, Y.,** Acute effects of marijuana smoking on maximal exercise performance, *Med. Sci. Sports Exerc.,* 18(6), 685, 1986.

Chapter 3

EXERCISE, DRUGS, AND TISSUE SPECIFIC ANTIOXIDANT SYSTEM

Satu M. Somani

CONTENTS

0-8493-8540-1/96/$0.00+$.50
© 1996 by CRC Press, Inc.

1. INTRODUCTION

A recent monograph on "exercise and oxygen toxicity" describes how the molecular and cellular environment of the body can be altered by exercise and how exercise provides benefits as well as harmful effects to health.[1] A second recently published monograph which examines "exercise for prevention and treatment of major illnesses"[2] and how exercise can provide health benefits adds an important dimension to our understanding. However, very little is known about exercise and drug interactions with respect to antioxidant enzymes and glutathione.

Exercise is known to exert numerous physiological changes in vital organ systems of the body. Among those changes, the most important is the enhanced respiration and utilization of oxygen in the body. Increased oxygen influx during exhaustive exercise may be potentially harmful to the body. During the last 10 years, much evidence has accumulated implicating enormous generation of reactive oxygen species and other free radicals especially during exercise in the muscles and heart.[3,4] However, cells contain several antioxidant defense mechanisms to protect themselves from free radical injury. These include endogenous antioxidants and antioxidant enzymes (AOE), simply referred to as the antioxidant system. The activities of AOE, which are well distributed in all organs of the body, are dependent on oxygen consumption rate, metabolic rate, and the amount of metal ions and fatty acids present. The AOE activities are prone to being altered by changes in oxygen consumption (oxidative stress). Oxidative stress can be described as a disturbance in the antioxidant system which is not able to adequately scavenge free radicals/reactive oxygen species and arrest lipid peroxidation chain reactions. This oxidative stress can occur due to strenuous exercise, some drugs, disease processes, and the combination of these and other factors.

The effects of exercise on antioxidant enzymes has been studied commonly in blood, heart, liver, and muscle, but there is scant information on other organs such as the brain, lung, kidney, and testes. Variations in antioxidant enzyme activities are dependent on the type of exercise, mode of exercise, intensity, frequency, and duration of exercise, animal species differences, tissue specificity, the time of sacrifice of the animal after exercise, and the tissue isolation and length of preservation until analysis. These aspects are elucidated precisely in this chapter and summarized in various tables. Internally, each section for AOE tissue specificity is organized in alphabetical order. This chapter explains the effect of exercise training and acute exercise on the rat antioxidant enzymes and glutathione in subcellular fractions of the heart[5] and the brain regions.[6] The chapter also describes the effect of exercise training on antioxidant enzyme kinetics (the maximum velocity V_{max} and K_m) in most tissues of aged rat.[7] The modulation of antioxidant enzyme activity primarily depends upon its substrate (reactive oxygen species), cosubstrate production, nature of catalytic center, affinity of the enzyme to the substrate, and selectivity and specificity of the substrate. The induction of antioxidant enzyme activity may occur through transcription/translation or posttranslational processes as a result of cumulative/ chronic physical or chemical stresses.[8] Posttranslational activation of antioxidant enzyme activity in the cells can occur through activation of the A_3 receptor.[9] Finally, this chapter provides examples of drugs, pesticides, and chemicals which may undergo metabolic alterations to produce free radicals and reactive oxygen species or which may be metabolized to biologically reactive intermediate metabolites that covalently bind to tissues to produce organ-specific toxicity.[10-14] If exercise is given along with the drugs, the question is whether exercise will serve as an inducer/activator of an antioxidant system or will exercise enhance the toxicity of the drug and/or metabolites by elevating reactive oxygen species. This chapter deals with the response of tissue-specific antioxidant enzymes and antioxidant glutathione to acute exercise and exercise training and also summarizes the interaction of exercise and drugs on the antioxidant system.

2. PATHWAYS OF THE ANTIOXIDANT SYSTEM

The potential harm of oxygen derives from its ability to be converted to reactive oxygen species (2 to 5%) such as superoxide anion, singlet oxygen, hydroxyl radicals, hydroperoxides, and lipid peroxides. These species are produced as a result of oxidation processes occurring in the mitochondria. The oxidation reactions involve addition of oxygen, removal of hydrogen or electrons, or partial reduction of oxygen. Mitochondria is the energy-producing organelle where oxygen undergoes four-electron reduction, catalyzed by cytochrome oxidase, wherein most oxygen combines with hydrogen to produce water. However, 2 to 5% of oxygen consumed forms superoxides. In this process, reduced co-enzyme Q (ubisemiquinone) is involved as an electron donor for molecular oxygen. Nicotinamide adenine dinucleotide phosphate (NADH) supplies electrons to co-enzyme Q (ubiquinone) which in turn is reduced to ubisemiquinone. Ubisemiquinones are lipophilic and diffuse through the organelle and come in contact with oxygen to produce superoxides.[15] The superoxide anions are readily dismutated by manganese superoxide dismutase in mitochondria and Cu-Zn superoxide dismutase in the cytosol and extracellular fluid to produce hydrogen peroxide and singlet oxygen (Figure 1). This enzyme makes the reaction happen 10 million times faster than its spontaneous rate. It is estimated that hydrogen peroxide production is highest in endoplasmic reticulum

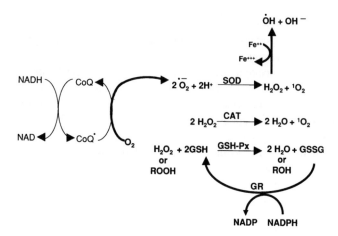

FIGURE 1. Pathways for the generation of reactive oxygen species and antioxidant enzyme reactions.

(45%) followed by metal-catalyzed oxidations in peroxisomes (35%); oxidative phosphorylation in mitochondria (15%), and oxidation of xanthine in cytosol (5%).[15,16] Endoplasmic reticulum is also the seat of drug metabolism, and mixed function oxidases generate H_2O_2. Hydrogen peroxide is then quickly converted by either catalase (CAT) or glutathione peroxidase (GSH-Px) to H_2O and singlet oxygen. If hydrogen peroxide escaped this enzymatic onslaught, then it can react immediately with the transition metals, usually iron, to produce a very toxic and reactive hydroxyl radical.[17] Lipid peroxides are converted to lipid alcohol by GSH-Px. GSH consumed in the GSH-Px reaction is recycled back to its reduced form by glutathione reductase (GR) as shown in Figure 1. This reduced glutathione is the most important antioxidant in the body, which helps scavenge reactive metabolites produced by drugs and chemicals. Other antioxidants, such as vitamins C and E in the cellular system, scavenges free radicals and reactive oxygen species and they "act in concert with their endogenous (mainly dietary) counterparts to provide protection against ravages of reactive oxygen."[1] The role of vitamins C and E as antioxidants have been discussed by others recently.[1] The basic level of antioxidant enzyme activity and antioxidants must be maintained at all times in all tissues irrespective of their aerobic power (O_2 consumption). Any disturbance in this basic level could cause a potential oxidative stress.

3. LIPID PEROXIDATION

Recently, Alessio[18] reviewed in detail the various aspects of lipid peroxidation processes in healthy and diseased models. Others have also described the phenomenon of lipid peroxidation.[17] Free radicals, or reactive oxygen species such as ˙OH, ˙OOH with sufficient energy, cause lipid peroxidation by abstracting a hydrogen atom from a methylene carbon of the unsaturated fatty acids which, in turn, is converted to a lipid free radical. In a process called lipid peroxidation, these free radicals of lipid can take up O_2 and form a chain reaction, producing lipid free radicals or lipid hydroperoxides. The rate of lipid peroxidation is dependent on the presence of transition metals iron or copper and NADPH in the membrane. These processes continue until the unsaturated fatty acids are depleted. One of the final products of lipid peroxidation is the malondialdehyde, which is measured spectrophotometrically in biological fluids and tissues. Lipid peroxidation (malondialdehyde levels) is considerably increased in blood and tissues during exercise. The various tables in this chapter show the extent of malondialdehyde formation in different tissues during exercise. Lipid peroxidation reactions can damage lipid membranes of cell structure and mitochondrial membrane, and interfere with mitochondrial and cell function.[17,18] An increase in antioxidant enzyme activity or intake of antioxidants depletes lipid peroxidation reactions.

4. EXERCISE AND ANTIOXIDANT ENZYMES

4.1. BLOOD

Blood is a circulating tissue and carries oxygen and other metabolic products throughout the body. The influence of exercise on the blood flow to various organs is explained in Chapter 1. Red blood cells have a competent antioxidant system. Any reactive oxygen species formed in the red blood cells is effectively scavanged by this system. However, a small amount of hemoglobin, Ferrous (Fe^{++}), is oxidized to methemoglobin, Ferric (Fe^{+++}), by autooxidation particularly during exercise[19] (Figure 2). During this oxidation process, superoxide anion radical $\bar{O}_2$ is formed by the transfer of a single electron. Methemoglobin is reduced to hemoglobin by NADPH generated by the hexose monophosphate shunt pathway (Figure 2). Superoxide dismutase (CuZnSOD), an abundant enzyme present in erythrocytes dismutates the superoxide radical to generate H_2O_2 and oxygen. Thus, this question remains unresolved: is the H_2O_2 or peroxide removal a rate-limiting factor in the processes of oxidative stress during exercise? Catalase and glutathione peroxidase degrade H_2O_2 to H_2O and singlet oxygen. The cosubstrate for glutathione peroxidase is a reduced glutathione, which is converted to oxidized glutathione (GSSG). Glutathione reductase enzyme in the presence of NADPH converts GSSG to GSH. The primary function of GR is to keep the glutathione in the reduced state.

Marathon runners (100-km race) remove the older erythrocytes due to metabolic and/or mechanical damage to body cells.[20] Thus, the older erythrocytes are replaced by the young ones in the peripheral blood. Red blood cells are also released from the spleen during exercise. Exposure of subjects with the sickle cell trait to treadmill exercise resulted in an increase not only in the susceptibility of red blood cells to oxidation but also in the density of red blood cell membranes.[21]

4.1.1. Blood Response to Exercise: Antioxidant Enzyme Activity

Young erythrocytes have substantially more CuZnSOD enzyme activity than the older cells.[22] Ohno et al.[23] reported that plasma CuZnSOD concentration was reduced to about one-third at 15 min and 24 h after only 15 min of

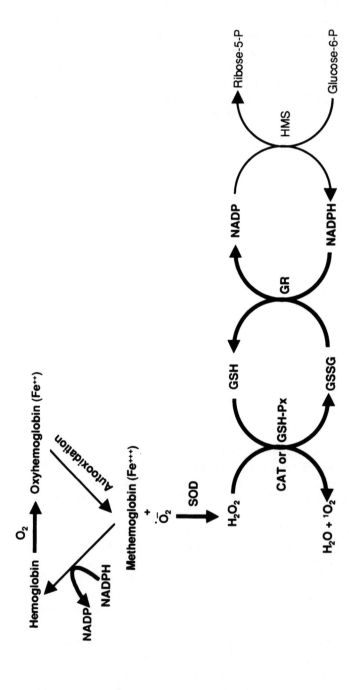

FIGURE 2. Superoxide production in the blood and antioxidant enzyme system. (Modified from Gohil, K., Viguie, C., Stanley, W. C., Brooks, G. A., and Packer, L., *J. Appl. Physiol.*, 64, 115, 1988. With permission.)

cycle ergometer exercise at ~75% VO_2 max, although MnSOD concentrations did not vary substantially. Recently, Ohno et al.[32] presented an excellent review on superoxide dismutase in exercise and disease. Superoxide dismutase (CuZnSOD and MnSOD) are widely distributed in various tissues and are abundantly present to dismutate to superoxide anion $\bar{O}_2$. The effects of exercise on the blood/plasma antioxidant system reported by various authors has been summarized in Table 1.[5,12,24-37] The most common features of this table are that the exercise induced the activity of SOD and GR and increased the levels of GSSG and malondialdehyde in spite of varying methodologies, exercise protocols, and species differences.

Most studies showed CAT and GSH-Px activity increased or remained unchanged due to exercise, with a few exceptions indicating decreased enzyme activity. Blood and plasma are easily obtainable biological fluids from animals and humans which showed an increase in GSSG and malondialdehyde levels indicating that oxidative stress occurred due to exercise. However, the increase in GR activity is indicative of conversion of GSSG to its reduced form (GSH), thus reducing oxidative stress. The data on GSH levels is conflicting. Some studies showed increased GSH levels and others showed the depletion of this antioxidant due to exercise. The importance of GSH as an antioxidant is discussed in Chapter 4.

During exercise, lactic acid is produced, which in turn decreases blood pH. Ray and Prescott[38] reported that low pH results in a reduced affinity of GR for NADPH. The blood pH will not remain depressed up to 24 h, keeping NADPH activity low. There are mechanisms that keep blood pH constant. We have shown that GR activity in the blood remained high even 23 h after the exercise.[5] An increase in GR activity seems to be due to an activation of a preexisting inactive enzyme.[29] In erythrocytes, GSH-Px activity was not altered by exercise.[39] Ono et al.,[28] however, reported a significant decrease in GSH-Px activity after exercise, a result similar to reports by Brady et al.[40] These differences in GSH-Px activity in erythrocytes could be attributed to differences in the intensity of exercise. Ono et al.[28] concluded that the decrease in GSH-Px activity in erythrocytes might be attributed to a protective action of the GSH-Px enzyme against exercise-induced lipid peroxidation.

Glutathione is depleted or is oxidized to GSSG due to exercise (Table 1). This depletion or oxidation of glutathione along with the status of AOE could lead to injury of red blood cells. The transport of oxidized glutathione from erythrocytes can occur.[35] Exercise enhances the blood flow in most organs, but depletes it in the liver, which in turn will influence the compartmentalization of GSH. Exercise may alter the transport of glutathione (extracellular and intracellular), alter synthesis or degradation of glutathione due to an increased uptake of oxygen, or alter an increase or decrease in conjugation of glutathione with exogenous or endogenous compounds. The effect of exercise on the compartmentalization of GSH influences the oxidation of GSH and the onset of injury to the tissues.[41] Blood is an easily obtainable tissue from humans and animals, and may be used as a diagnostic model for oxidative stress caused by exercise, drug administration, disease condition, or the combination of these.

TABLE 1
Blood Response to Exercise in Animals and Humans: Antioxidant Enzymes, Glutathione Systems, and Lipid Peroxidation

Species	Type of Exercise and Duration	Tissue/Cells	% Change in Activity/Level (+) Increase (−) Decrease							Ref.
			SOD	CAT	GSH-Px	GSH	GSSG	GR	MDA	
Mice	Swim exercise training 1 h/day, 5 days/wk (9 weeks) (21 weeks)	Blood							+59	Kanter et al. (12)
Rat	Exhaustive exercise	Plasma	+50	+63	+31	+65	+350			Sen et al. (24)
Rat	Exhaustive exercise treadmill (36 min)	Plasma	+123	+47	No change		+1471			Lang et al. (25)
Rat	Exhaustive exercise (90–120 min)	Plasma				+51	+751			Lew et al. (26)
Rat	Acute exercise 100% VO_2 max	Blood	+59	−16	+22					Somani et al. (5)
Rat	Exercise training (10 weeks)	Blood	+108	+8	+114					Somani et al. (5)
Dog	Exercise training (30 weeks)	Plasma				−22	No change			Marin et al. (27)
Equine	Running on a circular sand track for 1000 meters (15 m/sec)	Plasma/RBC	No change	No change	−6				+8	Ono et al. (28)
Equine	Running 2 Km in 7.4 min	RBC/Blood			−10	+15 +53		+38		Brady et al. (29)
Human	Prolonged exercise training (cycling) 60 min / 120 min / 134 min	Blood		No change No change No change	No change No change No change	+12.5 +25 +40	No change No change No change	+33 +24 +30	+33 +33 +33	Ji et al. (30)

Human	Running training 5 km, 6 times/wk (10 weeks)	RBC	12.5				+?8	Ohno et al. (31)
Human	Bicycle ergometer (30 min)	RBC	No change	No change	No change	No change	+?1	Ohno et al. (32)
Human	Running training (15 km)	Blood		No change	No change			Evelo et al. (33)
	(20 weeks)				+49		+?	
	(40 weeks)				−8		+●	
Human	Walking on treadmill (15 min)	Blood/RBC			No change		+?4	Chaney et al. (34)
Human	Prolonged submaximal exercise (cycle ergometer) 90 min. (3 days)	Blood			−60	+100		Gohil et al. (19)
Human	Prolonged submaximal exercise (cycle ergometer) 90 min. day 1	Blood			−55	+28		Viguie et al. (36)
	day 3				−55	+28		
Human	Acute exercise	Blood			−9	+88	+40	Sen et al. (37)

Note: SOD = superoxide dismutase; GSH = glutathione peroxidase; CAT = catalase; GSH = reduced glutathione; GSSG = oxidized glutathione; MDA = malondialdehyde; GR = glutathione reductase.

4.2. BRAIN

The brain is an important organ of the body and most difficult to fully understand. It controls the various physiological processes occurring centrally or peripherally. Exercise gives the feelings of well being and freshness of the mind through stimulation of the complex network of the brain which controls behavior.

Oxygen consumption increases nearly 20-fold in the body during high intensity aerobic exercise (100% VO_2 max). The brain typically takes 20% of the oxygen consumed under normal physiological conditions. However, a 20-fold increase in oxygen consumption during exercise may increase oxygen uptake by the brain. Molecular oxygen easily dissolves in a nonpolar compartment such as the brain; however, the oxygen is not stored in the tissue. Neuronal cells are rich in mitochondria and require a high concentration of adenosine triphosphate (ATP) since oxidative phosphorylation occurs extensively. The brain is one of the most oxygenated tissues of the body; it is rich in peroxidizable phospholipid and polyunsaturated fatty acids, and contains only low to moderate levels of antioxidant enzymes. Thus, the reactive oxygen species generation in the brain may increase due to exercise and cause lipid peroxidation.

4.2.1. Brain Response to Exercise: Antioxidant Enzyme Activity

The influence of exercise on the antioxidant system and malondialdehyde levels in different brain regions is shown in Table 2.[6,42] SOD activity decreased in the cerebral cortex with no significant change in other brain regions due to acute exercise (Table 2), indicating oxidative stress in this region.[42] Other brain regions have the lowest basal SOD activity and, therefore, seem to be less vulnerable to oxidative stress due to exercise. Since the cerebral cortex is responsible for the control of cognitive function, acute exhaustive exercise could result in a momentary impairment of cognitive function. Catalase activity preferentially increased due to acute exercise in the cerebral cortex and corpus striatum, whereas GSH-Px activity increased profoundly in the cortex and decreased in the striatum. This may reflect a compensatory mechanism to scavenge peroxides generated due to exercise-induced oxidative stress. However, the decreased GSH-Px activity in the striatum suggests that accumulated lipid peroxide due to exercise in this region may be utilizing more GSH-Px. GR activity, which controls the endogenous level of reduced glutathione, decreased due to acute exercise in most of the brain areas studied. Brain GSH is important in the regulation of blood pressure and has been reported to decrease during oxidative stress.[43] Decreased GR activity can be associated with an accumulation of GSSG, which is an index of oxidative injury to the brain[44] during acute exercise. However, exercise training has been reported to maintain endogenous GSH levels in different areas of the brain.[6] Acute exercise increased lipid peroxidation in different brain regions, as measured by malondialdehyde (MDA) generation. It is interesting that lipid peroxidation was inversely proportional to the activity of GSH-Px in this brain region. Thus, acute exercise caused peroxidative damage to the striatum.

TABLE 2
Brain/Brain Regions Response to Exercise in Rat: Antioxidant Enzymes, Glutathione Systems, and Lipid Peroxidation

Species	Type of Exercise and Duration	Brain Tissue/ Regions	% Change in Activity/Level (+) Increase (–) Decrease							Ref.
			SOD	CAT	GSH-Px	GR	GSH	GSSG	MDA	
Rat Sprague-Dawley	Exercise training on treadmill (5 day/week)	Cortex	No change		No change		No change	–18		Somani et al. (6)
	7.5 weeks	Brain stem	+30		No change		+9	–24		
		Striatum	+30		Slight decrease		No change	+7		
		Hippocampus	Slight increase		No change					
Rat Fisher-344	Acute Exercise on treadmill 100% VO$_2$ max	Cortex	–25	+55	+147	–17			+57	Somani et al. (42)
		Striatum	–6	+39	–64	–17			+112	
		Cerebellum	No change	No change	+34	–13			+8	
		Medulla	+7	+21	–21			+13		
		Hypothalamus	No change	No change	–9			+16		

TABLE 3
Effect of Exercise Training on Antioxidant Enzyme Kinetics in Brain

	Sedentary Control		Exercise Training	
Enzymes	K_m (mM)	V_{max} (μmol/min/mg p)	K_m (mM)	V_{max} (μmol/min/mg p)
CAT	11.1	4.0	33.3	18.0
GSH-Px (GSH as cosubstrate)	50.0	0.06	22.2	0.1
GSH-Px (t-butylhydroperoxide substrate)	25.0	0.06	5.9	0.04
GR	9.3	0.047	7.5	0.05

Note: p = Protein.

However, exercise training for 7.5 weeks gave a different picture. The brain stem and corpus striatum showed a significant increase in SOD enzyme activity due to exercise training[6] (Table 2). It seems that the exercise training caused either more oxidative stress in the brain stem and corpus striatum, or had a better ability to induce antioxidant enzymes to cope with superoxides formed. The brain stem and corpus striatum may be more sensitive to oxidative stress, whereas the cerebral cortex region might have acquired more resistance to oxidative stress due to a higher level of GSH. No significant change in the activity of GSH-Px is indicative of an adaptive response due to exercise training. Exercise training significantly increased the GSH to GSSG ratio in the brain stem and in the cerebral cortex, whereas this ratio did not change in the corpus striatum. The benefit of exercise training seems to be evident as GSSG levels decreased and GSH levels remained unaltered. This study concluded that the exercise training altered the SOD activity and GSH to GSSG ratio differentially in various brain regions to cope with oxidative stress.

Aerobic exercise increases the density of capillaries in the brain, providing increased blood flow and greater protection against loss of brain cells. The ability to make new capillaries in response to aerobic demands probably declines in middle age. But maintaining aerobic exercise helps offset the age-related loss of capillary production. Exercise possibly increases cerebral blood flow which can result in the release of adenosine. We describe in Chapter 7 that adenosine can induce angiogenesis. This new blood vessel formation could definitely be a health benefit of exercise training. Adenosine appears to activate the antioxidant enzyme activity which scavenges the ROS (reactive oxygen species), and thus protects the brain against oxidative stress.

4.2.2. Exercise Training and Antioxidant Enzyme Kinetics

Aged rats were subjected to progressive exercise for 9 weeks and sacrificed 23 h after the last exercise bout. The brain was isolated and enzyme kinetics were determined; the values are shown in Table 3.[7] The maximal velocity

(V_{max}) for CAT increased more than fourfold in the brain, indicating the potential activation of CAT due to exercise training. K_m also increased three-fold after exercise training, suggesting that the H_2O_2 generation exceeded the saturation point.[7] V_{max} for GSH-Px using GSH as a cosubstrate increased by 64%, whereas GR remained almost the same. It seems that the H_2O_2, which is predominantly produced during exercise training by enzymatic dismutation of $\bar{O}_2$, and also nonenzymatically, activates CAT activity much more than GSH-Px activity. GR activity remained almost the same, indicating that the GSSG level did not increase and the ratio of GSH to GSSG remained the same. This may be the result of adaptation due to exercise training. It is concluded that exercise training induces the antioxidant enzymes and thus aids in coping with oxidative stress in old age.

4.3. HEART

The heart is an aerobic organ and has one of the highest oxygen consumption rates in the body. Therefore, free radical generation is also higher. The heart is a postmitotic tissue and therefore the turnover of antioxidant enzymes is slow. Thus, the heart could be very susceptible to ROS, and the factors that cause oxidative stress are exercise, exposure to drugs or chemicals and their metabolites, etc. Ji[41] recently described an estimate of myocardial oxidative capacity based on the ratio of the various antioxidant enzyme activities over that of mitochondrial citrate synthase enzyme. The AOE activity ratio appears to be very low in the heart compared to the liver. The same author extensively discussed exercise-induced oxidative stress in the heart. A *New England Journal of Medicine* editorial recently asked: "Is exercise beneficial or hazardous to your heart?"[45] Physical exercise can trigger an acute myocardial infarction.[46] The risk of heart attack during strenuous physical exertion (within 1 h following it) was two times greater in Germany and six times greater in the U.S. than less strenuous exertion and no activity.

4.3.1. Heart Response to Exercise: Antioxidant Enzyme Activity

The effects of exercise on the alteration in antioxidant enzymes, GR, GSH, and GSSG due to exercise as reported by various investigators has been summarized in Table 4.[5,12,13,24,47-53] CuZnSOD activity either increased or showed no change due to exercise. Two studies showed a decrease in SOD activity. Our studies showed an increase in MnSOD, CAT, and GSH-Px in rat heart mito-chondria. CAT, in most studies, showed an increase in activity, whereas, GSH-Px activity increased in heart tissue due to acute exercise or exercise training, indicating an activation of this enzyme to scavenge excess lipid peroxides produced during exercise. However, MDA levels did not follow the same pattern as GSH-Px activity. MDA levels decreased during exercise training,[5] whereas exhaustive exercise showed an increase in MDA.[13] Recently, Somani et al.[5] compared the mitochondrial (M)/cytosolic (C) ratio for SOD, CAT, and GSH-Px in rat heart after acute exercise with that of exercise training (Table 5). This ratio for all antioxidant enzymes in acute exercise was much higher

TABLE 4
Heart Response to Exercise in Animals: Antioxidant Enzymes, Glutathione Systems, and Lipid Peroxidation

Species	Type of Exercise and Duration	Tissue Homogenate/ Mitochondria/ Cytosol	% Change in Activity/Level, (+) Increase, (−) Decrease								Ref.
			Cu-Zn SOD	Mn-SOD	CAT	GSH-Px	GSH	GSSG	GR	MDA	
Mice	Swim exercise training 1 h/day, 5 days/wk (9 weeks)	Homogenate	−8		+15	+22					Kanter et al. (12)
	(21 weeks)		+12		+71	+6					
Mice	Exercise training (5 weeks)	Homogenate	+13								Reznick et al. (47)
Rat	Acute exercise treadmill (25 min)	Mitochondria/ cytosol	+28		No change	No change			No change		Ji (48)
Rat	Exercise training treadmill 1 h/day, 5 days/week (12 weeks)	Mitochondria/ cytosol	No change	No change	+40	No change					Ji (48)
Rat	Swimming training 4 h/day, 194–200 h per rat	Homogenate	−25		−40	+8	+6		−7		Kihlstrom et al. (49)
Rat	Treadmill acute exercise (1 h)	Mitochondria/ cytosol	+33	No change	No change	No change					Ji et al. (50)
Rat	Exhaustive exercise	Homogenate					−23	−8	+13	No change	Sen et al. (24)

Species	Exercise	Tissue fraction								Reference
Rat	Exercise training 2 h/day, 5 days/week (12 weeks)	Homogenate	No change					+16	+33	Laughlin et al. (52)
Rat	Exercise training (10 weeks)	Homogenate/ Mitochondria/ cytosol	+33	+66M +4C	+32M +19H	-10C	+36C	+23	-24 No change	Somani et al. (5)
Rat	Acute exercise (30 min)	Homogenate/ Mitochondria/ cytosol	+66	+258 +34C	+32M +23H	+30C	-53C	+31	No change	Somani et al. (5)
Rat	Exercise training (10 weeks)	Homogenate	+30	No change	No change					Powers et al. (53)
Rat	Exhaustive exercise	Homogenate/ Mitochondria	+28	-12H	+12H			No change	+6	Ji and Mitchell (13)

Note: H = homogenate; M = mitochondria; C = cytosol; SOD = superoxide dismutase; CAT = catalase; GSH-Px = glutathione peroxidase; GSH = reduced glutathione; GSSG = oxidized glutathione; GR = glutathione reductase; MDA = malondialdehyde.

TABLE 5
Rat Heart Mitochondrial/Cytosolic Ratio for Antioxidant Enzyme
Activities Based on Percent of Sedentary Control

	SOD	CAT	GSH-Px
Acute Exercise	1.92	2.67	1.71
(100% VO$_2$ max)			
Trained Exercise	1.26	1.59	1.32
(7.5 weeks)			

Adapted from Somani, S. M., Rybak, L. P., and Frank, S., *Pharm. Biochem. Behav.*, 1995, in press. With permission.

than in exercise training, indicating the greater oxidative stress due to acute exercise.

Superoxide anions are excessively generated in mitochondria after acute exercise which influences the increase in MnSOD activity. MnSOD is utilized to dismutate $\bar{O}_2$ to H_2O_2. Thus, the excess H_2O_2 produced enhances the activity of CAT, thereby increasing the ratio of mitochondrial vs. cytosolic for CAT. Similarly, GSH-Px activity is also stimulated in mitochondria of acutely exercised rats, resulting in a higher ratio of mitochondria/cytosol for this group. GSH-Px primarily catalyzed lipid peroxide to lipid alcohol utilizing GSH as a cosubstrate which is converted to GSSG. GSSG levels were found to be almost twofold higher than GSH levels in the cytosolic fraction of the heart due to strenuous single exercise.[5] We could not determine GSH or GSSG in the mitochondrial fraction of the heart. Mitochondrial GSH was found to originate from the cytosol and was then imported into mitochondria by a system that contains a high affinity transporter.[54,55] Exercise training decreased the malondialdehyde level to 75% of sedentary control value in heart mitochondria, indicating a possible benefit of exercise training.[5] Exercise training increases antioxidant enzyme activity in mitochondria, indicating that this organelle might be more susceptible to oxidative stress. However, the mechanisms of activation/induction of antioxidant enzymes due to exercise or drug administration is not elucidated. We consider, based on our preliminary data, that the enzyme activation or induction in the tissues is mediated via adenosine receptor or is due to gene regulation. Chapter 7 discusses the adenosine hypothesis. Mitochondria consumes oxygen to produce ATP by oxidative phosphorylation; ATP is used as an energy source by the heart for contraction and other cellular functions.[56] However, during acute exercise, this ATP consumption increases. ATP is then simultaneously broken down to adenosine diphosphate, adenosine monophosphate and, finally, to adenosine. Thus, it is quite possible that the increase in adenosine level may be involved in the activation of antioxidant enzymes. Another possible mechanism of AOE induction, due to exercise training, is the gene regulation discussed in the following section.

4.3.2. Exercise and Antioxidant Enzyme Gene Expression in Heart Tissue

Recently, Somani and Rybak[8] compared the effect of exercise training on transcription of antioxidant enzymes and the activities in aged rat heart. Exercise training caused a sustained increase in antioxidant enzyme activity in rat heart which was found in an elevated state even 23 h after the last exercise bout. The enzyme activity of CAT ($255.32 \pm 7.29\%$ of sedentary control) and GR ($261.50 \pm 12.61\%$ of sedentary control) was found to increase two- to three-fold, whereas the increases in SOD ($153.24 \pm 19.65\%$ of sedentary control) and GSH-Px ($132.99 \pm 2.05\%$ of sedentary control) activities were moderate in these aged rats. The intracellular balance of these enzymes is important for overall sensitivity to counteract oxidative damage to cells.[57,58] The increase in SOD activity may generate lethal overproduction of H_2O_2 which should be counterbalanced by increased scavenging of H_2O_2 by CAT and/or GSH-Px. Exercise training resulted in enhanced resistance to oxidative damage acquired by heart tissue of aged rats. Such resistance can be illustrated by measuring the CAT/SOD ratio.[59] The CAT/SOD ratio increased twofold (from 4.92 to 8.20) after the exercise training; however, the GSH-Px/SOD ratio remained unaltered.[8] Also, the increased GR/GSH-Px ratio (from 46.60 to 91.63) is indicative of the ability acquired by heart tissue to generate excess reduced GSH moieties after exercise training. More importantly, these are long-term beneficial effects of exercise and are evident in the hearts of old animals. Such an increase in antioxidant enzyme activity is possible either by transcriptional activation of the respective gene or the posttranslational modification of enzyme molecules. Antioxidant enzymes contain metal (Cu, Zn, Mn, or Se) at the catalytic site. These cofactors are essential for enzyme activity and may potentially limit the expression of the enzyme activity. Harris[60] indicated that "the cofactor regulation shows an important departure from bacteria regulation in that the switch is put to posttranslational events." Although very little is known about the molecular basis for regulation of these enzymes in mammalian tissues, the demonstration of selective *in vitro* induction of AOE by different oxidant stresses[61] supported these observations. These authors showed that the addition of H_2O_2 caused a dose-dependent increase in CAT mRNA in cells, whereas the increase in the steady-state mRNA levels of MnSOD and GSH-Px were less striking. There is scant information on whether these antioxidant enzymes (SOD, CAT, and GSH-Px) show differential regulation in tissues after physical exercise in order to nullify the increased production of reactive oxygen species during exercise. The induction of antioxidant enzymes might be taking place after an intracellular concentration of free radicals or reactive oxygen species increase above normal levels.

We have recently studied whether an increase in activity of superoxide dismutase (MnSOD and CuZnSOD), CAT, and GSH-Px during exercise training was associated with the increased levels of respective mRNAs.[8] Male Fischer-344 rats (age 77 weeks) were given exercise training for 9 weeks on the treadmill. The exercise training was stopped 23 h prior to the sacrifice of animals. The heart tissues of trained and sedentary control rats were used to determine antioxidant enzyme activity and to isolate mRNAs encoding MnSOD, CuZnSOD, CAT, and GSH-Px by Northern blotting experiments. The intensities of mRNA bands were measured by densitometric scanning of the autoradiograms. Northern blot for tubulin was used to normalize the respective intensities. The results indicate that the level of mRNAs of enzymes MnSOD, CAT, and GSH-Px were found to increase by $126 \pm 5\%$, $133 \pm 6\%$, and $138 \pm 5\%$ of sedentary control (mean $\pm$ SEM), respectively, in the heart of the aged rat due to exercise training. These results of the Northern blotting experiments show an increase in mRNA levels of antioxidant enzymes. It is apparent that the increased enzyme activities of CAT and GR are not due to the transcriptional activation of respective genes since such an activation should produce higher copies of transcripts specific to the antioxidant enzymes. The increases in transcript levels are relatively low and are not concurrent with the increases in enzyme activities. This suggests other potential mechanisms by which exercise training can increase antioxidant enzyme activities. Our hypothesis is that the antioxidant enzyme induction might be regulated by both pretranslational (transcriptional) and posttranslation modification.

4.3.3. Exercise Training and Ascorbate Radical Formation

Ascorbate radicals play a pivotal role in the scavenging of ROS and function as free-radical chain-terminating agents by self-disproportionation.[62] The presence of ascorbate free (Asc•-) radical has been reported in myocardial tissues during ischemia using biochemical techniques.[63-65] A real-time continuous-flow electron spin resonance (ESR) study has shown that the ascorbate free radical is a reliable indicator of ROS-mediated myocardial ischemic and postischemic injury.[66] The ascorbate ion (-AH) seems to have cardioprotective properties and might play a critical role in a ROS-induced myocardial ischemia/reperfusion injury.[67] The ROS are extremely short-lived, making them difficult to detect. Direct electron paramagnetic resonance (EPR) as well as EPR-spin trapping are the only direct methods available for the detection of free radicals in aqueous solutions at room temperature. Recently, Buettner and Jurkiewicz[68] reported in *in vitro* studies that Asc•- can be used as an indicator of oxidative stress. As oxidative stress increases in a system, the steady-state Asc•- concentration also increases. Ascorbate free radicals have a much longer half-life (50 seconds) than the half-lives of superoxide ($\overset{\cdot}{\bar{O}}_2$) 1×10^{-6} sec; singlet oxygen ($^1O_2$) 1×10^{-6} sec; molecular oxygen (O_2) $> 10^2$ sec; hydroxyl radical ($\overset{\cdot}{O}H$) 1×10^{-9} sec; alkoxyl radical ($R\overset{\cdot}{O}$) 1×10^{-6} sec; peroxyl radical ($RO\overset{\cdot}{O}$) 1×10^{-2} sec, and lipid peroxide (ROOH) $> 10^2$ sec.[16,69] Since Asc•- is relatively stable, it is easily detectable by EPR.

We have recently reported that the ascorbate radicals are generated in the heart muscle during exercise training in aged rat (86 weeks old).[4] AH acts as an efficient "scavenger" of a variety of oxygen-containing radicals in addition to antioxidant enzymes and glutathione. The superoxide converts AH⁻ to ascorbate free radical (Asc•⁻). Electron paramagnetic resonance spectra of intact heart tissue from sedentary control and exercise trained rats are shown in Figure 3. The heart tissue of exercise trained rats generated an EPR spectrum of the ascorbate free radical doublet with a hyperfine coupling constant of 1.89 Gauss (0.189 mT). Using electron paramagnetic resonance spectra, the ascorbate radical showed a very defined signal peak similar to the peak elucidated by Yamazaki and Piette.[70] We roughly estimated the level of ascorbate radical to be 2.5 nM in 50 mg tissue due to exercise training, which could be extrapolated to about 50 nM/g of heart tissue of the exercise trained rat. The ascorbate EPR signal was not observed in sedentary control rat heart tissues.

An α-phenyl-N-t-butyl-nitrone (PBN)-spin adduct (of the aqueous phase) of the exercise trained heart tissue is shown in Figure 3. This PBN-adduct consists of a triplet of doublets with hyperfine constants of $a_N = 1.63$ mT and a$\text{ß}_H = 0.35$ mT. Similar hyperfine constants $a_N = 1.62$ mT and a$\text{ß}_H = 0.36$ mT have been attributed to a lipid peroxidation by-product (L•) in an application of EPR spin trapping to rat ischemic brain homogenate incubated with NADPH and iron-ethylene diamine-tetraacetic acid (EDTA).[71] However, we could not detect the Asc•⁻ EPR signal in the heart tissue of the young adult rat after acute exercise (unpublished data). Our findings showed the formation of ascorbate radical in the heart tissue even 23 h after the last bout of exercise. The steady-state concentration of Asc•⁻ and the Asc•⁻ EPR signal intensity can serve as a quantitative marker. Therefore, exercise training can provide protection to heart tissue against oxidative damage, via ascorbate ion radical and vitamin E (Figure 4).

4.4. KIDNEY

Recently, Painter[72] reviewed exercise aspects for individuals with end-stage renal disease. These patients treated with dialysis have marked reduction in exercise capacity compared to healthy individuals. Kidneys are master chemists of the internal environment and play an important part in the excretory function. Kidneys receive and filter about 25% of cardiac output, filtering endogenous or foreign compounds of molecular weight less than 60,000. However, kidneys extract only 6% of the oxygen from the blood. Recently Ohno et al.[73] reported the excretion of CuZnSOD (13.2 ± 3.3 ng min⁻¹) (molecular weight 33,000) in the urine of high school students immediately after 2 h exercise. After 30 min rest, however, less CuZnSOD was excreted (9.87 ± 3.37 mg min⁻¹) in urine. MnSOD (molecular weight 88,000) was not detected in the urine. Neither CuZnSOD nor MnSOD was detected in the urine prior to exercise (initial control). The physiological and pathological consequence of the depletion of CuZnSOD in serum is not known.

4.4.1. Exercise Training and Antioxidant Enzyme Kinetics

There is scant information on the renal antioxidant system specifically in relation to exercise. We have recently shown that exercise training for 9 weeks in aged rats alters the antioxidant enzyme activity in the kidney. CAT and

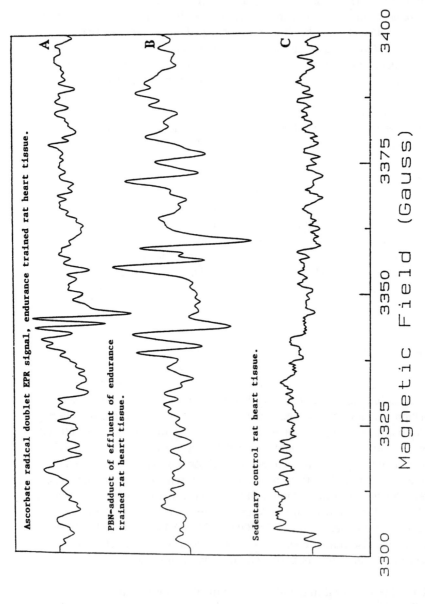

FIGURE 3. EPR species obtained from heart homogenized tissue of exercise trained rats: (A) Ascorbate radical doublet EPR signal of the exercise trained rat heart homogenized tissue; (B) PBN-adduct of effluent of the exercise trained rat heart homogenized tissue; (C) Sedentary control rat. Spectrophotometer conditions: receiver gain 1.25×10^5; microwave power 10 mW; time constant 0.5 sec; scan time 8 min.

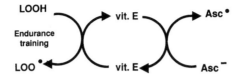

FIGURE 4. Sparing of vitamin E as a chain-breaking antioxidant by the formation of ascorbate radical during exercise training.

GSH-Px activities decreased by 59 and 16%, respectively, whereas GR activity increased by 9% due to exercise training. The values of V_{max} for CAT and GSH-Px decreased[7] (Table 6). These enzymes are responsible for scavenging H_2O_2 and organic hydroperoxides. The kidney is a highly filterable and excretory organ. Hydroperoxide generated elsewhere may find its way to the kidney via blood. It seems that these enzymes are inactivated due to high organic peroxides and other ROS concentrations. GR is slightly activated due to exercise training. The Michaelis-Menten constant (K_m) value for CAT decreased by 63%, indicating higher affinity of CAT for substrate H_2O_2 after exercise training. Similarly, lower values of K_m for enzymes GSH-Px and GR are also indicative of higher affinities for their substrates GSH and GSSG, respectively.[7] This phenomenon may be related to adaptation in response to exercise training.

4.5. LIVER

The liver has the highest activity of antioxidant enzymes and very high levels of antioxidants. This organ efficiently scavenges the ROS produced in the liver. It is the prime organ for most of the detoxification of foreign compounds (see Chapter 1). Endoplasmic reticulum of the liver metabolizes drugs, pesticides, and chemicals utilizing the cytochrome P-450 system. The

TABLE 6
Effect of Exercise Training on Antioxidant Enzyme Kinetics in Kidney

Enzymes	Sedentary Control		Exercise Training	
	K_m (m*M*)	V_{max} (μmol/min/mg p)	K_m (m*M*)	V_{max} (μmol/min/mg p)
CAT	55.5	3.20	20.8	1.3
GSH-Px (GSH is cosubstrate)	71.4	0.8	28.6	0.67
GSH-Px (t-butylhydro-peroxide as substrate)	5.0	0.22	4.0	0.21
GR	10.8	0.22	8.2	0.24

Note: p = Protein.

mixed function oxidases in this organelle also generate H_2O_2.[16] Although the liver contains high levels of antioxidants and AOE, enormous amounts of ROS and reactive drug metabolites are also produced, which are then efficiently scavenged and detoxified in this organ.

4.5.1. Liver Response to Exercise: Antioxidant Enzyme Activity

The effect of exercise on the antioxidant system and malondialdehyde levels studied by various investigators have been summarized in Table 7.[4-27,48,51,74-77] The common features of this table are that CuZnSOD and CAT activity increased and GSH levels decreased in most studies. SOD activity increased from 10 to 28% in liver due to acute exercise or exercise training in rats and mice. Enzyme activity did not change due to swim exercise in mice. CAT activity increased from 4 to 68% due to exercise. GSH-Px activity in liver also increased with both acute exercise or exercise training; however, when this activity was analyzed in mitochondria and cytosol, it was found to decrease in the subcellular fraction. GSH was depleted from 8 to 80% in the liver due to acute exercise as well as exercise training in all studies, with the exception of two studies where Sen et al.[75] found an increase of 8% in rats and 21% in dogs with exercise training. GSSG levels showed conflicting results with an increase or decrease or no change either with acute exercise or exercise training. GR activity was found to decrease with exercise. MDA was found to increase from 14 to 50% with exercise, with the exception of one study which showed a 36% depletion due to exercise.

4.5.2. Exercise Training and Antioxidant Enzyme Kinetics

Alteration in antioxidant enzyme kinetics in the liver was studied after 9 weeks of exercise training in rats. The maximum velocity (V_{max}) for CAT in the liver increased by 33% due to exercise training, whereas K_m increased by 18%. V_{max} and K_m for GSH-Px increased twofold using GSH as a cosubstrate[7] (Table 8). V_{max} and K_m for GR decreased by 26 and 43%, respectively. These results demonstrate a potential activation of CAT and GSH-Px to get rid of excess peroxides generated during exercise training. The affinity of GR for substrate GSSG shifted to higher levels due to exercise training, whereas CAT and GSH-Px affinity for their substrates (H_2O_2 and/or hydroperoxides) decreased due to exercise training, thus suggestive of adaptation to exercise training. Exercise training potentially activated the antioxidant enzymes in the liver and adapted in such a way that they were active at higher concentration of ROS; therefore, hepatic functions were maintained in old age.

4.6. LUNG

The lung is an oxygen organ of the body and experiences the oxygen tension directly along with airborne particles. Pulmonary ventilation and O_2 utilization increases considerably with physical exercise. Salminen et al.[78] reported that there was no increase in CAT and GSH-Px activity due to endurance training for 3, 10, or 20 days in mice or rats; neither was there any change in the level of vitamin E. Lipid peroxidation as measured by the expiration of pentane increased due to the physical exercise.[79,80] These authors also reported that the hyperoxia and hypoxia alters the antioxidant system in the lung. It is quite possible that acute exhaustive exercise will alter the antioxidant system. However, a number of drugs and chemicals such as bleomycin, paraquat,[81] etc., are known to produce ROS, which alters the pulmonary antioxidant system and increases lipid peroxidation. Bleomycin, a known superoxide generator, increases the SOD activity in the lung.[82] The interaction of these drugs, however, with exercise has not been explored.

4.6.1. Exercise Training and Antioxidant Enzyme Kinetics

Table 9 shows the V_{max} and K_m values of antioxidant enzymes in the lung tissue of sedentary control and exercise-trained rats.[7] An increase of 34% in the V_{max} value of CAT is indicative of induction of this enzyme after exercise training.[7] However, the V_{max} values for GSH-Px and GR decreased by 23.1 and 12.2%, respectively, due to exercise training. An increase in the K_m value for CAT indicated that there was more substrate (H_2O_2) production which led to low affinity of enzyme CAT for this substrate. During exercise, a very high intake of oxygen in the lung led to formation of the superoxide anion which was converted to H_2O_2 by SOD. This very high concentration of H_2O_2 resulted in a low K_m value of CAT, whereas K_m for GSH-Px decreased by 25%, indicating a higher affinity of GSH-Px for the substrate (hydroperoxides). The K_m value for GR slightly decreased, indicating a moderate increase in affinity of GR for GSSG during exercise training.

4.7. MUSCLE

During exercise, blood flow to skeletal muscles increases 10 times, thereby considerably increasing oxygen delivery to this tissue. The metabolic rates of skeletal muscles alter in order of $>10^2$.[83] Exercise intensity plays a direct role in modulating the antioxidant system in the skeletal muscles. The higher the intensity of exercise, the higher the alteration in antioxidant enzymes and in the glutathione status in this tissue. The status of the antioxidant system in muscle in response to exercise has been reported by several investigators and the results are summarized in Table 10.[24-27,51,52,74-76,84-88]

4.7.1. Muscle Response to Exercise: Antioxidant Enzyme Activity

Table 10 reviews the changes in the activity of antioxidant enzymes, GR, GSH, and GSSG and the extent of lipid peroxidation (malondialdehyde) in muscle during exercise in rats and mice. Acute exhaustive exercise increased CuZnSOD activity in the range of 16 to 23% in the skeletal muscle. Exercise training did not appreciably alter the SOD activity in the muscle. A recent study showed an increase of 50% in SOD activity during 10 weeks of exercise training.[88] Superoxide dismutase activity is dependent on superoxide formation.

TABLE 7
Liver Response to Exercise in Animals: Antioxidant Enzymes, Glutathione Systems, and Lipid Peroxidation

Species	Type of Exercise and Duration	Tissue Homogenate/ Mitochondria/ Cytosol	% Change in Activity/Level, (+) Increase, (−) Decrease								Ref.
			Cu-Zn SOD	Mn-SOD	CAT	GSH-Px	GSH	GSSG	GR	MDA	
Mice	Swim exercise training (1 h/day, 5 days/week) (9 weeks) (21 weeks)	Homogenate	No change +10		+8 +68	+102 +53					Kanter et al. (12)
Rat	Acute exercise treadmill (25 min)	Mitochondria/ cytosol	+12	No change	No change	+10			No change		Ji (48)
Rat	Exercise training treadmill (1 h/day, 5 days/week) (12 weeks)	Mitochondria/ cytosol	No change	No change	No change	−28M −24C					Ji (48)
Rat	Exhaustive exercise (90–120 min)	Homogenate					−8	+111			Lew et al. (26)
Rat	Acute exercise (1 h)	Mitochondria/ cytosol	+15	No change	+30	−23M −7C				+61	Ji et al. (74)
Rat	Exercise training (1 h/day, 5 days/week) (10 weeks)	Mitochondria/ cytosol	No change	No change	−10	−35M −27C				+32	Ji et al. (74)
Rat	Exercise training (8 weeks)	Homogenate				No change	+21		No change		Sen et al. (75)
Rat	Exhaustive exercise treadmill	Mitochondria/ cytosol	+13	−12	+4	+12	−19	No change	+8	+43	Ji and Fu (85)
Rat	Treadmill, acute exhaustive exercise (36 min)	Homogenate				+35		−25			Lang et al. (25)

Animal	Exercise	Fraction						Reference
Rat	Acute exercise	Homogenate	+15	+9			+22	Lew et al. (26)
Rat	Exercise training (1 h/day, 5 days/week) (13 weeks)	Homogenate	+28	−4			+14	Lew et al. (26)
Rat	Exhaustive exercise	Homogenate	No change	−29			−4	Sen et al. (75)
Rat	Submaximal exercise (2 h)	Homogenate		−80				Pyke et al. (77)
Rat	Exhaustive exercise	Homogenate		−25	+54		+50	Sen et al. (24)
Rat	Exercise training (30 weeks)	Homogenate			No change	No change		Marin et al. (27)
Rat	Exercise training (55 weeks)	Homogenate	−7	+8			−8	Sen et al. (75)

Note: M = mitochondria; C = cytosol; SOD = superoxide dismutase; CAT = catalase; GSH-PX = glutathione peroxidase; GR = glutathione reductase; GSH = reduced glutathione; GSSG = oxidized glutathione; MDA = malondialdehyde.

TABLE 8
Effect of Exercise Training on Antioxidant Enzyme Kinetics
in the Liver of Rat

Enzyme	Sedentary Control		Exercise Training	
	K_m (m*M*)	V_{max} (μmol/min/mg p)	K_m (m*M*)	V_{max} (μmol/min/mg p)
CAT	7.8	1430	9.1	1900
GSH-Px (GSH as cosubstrate)	33.3	1.0	66.6	2.0
GSH-Px (t-butyl-hydroperoxide as substrate)	28.6	0.63	26.7	0.77
GR	50.0	0.84	28.6	0.62

Note: p = Protein.

During acute exercise more superoxides are likely to be formed which need higher activity and levels of SOD to dismutate superoxide into hydrogen peroxide. Acute exercise increased CAT activity in the range of 29 to 50% in the skeletal muscle to scavenge the excess of H_2O_2 produced during the high intensity of exercise, while exercise training showed a depletion or no change in CAT activity in the majority of studies reported so far. One of the studies,[76] reported an increase of 98% in CAT activity.

TABLE 9
Effect of Exercise Training on Antioxidant Enzyme Kinetics
in the Lung of Rat

Enzyme	Sedentary Control		Exercise Training	
	K_m (m*M*)	V_{max} (μmol/min/mg p)	K_m (m*M*)	V_{max} (μmol/min/mg p)
CAT	33.3	50.0	80.0	67.0
GSH-Px (GSH as cosubstrate)	20.0	0.26	15.4	0.27
GSH-Px (t-butyl-hydroperoxide as substrate)	11.8	0.20	17.4	0.25
GR	9.3	0.07	8.2	0.06

Note: p = Protein.

Acute exercise increased GSH-Px (10 to 62%) in most studies reported so far. One study, however, reported a mild decline in mitochondrial GSH-Px activity.[74] GSH-Px scavenges hydroperoxides utilizing GSH as a cosubstrate. GSH level is also increased (18 to 20%) during acute exercise. GSH is converted to GSSG, which increased (50 to 145%), in muscle due to exhaustive exercise. The oxidized glutathione is converted to reduced glutathione by glutathione reductase enzyme, which also increased from 21 to 435% with the exception of one study reporting mild decrease in GR activity. During exercise training there was no appreciable change in GSH-GSSG levels and GR activity in the muscle, indicating an adaptive response to exercise training. Malondialdehyde levels increased in most studies due to acute exercise or exercise training; however, one study[74] showed a decrease in malondialdehyde levels in both types of exercise.

4.7.2. Exercise Training and Antioxidant Enzyme Kinetics

Table 11 shows the alteration in V_{max} and K_m values of antioxidant enzymes in the muscles during exercise training of 9 weeks.[7] The V_{max} value of catalase increased by 25% due to exercise training, indicating the induction of CAT enzyme. The K_m value for CAT also increased by 20%, indicating that higher levels of H_2O_2 are produced. This increase activated CAT to degrade the hydrogen peroxide. V_{max} for GSH-Px with exercise training showed no alteration; however, the K_m value decreased by 37%, suggesting the depletion in substrate (hydroperoxide) and cosubstrate GSH, and the affinity of GSH-Px for GSH increased. The V_{max} value for GR decreased by 20%, indicating that there is no substrate-induced activation of this enzyme. Similarly, K_m decreased by 21% due to exercise training because GSSG is not formed.

4.8. TESTES

There is no information on antioxidant enzyme activity in the testes in relation to exercise although the actions and interactions of testicular hormones and their relationship to exercise have been studied extensively. Recently, we have shown in *in vitro* studies using cell lines that the A_3 adenosine receptor is involved in the activation of antioxidant enzymes through the G-protein-Ca^{++}-protein kinase cascade.[9] This A_3-adenosine receptor is well distributed in the heart and testes. We have also shown that exercise activates antioxidant enzymes, possibly through A_3 adenosine receptor in the heart tissue of rats who have undergone acute exercise. It is quite possible that the antioxidant enzymes are activated in the testes during exercise training through the same receptor. Therefore, we have studied the kinetics of antioxidant enzymes in this tissue as shown in Table 12.

4.8.1. Exercise Training and Antioxidant Enzyme Kinetics

V_{max} for catalase increased by 21% in exercise-trained rat testes. This increase suggests the activation of catalase enzyme in this tissue. There is no

TABLE 10
Muscle Response to Exercise in Animals: Antioxidant Enzymes, Glutathione Systems, and Lipid Peroxidation

Species	Type of Exercise and Duration	Tissue Homogenate/ Mitochondria/ Cytosol	Cu-Zn SOD	Mn-SOD	CAT	GSH-Px	GSH	GSSG	GR	MDA	Ref.
			% Change in Activity/Level, (+) Increase, (−) Decrease								
Mice	Exhaustive Running (2–3 h)	Homogenate			+4	+10				+20	Salminen and Vihko (84)
Mice	Endurance training (1 h/day, 5 days/week) (3 weeks)	Homogenate			No change	No change	+13	+4		−22	Ji et al. (86)
Rat	Exercise training (2 h/day, 5 days/week) (12 weeks)	Homogenate	No change		−43	+11					Laughlin et al. (52)
Rat	Exhaustive exercise treadmill	Homogenate	+17		+29	+20	+18	+60	+45	+23	Ji and Fu (85)
Rat	Exercise training (8 weeks)	Homogenate				+15	No change		−15		Sen et al. (75)
Rat	Acute exercise (1 h)	Mitochondria/ cytosol	No change	+8	−12	−8C No change M				−25	Ji et al. (74)
	Exercise training (1 h/day, 5 days/week) (10 weeks)	Mitochondria/ cytosol	−6	+5	−17	+103M +10C				−38	
Rat	Exhaustive exercise	Homogenate					−26	+45		+64	Sen et al. (24)
Rat	Acute exhaustive exercise, Treadmill (1 h)	Homogenate	+23		+50	+62	+20	+50	+32	+30	Ji et al. (51)
Rat	Exhaustive exercise	Homogenate				No change	−33		−11		Painter (72)

Species	Exercise	Preparation								Reference
Rat	Exercise training treadmill (10 weeks)	Homogenate	No change	No change	+62					Ji et al. (86)
Rat	Exhaustive exercise (90–120 min)	Homogenate				−28	+62			Lew et al (26)
Rat	Acute exercise treadmill (25 min)	Homogenate	+20	+30	+25			+45		Ji (48)
Rat	Exercise training (1 h/day, 5 days/week) (12 weeks)	Homogenate/ mitochondria/ cytosol	No change	No change	+65M +40C					Ji (48)
Rat	Acute exercise	Homogenate	+16	−17					+34	Alessio and Goldfarb (76)
Rat	Exercise training (18 weeks)	Homogenate	−6	+98					+25	Alessio and Goldfarb (76)
Rat	Exercise training (10 weeks)	Homogenate			+24					Hammeren et al. (87)
Rat	Acute exhaustive exercise (36 min)	Homogenate				+145				Lang et al. (25)
Rat	Exercise training (10 weeks)	Homogenate	+50		+29					Powers et al. (88)
Dog	Exercise training (30 weeks)	Homogenate				+42				Marin et al. (27)
Dog	Exercise training (55 weeks)	Homogenate		+42	+42	+42		+21		Sen et al. (75)

Note: H = homogenate; M = mitochondria; C = cytosol; SOD = superoxide dismutase; CAT = catalase; GSH-Px = glutathione peroxidase; GR = glutathione reductase; GSH = reduced glutathione; GSSG = oxidized glutathione; MDA = malondialdehyde.

TABLE 11
Effect of Exercise Training on Antioxidant Enzyme Kinetics
in the Muscle of Rat

Enzyme	Sedentary Control		Exercise Training	
	K_m (mM)	V_{max} (μmol/min/mg p)	K_m (mM)	V_{max} (μmol/min/mg p)
CAT	33.3	16.0	40.0	20.0
GSH-Px (GSH as cosubstrate)	57.1	0.13	36.4	0.14
GSH-Px (t-butyl-hydroperoxide as substrate)	11.2	0.07	10.8	0.06
GR	19.0	0.030	13.3	0.024

Note: p = Protein.

activation of GSH-Px with GSH as a cosubstrate. GSH-Px is activated, however, when t-butyl hydroperoxide is used as a substrate. This suggests that any
hydroperoxide formed in the testes due to physical or chemical stressors will
activate GSH-Px enzymes. Steroid hormones present in the testes are likely to
form hydroperoxides which can activate GSH-Px enzymes; GR activity is also
activated. These observations clearly demonstrate an adaptation response in
testes tissue due to exercise training.

TABLE 12
Effect of Exercise Training on Antioxidant Enzyme Kinetics
in the Testes of Rat

Enzyme	Sedentary Control		Exercise Training	
	K_m (mM)	V_{max} (μmol/min/mg p)	K_m (mM)	V_{max} (μmol/min/mg p)
CAT	9.1	14.0	13.3	17.0
GSH-Px (GSH as cosubstrate)	133.3	0.67	14.3	0.25
GSH-Px (t-butyl-hydroperoxide as substrate)	33.3	0.29	50.0	0.44
GR	12.5	0.06	13.5	0.09

Note: p = Protein.

5. INTERACTION OF EXERCISE, DRUGS, AND ANTIOXIDANT SYSTEM

The metabolic pathways of drugs and chemicals utilizing the cyt P-450 system are described in Chapter 1. There are several metabolic pathways that could form electrophilic intermediate metabolites and also could generate superoxides and free radicals depending on the type of compound. Usually compounds containing nitro, amine, or iminium, or quinone functional groups form electrophilic intermediate metabolites which bind covalently with macromolecules and produce tissue-specific toxicity. Reduction of compounds by NADPH-cytochrome P-450 reductase[89] could be a source of generation of superoxides and free radicals. The metabolism of some compounds undergoes one-electron reduction under low oxygen tension.[90] The reduction reaction can generate a reactive metabolite which takes up molecular oxygen and converts it to superoxide anion $\bar{O}_2$. This superoxide is dismutated to form hydrogen peroxide (H_2O_2). Hydrogen peroxide in the presence of the ferrous atom produces hydroxyl radical ($\dot{O}H$) and hydroxyl ion ($\bar{O}H$). This hydroxyl radical is very reactive and causes lipid peroxidation while leading to toxic effects. H_2O_2 is degraded by CAT and GSH-Px to H_2O to $^1O_2$. We have shown that exercise stimulates the activity of SOD, CAT, GSH-Px, and GR. The question then arises: will exercise ameliorate the toxicities of drugs that produce reactive oxygen species and free radical?

Kanter et al.[12] reported that the life-threatening cardiac toxicity of adriamycin could be ameliorated by exercise training, enhancing antioxidant enzyme activity in the heart. Recently, Ji and Mitchel[13] reported that the administration of doxorubicin (adriamycin) interfered with the normal heart mitochondrial respiratory function and the administered dose did not impair myocardial antioxidant functions. However, this study pertains to interaction of acute exercise and doxorubicin on respiratory function.

Anticancer agents are administered to patients by continuous infusion and subjects are encouraged to carry on their daily routine activities. Some of these drugs cause severe toxicity, producing reactive oxygen species and free radicals, which can be reduced by administering glutathione, acetylcysteine, or other nucleophilic compounds. This process may lead to a decrease in toxicity; at the same time, this will also decrease the efficacy of anticancer agents. However, an exercise program can possibly help ameliorate these toxicities by stimulating antioxidant enzymes which scavenge reactive oxygen species produced by anticancer agents, other drugs, and chemicals. Table 13[10-13,42,82,90,92,106] lists some drugs and chemicals that produce superoxide, hydroxyl radicals, or biologically reactive intermediate metabolites. These drugs or metabolites cause tissue-specific toxicity. Ethanol produces α-hydroxy ethyl radical during its metabolism.[97] The study of both acute exercise and/or ethanol demonstrated that they exerted oxidative stress on the brain regions which may lead to functional impairment. The combined effect of acute exercise and ethanol

TABLE 13

**Examples of Some Drugs, Pesticides, and Chemicals that Produce
Toxicities Mediated via Free Radicals/Reactive Intermediate
Metabolites**

Drugs	Free Radicals/ROS	Toxicity	Ref.
Donorubicin (Anthracyclines)	$\dot{O}_2$, $\dot{O}H$	Heart	Pollakis et al. (90), Kanter et al. (12), Ji and Mitchell (13)
Belomycin	$\overline{O}_2$	Lung	Petering et al. (82)
Mytomycin	Free radical		Moore (92)
cis-Platin	Possibly free radical	Kidney/cochlea	Somani et al. (10), Rybak et al. (11)
BCNU-carmustine	Methyl radical	CNS	Reed et al. (93)
Procarbazine	Free radical	CNS	Sinha (94)
Acetoaminophen	Reactive intermediate metabolites	Liver	Kaysen et al. (95)
Isoniazid	Free radical	Liver	Mitchell et al. (96)
Ethanol	α-Hydroxyl ethyl radical	Liver and brain	Knecht et al. (97) Somani et al. (42)
Physostigmine	Eseroline to catechol to quinones	CNS	Somani et al. (98)
Quinones	Reactive metabolites	CNS	Kochli et al. (99)
Morphine	Covalent binding	Brain	Nagamatsu et al. (100)
Nitrofurantoin	Oxidant	Pulmonary	Suntres and Shek (101)
Paraquat	Oxidant	Lung	Bus and Gibson (102)
Parathion	Reactive metabolite	CNS	Chambers et al. (103)
Carbon tetrachloride	Trichlormethyl radical	Liver	Sipes et al. (104), Mehendale (105)
Polycyclic aromatic hydrocarbons	Epoxides	Liver	Das et al. (106)

seems to augment antioxidant enzymes. However, it also increases the level of MDA in various areas of brain.[42]

Cancer rates are lower among exercisers.[108] One of the reasons suggested is that the exercise depletes the level of serum iron[107] and also possibly the tissue iron. Iron is essential in generation of hydroxyl radicals which cause tissue damage. It is hypothesized that lower iron levels would cause less tissue injury and less cancer rates and less heart disease. Winningham[108] has recently reviewed exercise and cancer and has developed an exercise program for cancer patients. There have been no studies on exercise for cancer patients, obviously for reasons that the cancer chemotherapeutic agents produce many debilitating adverse effects due to formation of reactive metabolites.[109] For example, adrinmycin produces cardiotoxicity; bleomycin, BCNU, and busulfan cause pulmonary toxicity. Vincristine is a neurotoxic drug. Although all anticancer agents have severe toxic effects, some of them are related to reactive metabolites/free radicals; hence, low intensity exercise could potentially help in maintaining or elevating antioxidant enzyme activity to scavenge free radicals.

This area of research "interaction of exercise and drugs" in relation to antioxidant enzymes has not been explored, and needs to be investigated.

6. SUMMARY

The antioxidant system of the body comprises antioxidant enzymes (superoxide dismutase, catalase, glutathione peroxidase, and the ancillary enzyme, glutathione reductase) and antioxidants (vitamin C, vitamin E, and glutathione). This antioxidant system is well distributed in all organs. Exercise increases the oxygen influx in different organs and generates reactive oxygen species and free radicals which are scavenged by the antioxidant system. Variation in the activity of the antioxidant enzyme is reflected in different organs/tissues and subcellular fractions of the cell due to exercise. The tissue-specific activities of antioxidant enzymes are influenced by oxygen consumption rate, drugs, and disease processes. The activation of antioxidant enzymes may take place via the adenosine A_3 receptor. The induction of antioxidant enzymes may occur due to transcription/translation processes as a result of exercise training. Studies show that exercise increased the activity of SOD and GR, and also increased the level of GSSG and malondialdehyde in the blood irrespective of mode, intensity, and duration of exercise. Catalase and glutathione peroxidase activity also increased moderately due to exercise. Antioxidant enzyme activity in various brain regions differed, and exercise differentially induced enzyme activities. The antioxidant enzyme activity in the heart is low when compared to the liver. Exercise specifically increased the activity of antioxidant enzymes in the mitochondria of the heart. The presence of ascorbate radicals in heart tissue 23 h after the last bout of exercise was detected, indicating that exercise training can provide protection to heart tissues against oxidative damage via ascorbate and vitamin E. There is very little information about the antioxidant enzymes and exercise in kidney, lung, and testes tissues. The liver generates a very high amount of reactive oxygen species and correspondingly, there are high concentrations of antioxidants and high activity of the antioxidant enzymes to scavenge them. The liver also produces reactive drug metabolites that can covalently bind to macromolecules. Muscle has the largest mass in the body and enzyme activity is generally low, but exercise induces this enzyme activity in various types of muscle. The maximum velocity (V_{max}) of catalase, glutathione peroxidase, and glutathione reductase was favorably higher in most of the tissues of aged rats after exercise training. Similarly, K_m also generally increased due to exercise adaptation. Acute exercise increased membrane lipid peroxidation, whereas exercise training provided protection by depleting the level of malondialdehyde. Certain drugs can cause severe toxicity due to metabolic conversion to reactive intermediate metabolites. Exercise may ameliorate the toxicity of the drug by the activation of antioxidant enzymes, a topic which needs to be investigated. Finally, exercise can maximize the free radical scavenging system by inducing/activating antioxidant enzymes.

REFERENCES

1. **Sen, C. N., Packer, L., and Hanninen, O.,** *Exercise and Oxygen Toxicity,* Elsevier, Amsterdam, 1994.
2. **Goldberg, L. and Elliot, D. L.,** *Exercise for Prevention and Treatment of Illness,* F. A. Davis Co., Philadelphia, 1994.
3. **Sjodin, B., Hellsten Westling, Y., and Apple, F. S.,** Biochemical mechanisms for oxygen free radical formation during exercise, *Sports Med.,* 10, 236, 1990.
4. **Somani, S. M. and Arroyo, C. M.,** Endurance training generates ascorbate free radicals in rat heart, *Ind. J. Physiol. Pharmacol.,* 1995, in press.
5. **Somani, S. M., Frank, S., and Rybak, L. P.,** Effect of acute and trained exercise on antioxidant system in rat heart subcellular fraction, *Pharm. Biochem. Behav.,* 51, 627, 1995.
6. **Somani, S., Ravi, R., and Rybak, L. P.,** Effect of exercise training on antioxidant system in brain regions of rat, *Pharmacol. Biochem. Behav.,* 50, 635, 1995.
7. **Somani, S. M. and Husain, K.,** Exercise training alters kinetics of antioxidant enzymes in rat tissues, *Int. J. Sports Med.,* 1995, submitted.
8. **Somani, S. M. and Rybak, L. P.,** Comparative effects of exercise training on transcription of antioxidant enzymes and the activities in aged rat heart, *Ind. J. Physiol. Pharmacol.,* 1995, submitted.
9. **Maggirwar, S. B., Dhanjaj, D. N., Somani, S. M., and Ramkumar, V.,** Adenosine acts as an endogenous activator of the cellular antioxidant defense system, *Biochem. Biophys. Res. Commun.,* 201, 502, 1994.
10. **Somani, S. M., Ravi, R., and Rybak, L. P.,** Diethyldithiocarbamate protection against cisplatin nephrotoxicity: antioxidant system, *Drug Chem. Toxicol.,* 1995, in press.
11. **Rybak, L. P., Ravi, R., and Somani, S. M.,** Mechanism of protection by diethyldithiocarbamate against cisplatin ototoxicity: antioxidant system, *Fund. Appl. Toxicol.,* 26, 293, 1995.
12. **Kanter, M. M., Hamlin, R. L., Unverferth, D. V., Davis, H. W., and Merola, A. J.,** Effect of exercise training on antioxidant enzymes and cardiotoxicity of doxorubicin, *J. Appl. Physiol.,* 59, 1298, 1985.
13. **Ji, L. L. and Mitchell, E. W.,** Effects of adriamycin on heart mitochondrial function in rested and exercised rats, *Biochem. Pharmacol.,* 47, 877, 1994.
14. **Ghersi-Egea, J. F. and Livertoux, M. H.,** Evidence for drugs metabolism as a source of reactive species in the brain, in *Free Radicals and Aging,* Emerit, I. and Chance, B., Eds., Birkhauser Verlag, Basel Switzerland, 1992, 219.
15. **Chance, B., Sies, H., and Boveris, A.,** Hydrogen peroxide metabolism in mammalian organs, *Physiol. Rev.,* 59, 527, 1979.
16. **Weindruch, R., Warner, H. R., and Starke-Reed, P. E.,** Future directions of free radical research in aging, in *Free Radicals in Aging,* Yu, B. P., Ed., CRC Press, Boca Raton, FL, 1993, 269.
17. **Cadenas, E.,** Biochemistry of oxygen toxicity, *Annu. Rev. Biochem.,* 58, 79, 1989.
18. **Alessio, H. M.,** Lipid peroxidation processes in healthy and diseased models, in *Exercise and Oxygen Toxicity,* Sen, C. K., Packer, L., and Hamniner, O., Eds., Elsevier Science, Amsterdam, 1994, 269.
19. **Gohil, K., Viguie, C., Stanley, W. C., Brooks, G. A., and Packer, L.,** Blood glutathione oxidation during human exercise, *J. Appl. Physiol.,* 64, 115, 1988.
20. **Reinhart, W. H., Staubli, M., and Straub, P. W.,** Impaired red cell filterability with elimination of old red blood cells during a 100-km race, *J. Appl. Physiol.,* 54, 827, 1983.
21. **Das, S. K., Hinds, J. E., Hardy, R. E., Collins, J. C., and Mukherjee, S.,** Effects of physical stess on peroxide scavengers in normal and sickle cell trait erythrocytes, *Free Rad. Biol. Med.,* 14, 139, 1993.
22. **Bartosz, G., Tannert, C., Fried, R., and Leyko, W.,** Superoxide dismutase activity decreases during erythrocyte aging, *Experentia,* 34, 1464, 1978.

23. **Ohno, H., Yamashita, H., Ookawara, T., Saitoh, D., Mimura, K., and Taniguchi, N.,** Effects of brief physical exercise on the concentrations of immunoreactive superoxide dismutase isoenzymes in human plasma, *Tohoku J. Exp. Med.,* 167, 301, 1992.

24. **Sen, C. K., Atalay, M., and Hänninen, O.,** Exercise-induced oxidative stress: glutathoine supplementation and deficiency, *J. Appl. Physiol.,* 77, 2177, 1994.

25. **Lang, J. K., Gohil, K., Packer, L., and Burk, R. F.,** Selenium deficiency, endurance exercise capacity, and antioxidant status in rats, *Am. Physiol. Soc.,* 87, 2532, 1987.

26. **Lew, H., Pyke, S., and Quintanilha, A.,** Changes in the glutathione status of plasma, liver and muscle following exhaustive exercise in rats, *FEBS,* 185, 262, 1985.

27. **Marin, E., Kretzschmar, M., Arokoski, J., Hänninen, O., and Klinger, W.,** Enzymes of glutathione synthesis in dog skeletal muscles and their response to training, *Acta Physiol. Scand.,* 147, 369, 1993.

28. **Ono, K., Inui, K., Hasegawa, T., Matsuki, N., Watanabe, H., Takagi, S., and Hasegawa, A. D.,** The changes of antioxidant enzyme activities in equine erythrocytes following exercise, *Jpn. J. Vet. Sci.,* 52, 759, 1990.

29. **Brady, P. S., Shelle, J. E., and Ullrey, D. E.,** Rapid changes in equine erythrocyte glutathione reductase with exercise, *Am. J. Vet. Res.,* 38, 1045, 1977.

30. **Ji, L. L., Katz, A., Ronggen, F., Griffith, M., and Spencer, M.,** Blood glutathione status during exercise: effect of carbohydrate supplementation, *J. Appl. Physiol.,* 74, 788, 1993.

31. **Ohno, H., Yahata, T., Sato, Y., Yamamura, K., and Taniguchi, N.,** Physical training and fasting erythrocyte activities of free radical scavenging enzyme systems in sedentary men, *Eur. J. Appl. Physiol.,* 57, 173, 1988.

32. **Ohno, H., Suzuki, K., Fujii, J., Yamashita, H., Kizaki, T., Oh-ishi, S, and Taniguchi, N.,** Superoxide dismutases in exercises and disease, in *Exercise and Toxicity,* Sen, C. K., Packer, L., and Hänninen, O., Eds., Elsevier, Amsterdam, 1994, 127.

33. **Evelo, C. T. A., Palmen, N. G. M., Artur, Y., and Janssen, G. M. E.,** Changes in blood glutathione concentrations, and in erythrocyte glutathione reductase and glutathione S-transferase activity after running training and after participation in contests, *Eur. J. Appl. Physiol.,* 64, 354, 1992.

34. **Chaney, S., Blomquist, W., Muller, K., and Goldstein, G.,** Biochemical changes in humans upon exposure to sulfuric acid aerosol and exercise, *Arch. Environ. Health,* 35, 211, 1980.

35. **Srivastasra, S. K. and Beutler, E.,** The transport of oxidized glutathione from human erythrocytes, *J. Biol. Chem.,* 244, 9, 1969.

36. **Viguie, C. A., Frei, B., Shigenaga, M. K., Ames, B. N., Packer, L., and Brooks, G. A.,** Antioxidant status and indexes of oxidative stress during consecutive days of exercise, *J. Appl. Physiol.,* 75, 566, 1993.

37. **Sen, C. K., Rankinen, T., Väisänen, S., and Rauramaa, R.,** Oxidative stress after human exercise: effect of N-acetylcysteine supplementation, *J. Appl. Physiol.,* 76, 2570, 1994.

38. **Ray, L. E. and Prescott, J. M.,** Isolation and some characteristics of glutathione reductase from rabbit erythrocytes, *Proc. Soc. Exp. Biol. Med.,* 148, 402, 1975.

39. **Gallagher, K. and Stowe, H. D.,** Influence of exercise on serum selenium and peroxide reduction system of racing standardbred, *Am. Soc. Vet. Res.,* 41, 1333, 1980.

40. **Brady, P. S., Ku, P. K., and Ullrey, D. E.,** Lack of selenium supplementation on the response of the equine erythrocyte glutathione system and plasma enzymes to exercise, *J. Anim. Sci.,* 47, 492, 1978.

41. **Ji, L. L.,** Exercise-induced oxidative stress in the heart, in *Exercise and Oxygen Toxicity,* Sen, C. K., Packer, L., and Hanninen, O., Eds., Elsevier Science, Amsterdam, 1994, 249.

42. **Somani, S. M., Diaz-Phillips, L., Husain, K., Lanzotti, D. G., Kareti, K., and Trammell, G.,** Effect of exercise and ethanol of antioxidant enzyme and lipid peroxidation in brain regions of rat, *Neurotoxicology,* 1995, submitted.

43. **Murakami, E., Himada, K., and Kokuba, T.,** The role of brain glutathione in blood pressure regulation, *Jpn. Circ. J.,* 52, 1299, 1988.

44. **Warner, P. and Cohen, G.,** Glutathione disulfide (GSSG) as a marker of oxidative injury to brain mitochondria, *Ann. N.Y. Acad. Sci.,* 679, 364, 1993.
45. **Curfman, G. D.,** Is exercise beautiful — or hazardous — to your heart?, *N. Engl. J. Med.,* 329, 1730, 1993.
46. **Willich, S. N., Lewis, M., Lowel, H., Arntz, H. R., Schubert, F., and Schroder, R.,** Physical exertion as a trigger of acute myocardial infarction, *N. Engl. J. Med.,* 329, 1684, 1993.
47. **Reznick, A. Z., Steinhagen-Thiessen, E., and Gershon, D.,** The effect of exercise on enzyme activities in cardiac muscles of mice of various ages, *Biochem. Med.,* 28, 347, 1982.
48. **Ji, L. L.,** Antioxidant enzyme response to exercise and aging, *Med. Sci. Sports Exerc.,* 25, 225, 1993.
49. **Kihlstrom, M., Ojala, J., and Salminen, A.,** Decreased level of cardiac antioxidants in endurance-trained rats, *Acta Physiol. Scand.,* 135, 549, 1989.
50. **Ji, L. L., Dillon, D., and Wu, E.,** Myocardial aging: antioxidant enzyme systems and related biochemical properties, *Am. J. Physiol.,* 261, R386, 1991.
51. **Ji, L. L., Fu, R., and Mitchell E. W.,** Glutathione and antioxidant enzymes in skeletal muscle: effects of fiber type and exercise intensity, *J. Appl. Physiol.,* 73, 1854, 1992b.
52. **Laughlin, M. H., Simpson, T., Sexton, W. L., Brown, O. R., Smith, J. K., and Korthuis, R. J.,** Skeletal muscle oxidative capacity, antioxidant enzymes, and exercise training, *J. Appl. Physiol.,* 68, 2337, 1990.
53. **Powers, S. K., Criswell, D., Lawler, J., Martin, D., Lieu, F., Ji, L. L., and Herb, R. A.,** Rigorous exercise training increases superoxide dismutase activity in ventricular myocardium, *Am. J. Physiol.,* 34, 2094, 1993.
54. **Griffith, O. W. and Meister, A.,** Origin and turnover of mitochondrial glutathione, *Proc. Natl. Acad. Sci. U.S.A.,* 82, 4668, 1985.
55. **Martensson, J., Lai, J. C. K., and Meister, A.,** High affinity trasport of glutathione is part of a multi-component system essential for mitochondrial function, *Proc. Natl. Acad. Sci. U.S.A.,* 87, 7185, 1990.
56. **Copeland, J., Kosek, J. C., and Hurley, E. J.,** Early functional and ultrastructural recovery of canine cadaver hearts, *Circulation,* 37, 188, 1968.
57. **Amstad, P., Moret, R., and Cerrutti, P.,** Glutathione peroxidase compensates for the hypersensitivity of CuZn-superoxide dismutase overproducers to oxidant stress, *J. Biol. Chem.,* 269, 1606, 1994.
58. **Michiels, C., Raes, M., Houbion, A., and Remacle, J.,** Association of antioxidant systems in the protection of human fibroblast against oxygen derived free radicals, *Free Rad. Res. Commun.,* 14, 323, 1991.
59. **Mao, G., Thomas, P., Lopaschuk, G., and Poznansky, M.,** Superoxide dismutase catalase conjugates. Role of hydrogen peroxide and the fenton reaction in SOD toxicity, *J. Biol. Chem.,* 268, 416, 1993.
60. **Harris, E. D.,** Regulation of antioxidant enzymes, *FASEB J.,* 6, 2675, 1992.
61. **Shull, S., Heintz, N. H., Periasamy, M., Manohar, M., Janssen, Y. M., Marsh, J. P., and Mossman, B. T.,** Differential regulation of antioxidant enzymes in response to oxidants, *J. Biol. Chem.,* 266, 24398, 1991.
62. **Bielsi, B. H. J.,** *Ascorbic Acid: Chemistry, Metabolism and Uses,* Seib, P. A. and Tolbert, B. M., Eds., American Chemical Society, Washington, D.C., 1984, 81.
63. **Arroyo, C. M., Kramer, J. H., Dickens, B. F., and Weglicki, W. B.,** Identification of free radicals in myocardial ischemia/reperfusion by spin trapping with nitrone DMPO, *FEB. Paris,* 221, 101, 1987.
64. **Rao, P. S., Cohen, M. V., and Mueller, M. S.,** Production of free radicals and lipid peroxides in early experimental myocardial ischemia, *J. Mol. Cell Cardiol.,* 15, 713, 1983.
65. **Rao, P. S. and Mueller, M. S.,** Lipid peroxidation and acute myocardial ischemia, *Adv. Exp. Med. Biol.,* 161, 347, 1983.

66. **Pietri, S., Culcasi, M., Stella, L., and Cozzone, P. J.,** Ascorbyl free radical as a reliable indicator of free-radical-mediated myocardial ischemic and postischemic injury, *Eur. J. Biochem.,* 193, 845, 1990.

67. **Chambers, D. J., Astras, G., Takahashi, A., Manning, A. S., Braimbridge, M. V., and Hearse, D. J.,** Free radicals and cardioplegia: organic antioxidants as additives to the St. Thomas' Hospital cardioplegic solution, *Cardiovasc. Res.,* 23, 351, 1989.

68. **Buettner, G. R. and Jurkiewicz, B. A.,** Ascorbate free radical as a marker of oxidative stress: an EPR study, *Free Rad. Biol. Med.,* 14, 49, 1993.

69. **Florence, T. M.,** Free radicals, antioxidants and cancer prevention, *Proc. Nutr. Aust.,* 15, 88, 1990.

70. **Yamazaki, I. and Piette, L. H.,** Mechanisms of free radical formation and disappearance during the ascorbic acid oxidase and peroxidase reactions, *Biochim. Biophys. Acta,* 50, 62, 1961.

71. **Tominaga, T., Imaizumi, S., Yoshimoto, T., Suzuki, J., and Fujita, Y.,** Application of spin-trapping study to rat ischemic brain homogenate incubated with NADPH and iron-EDTA, *Brain Res.,* 402, 370, 1987.

72. **Painter, P.,** Exercise for individuals with end-stage renal disease, in *Exercise for Prevention and Treatment of Illness,* Goldberg, L. and Elliot, J., Eds., F. A. Davis Co., Philadelphia, 1994, 289.

73. **Ohno, H., Yamashita, H., Ookawara, T., Kizaki, T., Sato, Y., and Taniguchi, N.,** Effect of physical exercise on urinary exertion of CuZn-superoxide dismutase in male high school students, *Acta. Physiol. Scand.,* 148, 353, 1993.

74. **Ji, L. L., Stratman, F. W., and Lardy, H. A.,** Antioxidant enzyme systems in rat liver and skeletal muscle: influences of selenium deficiency, chronic training, and acute exercise, *Arch. Biochem. Biophys.,* 263, 150, 1988.

75. **Sen, C. K., Marin, E., Kretzschmar, M., and Hänninen, O.,** Skeletal muscle and liver glutathione homeostasis in response to training, exercise, and immobilization, *J. Appl. Physiol.,* 73, 1265, 1992.

76. **Alessio, H. M. and Goldfarb, A. H.,** Lipid peroxidation and scavenger enzymes during exercise: adaptive response to training, *J. Appl. Physiol.,* 64, 1333, 1988.

77. **Pyke, S., Lew, H., and Quintanilha, A.,** Severe depletion in liver glutathoine during physical exercise, *Biochem. Biophys. Res. Commun.,* 139, 926, 1986.

78. **Salminen, A., Kainulainen, H., and Vihko, V.,** Endurance training and antioxidants of lung, *Experentia,* 40, 822, 1984.

79. **Gee, D. L. and Tappel, A. L.,** The effect of exhaustive exercise on expired pentane as a measure of in vivo lipid peroxidation in the rat, *Life Sci.,* 28, 2425, 1981.

80. **Dillard, C. J., Litov, R. E., Savin, W. M., Mumelin, E. E., and Tappel, A. L.,** Effects of exercise, vitamin E, and ozone on pulmonary function and lipid peroxidation, *J. Appl. Physiol.,* 45, 927, 1978.

81. **Bus, J. S., Cagen, S. Z., Olgaard, M., and Gibson, J. E.,** A mechanism of paraquet toxicity in mice and rats, *Toxicol. Appl. Pharmacol.,* 353, 501, 1976.

82. **Petering, D. H., Byrnes, R. W., and Antholine, W. E.,** The role of redox-active metals in the mechanism of action of bleomycin, *Chem. Biol. Int.,* 73, 133, 1990.

83. **Hamaoka, T., McCully, K. K., Iwane, H., and Chance, B.,** Noninvasive measures of muscle metabolism, in *Exercise and Oxygen Toxicity,* Sen, C. K., Packer, L., and Hanninen, O., Eds., Elsevier Science, Amsterdam, 1994, 481.

84. **Salminen, A. and Vihko, V.,** Endurance training reduces the susceptibility of mouse skeletal muscle to lipid peroxidation in vitro, *Acta. Physiol. Scand.,* 117, 109, 1983.

85. **Ji, L. L. and Fu, R.,** Responses of glutathione system and antioxidant enzymes to exhaustive exercise and hydroperoxide, *J. Appl. Physiol.,* 72, 1, 1992a.

86. **Ji, L. L., Wu, E., and Thomas D. P.,** Effect of exercise training on antioxidant and metabolic functions in senescent rat skeletal muscle, *Gerontology,* 37, 317, 1991.

87. **Hammeren, J., Powers, S., Lawler, J., Criswell, D., Martin, D., Lowenthal, D., and Pollock, M.,** Exercise training-induced alterations in skeletal muscle oxidative and antioxidant enzyme activity in senescent rats, *Int. J. Sports Med.,* 13, 412, 1992.

88. **Powers, S. K., Criswell, D., Lawler, J., Martin, D., Ji, L. L., Herb, R. A., and Dudley, G.,** Regional training-induced alterations in diaphragmatic oxidative and antioxidant enzymes, *Resp. Physiol.,* 95, 227, 1994.

89. **Ortiz de Montellano, P. R.,** Oxygen activation and transfer, in *Cytochrome P-450, Structure, Mechanism, and Biochemistry,* Ortiz de Montellano, P. R., Ed., Plenum Press, New York, 1986, 217.

90. **DeGroot, H. and Noll, T.,** Halothane hepatotoxicity: relation between metabolic activation, hypoxia, covalent binding, lipid peroxidation and liver cell damages, *Hepatology,* 3, 601, 1983..

91. **Pollakis, G., Goormaghtigh, E., Delmelle, M., Lion, Y., and Ruysschaert, J. B.,** Adriamycin and derivatives interaction with the mitochondrial membrane: O_2 consumption and free radical formation, *Res. Commun. Chem. Pathol. Pharmac.,* 44, 445, 1984.

92. **Moore, H. W.,** Bioactivation as a model for drug design bioreductive alkylation, *Science,* 197, 527, 1977.

93. **Reed, D. J., May, H. E., Boorse, R. B., Gregory, K. M., and Beilstein, M. A.,** 2-Chloroethanol formation as evidence for a 2-chloroethyl alkylating intermediate during chemical degradation of 1-(2-chlorethyl)-3-cyclohexyl-1-nitrosourea and 1-(2-chlorOethyl)-3-(trans-4-methylcyclohexyl)-1-nitrosourea, *Cancer Res.,* 35, 568, 1985.

94. **Sinha, B. K.,** Metabolic activation of procarbazine: evidence for carbon-centered free-radical intermediates, *Biochem. Pharmacol.,* 33, 2777, 1984.

95. **Kaysen, G. A., Pond, S. M., Roper, M. H., et al.,** Combined hepatic and renal injury in alcoholics during therapeutic use of acetaminophen, *Arch. Int. Med.,* 145, 2019, 1985.

96. **Mitchell, J. R., Zimmerman, H. J., Ishak, K. G., Thorgeirsson, U. P., Timbrell, J. A., Snodgrass, W. R., and Nelson, S. D.,** Isoniazid liver injury: clinical spectrum, pathology, and probable pathogenesis, *Ann. Int. Med.,* 84, 181, 1976.

97. **Knecht, K. T., Thurman, R. G., and Mason, R. P.,** Role of superoxide and trace metals in production of α-hydroxy ethyl radical from ethanol by microsomes from alcohol dehydrogenase deficient deer mice, *Arch. Biochem. Biophys.,* 303, 339, 1993.

98. **Somani, S. M., Kutty, R. K., and Krishna, G.,** Eseroline, a metabolite of physostigmine, induces neuronal cell death, *Toxicol. Appl. Pharm.,* 106, 28, 1990.

99. **Kochli, H. W., Wermuth, B., and Von Wartburg, J. P.,** Characterization of a mitochondrial NADH-dependent nitro reductase from rat brain, *Biochem. Biophys. Acta,* 616, 133, 1980.

100. **Nagamatsu, K., Kido, Y., Terao, T., Ishida, T., and Toki, S.,** Studies on the mechanism of covalent binding of morphine metabilities to proteins in mouse, *Drug. Metab. Disp.,* 11, 190, 1983.

101. **Suntres, Z. and Shek, P. N.,** Nitrofurantoin-induced pulmonary toxicity: *in vivo* evidence for oxidative stress-mediated mechanisms, *Biochem. Pharmacol.,* 43, 1127, 1992.

102. **Bus, J. S. and Gibson, J. E.,** Paraquat: model for oxidant-initiated toxicity, *Environ. Health Perspect.,* 55, 37, 1984.

103. **Chambers, J. E., Munson, J. R., and Chambers, H. W.,** Activation of the phosphothionate insectivide parathion by rat brain in situ, *Biochem. Biophys. Res. Comm.,* 165, 327, 1989.

104. **Sipes, I. G., Krishna, G., and Gillette, J. R.,** Bioactivation of carbon tetrachloride, chloroform and bromotrichloromethane: role of cytochrome P-450, *Life Sci.,* 20, 1541, 1977.

105. **Mehendale, H. M.,** Amplified interactive toxicity of chemicals at nontoxic level: mechanistic considerations and implications to public health, *Environ. Health. Perspect.,* 102, 139, 1994.

106. **Das, M., Seth, P. K., and Mukhtar, H.,** NADPH-dependent inducible aryl hydrocarbon hydroxylase activity in rat brain mitochondria, *Drug. Metab. Dispos.,* 9, 69, 1981.

107. **Lauffer, R. B.,** Exercise as prevention: do the health benefits derive in part from lower iron levels?, *Med. Hypothesis,* 35, 103, 1991.
108. **Winningham, M. L.,** *Exercise and Cancer in Exercise for Prevention and Treatment of Illness,* Goldberg, L. and Elliot, D. L., Eds., F. A. Davis Co., Philadelphia, 1994, 301.
109. **Powis, G.,** *Anticancer Drugs: Reactive Metabolism and Drug Interaction,* Pergamon Press, Oxford, 1994.

Chapter 4

GLUTATHIONE AND EXERCISE

Li Li Ji and Christiaan Leeuwenburgh

CONTENTS

1. INTRODUCTION

Oxidative stress is involved in many pathological conditions and in aging.[1-3] Recently, free radical generation has been implicated in the etiology of exercise-induced cell and tissue damage.[3-6] Although the exact mechanism for the exercise-induced oxidative damage is still elusive, there is increasing evidence that the problem stems from the enhanced oxidative metabolism associated with exercise, since the whole body oxygen consumption can increase 10- to 20-fold during strenuous aerobic exercise, such as marathon running and cross-country skiing, whereas oxygen flux in the individual muscle fibers is believed to increase by as much as 100-fold.[3] Most of the oxygen consumed is utilized in the mitochondria for oxidative phosphorylation and is reduced to water. However, a small fraction of oxygen may be reduced univalently to several intermediates due to the increased "leakage" of electrons from the mitochondrial respiratory chain, primarily at the Complex III (ubiquinone dehydrogenase) step.[7] These oxygen species are, in the order of added electrons, superoxide

($\bar{O}_2$), hydrogen peroxide (H_2O_2), and hydroxyl radical ($\cdot OH$), and are collectively termed reactive oxygen species. Several investigators have shown, using electron paramagnetic resonance spectroscopy methods, that following heavy exercise free radical signals are increased in a number of metabolically active tissues.[8-10] The increased free radical production appears to coincide with oxidative tissue damage, such as alteration of cellular oxidoreductive (redox) status,[11-15] lipid peroxidation,[16-18] inactivation of specific enzymes,[19] and oxidative damage to genetic materials.[20]

Protection against oxygen free radicals in the cell is provided by an elaborate antioxidant defense system including antioxidant enzymes, antioxidant vitamins (α-tocopherol, ascorbate, and β-carotene), and thiols. Their functions in protecting the tissues from exercise-induced oxidative damage have been reviewed by a number of authors recently.[3-6,21,22] Each of the antioxidant systems assumes a unique role, while functionally cooperating and complementing one another. This review will focus on the role of glutathione (L-γ-glutamyl-L-cysteinyl-glycine; GSH) because of the pivotal functions it plays in the cellular antioxidant defense during acute and chronic exercise, and because of the increasing attention it receives in the recent literature of exercise physiology and biochemistry. The authors will review the basic biochemical properties of GSH as an antioxidant, its intracellular and interorgan regulation during exercise, and perturbation of its homeostasis caused by nutritional deficiency and supplementation.

2. BIOCHEMISTRY OF GLUTATHIONE

GSH is a thiol-containing tripeptide found in virtually all animal and plant cells and in some bacteria. It has been the subject of much research since its discovery by Rey-Pailhade in 1888. Its original name *philothione* (Greek for love-sulfur) reflects its tendency towards a spontaneous reaction with sulfur. Eventually, the molecule itself was found to contain sulfur and Hopkins (1921) named the structure glutathione. The elucidation of its tripeptide structure was not resolved until around 1930, revealing that glutamic acid, cysteine, and glycine were all part of its constituents. An explosive amount of information relating to the complex function of this simple compound has accumulated at just a few years past its centennial. There have been several comprehensive reviews of glutathione in recent years.[23-25]

2.1. FUNCTIONS OF GLUTATHIONE

GSH has three structural characteristics which facilitate its metabolic and antioxidant functions. First, the glutamyl-cysteine bond is formed at the γ-carboxyl group of glutamate instead of the common α-carboxyl site. This unique characteristic makes the γ-carboxyl bond resistant to all peptidases except γ-glutamyltranspeptidase. γ-Glutamyltranspeptidase is bound to the external surface of the cell membrane; therefore, it does not cleave intracellular GSH.[24] Second, the C-terminal glycine protects GSH from cleavage by

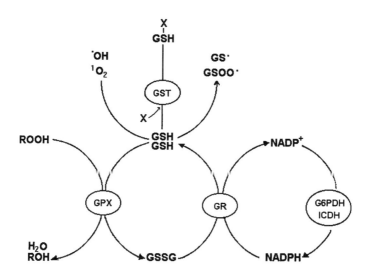

FIGURE 1. Antioxidant function of GSH. GPX, glutathione peroxidase; GR, glutathione reductase; GSH sulfur-transferase, glutathione sulfur-transferase; G6PDH, glucose 6-phosphate dehydrogenase; ICDH, isocitrate dehydrogenase. ROOH, alkyl peroxide or hydrogen peroxide; X, xenobiotics.

intracellular γ-glutamylcyclotransferase, increasing its stability. Finally, the most important moiety is the sulfhydryl on cysteine, responsible for many metabolic functions of GSH. These characteristics provide GSH with multiple roles in the cellular antioxidant defense. These roles include: (a) to serve as a cosubstrate for GSH peroxidase (GPX) wherein GSH is used as a hydrogen donor to reduce hydrogen peroxide and organic peroxide to water and alcohol, respectively; (b) to conjugate with exogenous and endogenous toxic compounds, catalyzed by GSH sulfur-transferase, rendering them more water-soluble and easier to be metabolized; (c) to reduce protein disulfide and GSH-protein mixed disulfide bonds, maintaining the sulfhydryl residues of certain proteins and enzymes in the reduced state; (d) to store cysteine in a nontoxic form and to provide a vehicle for cysteine transport between organs; (e) GSH plays an important role in the reduction of ribonucleotides to deoxyribonucleotides; and (f) GSH assumes a vital role in keeping α-tocopherol (vitamin E) and ascorbic acid (vitamin C) in the reduced states.

The most important antioxidant function of GSH is illustrated in Figure 1. The removal of the hydrogen and organic peroxides (e.g., lipid peroxide) is catalyzed by the selenium-dependent enzyme GPX, forming water and alcohol, respectively. By donating a pair of hydrogen ions, GSH is oxidized to glutathione disulfide (GSSG). Reduction of GSSG is catalyzed by glutathione reductase (GR), a flavin-containing enzyme, wherein nicotinamide-adenine dinucleotide phosphate (NADPH) is used as the reducing power. This reaction takes place simultaneously with GPX, thus providing a redox cycle for the regeneration of GSH.[26] GSSG levels in most tissues are kept very low, and the intracellular ratio of GSH:GSSG is believed to be much higher than reported in the literature.[1] NADPH is supplied by the hexose monophosphate pathway or by reactions catalyzed by isocitrate dehydrogenase and malic enzyme, depending on the tissue.[5,27] Although NADPH is a relatively abundant cellular reducing power, a shortage may occur when the hexose monophosphate pathway is severely constrained due to glucose 6-phosphate dehydrogenase deficiency or when the glucose source is limited.[26] In addition to the enzymatically catalyzed functions, GSH is also an efficient scavenger of $\bar{O}_2$, $\cdot OH$, and singlet oxygen ($^1O_2$). In these reactions, GSH is reduced to glutathione thiyl radical (GS$\cdot$), which is less reactive.[1]

Recently, GSH has been found to be involved in reducing a variety of antioxidants in the cell. For example, GSH has been postulated to reduce vitamin E (α-tocopheroxyl) radicals which are formed in the chain-breaking reactions with alkoxyl or lipid peroxyl radicals.[28,29] GSH may also be used to reduce semidehydroascorbate radical (vitamin C radical) derived in the recycling of vitamin E, and to reduce α-lipoic acid to α-dihydrolipoate. The latter have recently been hypothesized to play an important role in the recycling of ascorbate or ascorbic acid. Together, these reactions make the limited and valuable resources of vitamin E and C recyclable at the expense of GSH, a relatively abundant reducing power in the cell.

2.2. GLUTATHIONE HOMEOSTASIS

GSH is the most abundant short-chain peptide and nonprotein thiol source in the cell.[25] GSH concentration in the cell is in the millimolar range for most tissues, but there is a great variability in GSH content in different organs depending on their function and oxidative capacity. The eye lens has the highest GSH concentration (~10 mM) among all tissues, probably due to its essential role in protecting against photoradiation.[1] Next only to the eye lens, the concentration of GSH in the liver is between 5 to 7 mM. Hepatic GSH is used for a variety of antioxidant and detoxification functions.[24] Other important organs such as the lung, kidney, and heart contain 2 to 3 mM of GSH. It is noteworthy that the red blood cell contains a high level of GSH (~2 mM) compared to blood plasma (<0.05 mM) primarily due to its protective role against oxidative damage to haemoglobin.[26]

Skeletal muscle GSH concentration varies depending on muscle fiber type and animal species.[14,30] As shown in Table 1, Type I muscle (slow-twitch oxidative) such as the soleus contains sixfold higher GSH content (~3 mM) than the Type IIb muscle white vastus lateralis (fast-twitch glycolytic) in rats. However, the GSH:GSSG ratio appears remarkably consistent across various fiber types.

Although GSH is essential for the normal cell functions, most organs and tissues do not synthesize GSH *de novo*. Instead, GSH is taken up from the extracellular source and imported into the cell.[23,25] This process encompasses cross-membrane transport and resynthesis of GSH, known as the γ-Glutamyl Cycle.[25] The first enzyme in the translocation of GSH is γ-glutamyl-

TABLE 1
Glutathione Status in Skeletal Muscle

	GSH	GSSG	GSH+GSSG	GSH:GSSG
Rat				
White vastus	0.5	0.03	0.53	17
Red vastus	1.5	0.09	1.60	17
Soleus	2.2	0.18	2.40	18
Mice				
Quadriceps	0.5	0.03	0.53	17
Diaphragm	0.6	0.08	0.68	8

Note: All data are given in μmol/g wet wt.

transpeptidase, an enzyme located on the outer surface of the cell membrane which cleaves the extracellular GSH to glutamate and cysteinylglycine. The former is transported into the cell using a cystine or other available amino acid as a carrier. Once transported into the cell, cysteinylglycine is further cleaved to cysteine and glycine. The intracellular synthesis of GSH from the three amino acid precursors requires seven enzymes and two ATPs.[23] γ-Glutamylcysteine synthase, the rate-limiting enzyme, catalyses the formation of a peptide linkage between cysteine and glutamate. This reaction is inhibited by a negative feedback, controlled by the availability of GSH and is limited by the availability of cysteine. The final step of GSH synthesis is catalyzed by GSH synthase. Although the above description outlines the main pathway for tissue GSH synthesis, this is probably not the only way. There is some evidence that alternative pathways may exist for GSH import into the cell, including an intact uptake.[31,32]

The majority of the GSH in the body is synthesized *de novo* in the liver, supplying approximately 90% of the circulating GSH under physiological conditions.[24,25,33,34] The main portion of the synthesized GSH is exported into the plasma, whereas the remaining is excreted into the bile[34] (Figure 2). Hepatic GSH synthesis is controlled by both substrate (amino acids) availability and hormonal regulation. Thus, fasting decreases liver GSH content, whereas refeeding recovers it without affecting the activity of GSH synthesizing enzymes.[35] Cysteine and methionine concentrations play a major role in determining hepatic GSH synthesis upon fast-refeeding.[35] Insulin and glucocorticoids stimulate hepatic GSH synthesis by an induction of γ-glutamylcysteine synthase.[36] In contrast, glucagon and several other cAMP-stimulating agents down-regulate hepatic GSH synthesis by phosphorylating and inhibiting γ-glutamylcysteine synthase.[37] However, liver efflux of GSH is enhanced by glucagon.[38]

GSH turns over at a significant rate in virtually all mammalian tissues. It is estimated that the turnover rate amounts to 4.5, 2, 7, and 1.6 μmol/h, for the liver, kidney, and skeletal muscle, respectively.[39] Uptake of GSH into the liver is rather limited because of the low γ-glutamyltranspeptidase activity. Al-

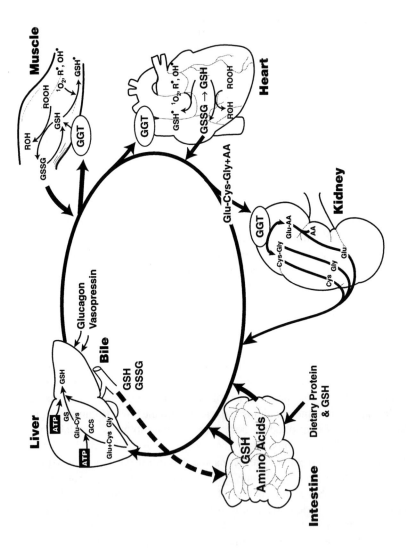

FIGURE 2. Postulated outline of interorgan transport of glutathione. GS·, glutathione thiyl radical; ROOH, hydroperoxide; ROH, alcohol; GGT-glutamyltranspeptidase; GCS, γ-glutamylcysteinyl synthase; GS, GSH synthase.

though human liver contains considerably higher amounts of γ-glutamyl-transpeptidase compared to other species, such as the rat, the γ-glutamyl-transpeptidase activity is still not sufficient for significant import of GSH.[24] The kidney, on the other hand, is responsible for 80 to 90% of plasma GSH removal due to its extremely high γ-glutamyltranspeptidase activity.[25,31] The constituent amino acids are taken up by the proximal tubular cells for resynthesis of GSH, or returned back into the circulation. Although GSH turnover rate is low in the skeletal muscle, primarily due to a low γ-glutamyltranspeptidase activity,[30,40] the skeletal muscle as a whole is an important GSH pool. The large muscle mass (~40% of the body weight) and the relatively high GSH concentration may exert an important influence on plasma GSH levels and GSH turnover under certain physiological and pathological conditions.[41]

Cells are capable of exporting GSSG to maintain the GSH:GSSG ratio and to alleviate oxidative stress, as has been demonstrated in skeletal muscle, liver, heart, and erythrocytes.[32,33,42,43] In addition, GSH seems particularly enriched in the membrane lipid bilayers of the cell such that the membrane-borne thiols and other antioxidants (e.g., α-tocopherol) are kept in the reduced state.[5] This profile of intracellular GSH distribution is especially favorable for some organelles such as the mitochondria, wherein the inner membrane is an important source of free radical generation. Since mitochondria lack the enzymes of the γ-Glutamyl Cycle, mitochondrial GSH is transported from the cytosol by specific carriers.[44,45]

3. GLUTATHIONE RESPONSE TO ACUTE EXERCISE

3.1. INTRACELLULAR GLUTATHIONE REDOX STATUS

Intracellular GSH status is regulated primarily by GPX and GR catalyzed reactions, as illustrated in Figure 1. This GSH-GSSG cycle is by no means a closed cycle since GSH is imported from the extracellular source and GSSG may be exported outside the cell, both processes requiring ATP.[23,31] In addition, supply of the reducing power NADPH relies on hexose monophosphate shunt which depends upon glucose availability. In most tissues GPX activity far exceeds that of GR, suggesting that the reducing capacity of the GSH-GSSG cycle may be limited by GR activity (Table 2). All these factors determine that during heavy aerobic exercise there is a tendency towards an accumulation of GSSG in the cell, because reactive oxygen species production are increased during exercise,[4,8] whereas intracellular availability of ATP and NADPH may be compromised due to an increased metabolic demand.

3.1.1. Skeletal Muscle

Skeletal muscle is a major site of free radical production, but has only a moderate reserves of GSH.[5] Therefore, exercise is expected to have a significant impact on muscle GSH status. Indeed, an acute bout of exhaustive exercise has been shown to cause a significant increase in GSSG content in rat skeletal muscle.[12,13] The levels of GSSG increase seem to depend on exercise intensity

TABLE 2
Enzyme Activities in the GSH-GSSG Cycle

	GPX	GR	G6PDH	ICDH
Rat Vastus L.	32	4	0.6	<1
Rat Soleus	80	9	0.6	<1
Rat heart	126	5	—	—
Rat liver	480	40	40	—

Note: All data are given in nmol/min × mg protein. Enzymes: GPX, glutathione peroxidase; GR, glutathione reductase; G6PDH, glucose 6-phosphate dehydrogenase; ICDH, isocitrate dehydrogenase.

as well as muscle fiber type. In the deep vastus lateralis muscle (Type IIa), GSSG was increased by 40% after 1 h of exercise at ~75% VO_2max, whereas in the soleus muscle (Type I) there was only a modest increase in GSSG at high workload (~90% VO_2max).[14] Type IIb muscle showed little change in GSSG at all workloads measured. These patterns probably reflect the different levels of reactive oxygen species production at the various workloads as well as the reducing capacity within the various muscle fibers. It is noteworthy that accumulation of GSSG in exercising muscle was associated with an activation of GPX and GR in these studies, indicating an increased hydroperoxide flux through the GSH-GSSG cycle.[13] Studies of the diaphragm muscle involved in resistive breathing showed similar results, as a significant loss of GSH and an increase in GSSG:GSH+GSSG ratio were apparent in the stressed diaphragms.[46] In contrast to heavy exercise, prolonged exercise at moderate intensity was found to result in no accumulation of GSSG in the skeletal muscle of mice swum to exhaustion.[47] Coincidentally, enzyme activities in the GSH-GSSG redox cycle also showed little alteration in response to the imposed exercise.

There have been conflicting reports regarding GSH response to acute exercise in skeletal muscle. Ji and co-workers,[13,14,47] have found that GSH content is significantly increased in rodent hindlimb muscles after an acute bout of exercise. Total glutathione content in working muscles was also found to be elevated after exercise. This unique response of muscle GSH was previously reported by Pyke et al.,[48] indicating that muscle might take up GSH to cope with the exercise-induced oxidative stress. In contrast, Sen et al.[30] showed that GSH content was decreased in rat muscle after an acute bout of exhaustive exercise, along with a down-regulation of γ-glutamyltranspeptidase activity. A marked decline of GSH in the soleus muscle after treadmill exercise has been reported by Duarte et al.,[49,50] in mice. Allopurinol, an endothelial xanthine oxidase inhibitor, was found to be effective in protecting the skeletal muscle from exercise-induced GSH loss.[49] Since muscle GSSG content was not measured in the above studies, it is not clear whether GSH was oxidized to GSSG or lost through circulation. Jackson et al.[51] showed that GSH release was preceded by creatine kinase release in rat skeletal muscle during electrical stimulation, indicating that GSH efflux might be a result of muscle damage.

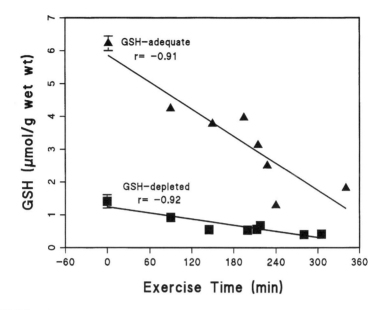

FIGURE 3. The relationship between swimming endurance time and glutathione content in the liver of acutely exercised mice. ▲, GSH-adequate (r = –0.91); ■, GSH-depleted mice (r = –0.92); injected with BSO for 12 days (2 mmol/kg body wt/day) combined with 20 m*M* BSO in drinking water. Values at zero time are means (± SEM) of 8 control mice for both GSH-A and GSH-D.

The ratio of GSH:GSSG, an indicator of intracellular redox status, was reported to be dramatically decreased in human skeletal muscle biopsy after marathon running.[52] However, in rodent studies, most authors found only moderate reduction or no change in the GSH:GSSG ratio after acute exercise.[12-14,47] The reported values of muscle GSH:GSSG ratio vary greatly from study to study (from 10 to several hundred), making comparisons difficult. This is probably caused by the different GSH assays used by the various investigators. One possible source of variability may hinge on whether or not the GSH-protein mixed disulfide was taken into account.

3.1.2. Liver

In the liver, a decreased GSH content after exercise has been reported consistently in several rodent studies.[12,30,40,47,48] Furthermore, hepatic residual GSH content was found to correlate inversely with endurance time in rats[48] and mice[47] exercising to exhaustion. The extent of GSH depletion in the liver also appears to depend on the length of exercise time (Figure 3). Thus, a 50% decrease in liver GSH was reported in mice after an exhaustive swimming bout for 4 to 6 h.[47] Villa et al.[53] reported a similar level of liver GSH depletion (–40%) with treadmill exercise in mice. The exercise-induced GSH decline was attenuated by injecting mice with S-adenosyl-L-methionine for 10 days. The observed decrease of liver GSH can be attributed to several factors. First, prolonged heavy exercise is known to increase free radical production in the liver.[8]

It is estimated that *in situ* 10 to 15% of the total oxygen uptake in the liver is converted to H_2O_2,[7] and this fraction may increase with an increased metabolic rate. Therefore, hepatic GSH consumption may be dramatically increased during exercise. Second, hepatic export of GSH into the plasma is stimulated by hormones, such as glucagon and vasopressin,[38,54] which both increase their releases during prolonged exercise. Finally, *de novo* GSH synthesis requires three ATPs, whereas recycling of GSSG to GSH requires NADPH. These pathways are heavily taxed during exhaustive exercise when other metabolic demands compete for ATP and NADPH.

There is a lack of clear consensus regarding GSSG response to exercise in the liver. Some investigators have reported increased GSSG content after exhaustive exercise in rats, presumably caused by an increased oxidation of GSH,[12] whereas others found it to be either unchanged[13] or decreased.[47,55] The decrease of liver GSSG may be explained by a possible release of GSSG into the bile under oxidative stress.[33]

3.1.3. Heart

There is little data available regarding heart GSH response to acute exercise. In one study, Packer et al.[56] found no significant difference in either total glutathione (GSH+GSSG) or GSSG in the heart between rested and exhaustively exercised guinea pigs. However, Sen et al.[57] were able to show a decrease in total myocardial GSH in rats exercised to exhaustion. The loss of heart GSH may have been caused by either a direct oxidation to GSSG or the reduction of α-tocopherol radicals and semihydroascorbate radicals produced in the myocardium during exercise.[58] Recently, we investigated GSH status in the myocardium of mice swimming to exhaustion.[59] Heart GSH content was found to decrease from 0.9 at rest to 0.7 μmol/g wet wt. after exercise, which was consistent with the findings of Sen et al.[57] Furthermore, myocardial GSH concentration was inversely correlated with exercise time. A remarkable finding was that GSSG concentration was also significantly decreased after exercise. Thus, while myocardial GSH+GSSG was decreased by ~20% at the end of the swimming lasting 3.5 h, the GSH:GSSG ratio was maintained relatively constant.[59] In light of the previous finding by Ishikawa and Sies[42] that isolated perfused hearts were able to export GSSG when oxidatively stressed with t-butylhydroperoxide, our data indicate that GSSG export may be an important mechanism for the heart to cope with an exercise-induced oxidative stress.

3.2. REGULATION OF GLUTATHIONE HOMEOSTASIS

Blood GSH homeostasis is determined by hepatic output and peripheral uptake of GSH, as illustrated in Figure 2. Furthermore, erythrocytes also contain a significant GSH pool and are capable of exchanging GSH with the blood plasma.[26] Physical exercise not only increases the whole-body oxidative metabolism, but also alters blood distribution to many organs and tissues which actively utilize GSH as an antioxidant. Thus, strenuous exercise can cause a disturbance in the blood GSH status. Although there is a large body of literature dealing with blood GSH response to exercise in both animal and human studies, the results are inconsistent and often confusing. Kretzschmar et al.[60] showed that plasma GSH concentration was significantly decreased after an acute bout of treadmill exercise in long-distance runners at different ages. However, untrained subjects did not show a GSH decline after treadmill running. Also, plasma GSSG levels were not altered by exercise. It has been shown in human subjects that blood GSH levels were significantly decreased, whereas GSSG levels were increased in a reciprocal fashion during the initial phase of 90 min exercise at ~60% VO$_2$max.[11,61] However, short-term maximal exercise did not alter blood GSH status.[11] Sen et al.[15] reported that blood concentration of GSSG, but not GSH, was significantly elevated after an acute bout of treadmill exercise in human subjects at both maximal and submaximal intensities. As a result, the ratio of GSSG:GSH was increased in the blood. Duthie et al.,[62] evaluating human erythrocyte response to a half-marathon (13.1 mile, 21 km), found a ~50% decrease of GSH content immediately after the race but no change in GSSG levels. GPX and glucose-6-phosphoglucose 6-phosphate dehydrogenase activities were found unaltered comparing pre- vs. postrace. These findings may reflect an increased oxidative stress to the red blood cells due to an enhanced oxygen transport during heavy exercise.

In contrast to the aforementioned studies, several investigators reported no significant change in blood GSH or GSSG levels in humans under various experimental conditions.[63-65] Ji et al.[66] reported that blood GSH and total glutathione levels were significantly elevated during prolonged bicycle exercise in human subjects. Sahlin et al.[67] also showed that total glutathione levels in the blood and plasma were significantly increased during bicycle exercise at progressively increased workloads. The reason for the discrepancies of exercise response of GSH is unknown, but may be related to the severity of the exercise protocols and the training status of the subjects. It should be kept in mind that blood GSH has two separate pools, i.e., erythrocyte (~2 m*M)* and plasma (<0.05 m*M).* In order to obtain meaningful results, the two GSH sources should be separated immediately after exercise. Caution also has to be practiced to prevent rapid oxidation of GSH to GSSG.

Interorgan transport of GSH has been proposed to occur during prolonged strenuous exercise.[12,47,66,68] However, there are two opposing scenarios regarding the roles of liver and skeletal muscle in the maintenance of GSH homeostasis. Lew et al.[12] and Ji et al.[66] hypothesized that liver exports GSH under the hormonal influence, such as glucagon and vasopressin, which are known to increase during prolonged exercise. Circulating GSH may be taken up by skeletal muscle to alleviate an exercise-induced oxidative stress. In support of this hypothesis, the authors[66] showed that blood GSH content was elevated without changing GSSG concentration during prolonged bicycle exercise at 75% VO$_2$max. When the subjects were supplied with a carbohydrate drink during exercise, the elevated GSH response to exercise was abolished. Presumably, carbohydrate ingestion inhibited glucagon response which under normal conditions stimulates hepatic efflux of GSH.[38,54] The finding that there is an increased GSH content in active skeletal muscles after acute exercise and chronic training seem to be consistent with this scenario.[13,14,30,47,69-71] Furthermore, concentrations of cysteine and glutamate in exercised muscles showed a significant increase compared to resting levels.[13,14] Since *de novo* synthesis of GSH is small in the muscle, the increased GSH must be imported from the circulation either through the γ-Glutamyl Cycle or by an intact absorption.[32]

In contrast to this hypothesis, Kretzschmar and Muller[68] proposed that skeletal muscle exports GSH into, instead of importing GSH from, the plasma during prolonged exercise to cope with the oxidative stress in the whole body. This hypothesis was supported by their finding that plasma GSH levels were sustained 6 h after the surgery in hepectomized rats.[41] It was also argued that skeletal muscle, like the liver, has low γ-glutamyltranspeptidase activity, making any uptake of GSH negligible. Given the large GSH pool in skeletal muscle, this hypothesis seems attractive. However, the mechanism of exporting GSH from muscle cells has not been postulated and the signals stimulating muscle GSH efflux also remain to be identified.

Given the current state of knowledge, it is difficult to evaluate the merit of the two hypotheses. Some critical information is still missing from this complex picture. For example, it is unclear whether muscle uptake of GSH requires the activation of γ-glutamyltranspeptidase. Several studies have shown that γ-glutamyltranspeptidase is down-regulated during heavy exercise in skeletal muscle,[30,40] which seems to argue against an uptake of GSH by muscle. However, it has been demonstrated that administration of acivicin, a γ-glutamyltranspeptidase inhibitor, did not completely prevent GSH transport into the L-6 muscle cell lines.[32] Another question is to what extent can muscle export GSSG during exercise. Regardless of the exact mechanism, it is clear that skeletal muscle increases GSH turnover rate during strenuous exercise, which may have a significant impact on GSH homeostasis.

4. TRAINING ADAPTATION OF THE GLUTATHIONE SYSTEM

4.1. TISSUE GLUTATHIONE LEVELS IN THE TRAINED STATE

Chronic exercise training at high intensity and long duration has been shown to increase GSH content in the liver, lung, and leg muscles of beagle dogs.[30,68,70] The data indicate that tissues are capable of adapting to exercise-induced oxidative stress by either synthesizing more GSH or increasing its uptake from extramuscular sources. Two lines of evidence appear to support this hypothesis: (a) along with an increased GSH, activities of enzymes in the γ-Glutamyl Cycle, such as γ-glutamyltranspeptidase, γ-glutamylcysteine synthase, and glutathione synthase were also significantly elevated in the trained muscle groups;[30,70] and (b) GSH content was increased in rat hindlimb muscle after a single bout of exercise.[12,13,48] However, the effect of training on GSH content seems to vary between animal species and muscle fiber types. Sen et al.[30] reported no alteration of GSH content in red gastrocnemius, mixed vastus lateralis, and longissimus dorsi of rats after 10 weeks of endurance training, but liver GSH content was significantly increased. Salminen and Vihko[69] found a training-induced increase in GSH content in the red vastus muscle, but not the white vastus muscle in the rat. Leeuwenburgh et al.[40] showed that GSH levels in the deep vastus lateralis muscle were unaltered after 8 weeks of endurance training, whereas in soleus muscle GSH content and the GSH:GSSG ratio were significantly decreased. The reason for these discrepancies is not clear. It may be related to the rate of GSH utilization vs. the capacity of GSH uptake within each fiber type. Recently, Hollander et al.[71] revisited the effect of endurance training on GSH status in female rats pair-fed a semi-purified diet containing equal amounts of cysteine and other antioxidants. Training consisted of 2 h treadmill running daily at 25 m/min, 10% grade, and lasted 10 weeks. GSH content was found to increase by 28% ($p < 0.05$) in the deep vastus lateralis muscle of trained rats, with no alteration of the GSH:GSSG ratio. This study verifies that training adaptation of GSH is not limited to the dog muscles and that workload is probably a determining factor in stimulating GSH uptake in skeletal muscle. The effect of exercise training on liver GSH status has been shown to vary between studies.[30,68,71,72]

In addition to skeletal muscle, myocardial GSH has been reported to be elevated after swim training in rats and this increase was hypothesized to provide a greater protection against ischemia-reperfusion injury.[58,73,74] Interestingly, training adaptation of GSH was limited to the subepimyocardium of the left ventricle.[73] Subendomyocardial tissues and the right ventricular tissues demonstrated no effect.[74] Furthermore, treadmill training seems to be ineffective in raising myocardial GSH content.[71,75] Since the myocardium utilizes a significant amount of GSH during vigorous exercise,[59] the GSH status in the heart may be subjected to a delicate balance between GSH consumption and uptake. Indeed, we have recently found that rigorous swim training (6 h/day for 4 weeks) can cause a significant deficit in myocardial GSH content in rats.[76]

Physically trained human subjects and animals generally demonstrate a greater tolerance of exercise-induced disturbance of blood GSH,[63,72,77] although there are exceptions.[60] Furthermore, erythrocyte GSH content has been shown to increase significantly after 20 weeks of physical training in previously sedentary men.[78] It has been reported that blood GSH concentration increases with running distance in long-distance runners during a training season.[77] GSH and total GSH concentration in the red blood cells were higher in moderately trained (16 to 43 km/week) and highly trained (80 to 147 km/week) runners compared to sedentary subjects.[77] However, highly trained runners also demonstrated a significantly higher blood GSSG concentration at rest, possibly indicating an overtraining effect. Kretzschmar et al.[60] found that both young and old trained individuals had higher resting plasma GSH concentrations than their sedentary counterparts, without changing GSSG levels. It was suggested that the observed training adaptation of blood GSH resulted from an increased GSH export from both the liver and skeletal muscle.[68] Table 3 summarizes the effect of exercise training on GSH levels reported in the recent literature.

TABLE 3
Training Adaptations of Glutathione

Species	Skeletal Muscle	Heart	Liver	Blood	Erythrocytes	Plasma	Ref.
Dog	↑ *(RG)		↑ *				30
	↑ *(RG)					↑ *	70
			↑			↑	68
Rat	→ *(RG, MVL)		↑ *				30
	→ (RVL)						40
	↓ (S)						40
			→ *			→ *	72
		↑					73
		→					74
		→					75
	↑ (RVL)	→	→				71
	↓ (S)						71
		↓					76
Mouse	↑ (RVL)						69
	→ (WVL)						69
Human						↑	60
				↑ →			78
					↑		77

Note: Training adaptations of glutathione in rat, dog, mouse, and man. RG, red gastrocnemius; MVL, mixed vastus lateralis; RVL, red vastus lateralis; WVL, white vastus lateralis; S, soleus. * Indicates total GSH is measured.

4.2. TRAINING ADAPTATION OF GSH-RELATED ENZYMES

The effects of endurance training on activities of enzymes associated with the GSH-GSSG redox cycle have been well studied. There have been consistent reports that GPX activity in skeletal muscle is increased after endurance training.[4,5,30,40,71] An increased production of hydroperoxide associated with heavy exercise has been hypothesized to be the inducer of this antioxidant enzyme, but so far there is a lack of experimental evidence to support this hypothesis in the mammalian tissues.[5] Training adaptation of GPX also appears to depend on muscle fiber type and exercise intensity. Thus, red gastrocnemius (Type IIa) and plantaris (mixed) muscles demonstrated greater levels of GPX training adaptation than white gastrocnemius and soleus muscles in rats,[79] whereas red gastrocnemius muscle in dogs displayed more prominent increases of GPX activity than extensor carpi radialis and triceps muscles involved in the same training program.[30] Those muscles showing a greater training adaptation typically have a relatively low endogenous GPX activity, whereas oxygen flux is tremendously increased during treadmill running. Furthermore, the levels of GPX induction in these muscle types were shown to be a direct function of running speed and grade, and training duration.[79] Presumably, an increased GPX activity facilitates the removal of hydrogen and organic peroxide produced during exercise and alleviates potential oxidative stress in skeletal muscle. It is interesting to note that the diaphragm, a highly specialized skeletal muscle, also displays a prominent training adaptation of GPX. Furthermore, training adaptation was limited to the coastal regions of the diaphragm, whereas crural diaphragm and parasternal muscle showed little response.[80] In contrast to skeletal muscle, training does not induce myocardial or hepatic GPX, probably due to a high basal GPX activity in these tissues.[5,58,73]

Despite the important function of GR in the maintenance of tissue GSH status, training does not seem to have a significant impact on GR activity. Most studies have failed to reveal a training adaptation of GR in either skeletal muscle, liver, or myocardium.[5,40,71] A decrease of GR activity has been reported in rat hindlimb muscles after endurance training.[30,40] However, a small but significant increase in muscle GR activity was found in dogs after 1 year of vigorous training.[30] Another GSH-related antioxidant enzyme GSH sulfur-transferase also showed no training adaptation in all tissues measured.[30,40]

Several investigators have reported significant training adaptation of GSH-related enzymes in the human blood. Erythrocyte GPX activity was shown to be higher in distance runners compared to sedentary men.[77] GR activity in the red blood cells showed a significant increase after 20 weeks of training, along with an increased GSH level, in previously sedentary men.[78] Mena et al.[81] compared erythrocyte antioxidant enzyme status in professional vs. amateur cyclists and found that the former had more than twofold higher GPX activity than the latter. These data suggest that training enhances the capacity of the GSH-GSSG cycle to metabolize hydroperoxides produced in the red blood cells.

Compared to the enzymes in the GSH-GSSG cycle, few studies have investigated the effect of training on enzymes in the γ-Glutamyl Cycle. However, available data suggest that γ-glutamyltranspeptidase, γ-glutamylcysteine synthase, and glutathione synthase are subjected to training-induced up- or down-regulation. Sen et al.[30] found a significant training induction of γ-glutamyltranspeptidase in rat hindlimb muscle, suggesting that muscle uptake of GSH might be enhanced after training. Marin et al.[70] demonstrated that high intensity endurance training increases activities of γ-glutamylcysteine synthase and glutathione synthase in dog hindlimb muscles. Adaptation of these two key enzymes is consistent with the finding that trained muscles contain higher levels of GSH compared to the untrained ones.[30,40,68,71] Furthermore, rigorous swim training in rats has been found to increase myocardial γ-glutamyltrans-peptidase activity (unpublished observation). In light of the important antioxidant function of GSH during acute exercise, these findings have provided additional support to the hypothesis that antioxidant systems can be induced by exercise training.[5]

5. GLUTATHIONE DEFICIENCY AND EXERCISE

The physiological role of GSH is best illustrated when tissues deprived of GSH are subjected to an oxidative challenge. Cellular GSH levels may be substantially decreased by radiation or by administration of oxidizing agents, compounds that conjugate with GSH, or inhibitors of the GSH synthesizing enzymes.[31] For example, high doses of tertbutylhydroperoxide can produce a significant decline of tissue GSH levels and increase levels of GSSG. This decrement of GSH may be temporary because the GSSG formed is rapidly reduced by GSSG reductase.[26] Other nonspecific agents include diethylmaleate and phorone, which conjugate with the thiol group of GSH, forming inactive compounds. However, these conjugation reactions occur not only at the thiol moiety of GSH but also at other thiols contained by cysteine and certain enzymes. Although these compounds lead to large decrements of GSH, they also produce a variety of undesirable side effects. One such effect of diethylmaleate is to inhibit the activity of various enzymes. Diethylmaleate administration can also lead to lipid peroxidation not related to GSH depletion.[31]

Although there has been active research concerning GSH regulation during exercise over the years, little is known regarding the consequence of GSH deficiency on exercise-induced oxidative stress in various tissues. A low GSH level in the liver and muscle is expected to reduce its antioxidant capacity against exercise-induced oxidative stress. Kramer et al.[82] found that rats injected with diethylmaleate 2 h before exercise showed a significant impairment of swimming performance. A decrease of liver GSH was suggested to cause the decline of exercise endurance. The effect of diethylmaleate on diaphragm fatigue during resistive breathing was investigated in a recent study by Morales et al.[83] Diethylmaleate treatment (1 mg/kg body wt) produced a profound depletion of GSH in the diaphragm muscle, associated with a significant reduction of maximum tetanic tension and twitch tension. Although these studies implied that depletion of GSH was the underlying reason for the observed physiological dysfunction, it is difficult to evaluate the role of GSH because of the nonspecific nature of diethylmaleate as mentioned previously.

A more established procedure to deplete tissue GSH is through the administration of L-buthionine SR-sulfoximine (BSO), an irreversible inhibitor of γ-glutamylcysteine synthase, the rate-limiting enzyme for the γ-Glutamyl Cycle.[31,84] Although BSO causes GSH depletion in all cells, the magnitude of depletion varies between tissues due to their different GSH synthesis and degradation rate. Griffith and Meister[39] showed that mice treated with 5 μmol/day of BSO for 15 days decreased GSH concentration in the liver, plasma, heart, kidney, and skeletal muscle to 56, 32, 15, 4, and 2% of the control levels, respectively. Martensson and Meister[84] found that heart and muscle GSH levels were decreased to 8 and 3% of controls, respectively, with 3 weeks of BSO treatment. The dramatic depletion of GSH in the heart and skeletal muscle is especially interesting. It was found that diminution of GSH in skeletal muscle demonstrated a biphasic pattern during *in vivo* BSO treatment.[84] A rapid and marked depletion of cytosolic GSH (to ~3% of controls) occurred before mitochondrial GSH was affected. This finding was consistent with the knowledge that the mitochondria do not synthesize GSH, but import GSH from the cytosolic source. Two ATP-stimulated transport components were identified, one with a K_m of 60 μM and the other with a K_m of 5.4 mM.[45] V_{max} for these two components was also markedly different. It was suggested that two different transport systems might exist, carrying cytosolic GSH into the mitochondrial matrix and the intermembrane space, respectively.[45]

The effects of BSO treatment on tissue GSH status, exercise capacity, and lipid peroxidation have been investigated by Sen et al.[57] Rats received BSO by i.p. injections (6 mmol/kg body wt) 2 times/day for 4 days before exercising on treadmill until exhaustion (30 m/min, 10% grade). Total glutathione contents in the liver, lung, blood, and plasma were decreased by ~50%, and in skeletal muscle and heart by 80 to 90%, in the BSO-treated rats compared to the controls. GSSG contents in most of these tissues also showed a significant decrease. Exhaustive exercise increased the GSSG:GSH ratio in the skeletal muscle, especially in the GSH-depleted animals. Furthermore, a 50% decrease of endurance time was observed in the GSH-depleted rats, suggesting that GSH plays an essential role in maintaining exercise performance during high intensity treadmill running.

Leeuwenburgh and Ji[47] recently studied the impact of chronic GSH depletion on tissue GSH regulation and antioxidant status by injecting mice with BSO for 12 days (2 mmol/kg body wt/day) combined with 20 mM BSO in drinking water. BSO treatment depleted GSH content in the plasma, liver, kidney, heart, and quadriceps muscle to 35, 23, 15, 10, and 7% of the normal values, respectively. During an acute bout of swimming to exhaustion lasting 4 to 6 h, GSH content was decreased as a function of time in all tissues, except plasma and muscle which showed slight increases. Figure 3 shows that liver GSH decreased as a function of exercise duration during a prolonged exercise bout. In the GSH-depleted mice, exercise further suppressed GSH levels in all tissues and increased lipid peroxidation in the liver and muscle. Furthermore, liver malondialdehyde content was found to correlate inversely with GSH concentration during exercise in both the GSH-adequate and depleted mice (Figure 4). Consistent with the findings of Sen et al.,[57] GSSG contents in the liver, muscle, and heart showed a concomitant decrease with GSH such that the GSH:GSSG ratios were kept relatively constant. However, GSH depletion was not found to affect endurance performance during the moderate swim exercise. It can be concluded from the above two studies that BSO-induced GSH depletion has a profound impact on tissue and whole-body GSH homeostasis during exercise.

GSH depletion was shown to be associated with significant increases in lipid peroxidation in the heart, skeletal muscles, and plasma of GSH-depleted rats by some authors.[57] It was hypothesized that tissue GSH levels control lipid peroxidation either directly or indirectly because of the crucial role of GSH in keeping vitamin E and ascorbate in the reduced state. However, other investigators[47] found no manifestation of lipid peroxidation in the various mouse tissues chronically deprived of GSH. These discrepancies may be explained by the different protocols used to deplete tissue GSH. It is plausible that long-term treatment of BSO used by the latter studies (10 to 14 days) might have triggered some biochemical adaptations in the GSH-depleted animals. These possibilities

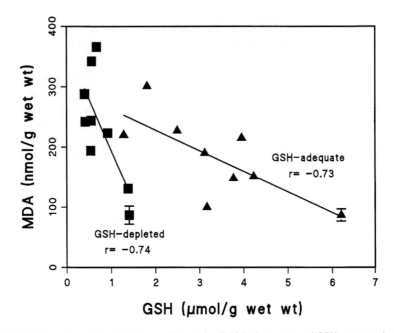

FIGURE 4. The relationship between liver malondialdehyde content and GSH concentration in acutely exercised mice. ▲, GSH-adequate (r = –0.73); ■, GSH-depleted (r = –0.74). The points with error bars indicate means (± SEM) of 8 control animals for GSH-A or GSH-D.

include, but are not limited to (a) an increased export of tissue GSSG under oxidative stress;[42] (b) an enhanced uptake of GSH by the cell membrane and mitochondria,[45] thus preventing free radical chain-reaction and excessive lipid peroxidation from occurring; and (c) an induction of antioxidant enzymes such that ROS are removed more efficiently (see the following discussions). Nevertheless, both studies showed that GSH depletion further suppressed the GSH:GSSG ratio in the exercise-stressed tissues.[47,57]

Antioxidant enzyme response to GSH depletion has been studied only sparsely and there is a paucity of data related to exercise. In a recent study, Leeuwenburgh and Ji [47] reported that chronic BSO treatment significantly decreased GPX activity in the liver, whereas GR and GSH sulfur-transferase activities were elevated. This finding agrees with Manning and Kranklin[85] who also showed an increase in hepatic GSH sulfur-transferase activity with GSH depletion, probably reflecting a compensation for a hampered GPX activity. In the kidney of GSH-depleted mice, activities of γ-glutamyltranspeptidase, GR, GSH sulfur-transferase, and SOD were found to be markedly increased.[47] Up-regulation of these enzymes may be indicative of an oxidative stress to this heavily involved organ in GSH homeostasis, as well as an adaptation to restore GSH redox status. γ-Glutamyltranspeptidase activity in the skeletal muscle showed a dramatic down-regulation with GSH depletion and a further decrease was evidenced in the exercised mice.[47] This down-regulation was proposed to be a compensatory mechanism to preserve plasma GSH which may be more vital to organs like heart, lung, and brain under oxidative stress. Furthermore, a down-regulation of the mitochondrial enzyme citrate synthase in the liver, kidney, and skeletal muscle has been reported with GSH depletion.[47,84]

6. GLUTATHIONE SUPPLEMENTATION AND EXERCISE

Cells deprived of GSH or exposed to an excessive oxidative stress can benefit from compounds targeted to increase the cellular thiol pool, particularly GSH concentration. Increased cellular GSH has been shown to protect cells against the deleterious effects of radiation and certain toxic compounds.[31] Thus, supplementation of GSH and GSH analogs have been used for therapeutic purposes such as drug-induced oxidative stress.[31] *N*-acetyl-L-cysteine (NAC), free GSH, and GSH ethyl ester are the most widely used compounds that protect against various redox disorders, such as myocardial ischemia-reperfusion damage,[86] hyperoxia-mediated lung injury,[87] mitochondrial damage by GSH depletion,[84] and HIV infection.[88]

Access of the target tissues to exogenously supplemented GSH is controlled by both circulatory and cellular regulatory mechanisms. Oral administration of GSH has been shown to increase plasma GSH, although the increase may be quite marginal.[89] Plasma GSH increases after GSH supplementation even in the presence of acivicin (a γ-glutamyltranspeptidase inhibitor); therefore, transepithelial transport of intact GSH must occur in the small intestine.[89] This indicates that not all GSH transport is γ-glutamyltranspeptidase-dependent and that there might exist a tripeptide transport channel in the intestinal membrane.[90] Furthermore, liver secretes GSH to the small intestine via the bile duct to assist in food detoxification.[91] Thus, circulatory GSH is dependent on both dietary and biliary derived GSH, transported by blood plasma into various organs.

Although GSH is absorbed by the gastrointestinal tract relatively efficiently, the uptake of GSH by most cells is limited by several factors. First, γ-glutamyltranspeptidase activity in most tissues, except for the kidney, is quite low. Second, resynthesis of GSH in the cell depends largely upon the availability of transported substrates, especially cysteine. Finally, γ-glutamylcysteine synthase, the rate-limiting enzyme of GSH synthesis, is strongly feedback-inhibited by GSH.[31] Supplementation of cysteine proves to be undesirable since administration of even moderate doses of L-cysteine is toxic.[92] To alleviate this toxic effect, analogous forms of cysteine such as L-2-oxothiazolidine-4-carboxylate or NAC have been used to promote GSH synthesis in the cell.[31] Another possible route of GSH supplementation is to avoid feedback inhibition on GSH synthesis by supplying GSH monoester which can be taken up readily by many types of cells as well as organelles, such as the mitochondria.[84,93]

Supplementation of NAC has been shown to cause variable results in tissue GSH status depending on the dose and method of supplementation. Jaeschke and Wendel[94] found that intraperitoneal injection of 0.5 mmol/kg body wt of

NAC caused an increase in liver GSH content. Others found GSH levels to be decreased using higher doses; almost 50% decrease of liver GSH was reported with NAC injection (0.5 to 1.0 g/kg, i.p.).[95] Orally administered NAC did not elicit such a large decrease of GSH compared to intraperitoneal administration.[95]

The effect of NAC supplementation on exercise-induced oxidative stress and performance has been investigated. Sen et al.[15] found that human subjects receiving 400 mg NAC/day for 2 days with an additional 800 mg before exercise showed an attenuated blood GSSG response during a maximal treadmill test. However, the sparing effect of NAC on the exercise-induced blood GSH oxidation in humans was not as pronounced as in rats.[57] The author attributed this difference to the different exercise duration between the human (~14 min) and the rat (2 h). It is possible that the oxidative stress associated with the longer exercise duration exceeded the protective capacity of exogenous NAC. Running performance of the animals was not different between the NAC-supplemented and control group. Sastre et al.[96] showed that oral supplementation of NAC (~1 g/kg body wt daily in the drinking water) was effective in preventing the increase in GSSG levels during exercise in rats. An *in situ* study by Shindoh et al.[97] showed that NAC supplementation by i.v. bolus attenuated the rate of diaphragmatic fatigue during repetitive isometric contraction. However, since none of the mentioned studies demonstrated an increase in tissue or blood GSH with NAC administration, the observed protective effects might simply be caused by a direct reductive function of NAC rather than a stimulation of GSH synthesis.

Supplementation of free GSH has generated limited promise in raising tissue GSH contents. Anderson et al.[93] found that addition of 10 mM GSH to a suspension medium did not increase GSH content in human red blood cells. Likewise, i.p. injection of 7.5 mmol/kg GSH had little effect on GSH levels in mouse tissues. It was reported in rats that after a single injection of GSH (1g/kg body wt, i.p.), plasma GSH was quickly elevated but returned to normal levels within several hours with little influence on tissue GSH content, whereas plasma GSSG levels were also elevated with GSH injection.[57] Although repeated injection of GSH raised plasma and kidney GSH significantly, it did not lead to a desirable increase in GSH content in skeletal muscle, heart, liver, or lung.[57] In contrast to free GSH, it has been shown that supplementation of GSH ethyl ester at equal doses to free GSH increased GSH content in the liver, kidney, and heart markedly in mice.[93] A ^{35}S-labeled GSH study revealed that administration of GSH ethyl ester (7.5 mmol/kg, i.p.) resulted in a significant increase in liver GSH within 2 h after injection. Recently, we investigated the effects of GSH and GSH ester supplementation in exercising mice.[98,99] Supplemented mice were fasted for 24 h and injected with either GSH or GSH ester (6 mmol/kg, i.p.) 1 h before exercise, whereas control animals were fasted for 24 h and injected with saline. GSH injection decreased GSH content in the liver (−15%), kidney (−26%), and heart (−17%), despite a 60% increase in plasma GSH. GSH content remained unchanged in the lung, diaphragm, and quadriceps muscle with GSH injection. GSH ester supplementation caused similar suppressions of liver and heart GSH; in addition, it decreased both plasma and quadriceps GSH contents by 22%. These findings mostly likely reflect the feedback inhibitory effect of exogenous GSH on tissue GSH synthesis, since hepatic γ-glutamylcysteine synthase activity was down-regulated significantly in both the GSH and GSH ester supplemented mice (unpublished data). It is not clear at present why GSH ester failed to circumvent the negative feedback inhibition on γ-glutamylcysteine synthase in the above study.

The effect of GSH supplementation on tissue oxidative damage during exercise has not been systematically evaluated. NAC supplementation in humans has not been found effective in preventing plasma lipid peroxidation or leukocyte DNA damage.[15] However, using immunoreactive MnSOD in the plasma as a marker of mitochondrial damage, Sen et al.[100] found that whereas plasma MnSOD content was significantly increased after exercise, endurance training and GSH supplementation attenuated this increase, suggesting a protective effect of GSH on mitochondrial membrane permeability.

The potential ergogenic effect of GSH supplementation on exercise performance has been an intriguing topic in the literature. Several studies indicate that supplementation of GSH can significantly improve exercise performance in experimental animals.[98,101,102] Acute GSH i.p. injection at dosages of 250 to 1000 mg/kg body wt was shown to increase swim endurance in mice.[102] However, since the entire exercise duration lasted only several minutes and no effort was made to evaluate oxidative stress imposed to the mice, it is uncertain whether the increased swimming time was related to the antioxidant function of GSH. Fiebig et al.[99] found that mice fasted for 24 h and injected with GSH or GSH ester significantly increased their endurance time (351 ± 22 and 348 ± 27 min, respectively) during an exhaustive bout of swimming compared to those fasted and injected with saline (237 ± 17 min). Because GSH contents in the liver and quadriceps muscle were decreased along with a diminished GSH:GSSG ratio in the quadriceps with GSH ester treatment, the authors concluded that the increased endurance time must be caused by some mechanisms independent of GSH antioxidant reserve.

7. CONCLUSION

Although the role of GSH in cellular antioxidant defense has been well established, its significance in protecting against free radical-induced oxidative stress and tissue damage during physical exercise has not been appreciated until recently. From the available evidence accumulated in the past decade, it becomes increasingly clear that GSH plays a pivotal role in the maintenance of the intracellular redox status, antioxidant vitamin levels, and antioxidant enzyme functions during acute and chronic exercise. The effectiveness of GSH protection in the various tissues depends on both the concentration of tissue GSH and the reducing capacity of the GSH-GSSG cycle, as well as the capacity of the tissue to import GSH and to export GSSG. Furthermore, an interorgan transport of GSH operates such that the liver exports GSH into the plasma under hormonal stimulation, whereas other organs and tissues take up GSH from the circulation. Despite a large reserve, GSH contents in a number of metabolically active tissues have been shown to decrease significantly, whereas GSSG levels increase, in response to an acute bout of heavy exercise. This disturbance of GSH status may be amplified with GSH deficiency, accompanied by enhanced lipid peroxidation and antioxidant enzyme dysfunction. Chronic training improves GSH antioxidant reserve by increasing both tissue GSH levels and enzyme activities associated with the GSH-GSSG cycle and the γ-Glutamyl Cycle, thus attenuating exercise-induced oxidative stress. Although GSH supplementation may provide some immediate benefit during acute exercise performance, its complex negative impact on intracellular and interorgan GSH homeostasis requires further investigation.

REFERENCES

1. **Halliwell, B. and Gutteridge, J. M. C.,** *Free Radicals in Biology and Medicine,* Clarendon Press, Oxford, 1989.
2. **Yu, B. P.,** Oxidative damage by free radicals and lipid peroxidation in aging, in *Free Radical in Aging,* Yu, B. P., Ed., CRC Press, Boca Raton, FL, 1993, 58.
3. **Meydani, M. and Evans, W. J.,** Free radicals, exercise, and aging, in *Free Radical in Aging,* Yu, B. P., Ed., CRC Press, Boca Raton, FL, 1993, 183.
4. **Jenkins, R. R.,** Free radical chemistry: relationship to exercise, *Sport Med.,* 5, 156, 1988.
5. **Ji, L. L.,** Exercise and oxidative stress: role of the cellular antioxidant systems, in *Exercise and Sports Science Review,* Holloszy, J., Ed., Williams and Wilkins, Baltimore, 1995.
6. **Kanter, M. M.,** Free radical and exercise: effect of antioxidant nutritional supplementation, in *Exercise and Sports Science Review,* Holloszy, J. O., Ed., Williams and Wilkins, Baltimore, 1995.
7. **Chance, B., Sies, H., and Boveris, A.,** Hydroperoxide metabolism in mammalian organs, *Physiol. Rev.,* 59, 527, 1979.
8. **Davies, K. J. A., Quantanilla, A. T., Brooks, G. A., and Packer, L.,** Free radicals and tissue damage produced by exercise, *Biochem. Biophys. Res. Comm.,* 107, 1198, 1982.
9. **Jackson, M. L., Edwards, R. H. T., and Symons, M. C. R.,** Electron spin resonance studies of intact mammalian skeletal muscle, *Biochim. Biophys. Acta,* 847, 185, 1985.
10. **Kumar, C. T., Reddy, V. K., Prasad, M., Thyagaraju, K., and Reddanna, P.,** Dietary supplementation of vitamin E protects heart tissue from exercise-induced oxidant stress, *Mol. Cell. Biochem.,* 111, 109, 1992.
11. **Gohil, K., Viguie, C., Stanley, W. C., Brooks, G. A., and Packer, L.,** Blood glutathione oxidation during human exercise, *J. Appl. Physiol.,* 64, 115, 1990.
12. **Lew, H., Pyke, S., and Quintanilha, A.,** Change in the glutathione status of plasma, liver and muscle following exhaustive exercise in rats, *FEBS Lett.,* 185, 262, 1985.
13. **Ji, L. L. and Fu, R. G.,** Responses of glutathione system and antioxidant enzymes to exhaustive exercise and hydroperoxide, *J. Appl. Physiol.,* 72, 549, 1992.
14. **Ji, L. L., Fu, R. G., and Mitchell, E. W.,** Glutathione and antioxidant enzymes in skeletal muscle: effects of fiber type and exercise intensity, *J. Appl. Physiol.,* 73, 1854, 1992.
15. **Sen, C. K., Rankinen, T., Vaisanen, S., and Rauramaa, R.,** Oxidative stress following human exercise: effect of N-acetylcysteine supplementation, *J. Appl. Physiol.,* 76, 2570, 1994.

16. **Dillard, C. J., Litov, R. E., Savin, W. M., Mumelin, E. E., and Tappel, A. L.,** Effect of exercise, vitamin E, and ozone on pulmonary function and lipid peroxidation, *J. Appl. Physiol.,* 45, 927, 1978.

17. **Alessio, H., Goldfarb, A. H., and Cutler, R.,** MDA content increases in fast- and slow-twitch skeletal muscle with intensity of exercise in a rat, *Am. J. Physiol.,* 255, 874, 1988.

18. **Kanter, M. M., Nolte, L. A., and Holloszy, J. O.,** Effect of an antioxidant vitamin mixture on lipid peroxidation at rest and postexercise, *J. Appl. Physiol.,* 74, 965, 1993.

19. **Ji, L. L., Stratman, F. W., and Lardy, H. A.,** Enzymatic downregulation with exercise in rat skeletal muscle, *Arch. Biochem. Biophys.,* 263, 137, 1988.

20. **Allessio, H. M.,** Exercise-induced oxidative stress, *Med. Sci. Sports Exerc.,* 25, 218, 1993.

21. **Goldfarb, A. H.,** Antioxidants: role of supplementation to prevent exercise-induced oxidative stress, *Med. Sci. Sports Exerc.,* 25, 232, 1993.

22. **Jenkins, R. R.,** Exercise, oxidative stress, and antioxidants: a review, *Int. J. Sports Nutr.,* 3, 356, 1993.

23. **Deneke, S. M. and Fanburg, B. L.,** Regulation of cellular glutathione, *Am. J. Physiol.,* 257, L163, 1989.

24. **Deleve, L. D. and Kaplowitz, N.,** Importance and regulation of hepatic glutathione, *Sim. Liv. Dis.,* 10, 251, 1990.

25. **Meister, A. and Anderson, M. E.,** Glutathione, *Ann. Rev. Biochem.,* 52, 711, 1991.

26. **Flohe, L.,** Glutathione peroxidase brought into focus, in *Free Radical in Biology and Medicine,* Vol. 5, Pryor, W., Ed., Academic Press, New York, 1982, 223.

27. **Reed, D.,** Regulation of reductive processes by glutathione, *Biochem. Pharm.,* 35, 7, 1986.

28. **Yu, B. P.,** Cellular defenses against damage from reactive oxygen species, *Physiol. Rev.,* 74, 139, 1994.

29. **Packer, L.,** Protective role of vitamin E in biological systems, *Am. J. Clin. Nutr.,* 53, 1050S, 1991.

30. **Sen, C. K., Marin, E., Kretzschmar, M., and Hanninen, O.,** Skeletal muscle and liver glutathione homeostasis in response to training, exercise and immobilization, *J. Appl. Physiol.,* 73, 1265, 1992.

31. **Meister, A.,** Glutathione deficiency produced by inhibition of its synthesis, and its reversal; applications in research and therapy, *Pharmacol. Ther.,* 51, 155, 1991.

32. **Sen, C. K., Rahkila, P., and Hanninen, O.,** Glutathione metabolism in skeletal muscle derived cells of the L6 line, *Acta Physiol. Scand.,* 148, 21, 1993.

33. **Adams, J. D., Lauterburg, B. H., and Mitchell, J. R.,** Plasma glutathione and glutathione disulfide in the rat: regulation and response to oxidative stress, *J. Pharmacol. Exp. Ther.,* 227, 749, 1983.

34. **Lauterburg, B. H., Adams, J. D., and Mitchell, J. R.,** Hepatic glutathione homeostasis in the rat: efflux accounts for glutathione turnover, *Hepatology,* 4, 586, 1984.

35. **Tateishi, N., Higashi, T., Shinya, A., Naruse, A., and Sakamoto, Y.,** Studies on the regulation of glutathione levels in rat liver, *J. Biochem.,* 75, 93, 1973.

36. **Lu, S. C., Ge, J. L., Kulenkamp, J., and Kaplowitz, N.,** Insulin and glucocorticoid dependence of hepatic γ-glytamylcysteine synthetase and glutathione synthesis in the rat, *J. Clin. Invest.,* 90, 260, 1992.

37. **Lu, S. C., Kulenkamp, J., Garcia-Ruiz, C., and Kaplowitz, N.,** Hormone-mediated down-regulation of hepatic glutathione synthesis in the rat, *J. Clin. Invest.,* 88, 260, 1991.

38. **Lu, S. C., Garcia-Ruiz, C., Kulenkamp, J., Ookhtens, M., Salas-Prato, M., and Kaplowitz, N.,** Hormonal regulation of glutathione efflux, *J. Biol. Chem.,* 265, 16088, 1990.

39. **Griffith, O. and Meister, A.,** Glutathione: interorgan translocation, turnover, and metabolism, *Natl. Acad. Sci. U.S.A.,* 76 5606, 1979.

40. **Leeuwenburgh, C., Fiebig, R., Chandwaney, R., and Ji, L. L.,** Aging and exercise training in skeletal muscle: response of glutathione and antioxidant enzyme systems, *Am. J. Physiol.,* 267, 439, 1994.

41. **Kretzschmar, M., Pfeifer, U., Machnik, G., and Klinger, W.,** Glutathione homeostasis and turnover in the totally hepatectomised rat: evidence for a high glutathione export capacity of extrahepatic tissues, *Exp. Toxic. Pathol.,* 44, 273, 1992.

42. **Ishikawa, T. and Sies, H.,** Cardiac transport of glutathione disulfide and S-conjugate, *J. Biol. Chem.,* 259, 3838, 1984.
43. **Srivastava, S. K. and Beutler, E.,** The transport of oxidized glutathione from human erythrocytes, *J. Biol. Chem.,* 244, 9, 1969.
44. **Griffith, O. W. and Meister, A.,** Origin and turnover of mitochondrial glutathione, *Proc. Natl. Acad. U.S.A.,* 82, 4668, 1985.
45. **Martensson, J., Lai, J. C. K., and Meister, A.,** High affinity transport of glutathione is part of a multicomponent system essential for mitochondrial function, *Proc. Natl. Acad. Sci. U.S.A.,* 87, 7185, 1990.
46. **Anzueto, A., Andrade, F., Maxwell, L. C., Levine, S. M., Lawrence, A., Gibbons, J., and Jenkinson, S. G.,** Resistive breathing activates the glutathione redox cycle and impairs performance of rat diaphragm, *J. Appl. Physiol.,* 72, 529, 1992.
47. **Leeuwenburgh, C. and Ji, L. L.,** Glutathione depletion in rested and exercised mice: biochemical consequence and adaptation, *Arch. Biochem. Biophys.,* 316, 941, 1995.
48. **Pyke, S., Lew, H., and Quintanilha, A.,** Severe depletion in liver glutathione during physical exercise, *Biochem. Biophys. Res. Comm.,* 139, 926, 1986.
49. **Duarte, J. A. R., Appell, H.-J., Carvalho, F., Bastos, M., and Soares, J. M.,** Endothelium-derived oxidative stress may contribute to exercise-induced muscle damage, *Int. J. Sports Med.,* 14, 440, 1993.
50. **Duarte, J. A., Carvalho, F., Bastos, M. L., Soares, J. M., Soares, C., and Appell, H.-J.,** Do invading leukocytes contribute to the decrease in glutathione concentration indicating oxidative stress in exercised muscle, or are they important for recovery?, *Eur. J. Appl. Physiol.,* 68, 48, 1994.
51. **Jackson, M. J., Brooke, M. H., Kaiser, K., and Edwards, H. T.,** Glutathione depletion during experimental damage to rat skeletal muscle and its relevance to Duchenne muscular dystrophy, *Clin. Sci.,* 80, 559, 1991.
52. **Corbucci, G. G., Montanari, G., Cooper, M. B., Jones, D. A., and Edwards, R. H. T.,** The effect of exertion on mitochondrial oxidative capacity and on some antioxidant mechanisms in muscle from marathon runners, *Int. J. Sports Med.,* 5, 135S, 1984.
53. **Villa, J. G., Collado, P. S., Almar, M. M., and Gonzalez, J.,** Changes in the biliary excretion of organic anions following exhaustive exercise in rats. *Biochem. Pharmacol.,* 40, 2519, 1990.
54. **Sies, H. and Graf, P.,** Hepatic thiol and glutathione efflux under the influence of vasopressin, phenylephrine and adrenaline, *Biochem. J.,* 226, 545, 1985.
55. **Lang, J. K., Gohil, K., Packer, L., and Burk, R. F.,** Selenium deficiency, endurance exercise capacity, and antioxidant status in rats, *J. Appl. Physiol.,* 63, 2532, 1987.
56. **Packer, L., Gohil, K., DeLumen, B., and Terblanche, S. E.,** A comparative study on the effects of ascorbic acid deficiency and supplementation on endurance and mitochondrial oxidative capacities in various tissues of the guinea pig, *Comp. Biochem. Physiol.,* 83, 235, 1986.
57. **Sen, C. K., Ataley, M., and Hanninen, O.,** Exercise-induced oxidative stress: glutathione supplementation and deficiency, *J. Appl. Physiol.,* 77, 2177, 1994.
58. **Ji, L. L.,** Exercise induced oxidative stress in the heart, in *Exercise and Oxygen Toxicity,* Sen, C. K., Packer, L., and Hanninen, O., Eds., Elsevier Science Publishers B.V., Amsterdam, 1994, 249.
59. **Leeuwenburgh, C., Leichtweis, S., Fiebig, R., Hollander, J., Gore, M., and Ji, L. L.,** Effect of acute exercise on glutathione depleted heart, *Mol. Cell. Biochem.,* submitted.
60. **Kretzschmar, M., Pfeifer, U., Machnik, G., and Klinger, W.,** Influence of age, training and acute physical exercise on plasma glutathione and lipid peroxidation in man, *Int. J. Sports Med.,* 12, 218, 1991.
61. **Viguie, C. A., Frei, B., Shigenaga, M. K., Ames, B., Packer, L., and Brooks, G. A.,** Antioxidant status and indexes of oxidative stress during consecutive days of exercise, *J. Appl. Physiol.,* 75, 566, 1993.

62. **Duthie, G. G., Robertson, J. D., Maughan, R. J., and Morrice, P. C.,** Blood antioxidant status and erythrocyte lipid peroxidation following distance running, *Arch. Biochem. Biophys.,* 282, 78, 1990.

63. **Marin, E., Hanninen, O., Muller, D., and Klinger, W.,** Influences of acute physical exercise on glutathione and lipid peroxides in blood of rat and man, *Acta Physiol. Hung.,* 76, 71, 1990.

64. **Laires, M. J., Madeira, F., Sergio, J., Colaco, C., Vaz, C., Felisberto, G. M., Neto, I., Breitenfeld, L., Bicho, M., and Manso, C.,** Preliminary study of the relationship between plasma and erythrocyte magnesium variations and some circulating pro-oxidant and anti-oxidant indices in a standardized physical effort, *Magnesium Res.,* 6, 233, 1993.

65. **Camus, G., Felekidis, A., Pincemail, J., Deby-Dupont, G., Deby, C., Juchmes-Ferir, A., Lejeune, R., and Lamy, M.,** Blood levels of reduced/oxidized glutathione and plasma concentration of ascorbic acid during eccentric and concentric exercises of similar energy cost, *Arch. Int. Physiol. Biochim. Biophys.,* 102, 67, 1994.

66. **Ji, L. L., Katz, A., Fu, R. G., Parchert, M., and Spencer, M.,** Alteration of blood glutathione status during exercise: the effect of carbohydrate supplementation, *J. Appl. Physiol.,* 74, 788, 1992.

67. **Sahlin, K., Ekborg, K., and Cizinsky, S.,** Changes in plasma hypoxanthine and free radical markers during exercise in man, *Acta. Physiol. Scand.,* 142, 275, 1991.

68. **Kretzschmar, M. and Muller, D.,** Aging, training and exercise: a review of effects of plasma glutathione and lipid peroxidation, *Sports Med.,* 15, 196, 1993.

69. **Salminen, A. and Vihko, V.,** Endurance training reduces the susceptibility of mouse skeletal muscle to lipid peroxidation in vitro, *Acta Physiol. Scand.,* 117, 109, 1983.

70. **Marin, E., Kretzschmar, M., Arokoski, J., Hanninen, O., and Klinger, W.,** Enzymes of glutathione synthesis in dog skeletal muscle and their response to training, *Acta Physiol. Scand.,* 147, 369, 1993.

71. **Hollander, J., Leeuwenburgh, C., Fiebig, R., Leichtweis, S., Griffith, M., and Ji, L. L.,** Training adaptation of antioxidant status in isocalorically fed female rats, Minneapolis, *Med. Sci. Sports. Exerc.,* 27, 544, 1995.

72. **Lew, H. and Quintanilha, A.,** Effects of endurance training and exercise on tissue antioxidative capacity and acetaminophen detoxification, *Eur. J. Drug Met. Pharmacol.,* 16, 59, 1990.

73. **Kihlstrom, M. T.,** Protection effect of endurance training against reoxygenation-induced injuries in rat heart, *J. Appl. Physiol.,* 68, 1672, 1990.

74. **Kihlstrom, M. T.,** Lipid peroxidation capacities in the myocardium of endurance-trained rats and mice *in vitro, Acta Physiol. Scand.,* 146, 177, 1992.

75. **Fiebig, R., Leeuwenburgh, C., and Ji, L. L.,** The effect of aging and training on myocardial antioxidant enzymes and lipid peroxidation. *Med. Sci. Sports Exerc.,* 26, S133, 1994.

76. **Leichtweis, S., Leeuwenburgh, C., Fiebig, R., Parmelee, D., Yu, X. X., and Ji, L. L.,** Rigorous swim training deteriorates mitochondrial function in rat heart, *Med. Sci. Sports Exerc.,* 26, S69, 1994.

77. **Robertson, J. D., Maughan, R. J., Duthie, G. G., and Morrice, P. C.,** Increased blood antioxidant systems of runners in response to training, *Clin. Sci.,* 80, 611, 1991.

78. **Evelo, C. T. A., Palmen, N. G., Artur, Y., and Janssen, G. M. E.,** Changes in blood glutathione concentrations, and in erythrocyte glutathione reductase and glutathione S-transferase activity after running training and after participation in contests, *Eur. J. Appl. Physiol.,* 64, 354, 1992.

79. **Powers, S. K., Criswell, D., Lawler, J., Ji, L. L., Martin, D., Herb, R., and Dudley, G.,** Influence of exercise intensity and fiber type on antioxidant enzyme activity in skeletal muscle, *Am. J. Physiol.,* 267, R375, 1994.

80. **Powers, S. K., Criswell, D., Lawler, J., Martin, D., Ji, L. L., and Dudley, G.,** Training-induced oxidative and antioxidant enzyme activity in the diaphragm: influence of exercise intensity and duration, *Resp. Physiol.,* 95, 226, 1994.

81. **Mena, P., Maynar, M., Gutierrez, J. M., Maynar, J., Timon, J., and Campillo, J. E.,** Erythrocyte free radical scavenger enzymes in professional bicycle racers. Adaptation to Training, *Int. J. Sports Med.,* 12, 563, 1991.

82. **Kramer, K., Dijkstra, H., and Bast, A.,** Control of physical exercise of rats in a swimming basin, *Physiol. Behav.,* 53, 271, 1993.

83. **Morales, C. F., Anzuato, A., Andrade, F., Levine, S. M., Maxwell, L. C., Lawrence, R., and Jenkinson, S. G.,** Diethylmaleate produces diaphragmatic impairment after resistive breathing, *J. Appl. Physiol.,* 75, 2406, 1993.

84. **Martensson, J. and Meister, A.,** Mitochondrial damage in muscle occurs after marked depletion of glutathione and is prevented by giving glutathione monoester, *Proc. Natl. Acad. Sci. U.S.A.,* 86, 471, 1989.

85. **Manning, B. W. and Kranklin, M.,** Induction of rat UDP-glucoronosyltransferase and glutathione S-transferase activities by L-buthionine-S, R-sulfoximine without induction of cytochrome P-450, *Toxicology,* 65, 149, 1990.

86. **Ferrari, R., Ceconi, C., Curello, S., Cargnoni, A., Alfieri, O., Pardini, A., Marzollo, P., and Visioli, O.,** Oxygen free radicals and myocardial damage: protective role of thiol-containing agents, *Am. J. Med.,* 91, 95, 1991.

87. **Suttorp, N., Kastle, S., and Neuhof, H.,** Glutathione redox cycle is an important defense system of endothelial cells against chronic hyperoxia, *Lung,* 169, 203, 1991.

88. **Malorni, W., Rivabene, R., Santini, M. T., and Donelli, G.,** N-Acethylcysteine inhibits apoptosis and decreases viral particles in HIV-chronically infected U937 cells, *FEBS,* 327, 75, 1993.

89. **Hagen, T. M., Wierzbicka, G. T., Sillau, A. H., Bowman, B. B., and Jones, D. P.,** Bioavailability of dietary glutathione: effect on plasma concentration, *Am. J. Physiol.,* 259, G524, 1990.

90. **Hagen, T. M. and Jones, D. P.,** Transepithelial transport of glutathione in vasculary perfused small intestine of rat, *Am. J. Physiol.,* 252, 607, 1987.

91. **Hagen, T. M., Wierzbicka, G. T., Bowman, B. B., Aw, T. Y., and Jones, D. P.,** Fate of dietary glutathione: disposition in the gastrointestinal tract, *Am. J. Physiol.,* 259, 530, 1990.

92. **Meister, A.,** Glutathione metabolism and its selective modification, *J. Biol. Chem.,* 263, 17205, 1988.

93. **Anderson, M. E., Powrie, F., Puri, R. N., and Meister, A.,** Glutathione monoethyl ester: preparation, uptake by tissues, and conversion to glutathione, *Arch. Bioch. Biophys.,* 239, 538, 1985.

94. **Jaeschke, H. and Wendel, A.,** Diurnal fluctuation and pharmacological alteration of mouse organ glutathione content, *Biochem. Pharmacol.,* 34, 1029, 1985.

95. **Estrale, J. M., Saez, G. T., and Such, L.,** The effect of cysteine and N-acetylcysteine on rat liver glutathione (GSH), *Biochem. Pharmacol,* 32, 3483, 1983.

96. **Sastre, J., Asensi, M., Gasco, E., Pallardo, F. V., Ferrero, J., Furukawa, T., and Vina, J.,** Exhaustive physical exercise causes oxidation of glutathione status in blood: prevention by antioxidant administration, *Am. J. Physiol.,* 263, R992, 1992.

97. **Shindoh, C., DiMarco, A., Thomas, P., Manubay, and Supinski, G.,** Effect of N-acetylcysteine on diaphragm fatigue, *J. Appl. Physiol.,* 68, 2107, 1990.

98. **Leeuwenburgh, C., Fiebig, R., Leichtweis, S., Hollander, J., and Ji, L. L.,** Effect of glutathione and glutathione ester supplementation during prolonged exercise, *Med. Sci. Sports Exerc.,* 27, 539, 1995.

99. **Fiebig, R., Leeuwenburgh, C., Leichtweis, S., Hollander, S., and Ji, L. L.,** Skeletal muscle glutathione status in exercise: effect of GSH and GSH ethyl ester supplementation, *Med. Sci. Sports Exerc.,* 27, S121, 1995.

100. **Sen, C. K., Ookawara, T., Suziki, K., Taniguchi, N., Hanninen, O., and Ohno, H.,** Immunoreactivity and activity of mitochondrial superoxide dismutase following training and exercise, *Pathophysiology,* 1, 165, 1994.

101. **Cazzulani, P., Cassin, M., and Ceserani, R.,** Increased endurance to physical exercise in mice given oral reduced glutathione (GSH), *Med. Sci. Res.,* 19, 543, 1991.
102. **Novelli, G. P., Falsini, S., and Braccioti, G.,** Exogenous glutathione increases endurance to muscle effort in mice, *Pharmacol. Res.,* 23, 149, 1990.

Chapter 5

DETOXIFICATION OF REACTIVE OXYGEN SPECIES: MOLECULAR STRATEGIES

Chandan K. Sen

CONTENTS

1. OXYGEN TOXICITY

Although the use of oxygen as metabolic fuel allows an attractive harvest of energy-rich phosphates per molecule of glucose, a significant fraction of oxygen utilized by the body is incompletely reduced and is known to be toxic. The concept of oxygen toxicity, referring to the adverse effects of oxygen at high pressure (as during diving, hyperbaric O_2 therapy, aerospace travel, etc.), was first reported by French scientist Paul Bert in 1878 just a century after the discovery of gas by Joseph Priestly. In Bert's classic work *La Pression Barometrique* he described the incidence of convulsions in various animal species exposed to oxygen at high pressure.[1] Today's concept of oxygen toxicity is not only restricted to hyperbaric oxygen but primarily focuses on the stress caused by reactive metabolites (oxygen free radicals/reactive oxygen species) of oxygen generated as an integral part of our daily life.[2,3] In 1924, it was established that molecular oxygen has two unpaired electrons in its valence orbit. Ground state O_2 is therefore a "diradical" (often referred to as

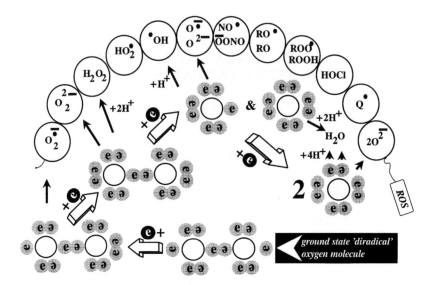

FIGURE 1. The four-step univalent reduction of "diradical" oxygen. Some commonly known members of the reactive oxygen species (ROS) family are: ·OH, hydroxyl radical; Q·, semiquinone; $O_2^{·-}$, superoxide anion radical; $^1O_2$, singlet oxygen; NO·, nitric oxide; ONOO⁻, peroxynitrite anion; O_2^{2-}, peroxide ion; RO·, alkoxyl radical; ROO·, peroxyl radical; ROOH, alkyl hydroperoxide; ROH, alkyl hydroxide; HOCl, hypochlorous; H_2O_2, hydrogen peroxide; HO_2·, perhydroxy radical. **e**, electron; directional orientation of **e** represents the direction of spin.

"dioxygen") the two unpaired electrons being accommodated, formally, in the degenerate pair of antibonding π^* orbital, π^1_x and π^1_y. However, because of quantum-mechanical restrictions, O_2 is not extremely reactive. Univalent (stepwise) addition of four electrons (tetravalent reduction) to O_2 produces water (Figure 1). Oxygen radicals and their byproducts collectively referred to as the reactive oxygen species (ROS) are capable of inciting oxidative tissue damage. In a biological system, *oxidative stress* refers to a disturbance in the pro- and antioxidant balance in favor of the prooxidant. Oxidative stress ensues when ROS manage to evade or overwhelm the antioxidant protective mechanisms of the cells and tissues.

In the biological system, molecular oxygen is reduced by one electron giving rise to superoxide radicals ($O_2^{·-}$) which can be further reduced to hydrogen peroxide and hydroxyl radicals (HO·) and finally to water. Formation of superoxide and hydrogen peroxide can be regulated by either enzymatic or nonenzymatic mechanisms, whereas no enzymes are required for the formation of hydroxyl radical. The hydroxyl radical is the most reactive oxygen species and may be formed either through transition metal ion catalyzed Fenton (Fe^{2+} + $H_2O_2 \rightarrow Fe^{3+}$ + OH^- + HO·) or Haber-Weiss (O_2^- + H_2O_2 + $Fe^{2+} \rightarrow O_2$ + OH^- + HO· + Fe^{3+}) reactions. The hydroxyl radical is a very reactive species capable of initiating deleterious reactions like lipid peroxidation, DNA damage, etc. Cells of macrophage lineage (e.g., endothelial cells, neutrophils, osteoclast, etc.) that are capable of synthesizing nitric oxide (NO) and producing super-oxide host the production of peroxynitrite anion ($^-$OO–N=O), a powerful long-lived oxidant.[4] ROS are also produced intracellularly by a variety of environmental agents, particularly redox cycling drugs, that divert electrons from NADPH to O_2 to generate a flux of $O_2^{\cdot-}$.

Partial (univalent or divalent) reduction of oxygen, an event primarily underlying the generation of ROS, has been also shown to be catalyzed by a number of enzymes of rat liver. Some such enzymes responsible for the generation of hydrogen peroxide or superoxide anion are listed below with their respective subcellular localization indicated in adjacent parentheses:[5] glycolate oxidase (EC 1.1.3.1; peroxisome), L-α-hydroxyacid oxidase (EC 1.1.3α; peroxisome), L-gulonolactone oxidase (EC 1.1.3.8; cytosol), aldehyde oxidase (EC 1.2.3.1; cytosol), xanthine oxidase (EC 1.2.3.2; cytosol), D-amino-acid oxidase (EC 1.4.3.3; peroxisome), monoamine oxidase (EC 1.4.3.4; mitochondrial outer membrane), pyridoxamine oxidase (EC 1.4.3.5; endoplasmic reticulum), diamine oxidase (EC 1.4.3.6; endoplasmic reticulum), NADPH-cytochrome *c* reductase (EC 1.6.99.1; endoplasmic reticulum), NADPH-cytochrome *c* reductase (EC 1.6.99.3; peroxisome "core"), urate oxidase (EC 1.7.3.3; peroxisome core), superoxide dismutase (EC 1.15.1.1; cytosol and mitochondrial matrix). Boveris et al.[6] have shown that mitochondria, microsomes, peroxisomes, and cytosolic enzymes are effective H_2O_2 generators, contributing in the rat liver, respectively, 15, 45, 35, and 5% to the cytosolic H_2O_2 at a PO_2 of 158 mmHg when fully supplemented by their substrates. Biotransformation of xenobiotics, especially via cytochrome P_{450} dependent mechanisms, may also remarkably contribute to the generation of reactive oxygen species.[7,8]

2. ANTIOXIDANT DEFENSES

With a rapid unfolding of knowledge in the area of antioxidant biochemistry, it appears that the body's arsenal to defend against oxidative stress is diverse and far from being precisely understood.[10,11] Broadly, the possible mechanisms by which antioxidants may protect against ROS toxicity are: (1) prevention of ROS formation, (2) interception of ROS attack by scavenging the reactive metabolites and converting them to less reactive molecules and/or by enhancing the resistivity of sensitive biological targets to ROS attack, (3) avoiding the transformation of less reactive ROS (e.g., $O_2^{\cdot-}$) to more deleterious forms (e.g., $\cdot$OH), (4) facilitating the repair of damage caused by ROS and triggering the expression of genes encoding antioxidant proteins, and (5) providing (e.g., as a cofactor or by acting to maintain a suitable redox status) a favorable environment for the effective functioning of other antioxidants. Although a large number of enzymatic and nonenzymatic physiological substances are known to have "antioxidant-like" functions, the primary contributors are superoxide dismutase (EC 1.15.1.1) and catalase (EC 1.11.1.6) enzymes, and the glutathione system.

Superoxide dismutases are enzymes involved in cellular defense against uncontrolled oxidative processes which catalyze the dismutation of the superoxide radical anion (to hydrogen peroxide) and hence diminish toxic effects due to this radical or to other free radicals derived from secondary reactions.[12] Present virtually in all mammalian cells, catalase plays a dual role: (1) a true catalytic role in the decomposition of H_2O_2, $2H_2O_2 \rightarrow 2H_2O + O_2$; and (2) a peroxidic role in which the peroxide is utilized to oxidize a range of H donors (AH_2) such as methanol, ethanol and formate, $AH_2 + H_2O_2 \rightarrow A + 2H_2O$. Glutathione (L-γ-glutamyl-L-cysteinylglycine, GSH) is well implicated in the circumvention of cellular oxidative stress and maintenance of intracellular thiol redox status.[10] The antioxidant function of the thiol is implicated through two general mechanisms of reaction with reactive oxygen species: direct or spontaneous, and glutathione peroxidase catalyzed. Glutathione peroxidase (GSHPx, EC 1.11.1.9) is specific for its hydrogen donor, reduced glutathione (GSH), but may use a wide range of substrates extending from H_2O_2 to organic hydroperoxides. GSH is a major cellular electrophile conjugator as well. Glutathione S-transferases (GST, EC 2.5.1.18) catalyze the reaction between the –SH group of GSH and potential alkylating agents, thereby neutralizing their electrophilic sites and rendering them more water soluble. Glutathione disulfide reductase (GRD, EC 1.6.2.4) regenerates GSH from its oxidized form glutathione disulfide (GSSG, produced as a by-product of GSHPx reaction) in the presence of an adequate supply of NADPH. Antioxidants like vitamins E, C, reduced lipoic acid, and glutathione are known to act synergistically in the form of an *antioxidant chain reaction*.[13,14] As can be observed from the scheme (Figure 2), reduced glutathione plays a critical central role in regenerating vitamins C and E from their oxidized by-products. In this context it should be noted that the antioxidant activity of selenium and vitamin B_6 is also glutathione dependent.[10] Biochemical details of how primary and ancillary antioxidants function to detoxify reactive oxygen species have been presented elsewhere in this volume.

3. PHYSICAL EXERCISE INDUCED OXIDATIVE STRESS

The traditional approach to estimate physical fitness is primarily based on the physiological capacity of an individual to utilize atmospheric oxygen in a given interval of time per kg body weight, i.e., the aerobic capacity. Therefore, trainees are left with the primary target to enhance their aerobic capacity to the highest possible limit. Supply of more and more oxygen to the tissues fuels oxidative metabolism that produces higher amounts (compared to anaerobic metabolism) of energy-rich phosphates and avoids the formation of lactate during the energy supply process. Physical exercising is associated with a 10- to 15-fold increase in the rate of oxygen uptake by the body. Oxygen flux in the active peripheral skeletal muscle tissue may increase by over 100-fold with a ~30-fold increase in blood flow and ~3-fold increase in arteriovenous

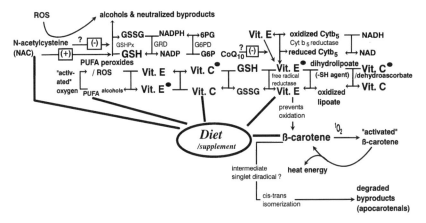

FIGURE 2. The antioxidant chain reaction. PUFA, polyunsaturated fatty acids; ROS, reactive oxygen species; a superscript dot symbolizes the radical form of the respective compounds; (+), NAC is a pro-GSH drug; ? (–), NAC and ubiquinone are suggested to "spare" the oxidation of GSH to GSSG and vitamin E to the tocopheroxyl radical, respectively; GSHPx, glutathione peroxidase; GRD, GSSG reductase; G6PD, glucose 6-phosphate dehydrogenase; G6P, glucose 6-phosphate; 6PG, 6-phosphogluconate; Cytb$_5$, cytochrome b$_5$; GSH, reduced glutathione; GSSG, glutathione disulfide. (From Sen, C. K. and Hänninen, O., in *Exercise and Oxygen Toxicity*, Sen, C. K., Packer, L., and Hänninen, O., Eds., Elsevier Science Publishers B.V., Amsterdam, 1994, chap. 5. Reprinted with due permission.)

O$_2$ difference. A large number of recent studies indicate that exercise induced increase in O$_2$ flux through the body is associated with a remarkable increase in the formation of reactive oxygen species.[3] This issue has been of particular concern especially because exercising is not only a recreational activity but is also well established to have diverse therapeutic benefits.[9] A vivid understanding of the possible mechanisms that contribute to exercise-induced oxidative stress, associated physiological response and designing of appropriate measures to circumvent/minimize such stress is fundamental to (1) uplift the merit of physical exercise as a therapeutic tool in clinical practice, (2) control exercise induced reactive oxygen species dependent tissue damage and other possible health risks, and (3) perhaps to enhance performance capacity in sports as well. The area of exercise and oxygen toxicity has been comprehensively addressed in a recent multi-author volume.[3]

It is well documented that several global regulatory mechanisms exist for the coordinated expression of enzymes and proteins needed for cellular defense against oxidative stress. For such a defense response, it is required that the cells sense oxidants and transduce the signal into changes in gene expression. This chapter presents a brief overview of the molecular aspects of oxidative stress sensing, response, and management. Several studies have examined the effect of acute and chronic exercise on the activity of physiological antioxidant enzymes in different tissues. A vast body of information appears to lend firm support to the hypothesis that exercise training significantly enhances the physiological antioxidant defenses of various tissues, especially skeletal muscle.[10,12] It has also been shown that chronic physical inactivity, on the other hand, decreases such defenses. Therefore, it appears that the endogenous antioxidant defense status of certain tissues, e.g., the skeletal muscle is influenced by the state of physical activity.[15] Although several studies have tested the effect of exercise on antioxidant enzyme activities and have reported significant changes, there is almost no information on the possible intracellular mechanisms that regulate such effects.

4. OXIDATIVE STRESS REGULONS

Antioxidant enzyme activities have been observed to be responsive to oxidative stress. Chronic exposure to increased oxygen flux through various tissues as occurs during exercise training has been shown to influence antioxidant enzyme activities.[10,12] However, information regarding the constitutive expression of antioxidant proteins is scanty. Most of the work in this area has been directed towards the understanding of processes that regulate the adaptation of cells exposed to oxidative stress. The models currently in use for such experiments are (1) prokaryotic enteric bacterial (*Escherichia coli, Salmonella typhimurium*) and eukaryotic yeast (*Saccharomyces cerevisiae*) cells with well-developed genetic and recombinant DNA techniques available in these species, and (2) mammalian cells (including that of human). *E. coli* and *S. typhimurium* must withstand at least transient exposure to oxidative conditions, as in sewage. In hosts, these enteric bacteria must also defend against oxidants ($O_2^{\cdot-}$, hydrogen peroxide and others) produced by macrophages. *S. cerevisiae* cells carry two superoxide dismutase genes *SOD1* (encoding cytosolic copper-zinc superoxide dismutase) and *SOD2* (encoding mitochondrial manganese superoxide dismutase; homologous to bacterial Mn superoxide dismutase) and two catalase genes: *CTT1* (encoding cytosolic catalase T) and *CTA1* (encoding peroxisomal catalase A).[16]

5. SUPEROXIDE INDUCIBLE *sox* AND *mar* SYSTEMS

Superoxides ($O_2^{\cdot-}$) , the one-electron reduction product of oxygen, is a basic form of reactive oxygen species (Figure 1). Spontaneous or enzymatic dismutation of superoxides produce hydrogen peroxide. During exercise, excess superoxides may be produced by a number of possible mechanisms.[10,17] Some of the major possible sources of exercise-induced excess superoxides are: (1) increased escape of these partially reduced forms of oxygen from the mitochondrial electron transport chain, (2) conversion of the enzyme xanthine dehydrogenase to the superoxide producing xanthine oxidase form, (3) stimulated neutrophils containing myeloperoxidases and NADPH oxidases, (4) ischemia — reflow at certain sites (e.g., synovial joint), and possibly also (5) altered intracellular signaling following oxidative modification of membrane receptors.

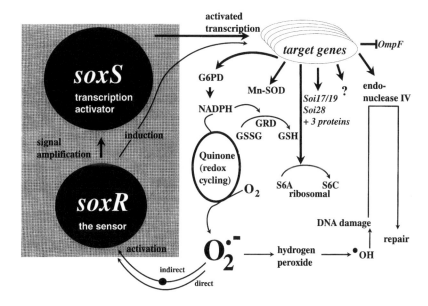

FIGURE 3. The superoxide (and nitric oxide) inducible *soxRS* regulon in *E. coli*. Directly or indirectly superoxides activate the soxR protein to an activated SoxR* form. Activated SoxR* acts as a transcriptional activator of *soxS*. Overproduced SoxS protein activates the transcription of target genes, e.g., *sodA* (for MnSOD), *nfo* (for DNA repair endonuclease IV), *zwf* (for glucose 6-phosphate dehydrogenase or G6PD), *fumC* (for fumarase C), *micF* (an antisense RNA regulator responsible for the OmpF effect) and others. It is possible that in addition to *soxS*, soxR may directly activate some target genes. In the absence of *soxR*, overproduction of soxS from a foreign promoter can induce the regulon. S6A and S6C, the unmodified and modified forms of the ribosomal protein S6; GRD, glutathione disulfide reductase; GSH and GSSG, reduced and oxidized forms of glutathione.

Oxidative stress generated by the redox-cycling compounds, such as naphthoquinone menadione or the aromatic quaternary amine paraquat induces the expression of around 80 polypeptides.[18,19] About half of these proteins are also induced by hydrogen peroxide, indicating that they are triggered indirectly by redox-cycling agents through the H_2O_2 formed by the dismutation of $O_2^{\cdot-}$. Nine superoxide stress proteins that are induced by menadione and paraquat exposure but not by hydrogen peroxide, are members of a regulon that is known to be under the positive transcriptional control of a locus called *soxR*.[20,21] *soxR* together with the adjacent soxS gene governs a superoxide response regulon. Induction of this regulon has been observed to be associated with increased transcription of soxS which in turn activates target genes. Therefore, induction of the regulon may actually be considered to be a two-stage process:[22] *soxR* probably acts as a superoxide sensor and responds by triggering the activation of the signal amplifier *soxS;* this is followed by the soxS-dependent induction of other genes (Figure 3). A recent work by Hidalgo and Demple[23] identified two forms of the soxR protein, an apoprotein and an iron-sulfur cluster containing the form referred to as the Fe-soxR. When activated, both forms of soxR could bind to the *soxS* promoter to induce it; however, only the Fe-soxR activated transcription *in vitro*. It is assumed that the redox-sensitive FeS cluster of soxR is modified upon exposure to superoxide anion radicals.

Some of the soxR regulon proteins are known to possess discrete antioxidant properties. For example, manganese superoxide dismutase scavenges superoxide, endonuclease IV repairs oxidative DNA damage, and glucose 6-phosphate dehydrogenase supplies NADPH to glutathione reductase, thereby helping to maintain a favorable redox status of the key antioxidant glutathione. *Soi-17, soi-19,* and *soi-28* have been identified as *soxR* controlled genes. The definite functions of these genes are yet unclear, however, the disruption of these genes by Mu d(*lac*) insertions renders *E. coli* highly sensitive to paraquat exposure.[24] *soxR* represses the expression of the outer membrane porin OmpF and increases the C-terminal glutamate modification of the ribosomal protein S6.[20] Such changes may limit the accumulation of intracellular toxins, increase resistance to a variety of antibiotics, and alter cellular targets for oxidative or other damage.

Greenberg et al.[20] have shown that mutants with constitutive alleles of *soxR* [*soxR* (Con)] are highly resistant to oxidants and many antibiotics. In a later report,[25] the authors showed that certain mutations at a different locus, named *soxQ,* confer some of the phenotypes seen in *soxR* constitutive strains, including resistance to menadione. A previously reported mutation called *cfxB,* identified through antibiotic resistance, was suggested to be likely an allele of *soxQ.* The *soxQ1* and *cfxB* mutations caused transcriptional activation of the genes that encode MnSOD, glucose 6-phosphate dehydrogenase, and the soi-17/19: lac fusions. *soxQ1* and *cfxB* mutations increase the synthesis of seven other proteins not influenced by *soxR.* The *soxQ1* and *cfxB* mutations were shown not to be dependent on the *soxR* gene, and gene induction by *soxR* in response to redox changes did not depend on the *soxQ* locus. The authors proposed that *soxQ* helps control some oxidative stress proteins as part of another regulon that responds to an unknown environmental signal.[25]

MarA (Mar stands for multiple antibiotic resistance) is another important regulator that contributes to defense against superoxide.[25] The *marRAB* operon is induced by various compounds including antibiotics and redox-cycling agents. The *marRAB* locus encodes three proteins and MarA shows a remarkable homology to SoxS.[26] In the absence of MarR, the repressor of the operon, *marA* expression increases. The increased MarA protein thus produced appears to induce the expression of *sodA, zwf, fumC, micF* (see the legend of Figure 3 for an explanation of abbreviations) and also that of some *soxRS* independent genes.[27] In addition to *SoxS* and *MarA,* the regulation of *sodA* (encoding MnSOD) expression is also known to be carried out by four other global transcription regulators. Compan and Touati[28] have identified these regulators as ArcA (aerobic respiration control), Fnr (fumarate nitrate reductase), Fur (ferric uptake regulation), and IHF (integration host factor). The ArcB sensor may be stimulated by an electron carrier in the transport chain. ArcA is posttranslationally activated by phosphorylation via ArcB.[29] Carrying an iron cofactor, Fnr is a redox-sensitive transcriptional regulator of anaerobically-induced genes.[30] Fur is also an iron-binding protein that represses genes involved in iron assimilation in the presence of high iron concentration.[31]

6. HYDROGEN PEROXIDE INDUCIBLE *oxyR* SYSTEM

Exposure to low levels (micromolar) of hydrogen peroxide increases the synthesis of around 30 polypeptides. Some of these proteins overlap with heat shock proteins and proteins induced in response to stress caused by other oxidants. Such an adaptive response allows bacterial cells to survive otherwise toxic (millimolar) doses of hydrogen peroxide and other agents.[32,33] A group of nine proteins induced as a result of the above-described response has been shown to be under the positive control of the *oxyR* gene. Such *oxyR* controlled proteins include the classic antioxidant enzymes catalase, glutathione reductase, and alkyl hydroperoxide reductase. The OxyR protein negatively regulates its own expression. Mutant varieties of bacteria that lack *oxyR* can still induce 21 other proteins. However, functional *oxyR* deficient bacteria have been observed to be sensitive to hydrogen peroxide and alkyl hyroperoxide toxicity.[33] OxyR possibly functions as a redox sensor. Oxidized but not reduced OxyR protein activates transcription of oxidative stress inducible genes *in vitro*. Storz et al.[34] have shown that direct oxidation of the OxyR protein brings about a conformational change by which OxyR transduces an oxidative stress signal to RNA polymerase (Figure 4). Tao et al.[35] showed that direct protein-protein contact between the OxyR protein and the C-terminal contact site I region of the RNA polymerase α subunit plays an essential role in transcription activation at the OxyR-dependent promoters.

The mutant *oxyR1*, overexpressing the nine *oxyR*-controlled proteins, was observed to be resistant to hydrogen peroxide, organic hydroperoxides, and to heat killing compared with the wild-type parent strain.[33] However, *oxyR1* was more sensitive to killing by menadione, 6-amino-7-chloro-5,8-dioxoquinone and 1-chloro-2,4-dinitrobenzene. *oxyR1* did not have any added protection against oxidants such as cadmium chloride, diamide, paraquat, and N-ethylmaleimide. Therefore, *oxyR1* mutants are resistant to a subset of oxidants to which hydrogen peroxide adapted cells are resistant. Storz et al.[36] observed that strains containing deletions of *oxyR* show 10- to 55-fold higher frequencies of spontaneous mutagenesis compared to otherwise isogenic *oxyR*+ control strains. Strains that contained a dominant *oxyR* mutation and overexpressed proteins regulated by *oxyR* showed lower spontaneous mutation frequencies by a factor of two. The authors suggested that *oxyR* and *oxyR* regulated genes protect against spontaneous oxidative DNA damage.[36]

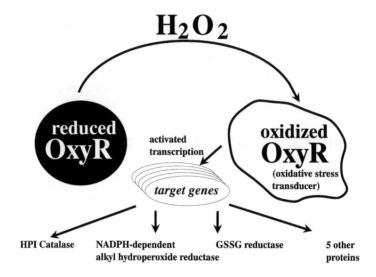

FIGURE 4. The *oxyR*-controlled regulon of hydrogen peroxide inducible (HPI) genes (in *S. typhimurium* and *E. coli*). Direct oxidation of the OxyR protein most likely brings about a conformational change by which OxyR transduces an oxidative stress signal to RNA polymerase. Most likely, oxidized OxyR activates transcription by recruiting RNA polymerase to the promoters. Conversion between the oxidized and reduced forms of OxyR is rapid and reversible. OxyR purified in the absence of reductants is oxidized but can be reduced by the addition of dithiothreitol. OxyR activates certain genes, e.g., *katG* (encoding catalase), *ahpCF* (encoding alkyl hydroperoxide reductase), *dps* (a nonspecific DNA binding protein), *gorA* (encoding glutathione reductase, GSSG reductase) and others, and negatively regulates its own expression.

7. NUCLEAR FACTOR-κB AND ACTIVATOR PROTEIN-1: ROS RESPONSIVE TRANSCRIPTION FACTORS

Nuclear factor (NF)-κB is a multiunit transcription factor that is activated by a variety of primary (viruses, bacteria, stress factors) and secondary (inflammatory cytokines) pathogenic stimuli. The protein is found in many different cell types and tissues; however, it has been characterized best in cells of the immune system such as pre-B, B, and T lymphocytes, macrophages, and monocytes. Activated NF-κB causes a rapid induction of genes encoding defense and signaling proteins. In most cells, NF-κB is present in a non-DNA binding form in the cytoplasm. The NF-κB complex is composed of three subunits: a DNA-binding 48 to 55 kDa protein (p50), a DNA-binding 65 to 68 kDa protein (p65, also known as Rel A), and a third inhibitory subunit (IκB) bound to p65. One of the well-studied stimuli that activates the transcription factor in a number of cell types is oxidative stress. Schreck et al.[37] showed that in Jurkat T cells, NF-κB is posttranslationally activated by low (micromolar) concentrations of hydrogen peroxide. Further studies by this group revealed that the activation of NF-κB in response to all inducing agents could be

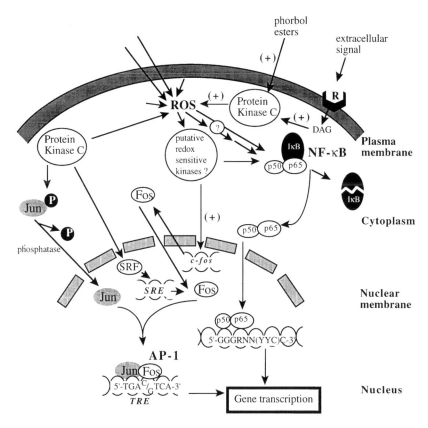

FIGURE 5. Hypothetical model outlining the activation of nuclear factor (NF) NF-κB and activator protein (AP)-1. Arrows from outside and inside the cell towards ROS are from extracellular and intracellular sites of ROS generation, respectively. R, receptor; DAG, diacylglycerol; SRF, serum responsive factor; *SRE*, serum responsive element; *TRE*, 12-O-tetradecanoylphorbol 13-acetate responsive element; (+), activation or increase. Winding lines in the nucleus represent DNA. R = any of the purine nucleotides, i.e., A or G; N = any of the four nucleotides A, T, G, or C; Y = any of the pyrimidine nucleotides, i.e., T or C; fragment in parenthesis may or may not be present in the binding site.

blocked by various chemically distinct antioxidants.[37,38] It has been also reported that various agents that induce oxidative stress e.g., tumor necrosis factor, interleukin-1, phorbol ester, lipopolysaccharide, anti-IgM, and ultraviolet light are also capable of activating NF-κB. Therefore, it appears that reactive oxygen species may play a messenger function in the activation of the factor. However, the actual mechanism of activation, i.e., the series of events that trigger the dissociation of IκB from the p50-p65-IκB complex is yet unclear. The cysteine at the amino acid position 62 in the p50 subunit has been suggested to be the redox-sensor.[39] Once activated, the p50-p65 dimer is rapidly translocated to the nucleus where it binds to the consensus sequence 5'-GGGRNN(YYC)C-3' in the κ enhancer as *trans*-acting factor (Figure 5). This

TABLE 1
Inducers of the Expression of the Mouse *GST Ya* Gene[60-62]

Planar aromatic hydrocarbons
Diphenols
Phorbol esters
Barbiturates
Electrophilic compounds

factor initiates transcription of genes. It is interesting to investigate whether strenuous exercise, known to oxidize thiols to disulfides, can induce NF-κB activation and the possible mechanism involved.

The activator protein-1 (AP-1) family comprises both Fos and Jun related proteins, the functional form being a dimer that is composed of either two Jun monomers or one Jun and one Fos related monomer (Figure 5).[40-44] This dimerization is very critical for AP-1 function and has been shown to take place through a *leucine zipper domain* that is currently referred to as the *coiled coil*.[45,46] The coiled coil is common to both dimerizing proteins and acts to juxtapose two basic regions that are capable of forming a complex with AP-1 DNA binding sites.[47,48] The activated AP-1 dimer binds to the TPA (12-O-tetradecanoylphorbol 13-acetate, also known as PMA) responsive element, or TRE.[49,50] The consensus TRE, 5′-TGAC/GTCA-3′, is found in promoter and enhancer region of genes. Phorbol esters are sensitive activators of AP-1. The effect is thought to be mediated via the activation of protein kinase C (PKC).[51] In response to PKC activation, Fos and Jun proteins are encoded by the rapidly inducible c-*fos* protooncogene and c-*jun* oncogene, respectively. It has been shown that reactive oxygen species can also directly induce the expression of c-*fos* mRNA and DNA synthesis.[52,53] Agents that are known to induce AP-1 activation are listed in Table 2. The activation of AP-1 is regulated by complex mechanisms consisting of posttranscriptional events acting on preexisting AP-1 molecules and transcriptional activation leading to the formation of increased amounts of AP-1-binding proteins. The regulation of AP-1 activation has been discussed in further details in a later section.

8. THIOL REDOX STATUS AND TRANSCRIPTION FACTORS

In a number of studies it has been observed that acute strenuous exercise induces blood and other tissue glutathione oxidation.[10] Reduced glutathione (GSH), a key physiological antioxidant (see Chapter 4 and Reference 10), is transformed to glutathione disulfide (GSSG) in response to strenuous exercise. Recent evidence suggests that GSSG may play a very crucial role in intracellular oxidative stress signaling. Results from human T-cells suggest that the hydrogen peroxide induced activation of NF-κB may also involve GSSG.[54]

TABLE 2
Inducers of AP-1 Activation

β-Naphthoflavone
3-Methylcholanthrene
tert-Butylquinone
trans-4-Phenyl-3-butene-2-one
Phorbol esters
Hydrogen peroxide
Phenobarbital
Arsenite
Arsenate
Heavy metals

Phorbol ester-induced activation of NF-κB was remarkably enhanced following BCNU (bischloroethylnitrosourea) treatment of human T-cells. BCNU is known to inhibit GSSG reductase activity and thus paralyze the regeneration of GSH from GSSG. BCNU cells are therefore characterized by the presence of high concentrations of intracellular GSSG. Other manipulations to lower intracellular GSSG levels (e.g., inhibition of GSH synthesis) inhibited the effect of BCNU in enhancing the phorbol ester-induced activation of NF-κB.[54] A complex aspect of the GSSG-mediated signaling process is that DNA binding of NF-κB is inhibited by physiologically relevant concentrations of GSSG. Thus, GSSG appears to have two mutually antagonistic effects. It appears that a certain optimal concentration of intracellular GSSG is required to enhance NF-κB activation. Concentration below this level is ineffective to cause any change in IκB dissociation whereas higher concentrations may trigger the IκB dissociation but inhibit the DNA-binding activity of the activated heterodimer. These effects of GSSG appear to be antagonized by the well-known oxidoreductase thioredoxin. Thiols such as thioredoxin, dithiotreitol, cysteine, and GSH has been observed to enhance NF-κB DNA-binding activity.[54-56] However, reduced thiols, e.g., thioredoxin have shown to strongly inhibit the induction of NF-κB activation and translocation to the nucleus.[57,58] It may be thus speculated that NF-κB response is regulated by the GSSG-thioredoxin balance in the cell. The proglutathione agent N-acetylcysteine, and reduced glutathione itself has been also shown to inhibit AP-1 activation.[39]

9. DNA REGULATORY ELEMENTS

Xenobiotic metabolism is associated with an increased production of reactive oxygen species. Therefore, enzymes involved in the metabolism of such foreign compounds contribute as antioxidants by decreasing the levels of compounds capable of generating ROS.[59] Mammalian cells exposed to a variety of chemical agents respond by increasing the activities of their xenobiotic metabolizing enzymes e.g., glutathione S-transferases (GST), glucuronosyl transferases, and NAD (P) H:quinone reductase. The GST Ya and NAD (P) H:quinone reductase genes are known to be implicated in such antioxidant-detoxicant defense responses.

Friling et al.[61] observed that the induction of the GST Ya gene in mouse was mediated by a DNA-regulatory element known as EpRE. EpRE was shown to be composed of two adjacent AP-1-like binding sites that bind and are transactivated by the Fos/Jun heterodimeric complex AP-1. Enhancers similar to the EpRE of the mouse GST Ya gene have been found to be implicated in the regulation of a number of other chemical-inducible genes. Such enhancers, as exemplified by the antioxidant responsive element (ARE) of the GST Ya gene[63] and rat quinone reductase genes,[64] are also known to be activated by the AP-1 complex.[65] Phenolic antioxidants related to butylated hydroxyanisole (BHA) and butylated hydroxytoluene (BHT) can trigger an ARE-mediated induction of the expression of genes encoding NAD(P)H:quinone reductase and the Ya subunit of GST. Choi and Moore[66] showed that such phenolic antioxidants specifically induce expression of the c-*fos* and c-*jun* protooncogene mRNAs. The response was antioxidant-specific and dose-dependent. The activity of the c-*fos* promoter was also induced in transient transfections, and results with deletions and point mutations revealed that a serum response element (SRE) existing upstream of c-*fos* gene was required for this response. This study confirmed that antioxidant treatment increases AP-1 activity.[66] Increased AP-1 binding was also observed when HepG2 or H4II hepatoma cells were treated with chemical inducers listed in Table 2.[62,65,67]

Because a wide variety of chemical agents can all activate the GST Ya and quinone reductase genes through the induction of AP-1 complex interacting with respective enhancers, it is speculated that all such chemicals may actually act by producing a common transduction signal for AP-1. This common signal, however, is yet to be characterized. Abate et al.[68] suggested that transcriptional activity mediated by AP-1 binding factors may be regulated by a redox mechanism. Xanthoudakis and Curran identified and characterized Ref-1 (a nuclear factor denoted redox factor-1), a 37-kDa nuclear protein that was observed to facilitate AP-1 DNA-binding activity.[69] Ref-1 is suggested to represent a novel redox component of the signal transduction processes that regulate eukaryotic gene expression. The yeast AP-1 (YAP1) protein of *Saccharomyces cerevisiae* is homologous to the AP-1 family of eukaryotic transcription factors.[70] YAP1-deleted strains have been found to be sensitive to superoxide and hydrogen peroxide generating compounds and also had decreased levels of glucose 6-phosphate dehydrogenase, superoxide dismutase, and glutathione reductase activity. It is not known whether the genes encoding these enzymes are directly regulated by YAP1. However, it seems likely that YAP1 contributes to antioxidant defense.

10. OXYGEN TENSION INDUCIBLE OREs IN HUMANS

In general, the hydrogen peroxide decomposing glutathione-dependent selenoenzyme glutathione peroxidase has been observed to respond to acute and chronic bouts of physical exercise (see Chapter 4 and Reference 10). The possible mode of this regulation is, however, unknown. It has been recently observed that the expression of the antioxidant enzyme glutathione peroxidase is modulated by a large number of factors including oxygen tension. Two *cis*-acting oxygen responsive elements (ORE1 and ORE2) were discovered in the 5′-flanking region of the glutathione peroxidase gene.[71] Two distinct regions (ORE1 and ORE2) located upstream from the transcription start site were observed to be responsive to oxygen tension in culture (pO_2 values of 150 or 40 mmHg). The OREs were observed to sense oxygen tension and trigger transcriptional changes. It was suggested that the effect is possibly mediated through some oxygen responsive regulatory factor (ORRF, e.g., USF, AP-1, and NF-κB) that activates or represses transcription through its direct or indirect contact with ORE sequences. Insertion of the OREs into a reporter gene governed by a SV40 promoter regulated chloramphenicol acetyltransferase activity according to the oxygen tension in culture.[71]

11. PHYTOALEXIN-INDUCED OXIDATIVE STRESS: THE [*Ah*] GENE BATTERY

Plant stress metabolites known as phytoalexins, a major source of oxidative stress to animals, have been useful to unveil a novel aspect of oxidative stress sensing. Phytoalexins are low molecular weight antimicrobial compounds that are both synthesized by, and accumulate in, plant cells exposed to microorganisms.[72] Phytoalexins include phenylpropanoid-, terpenoid-, and ethylene-derived chemicals, in addition to hydroxy-proline-rich glycoproteins and proteinase inhibitors. These compounds are toxic to animals ingesting the plants. Quinones represent the most electrophilic and therefore the most reactive and toxic phytoalexins. One-electron reduction of quinone produces semiquinone-radical. In the presence of (di)oxygen, the semiquinone radical can regenerate quinone and form $O_2{}^{\cdot-}$. Thus, redox cycling of quinone produces reactive oxygen. Phytoalexins are believed to be among the ligands that bind to the aromatic hydrocarbon-response (Ah) receptor. In animals, the Ah receptor appears to be a transducer pathway for detecting toxic plant flavones and providing a defense response i.e., the induction of appropriate enzymes.[73,74] A group of six genes has been defined as the [*Ah*] gene battery. There are two Phase I (almost exclusively cytochrome P-450) genes, cytochrome P_1-450 (CYP1A1) and cytochrome P_3-450 (CYP1A2), and four Phase II (enzymes that act on oxygenated intermediates) genes, NAD(P)H:menadione oxidoreductase (*Nmo-1*), aldehyde dehydrogenase (*Aldh-1*), UDP-glucuronosyltransferase (*Ugt-1*), and glutathione transferase (*Gt-1*). Whether *Gt-1* is certainly a part of the [*Ah*] gene battery demands further evidence. The inducer-receptor complex undergoes a temperature-dependent modification before gaining chromatin binding capacity. As a result, Ah receptor-mediated positive transcriptional activation of each of the genes in the [*Ah*] gene battery takes place.[73,74] Experiments with inbred mouse lines with overlapping radiation-induced chromosomal deletions involving the albino locus on chromosome 7 provide indirect evidence for regulatory genes located within the missing region of deletion homozygote mice (c^{14Cos}/c^{14Cos}). The region of the mouse chromosome 7 missing in the c^{14Cos}/c^{14Cos} mouse appeared to contain a master switch gene that responds to oxidative stress.[75-82]

12. METAL BINDING TRANSCRIPTION FACTORS IN ANTIOXIDANT DEFENSE

Cytosolic superoxide dismutase expression is regulated by the availability of intracellular free copper. The ACE1 activator protein is known to bind several Cu-(I) ions in a cooperative fashion. Such copper binding produces a conformation change of ACE1 to form the *copper fist*. This *copper fist* allows the ACE1 protein to bind to its target DNA.[83] The increased availability of copper induces the expression of the CuZnSOD. Such an effect has been observed to be mediated via ACE1.[84,85] Because transition copper ion is known to drive Fenton-type reactions and contribute to oxidative stress, ACE1-dependent induction of *SOD1* may actually help to protect the cells against oxidative stress. The same organism, *S. cerevisiae,* is known to contain the *MAC1* gene that encodes a protein (MAC1) homologous to ACE1.[86] Strains with disrupted *MAC1* were hypersensitive to heat, cadmium, zinc, lead, and hydrogen peroxide, and showed decreased hydrogen peroxide-dependent induction of the *CTT1* gene encoding the cytosolic catalase T enzyme. MAC1 is also known to regulate the expression of *FRE1* gene that encodes the ferric reductase enzyme (involved in iron reduction and uptake).[87]

13. Bcl-2 IN ANTIOXIDANT DEFENSE

Recent reports propose a crucial role of the protooncogene Bcl-2 in the prevention of cell death. Bcl-2 is localized to intracellular sites of oxygen free radical generation including mitochondria, endoplasmic reticula, and nuclear membranes. Zhong et al.[88] revealed that expression of the protooncogene may protect Ca^{2+} ionophore-induced apoptotic cell death. This effect was not mediated by a change in intracellular free Ca^{2+} level, indicating that Bcl-2 did not modify the rate of extracellular Ca^{2+} influx, but acted at a different point. It appears likely that Bcl-2 is implicated in the inhibition of a process that may cause apoptosis or necrosis. Necrotic death of GSH-deficient (produced following the inhibition of glutathione synthesis), oxidative stress-susceptible GT1-7 neural cells, was inhibited by the expression of Bcl-2.[89] Stable expression of Bcl-2 was achieved by the use of a retroviral vector. Bcl-2 expressed cells were also GSH deficient; however, it appeared that cells expressing Bcl-2 had two to three times the basal concentration of GSH and correspondingly higher concentration during GSH synthesis blockade. It was suggested that the elevated level of GSH associated with Bcl-2 might have resulted from a decreased utilization of the thiol in the Bcl-2 expressing cells. Interestingly, even after the excess GSH of Bcl-2 expressing cells was removed using a GSH conjugator, the cells exhibited a higher protection against cytotoxicity. This enhanced defense of Bcl-2 expressing cells was maintained in cells that were treated for a depletion of both cytosolic and mitochondrial pools of GSH. Results of this study showed that the net intracellular generation of reactive oxygen species and lipid peroxidation in Bcl-2 expressing cells was lower compared to the controls. Using nitro-L-arginine methyl ester (an inhibitor of NO synthesis) and *S*-nitroso-*N*-acetylpenicillamine (an inducer of NO production), the authors showed that NO is not involved in the mode of Bcl-2 action with respect to reactive oxygen species production or cell death. The contention that Bcl-2 acts by down-regulating the generation of reactive oxygen species was supported by the observation that *sod2* yeast mutants (null mutation for mitochondrial MnSOD) expressing Bcl-2 grew well in 21% oxygen. Bcl-2 expression also enhanced the growth of *sod1* mutants (null mutation for cytosolic CuZnSOD). The following possible function of Bcl-2 were proposed: (1) direct radical-scavenging protein, (2) metal-binding protein, and/or (3) inhibitor of mitochondrial superoxide generation. Recently, Hockenbery et al.[90] proposed that Bcl-2 regulates an antioxidant pathway at sites of free radical generation to prevent apoptosis.

14. SUMMARY

The hypothesis that physical exercise may induce oxidative stress, a state where the reactive oxygen species generated in excess overwhelm the tissue antioxidant defenses, is supported by a large number of recent studies.[3] Regular exercise training has been shown to enhance the physiological antioxidant defense status of various tissues. Training-induced increase in the antioxidant defenses in various tissues may be expected to be a genetically-regulated transient adaptation process. However, the possible mechanisms by which exercising may regulate the expression or activation of antioxidant proteins are not known and demand attention.

The contention that reactive oxygen species (either themselves or by-products of reactions kicked in by ROS) may act as crucial intercellular messengers regulating gene expression is gaining momentum. It is interesting to note that although antioxidant enzymes from bacterial to mammalian cells are highly conserved, homologs of bacterial OxyR and SoxR proteins have not been identified in yeast and mammalian cells. Coping with oxidative stress in this oxygen-rich atmosphere is a significant evolutionary factor, and the various positive control systems involved may be expected to both coordinate and compete with other global regulators acting on the same genes. Little is known about the possible cross-talk between the different global regulatory mechanisms that regulate the expression of enzymes and other proteins needed for cellular defense against the ravages of reactive oxygen. It may be speculated that identification and characterization of the intracellular redox sensors that are implicated in sensing and relaying exercise-induced oxidative stress signals to the nucleus may open up new avenues to control exercise-induced oxygen toxicity, especially through pharmacological interventions.

REFERENCES

1. **Bert, P.,** *La Pression Barometrique* (1878), [Eng. trans.: M. Hitchcock and A. Hitchcock], College Book Company, Columbus, Ohio, 1943.
2. **Packer, L.,** Oxygen is a dangerous friend, in *Cell Function and Disease,* Canedo, L. E., Todd, L. E., Packer, L., and Jaz, J., Eds., Plenum Press, New York, 1988, 199.
3. **Sen, C. K., Packer, L., and Hanninen, O.,** *Exercise and Oxygen Toxicity,* Elsevier Science Publishers B.V., Amsterdam, 1994, 36.
4. **Huie, R. E. and Padmaja, S.,** The reaction of NO with superoxide, *Free Rad. Res. Commun.,* 18, 195, 1993.
5. **Sies, H.,** Biochemistry of the peroxisome in the liver cell, *Angew. Chem. Int. Ed. Engl.,* 13, 706, 1974.
6. **Boveris, A., Oshino, N., and Chance, B.,** The cellular production of hydrogen peroxide, *Biochem. J.,* 128, 617, 1972.
7. **Archakov, A. I. and Bachmanova, G. I.,** *Cytochrome P-450 and Active Oxygen,* Taylor and Francis, London, 1990, 339.
8. **Roy, S. and Hänninen, O.,** Biochemical monitoring of the aquatic environment: possibilities and limitations, in *Ecotoxicology Monitoring,* Richardson, M., Ed., VCH Publishers, New York, 1993, 119
9. **Åstrand, P.-O. and Sen, C. K.,** The significance of exercise science in the maintenance of general health and enhancement of performance, *Ind. J. Physiol. Allied Sci.,* 48, 56, 1994.
10. **Sen, C. K. and Hänninen, O.,** Physiological antioxidants, in *Exercise and Oxygen Toxicity,* Sen, C. K., Packer, L., and Hänninen, O., Eds., Elsevier Science Publishers, Amsterdam, 1994, chap. 5.
11. **Goldfarb, A. and Sen, C. K.,** Antioxidant supplementation and the control of oxygen toxicity during exercise, in *Exercise and Oxygen Toxicity,* Sen, C. K., Packer, L., and Hänninen, O., Eds., Elsevier Science Publishers, Amsterdam, 1994, chap. 7.
12. **Ohno, H., Suzuki, K., Fujii, H., Yamashita, H., Kizaki, T., Ohishi, S., and Taniguchi, N.,** Superoxide dismutases in exercise and disease, in *Exercise and Oxygen Toxicity,* Sen, C. K., Packer, L., and Hänninen, O., Eds., Elsevier Science Publishers, Amsterdam, 1994, chap. 6.
13. **Sen, C. K., Rankinen, T., Väisänen, S., and Rauramaa, R.,** Oxidative stress after human exercise: effect of N-acetylcysteine supplementation, *J. Appl. Physiol.,* 76, 2570, 1994.
14. **Sen, C. K., Atalay, M., and Hänninen, O.,** Exercise induced oxidative stress: glutathione supplementation and deficiency, *J. Appl. Physiol.,* 77, 2177, 1994.
15. **Sen, C. K., Marin, E., Kretzschmar, M., and Hänninen, O.,** Skeletal muscle and liver glutathione homeostasis in response to training, exercise, and immobilization, *J. Appl. Physiol.,* 73, 1265, 1992.
16. **Gralla, E. B. and Kosman, D. J.,** Molecular genetics of superoxide dismutases in yeasts and related fungi, *Adv. Genet.,* 30, 251, 1992.
17. **Jackson, M. J.,** Exercise and oxygen radical production by muscle, in *Exercise and Oxygen Toxicity,* Sen, C. K., Packer, L., and Hänninen, O., Eds., Elsevier Science Publishers, Amsterdam, 1994, chap. 2.

18. **Greenberg, J. T. and Demple, B.,** A global response induced in *Eschherichia coli* by redox-cycling agents overlaps with that induced by peroxide stress, *J. Bacteriol.,* 171, 3933, 1989.

19. **Walkup, L. K. B. and Kogoma, T.,** Escherichia coli proteins inducible by oxidative stress mediated by the superoxide radical, *J. Bacteriol.,* 171, 1476, 1989.

20. **Greenberg, J. T., Monach, P., Chou, J., Josephy, P. D., and Demple, B.,** Positive control of a multilevel antioxidant defense regulon activated by superoxide-generating agents in *Escherichia coli, Proc. Natl. Acad. Sci. U.S.A.,* 87, 6181, 1990.

21. **Tsaneva, I. R. and Weiss, B.,** soxR, a locus governing a superoxide response in *Escherichia coli* K-12, *J. Bacteriol.,* 172, 4197, 1990.

22. **Wu, J. and Weiss, B.,** Two-stage induction of the soxRS (superoxide response) regulon of *Escherichia coli, J. Bacteriol.,* 174, 3915, 1992.

23. **Hidalgo, E. and Demple, B.,** An iron-sulfur center essential for transcriptional activation by the redox-sensing SoxR protein, *EMBO J.,* 13, 138, 1994.

24. **Kogoma, T., Farr, S. B., Joyce, K. M., and Natvig, D. O.,** Isolation of gene fusions (soi::lacZ) inducible by oxidative stress in *Escherichia coli, Proc. Natl. Acad. Sci. U.S.A.,* 85, 4799, 1988.

25. **Greenberg, J. T., Chou, J. H., and Monach, P. A.,** Activation of oxidative stress genes by mutations at the *soxQ/cfx/marA* locus of *Escherichia coli, J. Bacteriol.,* 173, 4433, 1991.

26. **Cohen, S. P., Hächler, H., and Levy, S. B.,** Genetic and functional analysis of the multiple antibiotic resistance (*mar*) locus in *Escherichia coli, J. Bacteriol.,* 175, 1484, 1993.

27. **Ariza, R. R., Cohen, S. P., Bachhawat, N., Levy, S. B., and Demple, B.,** Repressor mutations in the *marAB* operon that activate oxidative stress genes and multiple antibiotic resistance in *Escherichia coli, J. Bacteriol.,* 176, 143, 1994.

28. **Compan, I. and Touati, D.,** Interaction of six global transcription regulators in expression of manganese superoxide dismutase in *Escherichia coli* K-12, *J. Bacteriol.,* 175, 1687, 1993.

29. **Iuchi, S. and Lin, E. C. C.,** Adaptation of *Escherichia coli* to redox environments by gene expression, *Mol. Microbiol.,* 9, 9, 1993.

30. **Spiro, S. and Guest, J. R.,** Adaptive responses to oxygen limitation in *Escherichia coli, Trends Biochem. Sci.,* 16, 310, 1991.

31. **Bagg, A. and Neilands, J. B.,** Molecular mechanisms of regulation of sideroshore-mediated iron-assimilation, *Microbiol. Rev.,* 51, 509, 1987.

32. **Demple, B. and Hallbrook, J.,** Inducible repair of oxidative DNA damage in *Escherichia coli, Nature,* 304, 466, 1983.

33. **Christman, M. F., Morgan, R. W., Jacobson, F. S., and Ames, B. N.,** Positive control of a regulon for defenses against oxidative stress and some heat-shock proteins in *Salmonella typhimurium, Cell,* 41, 753, 1985.

34. **Storz, G., Tartaglia, L. A., and Ames, B. N.,** Transcriptional regulator of oxidative stress-inducible genes: direct activation by oxidation, *Science,* 248, 189, 1990.

35. **Tao, K., Fujita, N., and Ishihama, A.,** Involvement of the RNA polymerase alfa subunit C-terminal region in co-operative interaction and transcriptional activation with OxyR protein, *Mol. Microbiol.,* 7, 859, 1993.

36. **Storz, G., Christman, M. F., Sies, H., and Ames, B. N.,** Spontaneous mutagenesis and oxidative damage to DNA in Salmonella typhimurium, *Proc. Natl. Acad. Sci. U.S.A.,* 84, 8917, 1987.

37. **Schreck, R., Rieber, P., and Baeuerle, P. A.,** Reactive oxygen intermediates as apparently widely used messengers in the activation of the NF-kappaB transcription factor and HIV-1, *EMBO J.,* 10, 2247, 1991.

38. **Schreck, R., Meier, B., Männel, D., Dröge, W., and Baeuerle, P. A.,** Dithiocarbamates as potent inhibitors of nuclear factor kappa B activation in intact cells, *J. Exp. Med.,* 175, 1181, 1992.

39. **Devary, Y., Gottilieb, R. A., Smeal, T., and Karin, M.,** The mammalian ultraviolet response is triggered by activation of Src tyrosine kinases, *Cell,* 71, 1081, 1992.

40. **Bohmann, D., Bos, T. J., Admon, A., Nishimura, T., Vogt, P. K., and Tjian, R.,** Human proto-oncogene c-jun encodes a DNA binding protein with structural and functional properties of transcription factor AP-1, *Science,* 238, 1386, 1987.

41. **Angel, P., Allegretto, E. A., Okino, S. T., Hattori, K., Boyle, W. J., Hunter, T., and Karin, M.,** Oncogene jun encodes a sequence-specific transactivator similar to AP-1, *Nature,* 332, 166, 1988.

42. **Curran, T. and Franza, B. R. J.,** Fos and Jun: the AP-1 connection, *Cell,* 55, 395, 1988.

43. **Rauscher, F. J. I., DR, C., Curran, T., Bos, T. J., Vogt, P. K., Bohmann, D., Tjian, R., and Franza, B. R. J.,** Fos-associated protein p39 is the product of the c-jun protooncogene, *Science,* 240, 1010, 1988.

44. **Bohmann, D. and Tjian, R.,** Biochemical analysis of transcriptional activation by Jun: differential activity of c- and v-Jun, *Cell,* 59, 709, 1989.

45. **O'Shea, E. K., Rutkowski, R., and Kim, P. S.,** Evidence that the leucine zipper is a coiled coil, *Science,* 243, 538, 1989.

46. **Landschulz, W. H., Johnson, P., F., and McKnight, S. L.,** The leucine zipper: a hypothetical structure common to a new class of DNA binding proteins, *Science,* 240, 1759, 1988.

47. **Halazonetis, T. D., Georgopoulos, K., Greenberg, M. E., and Leder, P.,** c-Jun dimerizes with itself and with c-Fos, forming complexes of different DNA binding affinities, *Cell,* 55, 917, 1988.

48. **Sassone-Corsi, P., Ransone, L. J., Lamph, W. W., and Verma, I. M.,** Direct interaction between fos and jun nuclear oncoproteins: role of the 'leucine zipper' domain, *Nature,* 336, 692, 1988.

49. **Angel, P., Pöting, A., Mallick, U., Rahmsdorf, H. J., Jonat, C., Herrlich, P., and Karin, M.,** Phorbol ester-inducible genes contain a common cis element recognized by a TPA-modulated transacting factor, *Cell,* 49, 729, 1987.

50. **Lee, W., Haslinger, A., Karin, M., and Tjian, R.,** Activation of transcription by two factors that bind promoter and enhancer sequences of the human metallothionein gene and SV40, *Nature,* 325, 368, 1987.

51. **Nishizuka, Y.,** The role of protein kinase C in cell surface signal transduction and tumour promotion, *Nature,* 308, 693, 1984.

52. **Shibanuma, M., Kuroki, T., and Nose, K.,** Induction of DNA replication and expression of protooncogene c-myc and c-fos in quiescent Balb/3T3 cells by xanthine/xanthine oxidase, *Oncogene,* 3, 17, 1988.

53. **Shibanuma, M., Kuroki, T., and Nose, K.,** Stimulation by hydrogen peroxide of DNA synthesis, competence, familiy gene expression and phosphorylation of a specific protein in quiescent Balb/3T3 cells, *Oncogene,* 5, 1025, 1990.

54. **Galter, D., Mihm, S., and Droge, W.,** Distinct effects of glutathione disulphide on the transcription factors NF-κB and AP-1, *Eur. J. Biochem.,* 221, 639, 1994.

55. **Okamoto, T., Ogiwara, H., Hayashi, T., Mitsui, A., Kawabe, T., and Yodoi, J.,** Human thioredoxin/adult T cell leukemia-derived factor activates the enhancer binder protein of human immunodeficiency virus type 1 by thiol redox control mechanism, *Int. Immunol.,* 4, 811, 1992,

56. **Matthews, J. R., Wakasugi, N., Virelizier, J.-L., Yodoi, J., and Hay, R. T.,** Thioredoxin regulates the DNA binding activity of NF-κB by reduction of a disulphide bond involving cysteine 62, *Nucl. Acids Res.,* 20, 3821, 1992.

57. **Meyer, M., Schreck, R., and Bauerle, P.,** H_2O_2 and antioxidants have opposite effects on activation of NFκB and AP-1 in intact cells: AP-1 as secondary antioxidant responsive factor, *EMBO J.,* 12, 2005, 1993.

58. **Schenk, H., Klein, M., Droge, W., and Schulze-Osthoff, K.,** Distinct effects of thioredoxin and antioxidants on the activation of NFκB and AP-1, *Proc. Natl. Acad. Sci. U.S.A.,* 91, 1672, 1992.

59. **Sies, H.,** Oxidative stress: from basic research to clinical application, *Am. J. Med.,* 91, 31S, 1991.

60. **Friling, R. S., Bensimon, A., Tichauer, Y., and Daniel, V.,** Xenobiotic inducible expression of murine glutathione S-transferase Ya subunit gene, *Proc. Natl. Acad. Sci. U.S.A.,* 87, 6258, 1990.

61. **Friling, R. S., Bergelson, S., and Daniel, V.,** Two adjacent AP-1-like binding sites form the electrophile responsive element of murine glutathione S-transferase Ya subunit gene, *Proc. Natl. Acad. Sci. U.S.A.,* 89, 668, 1992.

62. **Pinkus, R., Bergelson, S., and Daniel, V.,** Phenobarbital induction of AP-1 binding activity mediates activation of glutathione S-transferase and quinone reductase gene expression, *Biochem. J.,* 290, 637, 1993.

63. **Rushmore, T. H., Morton, M. R., and Pickett, C. B.,** The antioxidant responsive element, *J. Biol. Chem.,* 266, 11632, 1991.

64. **Favreau, L. V. and Pickett, C. B.,** Transcriptional regulation of the rat NAD(P)-H.quinone reductase gene. Identification of regulatory elements controlling basal level expression and inducible expression by planar aromatic compounds and phenolic antioxidants, *J. Biol. Chem.,* 266, 4556, 1991.

65. **Bergelson, S., Pinkus, R., and Daniel, V.,** Induction of AP-1 (Fos/Jun) by chemical agents mediates activation of glutathione S-transferase and quinone reductase gene expression, *Oncogene,* 9, 565, 1994.

66. **Choi, H. S. and Moore, D. D.,** Induction of C-Fos and C-Jun gene expression by phenolic antioxidants, *Mol. Endocrinol.,* 7, 1596, 1993.

67. **Daniel, V., Bergelson, S., and Pinkus, R.,** The role of AP-1 transcription factor in the regulation of glutathione S-transferase Ya subunit gene expression by chemical agents, in *Structure and Function of Glutathione S-Transferases,* Tew, K. D., Pickett, C. B., Mantle, T. J., Mannervik, B., and Heys, J., Eds., CRC Press, Boca Raton, FL, 1993, 129.

68. **Abate, C., Patel, L., Rauscher, F. J., III, and Curran, T.,** Redox regulation of Fos and Jun DNA-binding activity *in vitro, Science,* 249, 1157, 1990.

69. **Xanthoudakis, S. and Curran, T.,** Identification and characterization of Ref-1, a nuclear protein that facilitates AP-1 DNA-binding activity, *EMBO J.,* 11, 653, 1992.

70. **Moye-Rowley, W. S., Harshman, K. D., and Parker, C. S.,** Yeast *YAP1* encodes a novel form of the jun family of transcriptional activator proteins, *Genes Dev.,* 3, 283, 1989.

71. **Cowan, D. B., Weisel, R. D., Williams, W. G., and Mickle, D. A. G.,** Identification of oxygen responsive elements in the 5′-flanking region of the human glutathione peroxidase gene, *J. Biol. Chem.,* 268, 26904, 1993.

72. **Paxton, J. D.,** Phytoalexins — a working redefinition, *Phytopathol. Zeitschr.,* 101, 106, 1981.

73. **Nebert, D. W. and Gonzalez, F. J.,** P450 genes: structure, evolution and regulation, *Annu. Rev. Biochem.,* 56, 945, 1987.

74. **Nebert, D. W.,** The *Ah* locus: genetic differences in toxicity, cancer, mutation and birth defects, *CRC Crit. Rev. Toxicol.,* 20, 153, 1989.

75. **Thaler, M. M., Erickson, R. P., and Pelger, A.,** Genetically determined abnormalities of microsomal enzymes in liver of mutant newborn mice, *Biochem. Biophys. Res. Commun.,* 72, 1244, 1976.

76. **Gatmaitan, Z., Lewis, S., Turchin, H., and Arias, I. M.,** Premature development of ligandin (GSH transferase B) in mice with an inherited defect in endoplasmic reticulum-Golgi structure and function, *Biochem. Biophys. Res. Commun.,* 75, 337, 1977.

77. **Gluecksohn-Waelsch, S.,** Genetic control of morphogenetic and biochemical differentiation: lethal albino deletions in the mouse, *Cell,* 16, 225, 1979.

78. **Russell, L. B., Montgomery, C. S., and Raymer, G. D.,** Analysis of the albino locus region of the mouse: characterization of 34 deficiencies, *Genetics,* 100, 427, 1982.

79. **Schmid, W., Muller, G., Shutz, G., and Gluecksohn-Waelsch, S.,** Deletions near the albino locus on chromosome 7 of the mouse affect the level of tyrosine aminotransferase mRNA, *Proc. Natl. Acad. Sci. U.S.A.,* 82, 2866, 1985.

80. **Loose, D. S., Shaw, P. A., Krauter, K. S., Robinson, C., England, S., Hanson, R. W., and Gluecksohn-Waelsch, S.,** *Trans*regulation of the phosphoenolpyruvate carboxykinase (GTP) gene, identified by deletions in chromosome 7 of the mouse, *Proc. Natl. Acad. Sci. U.S.A.,* 83, 5184, 1986.
81. **DeFranco, D., Morris, S. M., Jr., Leonard, C. M., and Gluecksohn-Waelsch, S.,** Metallothionein mRNA expression in mice homozygous for chromosomal deletions around the albino locus, *Proc. Natl. Acad. Sci. U.S.A.,* 85, 1161, 1988.
82. **Petersen, D. D., Gonzalez, F. J., Rapic, V., Kozak, C. A., Lee, J. Y., Jones, J. E., and Nebert, D. W.,** Marked increase in hepatic NAD(P)H:menadione oxidoreductase gene transcription and mRNA levels correlated with a mouse chromosome 7 deletion, *Proc. Natl. Acad. Sci. U.S.A.,* 86, 6699, 1989.
83. **Fürst, P., Hu, S., Hackett, R., and Hamer, D.,** Copper activates metallothionein gene transcription by altering the conformation of a specific DNA binding protein, *Cell,* 55, 705, 1988.
84. **Carri, M. T., Galiazzo, F., Ciriolo, M. R., and Rotilio, G.,** Evidence for coregulation of Cu,Zn superoxide dismutases and metallothionein gene expression in yeast through transcriptional control by copper via the ACE1 factor, *FEBS Lett.,* 278, 263, 1991.
85. **Gralla, E. B., Thiele, D. J., Silar, P., and Valentine, J. S.,** ACE1, a copper-dependent transcription factor, activates expression of the yeast copper, zinc superoxide dismutase gene, *Proc. Natl. Acad. Sci. U.S.A.,* 88, 8558, 1991.
86. **Jungmann, J., Reins, H. A., Lee, J., Romeo, A., Hasset, R., Kosman, D., and Jentsch, S.,** MAC1, a nuclear regulatory protein related to Cu-dependent transcription factors is involved in Cu/Fe utilization and stress resistance in yeast, *EMBO J.,* 12, 5051, 1993.
87. **Marchler, G., Schüller, C., Adam, G., and Ruis, H. A.,** *Saccharomyces cerevisiae* UAS element controlled by protein kinase A activates transcription in response to a variety of stress conditions, *EMBO J.,* 12, 1997, 1993.
88. **Zhong, L. T., Sarafian, T., Kane, D. J., Charles, A. C., Mah, S. P., Edwards, R. H., and Bredesen, D. E.,** Bcl-2 inhibits death of central neural cells induced by multiple agents, *Proc. Natl. Acad. Sci. U.S.A.,* 90, 4533, 1993.
89. **Kane, D. J., Sarafian, T. A., Anton, R., Hahn, H., Gralla, E. B., Valentine, J. S., Örd, T., and Bredesen, J. E.,** Bcl-2 inhibition of neural death: decreased generation of reactive oxygen species, *Science,* 262, 1274, 1993.
90. **Hockenbery, D. M., Oltvai, Z. N., Yin, X. M., Milliman, C. L., and Korsmeyer, S. J.,** Bcl-2 functions in an antioxidant pathway to prevent apoptosis, *Cell,* 75, 241, 1993.

Chapter 6

INDUCTION OF HEAT SHOCK PROTEINS BY EXERCISE

Ching-Yuan Su, Chawnshang Chang, and Chen-Ching Lai

CONTENTS

1. INTRODUCTION

Cells or whole organisms exposed to a mild thermal stimulus acquire a transient tolerance to subsequent, more severe heat challenge (Figure 1).[1] This inducible resistance by thermal incubation known as the heat shock response (HSR) was first observed in *Drosophila* larvae in 1962.[2] Normally, *Drosophila* larvae are grown at 25°C. When subjected to a 30-min incubation at 30°C followed with a short period of recovery, larvae developed thermotolerance. This was evident with a better survival rate of the preheated larvae in a second thermal challenge. The heat-induced response was later found to exist in a broad range of organisms or cultured cells. The list includes *Escherichia coli, dictyostelium, tetrahymena,* sea urchin embryos, yeast, fibroblasts, Chinese hamster ovary cells, human HeLa ascites cells, and many more, suggesting that this response is evolutionarily conserved and biologically important. Studies conducted so far indicate that the induction of the HSR confers not only

0-8493-8540-1/96/$0.00+$.50
© 1996 by CRC Press, Inc.

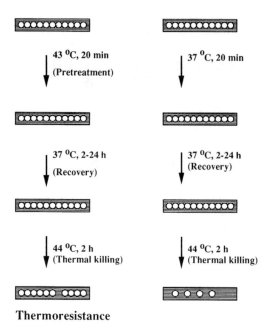

Thermoresistance

FIGURE 1. Illustration of the induction of the heat shock response by a brief thermal exposure. Mammalian cells were preheated at 5°C above optimum for a short interval, 20 to 30 min. After recovery from the initial heat stimulation, which usually requires several hours of incubation at 37°C, pretreated cells and unheated controls were subjected simultaneously to a severe heat shock. It was found that pretreated cells tended to survive better than untreated controls during the severe heat killing. This enhanced endurance to thermal challenge is due to the activation of a protective response, the heat shock response, in heat-preconditioned cells.

thermotolerance but also cross-resistance to other forms of insults, such as exposure to anoxia or alcohol.[1] More recently, whole-body thermal pretreatment has been shown to limit ischemic damage in the myocardium (Figure 2),[3] and reduce light-associated injury in the retina.[4] Furthermore, in an *in vitro* model for neuronal study, heat shock was demonstrated to confer protection against glutamate-induced excitotoxicity.[5] Thus, induction of the HSR may benefit cells or tissues when exposed to physical, chemical, or pathological insults, and activating this response by mild intervention could provide benefit.

At present, how to elicit the HSR "safely" *in vivo* is the subject of intense research. Various stressors, other than heat shock, induce this response.[1] Upon a mild thermal treatment, *Drosophila* larvae displayed a clear cut change in the puffing pattern of polytene chromosomes. Inhibitors that alter the mitochondrial electron transport or oxidative phosphorylation, such as amytal, antimycin, rotenone, oligomycin, and KCN, have been shown to cause the same heat shock change when incubated with the isolated salivary glands from fruit fly. Alternatively, the puffing phenomenon is also inducible by incubation of the salivary glands with alcohol, dinitrophenol, menadione, or hydrogen peroxide. The latter group of chemicals is known to affect the redox state and oxidatively

Whole-Body Hyperthermal Treatment

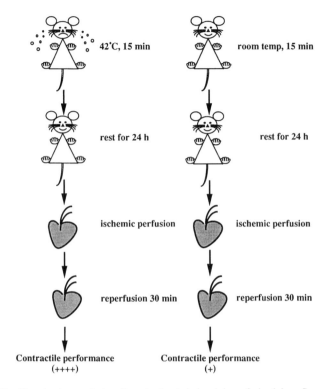

FIGURE 2. Heat shock-provoked cardioprotection to ischemia/reperfusion injury. Several groups have observed heat shock protection against metabolic imbalance in the myocardium during ischemia/reperfusion exposure. In this type of study, animals were often made hyperthermia to have a rectal temperature at 42°C for 15 min. Following a 24-h rest at room temperature, hearts were isolated from control and heat-preconditioned rats and retrogradely perfused. To simulate the ischemia/reperfusion insult, the myocardium was perfused first with low flow for several minutes and then normal flow for another period. Hearts obtained from the whole-body preheated rats were found to recover better than control after this insult.

damages the cells. Clearly, manipulating the mitochondrial functions or cellular redox potential activates the HSR. Nevertheless, these mitochondrial inhibitors or oxidative stressors are not suitable for use *in vivo*, because they are extremely toxic, and may affect intracellular sites other than their primary targets. Therefore, to develop some treatments that promote the HSR but generate no side effect is needed.

Increasing the body temperature is considered to be an excellent way to induce the HSR. However, overexposure to a uncontrolled exogenous heat stress may be dangerous. A physiological, and more natural, stressor that elicits a progressive increase in body temperature is exercise. During physical exertion, heat is generated from the conversion of adenosine triphosphate (ATP) to mechanical force in the contracting muscle, and then dissipated via circulation to form a general heat stress to other tissues. The magnitude of the induced heat load by physical activity is stringently controlled by complex physiological adjustments and regulatory systems. This normal function offers exciting possibilities of developing exercise into a safe method to induce the HSR *in vivo*. Several groups have studied this feasibility and demonstrated that exercise promotes the expression of heat shock proteins (HSPs) in certain tissues.[6-14] In this chapter, we first will present a brief overview of the well-known features of the HSR, and then compare the results of the present studies conducted to investigate the HSP-promoting effect of exercise. We hope that this comprehensive review and discussion will stimulate more research into the use of exercise as an inducer of the HSR. Exercise has been shown to bring in numerous health advantages for humans. To optimize the usefulness of exercise as a stimulant of a new beneficial response *in vivo* will further expand its therapeutic value in preventive medicine.

2. CONSERVED FEATURES OF THE HEAT SHOCK RESPONSE

The earliest observation of the HSR was reported by Ritossa.[2] During the normal development of the larval salivary gland of *Drosophila*, considerable changes occur in the pattern of chromosomal puffing activity. These are the consequences of the alteration in the titer of the insect's growth and molting hormone, ecdysone. Ritossa observed that other than exposure to ecdysone, temperature shock also induced a well-defined variation in the puffing pattern. The heat shock puffs were elicited by either whole-body thermal treatment of the larvae or *in vitro* heat incubation of the isolated salivary glands. Thus, upon thermal stimulation, isolated tissues or cells are capable of exhibiting HSR by themselves. Since then, investigations on thermal effects gradually shifted from intact animals to cultured cells or tissues, because the latter are more easily manipulated and amenable to biochemical analysis, and the pace of study is accelerated. During the past three decades, HSR has been studied in many organisms, as well as in many cell or tissue types of multicellular organisms. Based upon the accumulated observations of *in vivo* and *in vitro* models, it has been found that an exposure for 10 to 30 min to a heat stress at ~5°C above the optimum is generally sufficient to activate a rapid change in most cells previously mentioned. Under such conditions, the induced biological adaptations to thermal stress are remarkably similar, and can be summarized as the following.

2.1. INHIBITION OF NORMAL TRANSCRIPTION AND TRANSLATION

Cells respond intensely and rapidly to an increase in surrounding temperatures. Within minutes of heat exposure, there was a general reduction in the constitutive expression of the "normal" genes. This can result from (1) decreased transcription of the "normal" genes, (2) less efficient processing of the nascent transcripts, or (3) a reduced stability of their mRNA products.[1] The specific mechanisms involved in these regulations are complex. For example, redistribution of RNA polymerase molecules from "normal" or previously active genes to heat shock genes occurs rapidly at this stage. This has been demonstrated by Jamrich et al.[15] using indirect immunofluorescence to locate RNA polymerase B on the salivary gland polytene chromosome. With this technique, the chromosomal regions that are transcriptionally active give a bright fluorescence when stained with the antibodies against RNA polymerase B. The heat shock treatment led to a general reduction of fluorescence in the previously active puffs, and the appearance of brightly stained heat shock puffs. Consistent with this observation, the activity of the RNA polymerase II C-terminal-domain (CTD) kinase has been reported to increase after thermal stress.[16] The stimulation ratio of the RNA polymerase II CTD kinase ranged over 8- to 10-fold. Hyperphosphorylation of the RNA polymerase II CTD by the CTD kinase upon heat shock might diminish the interaction between the RNA polymerase and non-heat shock genes, and result in dissociation of initiation complexes from these genes. Additionally, thermal treatment also interrupts the splicing of nascent RNAs.[17] The transcripts of most eukaryotic genes contain intervening sequences and must be spliced to yield functional mRNAs. Inhibition of mRNA splicing further reduces the expression of non-heat shock genes. As for the mechanism that has been shown to affect the translation of non-heat shock mRNAs, it includes a breakdown or sequestration of these mRNAs in heat stressed cells.[18] Furthermore, the increased activity of another kinase, hemin-regulated initiation factor-2 (eIF-2) kinase, at high temperatures may also contribute to the inhibition of protein synthesis during heat shock.[19] It has been shown that hemin-regulated eIF-2 kinase catalyzes the phosphorylation of the α subunit of eukaryotic eIF-2. The phosphorylation of eIF-2 correlates with a suppression in mRNA translation. Overall, the impact of these changes upon heat shock may reflect a survival strategy that cells employ to curtail the production of aberrant proteins during and/or immediately after heat exposure.

2.2. SYNTHESIS OF HEAT SHOCK PROTEINS

When temperatures gradually return to normal, the accumulation of a specific set of proteins, the heat shock proteins, is detected. The presence of these proteins in cells was first discovered by Tissieres et al.[20] They incubated the *Drosophila* salivary glands with [^{35}S]methionine to correlate a protein change with the occurrence of heat shock puffs. Radiolabeled proteins, after isolation, were separated by electrophoresis on sodium dodecyl sulfate-polyacrylamide gel (SDS-PAGE), and identified with autoradiography of the gel. HSPs were classified as those rapidly and actively synthesized upon thermal treatment. After thermal stress, most cells produce HSPs having the apparent molecular masses around 110, 90, and 70 kDa, which are named HSP110, HSP90, and HSP70, accordingly. A representative example is shown in Figure 3, which depicts the synthesized HSPs in a rat myogenic cell line after a brief heat shock.

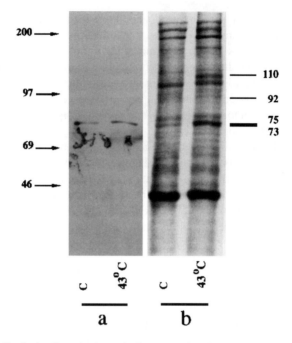

FIGURE 3. Synthesis of heat shock proteins in a myogenic cell line after heat stress. Fetal heart-derived H9c2 myocytes were subjected a 20-min incubation at 43°C followed with a 1-h recovery at 37°C. Subsequently, these heat-stressed cells were incubated with [35S]methionine for 1 h to label the newly synthesized protein during the post-heat shock period. Proteins were extracted, separated by SDS-PAGE, and then transferred to nylon filter membranes using a standard method. The immobilized proteins in the filters were identified with autoradiography or Western blot analysis using antibodies against HSP68 and HSC70. The latter technique is extremely useful for identification of a specific protein in a mixture, because it is difficult to recognize a protein solely based upon the estimated molecular size from the SDS-PAGE system. (**a**) Signals appeared in both control and heated samples when the filter was stained with an alkaline phosphatase-conjugated secondary antibody following an incubation with anti-HSP68/HSC70 antibodies. (**b**) Autoradiogram of the filter indicates the induction of several potential HSPs in H9c2 myocytes after heat shock. The locations of molecular weight standards are indicated by arrows. Note that the protein interacting with anti-HSP68/HSC70 antibodies has an apparent molecular mass around 75 kDa in our SDS-PAGE system.

The rapid increase in the cellular concentrations of HSPs is attributable to several mechanisms: (1) increased transcriptional activation of the heat shock genes, (2) prolonged half-lives for the heat shock mRNAs, and (3) more efficient translation of the HSP mRNAs.[1] In cultured *Drosophila* cells, the transcripts of the HSP70-encoding genes have been reported to increase within minutes of thermal incubation, and after a short period, they are abundant, accounting for 2 to 3% of the total nuclear RNAs.[21] This increase in heat shock transcripts resulted from the above-mentioned alteration in the specificity of RNA polymerase B in heat shocked cells. Also, it is noteworthy that most of the heat shock genes identified so far have no intron.[1] This unique feature allows heat shock transcripts to bypass the general block of RNA splicing encountered at high temperatures. Heat shock also exerts a marked effect on the stability of heat shock mRNAs. For one example, the half-lives of HSP70 mRNAs have been reported to increase at least 10-fold in heat treated HeLa cells.[22] In addition, heat shock mRNAs, compared to non-heat shock mRNAs, are preferentially translated.[18] This selective translation is partly due to features within the 5′ noncoding region of the heat shock mRNAs, and strongly suggests the involvement of a heat-shock translational regulation. The biological significance of HSP increases at this stage is not clearly known. However, it has been noted that following the accumulation of HSPs, the transcription of "normal" genes as well as the translation of "normal" mRNAs gradually return. Thus, HSPs have been implicated in facilitating the repairing process in heated cells.

2.3. ACQUISITION OF THERMOTOLERANCE

Generally speaking, a resistant state to thermal killing is acquired within 4 to 8 h after the initial heat stimulation. The development of thermotolerance correlates with the kinetics of the synthesis of HSPs, and reaches a maximum when the accumulation of these proteins plateaus.[1] The acquired thermotolerance eventually disappears between 40 to 80 h following the initial thermal stimulation. During this period, there is a reduction in the cellular concentrations of HSPs. By the time thermotolerance completely disappears, the expression of HSPs gradually returns to basal levels. This finding suggests that HSPs are involved in the acquisition, maintenance, and decay of thermotolerance. At least two lines of observation support this hypothesis. First, when HSPs are induced by amino acid analogs, thermotolerance is not detected.[23] Presumably, these amino acid analogs are incorporated into the newly synthesized HSPs, destroying their protective functions. Second, heat-induced lethality is increased in cells microinjected with antibodies against the major HSPs, HSP70s,[24] but reduced in cells that have been transfected with a constitutively expressed recombinant HSP70-encoding gene.[25] Taken together, these studies demonstrate an "active" role of HSPs in thermoprotection.

3. POTENTIAL FUNCTIONS OF HEAT SHOCK PROTEINS (THE FAMILY OF HSP70s)

So far, the identified HSPs can be categorized into several major families with distinct molecular weights: HSP110, HSP90s, HSP70s, HSP60s, and other small HSPs including ubiquitin.[1] The list could be expanded, because there may be yet to be identified, minor HSPs. HSPs are highly conserved in view of the encoding nucleotide sequences, predicted protein structures, or intracellular distribution. Most of the proteins also are expressed in resting cells. Therefore, it has been suggested that HSPs are important for cell survival at both normal and high temperatures. All cells or organisms examined to date produce HSP70s in response to an increase in temperature. In addition, the members of the HSP70 family are the most highly conserved HSPs previously identified. These proteins have been purified and extensively characterized. The studies of the 70-kDa proteins shed light on the potential protective function of HSPs.

The 70-kDa HSP family includes at least four members, which are HSP68 (no basal expression, heat-inducible), HSC70 (high basal expression, slightly heat-inducible), GRP78 (a glucose regulated protein located in the endoplasmic reticulum), and P75 (the HSP70 present in the mitochondrial compartment).[1] Accumulated evidence suggests that both heat-inducible and constitutively expressed members of the HSP70 family are required for essential functions in nonstressed or heat-stressed cells.

3.1. NONSTRESSED CELLS

Newly synthesized peptides or precursor proteins temporarily interact with the cytosolic HSP70s in normal cells (Figure 4).[26] The cytosolic HSP70s, HSP68, and HSC70, also bind to actin.[27] Therefore, the formation of the HSP70-nascent protein complex may facilitate the transport of protein precursors in the cytoplasmic reticulum through interaction with the actin microfilament network. Precursor proteins or peptides, when associated with the carrier HSP70s, are prevented from premature folding. Upon reaching their final destinations, unfolded peptides are handed over to another set of carrier HSP70s located in the organelles for proper transmembrane relocation. Mitochondrial HSP70 and GRP78 are also shown to be essential for protein transportation into the mitochondria and endoplasmic reticulum, respectively.[28,29] Once inside the organelles, the newly transferred proteins can conjugate with other proteins, such as HSP60s.[30] With the assistance of HSP60s, precursor proteins are eventually folded into their proper conformations. Other than being a cytosolic carrier, HSC70 also serves as the clathrin decoating protein.[31] This protein catalyzes the disassembly of clathrin cages using the chemical energy released from ATP hydrolysis. In view of the known features of HSP70s, it is clear that these proteins are capable of coordinating or modifying intramolecular or intermolecular protein-protein interaction.

3.2. HEAT-SHOCKED CELLS

HSP70s have a high stability at elevated temperatures.[32] This stability is enhanced by binding to nucleotides. The bacterial HSP70 homolog, DnaK protein, was originally identified as a host protein required for the replication of bacteriophage lambda. Recent studies indicate that it prevents *E. coli* RNA polymerase from aggregation upon thermal treatment, and de-aggregates or reactivates the "bad" polymerase that has been inactivated by heat denaturation.[33] Upon thermal stimulation, HSP68 and HSC70 concentrate primarily within the nuclei, and, secondarily, near the cell membranes.[1] After a downshift in temperature (the recovery stage), these proteins disappear from the nuclei and return to the cytoplasm. Recent work showed that the accumulation of HSP70s in the myocardium was associated with an enhanced structural stabilization in cardiac tissues.[34] HSP70s therefore could be viewed as molecular

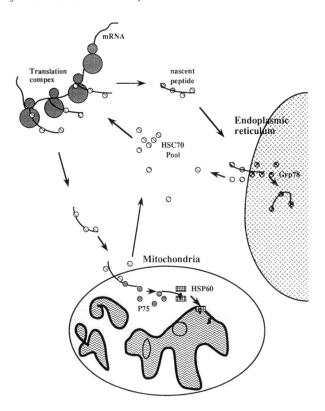

FIGURE 4. Proposed functions of HSP70s in nonstressed cells. The members of the HSP70 family are essential for several normal cellular functions. HSC70 binds with virtually every nascent peptide or translocation-competent protein to prevent it from premature folding. This protein also binds with action. Therefore, the association between HSC70 and nascent peptides or protein precursors allows efficient protein transfer via the actin cytoskeleton network. Organellar HSP70s, such as Grp78 and P75, orchestrate with HSC70 to facilitate the import of nascent peptides or precursor proteins into the endoplasmic reticulum and mitochondria. Once inside the organelles, protein precursors will be transferred to HSP60s, in which they fold into their final conformations in an ATP-dependent fashion.

chaperones that preserve preexisting biostructures during heat shock, or facilitate the disassembly of damaged structures after heat shock. Both features might be extremely important for the survival of thermally stressed cells. Other HSPs that are similarly induced during, or after, heat stimulation probably share the same protective features with HSP70s.

4. REGULATION OF THE HEAT SHOCK RESPONSE

Almost all heat shock-activated genes contain similar sequences in their 5′-promoter regions.[1] These sequences, known as the heat shock responsive element, are a contiguous array of variable numbers of nGAAn. In parallel action, a transcription factor, the heat shock factor, that displays a high affinity for the heat shock responsive element has been identified in many cells. *In vitro*, its presence transcriptionally activates the cloned HSP70 gene, but has no effect on non-heat shock genes. These discoveries focus attention on the transcriptional control of the heat shock genes. The current belief regarding the activation of heat shock responsive genes evolved around the presence of a universal inducing signal.[36] Recent studies demonstrated that introduction of protein aggregates into *E. coli* or oocytes activates the transcriptional activity of the promoter of a HSP70 gene.[37-39] Thus, denatured proteins or protein aggregates have been suggested to be the top candidates that present features recognized by the HSR induction system. In vertebrates, the heat shock transcription factor is maintained in an inactive state under nonstress conditions and acquires the ability to bind to the heat shock responsive element after a thermal stress. Biochemical studies indicate that the heat shock transcription factor associates with HSP70s,[40,41] and HSP70s negatively regulate the activity of the factor by keeping it in an inactive state. It is well established that HSP70s have a higher affinity to denatured or misfolded proteins.[32] Upon temperature upshift, the denatured proteins or protein aggregates thus generated can deplete the intracellular pool of free HSP70s. Such a change will release HSP70s and the heat shock factor from the heat shock factor/HSP70 complex. The free heat shock transcription factor will then be converted to an active form capable of DNA binding and trans-activating the heat-responsive gene expression (Figure 5). There is an indication that the activity of the heat shock factor may be regulated by a specific phosphorylation/dephosphorylation system. This is supported by the report that the phosphorylated level of heat shock factor increases upon thermal treatment, and the increased phosphorylation correlates with an enhanced ability of the factor to promote the transcription of heat shock genes.[42]

The existence of a universal signal for HSR induction could explain why divergent environmental stressors activate the same adaptive response in treated cells. Other than thermal treatment, exposure to ethanol, transition metals, uncouplers of the mitochondrial electron transport chain, and chemotherapeutic agents all induce the HSR.[1] Additionally, several disease states, such as viral infection, fever, inflammation, ischemia, hypertrophy, oxidant injury, and malignancy have a similar effect.[43] Exposure to each of these inducing agents or conditions may stimulate the production of abnormal proteins, which consume free HSPs and activate a demand for more HSP proteins.

There are, however, circumstances in which the induction of HSPs is not necessary to be accompanied with increases in aberrant proteins. For example, HSPs have been reported to be induced by the steroid hormone, ecdysone, in cultured *Drosophila* cells,[1] and by insulin in a hepatoma cell line.[44] This suggests that the induction of HSR could involve multiple regulatory signals. The supporting evidence for this theory is that cis-regulatory sequences responsible for serum or thermal induction of the HSP70 gene in human cells have

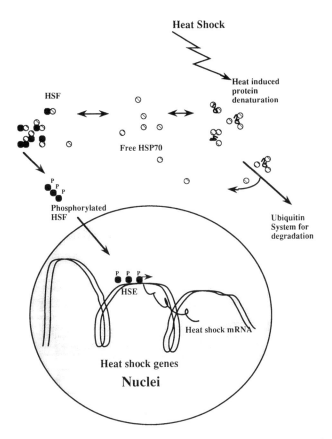

FIGURE 5. A model depicting the regulatory role of HSP70s in activating the expression of heat shock genes. Free and bound HSP70s are maintained at equilibrium in normal cells. At normal temperatures, a large fraction of the heat shock factor (HSF), which is required for the activation of heat shock responsive genes, is associated with HSP70s. Through this association, HSP70s either catalyze the inactivation of HSF or constitute a device that keeps HSF at a monomeric, inactive state. Thermal treatment increases the production of aberrant or denatured proteins. These proteins have a high affinity for HSP70s. Therefore, their increased production at temperature upshift will deplete the cellular reservoir of free HSP70s, and stimulate a release of HSP70s from the HSF/HSP70 complex. Freed HSF thus becomes active, and is capable of transfer from cytosol to the nuclei. During this process, the phosphorylation of this factor occurs. The increased phosphorylation enhances the ability of HSF to bind as a trimer to the heat shock responsive element (HSE) at the promoter region of heat shock genes. This binding attracts RNA polymerases to the heat shock promoter, and eventually stimulates the transcription of downstream genes.

been identified at different locations 5′-upstream from the transcription start site of the target genes.[45] Moreover, there are multiple heat shock factors present in vertebrate cells, and at least one is not activated by heat shock stimulation.[46] This theory may explain why some details of the HSR are regulated so differently among different cells or organisms.

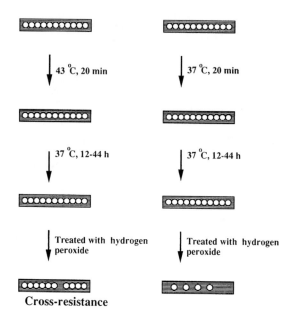

FIGURE 6.   Illustration of the cross-protective effect of the heat shock response. Cultured cells were incubated at a high temperature to activate the heat shock response. Afterward, they were subjected with unheated controls to a different type of insult, such as exposure to ethanol or hydrogen peroxide. Preheated cells tended to survive better than unheated controls in the latter insult, suggesting that the induction of the heat shock response cross-protects against the detrimental effects of other insults.

5. HEAT SHOCK AND CARDIOPROTECTION

Mild alcohol consumption was reported to reduce the risk of stroke and atherosclerosis. The detailed mechanism for this cardiovascular protection by alcohol is unclear. However, it is well recognized that treatment with this stressor enhances the production of HSPs and elicits the HSR in cells.[1] Associated with this biochemical change is an enhanced cross-resistance to subsequent lethal heat shock. Consistent with the observed protective effect of alcohol, heat-induced thermotolerance is noticed to cross-protect against other noxious stressors, such as anoxia or H_2O_2 (Figure 6).[1] Together, these findings suggest that HSR may be a general adaptive process that is stimulated to defend against the toxic effects of various insults. Thus, the induction of this protective response may, at least partly, account for the beneficial effect of alcohol previously observed in moderate drinkers. The induction of the HSR *in vivo* may have other clinical significance. In view of cardioprotection, an interesting observation was first reported by Currie et al. (Figure 2).[3] Their pioneer study reveals that a 15-min preincubation of intact animals at 42°C enhances myocardial tolerance to ischemia/reperfusion episodes. This observation was later confirmed by several groups.[47-49] A recent report further demonstrated that infusion of warm blood cardioplegia conferred a similar protection to the myocardium after 2 h of cardioplegic arrest.[50] Thus, whatever change brought about by thermal pretreatment is beneficial for the myocardium under hostile conditions. At present, the mechanism underlying the heat-induced cardiac protection is not clearly known. Using rat heart-derived H9c2 myocytes as an experimental model, we have found that thermal pretreatment elicited resistance to H_2O_2.[51] Similarly, myocytes preconditioned with ethanol survived better than controls in subsequent exposure to this reactive oxygen species.[52] Thus, HSR stimulants evoke the expression of oxidative protectants. It is noteworthy that in all cases examined, there is a temporal relationship between the heat-induced expression of HSP70s and the observed stress protection in cardiac cells. This observation suggests that HSP70s may be important for cardiac preservation in oxidative encounters. Elevated production of HSPs could also reduce pathological damage other than ischemia/reperfusion injury. For example, Barbe et al.[4] has reported that the retina isolated from rats that had been made hyperthermic, 41°C, for 15 min, had reduced photoreceptor damage in subsequent exposure to strong light. Furthermore, a hyperthermic treatment, 42.2°C for 20 min, was shown to elicit resistance to glutamate-induced neurotoxicity in cultured cells.[5] More recently, we also observed that thermal incubation of porcine aortic endothelial cells at 39°C for 2 to 4 days protected the cells against the detrimental effect of oxidized low density lipoprotein.[53] The molecular action of HSPs that confer these protection is under active investigation.

6. EFFECTS OF EXERCISE-INDUCED THERMAL STRESS

6.1. ANIMAL MODELS

Physical activity induces hyperthermia *in vivo*. Exercise performed at a regular interval decreases the development of coronary artery diseases. The latter observation is in good resonance with the above-reported cardiac protection in thermally treated animals. Therefore, it is of interest to investigate if exercise is an effective stimulant to evoke the HSR. The pioneer study to investigate the effect of exercise on HSPs was conducted in 1982 by Hammond et al.[6] In that particular study, rats were physically stressed by one bout of exhaustive swimming. At the completion of the exercise, the hearts of the experimental animals showed signs of cardiac malfunction, indicating that this type of physical activity exerts a marked burden on cardiac cells. Analysis of the extracted cardiac mRNAs from these animals, however, showed no sign of newly synthesized heat shock mRNAs. It was concluded that the physiological change provoked by exhaustive swimming is not sufficient for heat shock gene induction. Note that this observation is opposite to what Pshendin et al.[14] recently reported at the 40th anniversary meeting of the American College of Sports Medicine. The latter group subjected rats to 4 weeks of exhaustive swimming. Using Western blot analysis, they observed an increase of HSP68 in the isolated soleus muscle from exercisers. The contradiction between these two studies might arise from the differences in examined tissues (cardiac vs. skeletal muscles), employed exercise regimens (an acute bout of exercise vs. prolonged training), or detection methods (*in vitro* mRNA translation vs. Western blot analysis). Alternatively, it could simply be the result of the different temperature in the surrounding water in which swimming was conducted. Water has a high capacity to absorb and deliver heat. If exercise was carried out in a large body of cold water, hyperthermia thus generated will be quickly dissipated. On the other hand, if exercisers were swimming in warm water, the generated heat will accumulate quickly and become a marked internal stress to the body. Thus, the temperature in the aqueous environment has a dramatic impact on the adaptive physiology of swimmers. Unfortunately, the water temperature at which swimming was executed was not mentioned in either study.

It is realized only recently that hyperthermia accompanied with exercise is an effective stimulant to activate the formation of HSPs *in vivo*. In a study conducted by Locke et al.,[7] rats were run to exhaustion on a treadmill. At the end point, the rectal temperature was increased up to $41.6°C$. Exercised animals were sacrificed immediately to isolated spleen cells, peripheral lymphocytes, and soleus muscle. When subsequently incubated *in vitro* with [^{35}S]methionine, these cells or tissues, compared to their counterparts isolated from nonexercised animals, exhibited an enhanced ability to synthesize proteins of ~65, 72, 90, and 100 kDa. Salo et al.[8] also noticed the stimulatory effect of exhaustive treadmill exercise on HSPs. They reported that the concentrations of ~15 potential HSPs in skeletal muscle, heart, and liver were significantly higher in exercisers than in nonexercisers. In their study, Northern blot analysis was employed to assay for the change of heat shock mRNAs. The results of this analysis showed that the levels of HSP70 mRNAs in both cardiac and skeletal muscles peaked at 30 to 60 min after exercise, and then gradually returned to normal concentrations afterward.

Motor nerve stimulation was also effective to elicit the expression of HSPs in skeletal muscles. Essig et al.[10] reported that a 3-h stimulation of the peroneal nerve of rat tibialis arterial muscle followed with a 1.5 h recovery elevated the mRNA level of the heme oxygenase, a minor HSP, in the muscle. Separately, Hand et al.[11] demonstrated a marked increase in HSP70 and 60 mRNAs in the tibialis arterial muscle of rabbit after 1 day of chronic motor nerve stimulation. Stimulation of motor nerve causes muscle contraction, which generates a heat load with a magnitude correlating to the duration and intensity of the applied electric current. Thus, the results of these studies are compatible with those obtained from the treadmill exercise studies. Together, they demonstrate that contracting muscles respond rapidly to exercise-induced hyperthermia by activating an HSR.

6.2. HUMAN SUBJECTS

Exercise-induced hyperthermia also enhances the ability of human cells to generate HSPs. In a study by Ryan et al.,[9] five male subjects were subjected to different degrees of *in vivo* heat stress by treadmill exercise. To test for the induced change in HSP synthesis, leukocytes were isolated at the end of the regimens. The steady-state concentrations of HSP70s in the isolated leukocytes were determined by Western blot analysis. In parallel, another set of the leukocytes was further incubated at 41°C in the presence of [^{35}S]methionine to determine the extent of HSP inducibility *in vitro*. The rationale for the latter test is that induction of HSP70s is inversely affected by the level of the preexisting HSP proteins in the previously *in vivo* heat-stressed cells. Thus, if physical exertion activates the expression of HSP70s *in vivo,* the subsequent, *in vitro* induction of these proteins will be compromised. The results from this study indicated that no matter whether a mild or severe heat stress was imposed on exercisers, no significant difference of the steady-state contents of HSP70s was observed in leukocytes isolated immediately after exercise. However, using the radiolabeling assay to entail the induced change in protein synthesis, it was found that leukocytes isolated from exercisers whose rectal temperatures were elevated up to >40°C had a suppressed induction of HSP70s upon subsequent *in vitro* incubation at a high temperature. On the other hand, leukocytes obtained from exercisers who had a rectal temperature <40°C displayed a normal induction of HSP70s when exposed to the subsequent *in vitro* heat incubation. This observation strongly implies that a physiologically significant HSR has been induced in human subjects by exercise in a hot environment that raises the rectal temperature up to >40°C.

Thompson et al.[12] recently provided direct evidence confirming the efficacy of exercise to enhance the production of HSPs in humans. They recruited eight subjects to perform 70% maximum eccentric-isokinetic actions of the forearm flexor on one arm, with the other arm serving as control. A biopsy of the biceps muscle of each arm was taken 2 days later to analyze for the induced change in HSPs. Western blot analysis of the samples indicated a marked increase in the concentrations of HSP70s, HSP27, and ubiquitin in the exercised samples. This suggests that HSPs accumulate during the postexercise recovery stage.

Overall, the results from these animal and human studies support the hypothesis that a core temperature rise encountered during physical exercise is a sufficient stimulant for HSP formation. It is expected that future research to investigate more specific issues, such as which HSPs are responsive to the exercise stressor, and the timing of their induction, will soon be performed in a detailed manner. Additionally, it would be interesting to study if the production of HSPs in exercised subjects is solely a consequence of exercise-induced hyperthermia, or secondary to other alterations or adaptations activated during physical activity. To answer this question, one might want to directly assess the similarity and dissimilarity between the exercise- and hyperthermia-induced changes in gene expression. This information will greatly improve our understanding of the interaction between exercise and the regulatory mechanism of the HSR.

7. FUTURE PERSPECTIVES

It is noteworthy that most of the research conducted so far on exercise promotion of HSPs employed exhaustive exercise to stress experimental subjects. This form of exercise requires experimental subjects to perform a high intensity of physical activity. Under such conditions, the core temperature is pushed within a relatively short period to the range of 40 to 42°C, which is effective to induce an HSR *in vivo*, but may cause undesirable damage to the body. As described in a previous report, exposure to high temperature that accompanies exhaustion produces an overall acceleration of cellular metabolism.[54] This change will increase the risk for cardiac arrhythmias,[55,56] heat stroke,[57,58] and oxidative injury.[59,60] Factors involved in the potentiation of exercise-related cardiac arrhythmias include an increase in sympathetic tone, and oxygen and energy demands in the cardiac tissue. The combined effects of these factors leads to the development of myocardial ischemia and local acidosis. When the intensity of exercise reaches a level at which the generated heat load overcomes the capacity of normal circulatory adjustments to dissipate heat, thermal injury of tissues occurs. Exhaustive exercise also stimulates oxygen flux through the mitochondrial respiratory chain to produce more oxygen free radicals than usual. These oxygen species, being chemically reactive, could interact with lipids or proteins to alter their biological properties. Therefore, it is predictable that if HSP proteins are induced by strenuous physical exertion, their beneficial effects will be highly compromised. In the future, the safety limit of the length and intensity of exercise that will be performed to induce HSPs should be carefully defined.

The question whether exhaustive exercise is the only form of physical activity that stimulates the formation of HSPs needs to be addressed. For working muscles, such as the heart and skeletal muscles, which are the major sites of heat generation, the answer to the above question is probably no. The reason is that during exercise, the temperature in contracting muscles is usually higher than the rectal temperature by 1 to 2°C.[61] Therefore, the temperatures in the cardiac or skeletal muscles of an exhaustive exerciser should have far exceeded the level sufficient for HSP formation. Besides, it is acknowledged that HSP genes can be activated by incubation at either high or moderate temperatures, with the incubation interval being slightly prolonged at the moderately elevated temperatures.[1] We observed no significant difference in the synthesized HSPs in a myogenic cell line after incubation at 43°C for 20 min or at 40°C for 1 h (unpublished data). Consistent with this finding, Kregel et al.[13] have reported a stimulatory effect of submaximal exercise on HSPs. In that study, rats were subjected to an exercise regimen that caused no significant change in body temperature. Cardiac and skeletal muscle samples were isolated

30 min after the conclusion of exercise to analyze the induced change in HSPs. The data of Western blotting indicated that a prolonged bout of submaximal exercise is sufficient to increases the levels of HSP70s in these tissues. Some other current findings also promise the possibility to boost the intrinsic production of HSPs in various tissues without resorting to exhaustive exercise. This beneficial response might be induced by a combined use of the exercise stressor with other stressors, or with so-called "stress modifiers." The new notion is strongly supported by recent reports that there is a synergistic interaction between hyperthermia and alcohol, or hyperthermia and heavy metals, to elevate the expression of HSPs,[62] as well as the existence of a "stress modifier" that can augment the ability of heat stress to produce the protective proteins.[63] Further understanding of the stress mechanism will facilitate the design of specific exercise regimens to induce HSR without overstressing the subjects.

Biochemical and physiological adjustments to exercise are complex. The actual mechanism by which exercise accomplishes numerous health benefits remains unknown. At the present time, it may be premature to predict what specific advantages will be gained from the recurrent expression of HSPs in routine exercisers, because the final outcome may vary markedly with the type, intensity, and frequency of physical exertion that will be executed to stimulate the formation of the proteins. Nevertheless, based upon the known salutary features of HSPs,[64] it is reasonable to suggest that a sustained elevation of the protectants *in vivo* has physiological significance. It is true that healthy subjects have had various defense mechanisms to cope with the metabolic imbalance caused by physiological or environmental hazards. However, when situations occur that prevent the other defense mechanisms from coming into play, the presence of HSPs could be highly significant for survival through hostile conditions.

8. SUMMARY

HSR represents a novel defense mechanism protecting cells or whole organisms against the toxic effects of stress. From the "preventive" point of view, a persistent activation of this response *in vivo* may be beneficial for health. Exercise-induced hyperthermia is a stimulant provoking the HSR *in vivo*. With a large percent of the U.S. population participating in physical activity on a regular basis, this HSR stimulant has a great potential to be developed into an attractive tool to induce the protective response in humans. Studies conducted so far have demonstrated the feasibility of using exhaustive exercise to promote the endogenous production of HSPs, which are important determinants to the salutary effects of the HSR. Nevertheless, strenuous exercise is associated with various potential dangers. Therefore, it would be unwise to exercise regularly under such conditions. At the present time, whether other forms of exercise are more appropriate than exhaustive exercise to induce HSR is not clearly known. Therefore, an important task in the near future is to investigate this question, and to define carefully the amount and frequency of the exercise needed to achieve an optimal effect. This type of study will uplift the merit of exercise as a safe inducer of HSR, and to eventually benefit human health.

REFERENCES

1. **Lindquist, S.,** The heat shock response, *Ann. Rev. Biochem.,* 55, 1151, 1986.
2. **Ritossa, F. M.,** A new puffing pattern induced by temperature shock and DNP in *Drosophila, Experienta,* 18, 571, 1962.
3. **Currie, R. W., Karmazyn, M., Kloc, M., and Mailer, K.,** Heat-shock response is associated with enhanced postischemic ventricular recovery, *Circ. Res.,* 63, 543, 1988.
4. **Barbe, M. F., Tytell, M., Gower, D. J., and Welch, W. J.,** Hyperthermia protects against light damage in the rat retina, *Science,* 241, 1817, 1988.
5. **Rordorf, G., Koroshetz, W. J., and Bonventre, J. V.,** Heat shock protects cultured neurons from glutamate toxicity, *Neuron,* 7, 1043, 1991.
6. **Hammond, G. L, Lai, Y.-K., and Markert, C. L.,** Diverse forms of stress lead to new patterns of gene expression through a common and essential metabolic pathway, *Proc. Natl. Acad. Sci. U.S.A.,* 79, 3485, 1982.
7. **Locke, M., Noble, E. G., and Atkinson, B. G.,** Exercising mammals synthesize stress proteins, *Am. J. Physiol.,* 258, C723, 1990.
8. **Salo, D. C., Donovan, C. M., and Davies, K. J. A.,** HSP70 and other possible heat shock or oxidative stress proteins are induced in skeletal muscle, heart, and liver during exercise, *Free Rad. Biol. Med.,* 11, 239, 1991.
9. **Ryan, A. J., Gisolfi, C. V., and Moseley, P. L.,** Synthesis of 70K stress protein by human leukocytes: effect of exercise in the heat, *J. Appl. Physiol.,* 70, 466, 1991.
10. **Essig, D. A., Jackson, D. A., and Borger, D. R.,** A heme oxygenase mRNA is induced in skeletal muscle following 3 hours of nerve stimulation, *Med. Sci. Sports Exerc.,* 26, S94, 1994.
11. **Hand, G. A., Williams, R. S., Michel, J. B., and Ordway, G. A.,** Chronic motor nerve stimulation induces expression of cytosolic and mitochondrial heat shock RNAs, *Med. Sci. Sports Exerc.,* 26, S134, 1994.
12. **Thompson, H. S., Scordilis, S. P., and Clarkson, P. M.,** Muscle heat/stress protein changes after eccentric exercise, *Med. Sci. Sports Exerc.,* 26, S134, 1994.
13. **Kregel, K. C., Skidmore, R. L., Gutierrez, J. A., and Guerriero, V., Jr.,** HSP70 induction during exercise and heat stress in rats: Role of internal temperature, *Med. Sci. Sports Exerc.,* 26, S134, 1994.
14. **Pshendin, A., Kinev, A., and Rogozkin, V.,** The endurance training and accumulation of HSP-72 in various rat skeletal muscles, *Med. Sci. Sports Exerc.,* 26, S134, 1994.
15. **Jamrich, M., Greenleaf, A. L., and Bautz, E. K. F.,** Localization of RNA polymerase in polytene chromosomes of *Drosophila melanogaster, Proc. Natl. Acad. Sci. U.S.A.,* 74, 2079, 1977.
16. **Legagneux, V., Morange, M., and Bensaude, O.,** Heat-shock and related stress enhance RNA polymerase II C-terminal-domain kinase activity in HeLa cell extracts, *Eur. J. Biochem.,* 193, 121, 1990.
17. **Yost, H. J. and Lindquist, S.,** RNA splicing is interrupted by heat shock and is rescued by heat shock protein synthesis, *Cell,* 45, 185, 1986.
18. **Lindquist, S.,** Regulation of protein synthesis during heat shock, *Nature,* 293, 311, 1981.
19. **De Benedetti, A. and Baglioni, C.,** Activation of hemin-regulated initiation factor-2 kinase in heat-shocked HeLa cells, *J. Biol. Chem.,* 261, 338, 1986.

20. **Tissieres, A., Mitchell, H. K., and Tracy, U. M.,** Protein synthesis in salivary glands of *Drosophila melanogaster, J. Mol. Biol.,* 84, 389, 1974.
21. **Findly, R. C. and Pederson, T.,** Regulated transcription of the genes for actin and heat-shock proteins in cultured *Drosophila* cell, *J. Cell Biol.,* 88, 323, 1981.
22. **Theodorakis, N. G. and Morimoto, R. I.,** Posttranscriptional regulation of hsp70 expression in human cells: Effects of heat shock, inhibition of protein synthesis, and adenovirus infection on translation and mRNA stability, *Mol. Cell. Biol.,* 7, 4357, 1987.
23. **Mizzen, L. A. and Welch, W. J.,** Characterization of the thermotolerant cell. I. Effects on protein synthesis activity and the regulation of heat-shock proteins 70 expression, *J. Cell Biol.,* 106, 1105, 1988.
24. **Riabowol, K. T., Mizzen, L. A., and Welch, W. J.,** Heat shock is lethal to fibroblasts microinjected with antibodies against hsp70, *Science,* 242, 433, 1988.
25. **Li, G. C., Li, L., Liu, Y.-K., Mak, J. Y., Chen, L., and Lee, W. M. F.,** Thermal response of rat fibroblasts stably transfected with the human 70-kDa heat shock protein-encoding gene, *Proc. Natl. Acad. Sci. U.S.A.,* 88, 1681, 1991.
26. **Beckmann, R. P., Mizzen, L. A., and Welch, W. J.,** Interaction of hsp70 with newly synthesized proteins: implications for protein folding and assembly, *Science,* 248, 850, 1990.
27. **Tsang, T. C.,** New model for HSP70s' potential mechanisms of function, *FEBS Lett.,* 323, 1, 1993. (Cited as the ref for HSP70s as actin-binding proteins, and to facilitate the transport of proteins.)
28. **Kang, P. J., Ostermann, J., Shilling, J., Neupert, W., Craig, E. A, and Pfanner, N.,** Requirement for hsp70 in the mitochondrial matrix for translocation and folding of precursor proteins, *Nature,* 348, 137, 1990.
29. **Munro, S, and Pelham, H. R. B.,** An hsp70-like protein in the ER: identity with the 78 kDa glucose-regulated protein and immunoglobulin heavy chain binding protein, *Cell,* 46, 291, 1986.
30. **Langer, T., Lu, C., Echols, H., Flanagan, J., Hayer, M. K., and Hartl, F.-U.,** Successive action of DnaK, DnaJ, and GroEL along the pathway of chaperone-mediated protein folding, *Nature,* 356, 683, 1992.
31. **Ungewickell, E.,** The 70kD mammalian heat shock proteins are structurally and functionally related to the uncoating protein that releases clathrin triskelion from coated vesicles, *EMBO J.,* 4, 3385, 1985.
32. **Palleros, D. R., Welch, W. J., Fink, A. L.,** Interaction of hsp70 with unfolded proteins: Effects of temperature and nucleotide on the kinetics of binding, *Proc. Natl. Acad. Sci. U.S.A.,* 88, 5719, 1991.
33. **Skowyra, D., Georgopoulos, C., and Zylicz, M.,** The *E. coli* dna K gene product, the hsp70 homologue, can reactive heat-inactivated RNA polymerase in an ATP hydrolysis-dependent manner, *Cell,* 62, 939, 1990.
34. **Velazquez, J. M. and Lindquist, S.,** HSP70: nuclear concentration during environmental stress and cytoplasmic storage during recovery, *Cell,* 36, 655, 1984.
35. **Meerson, F. Z., Malyshev, I. Y., and Zamotrinsky, A. V.,** Differences in adaptive stabilization of structures in response to stress and hypoxia relate with the accumulation of hsp70 isoforms, *Mol. Cell. Biochem.,* 111, 87, 1992.
36. **Craig, E. A. and Gross, C. A.,** Is HSP70 the cellular thermometer?, *Trends Biochem. Sci.,* 16, 135, 1991.
37. **Goff, S. A. and Goldberg, A. L.,** Production of abnormal proteins in *E. coli* stimulates transcription of *lon* and other heat shock genes, *Cell,* 41, 587, 1985.
38. **Parsell, D. A. and Sauer, R. T.,** Induction of a heat shock-like response by unfolded protein in *Escherichia coli:* dependence on protein level not protein degradation, *Genes Dev.,* 3, 1226, 1989.
39. **Mifflin, L. C. and Cohen, R. E.,** Characterization of denatured protein inducers of the HSR in Xenopus laevis oocytes, *J. Biochem. Chem.,* 269, 15710, 1994.

40. **Baler, R., Welch, W. J., and Voellmy, R.,** Heat shock gene regulation by nascent polypeptides and denatured proteins: hsp70 as a potential autoregulatory factor, *J. Cell. Biol.,* 117, 1151, 1992.

41. **Abravaya, K., Myers, M. P., Murphy, S. P., and Morimoto, R. I.,** The human heat shock protein hsp70 interacts with HSR, the transcription factor that regulates heat shock gene expression, *Genes Dev.,* 6, 1153, 1992.

42. **Sorger, P. K.,** Yeast heat shock factor contains separable transient and sustained response transcriptional activators, *Cell,* 62, 793, 1990.

43. **Knowlton, A. A.,** HSPs, stress and the heart, *Ann. N.Y. Acad. Sci.,* 723, 128, 1993.

44. **Ting, L.-P., Tu, C.-L., and Chou, C.-K.,** Insulin-induced expression of human heat-shock protein gene hsp70, *J. Biol. Chem.,* 264, 3404, 1989.

45. **Wu, B. J. and Morimoto, R. I.,** Transcription of the human hsp70 gene is induced by serum stimulation, *Proc. Natl. Acad. Sci. U.S.A.,* 82, 6070, 1985.

46. **Sistonen, L., Sarge, K. D., Phillips, B., Abravaya, K., and Morimoto, R. I.,** Activation of heat shock gene factor 2 during hemin-induced differentiation of human erythroleukemia cells, *Mol. Cell. Biol.,* 12, 4104, 1993.

47. **Donnelly, T. J., Seivers, R. E., Vissern, F. L. J., Welch, W. J., and Wolfe, C. L.,** Heat shock protein induction in rat hearts: a role for improved myocardial salvage after ischemia and reperfusion?, *Circulation,* 85, 769, 1992.

48. **Yellon, D. M., Pasini, E., Cargnoni, A., Marber, M. S., Latchman, D. S., and Ferrari, R.,** The protective role of heat stress in the ischaemic and reperfused rabbit myocardium, *J. Mol. Cell Cardiol.,* 24, 895, 1992.

49. **Marber, M. S., Latchman, D. S., Walker, J. M., and Yellon, D. M.,** Cardiac stress protein elevation 24 hours after brief ischemia or heat stress is associated with resistance to myocardial infarction, *Circulation,* 88, 1264, 1993.

50. **Liu, X., Engelman, R. M., Moraru, I. I., Rousou, J. A., Flack, J. E., Deaton, D. W., Maulik, N., and Das, D. K.,** Heat shock: a new approach for myocardial preservation in cardiac surgery, *Circulation,* 86(Suppl. II), 358, 1992.

51. **Su, C.-Y., Dillmann, W. H., Woods, W. T., and Owen, O. E.,** Heat shock-induced oxidative tolerance in muscle cells, *Circulation,* 86, (Suppl. I), 33, 1992.

52. **Su, C.-Y., Lai, C.-C., Dillmann, W. H., Chang, C., and Owen, O. E.,** Modulation of the cellular antioxidant defense by heat shock or ethanol in rat heart H9c2 myocytes, *Am. J. Physiol.,* 1995, submitted.

53. **Su, C.-Y., Ishine, T., Lee, T. J.-F., and Lai, C.-C.,** Heat shock prevent the damages cause by oxidized low density lipoprotein in the porcine aortic endothelial cells (abstract), *FASEB J.,* 9, A895, 1995.

54. **Brinnel, H., Cabanac., M., and Hales, J. R. S.,** Critical upper limits of body temperature, tissue thermosensitivity and selective brain cooling in hyperthermia, in *Heat Stress, Physical Exertion and Environment,* Hales, J. R. S. and Richardson, D. A. B., Eds., Elsevier, Amsterdam, 1987, 209.

55. **Goldschlager, N., Cohn, K., and Goldschlager, A.,** Exercise-related ventricular arrhythmias, *Mod. Con. Cardiovasc. Dis.,* 48, 67, 1979.

56. **Koplan, J. P.,** Cardiovascular deaths while running, *JAMA,* 242, 2578, 1979.

57. **Sprung, C. L.,** Heat stroke, modern approach to an ancient disease, *Chest,* 77, 461, 1980.

58. **Sutton, J. R.,** Heat stroke from running, *JAMA,* 243, 1896, 1980.

59. **Davis, K. J. A, Quintanilha, A. T., Brooks, G. A., and Packer, L.,** Free radicals and tissue damage produced by exercise, *Biochem. Biophys. Res. Commun.,* 107, 1198, 1982.

60. **Quintanilha, A. T. and Packer, L.,** Vitamin E, physical exercise, and tissue oxidative damage, in *Biology of Vitamin E,* Ciba Foundation Symposium 101, Pitman Books, London, 1983, 56.

61. **Brooks, G. A., Hittleman, K. J., Faulkner, J. A., and Beyer, R. E.,** Tissue temperature and whole-animal oxygen consumption after exercise, *Am. J. Physiol.,* 221, 427, 1971.

62. **Rodenhiser, D. I., Jung, J. H., and Atkinson, B. G.,** The synergistic effect of hyperthermia and ethanol of changing gene expression of mouse lymphocytes, *Can. J. Cytol.,* 28, 1115, 1986.

63. **Hahn, G. M., Shiu, E. C., and Auger, E. A.,** Mammalian stress proteins HSP70 and HSP28 coinduced by nicotine and either ethanol or heat, *Mol. Cell Biol.,* 11, 6034, 1991.

64. **Morimoto, R.I., Tissieres, A., and Georgopoulos C.,** *The Biology of Heat Shock Proteins and Molecular Chaperones,* Cold Spring Harbor Laboratory Press, Cold Spring Harbor, New York, 1994.

Chapter 7

ROLE OF ADENOSINE IN EXERCISE

Satu M. Somani and Kazim Husain

CONTENTS

1. INTRODUCTION

Exercise evokes a number of physiological and pharmacological changes in various organs of the body especially in the muscular, cardiovascular, and cerebrovascular systems; and adenosine plays an important role in the regulation of these responses. During the last few decades, most reviews focused upon the changes in cellular energy, carbohydrates,[1] lipids,[2] and protein metabolism[3] during exercise. Recent reviews have emphasized numerous advances in the control of cellular and molecular events associated with exercise adaptations in the muscles.[4-6] Several metabolites have been proposed to influence muscular, cardiovascular, and cerebrovascular tones during exercise: adenosine,[7] lactate and pyruvate;[8,9] nitric oxide,[10] acetate,[11] and ammonia.[12] Adenosine, an endogenous purine nucleoside, is a metabolic product of adenosine triphosphate (ATP) and is also considered a regulator of biological functions. It occurs naturally in all organs of the body and has been extensively studied in skeletal muscle, heart, and brain systems. Increased concentrations of adenosine appear in the extracellular space when the delivery of oxygen is reduced (hypoxia) or when the utilization of ATP in tissues is raised (exercise).

0-8493-8540-1/96/$0.00+$.50
© 1996 by CRC Press, Inc.

The actions of adenosine are mediated by specific receptors that reside in the plasma membrane of every cell. The most important role of adenosine is the control of coronary,[13] cerebral,[14] and skeletal muscle[15] blood flow. It is a potent vasodilator in most of the cerebral and peripheral vascular beds, but seems to be a vasoconstrictor in the renal artery.[16,17] Adenosine acts as a neuromodulator and participates in numerous local regulatory mechanisms in the nervous system.[18] The most recent role of adenosine (as an endogenous modulator of antioxidant enzymes via A_3 receptors) provided a strong basis for writing this chapter. The chapter will focus on current knowledge of the physiological and pharmacological roles of endogenously released adenosine during exercise, particularly in the heart, skeletal muscle, and brain; it will focus on the role of adenosine in activation of antioxidant enzymes as well as interaction of adenosine receptors with agonists or antagonists during exercise.

2. EXERCISE AND METABOLISM OF ADENOSINE

Metabolism of adenosine has been well illustrated in several reviews.[7,19] As shown in Figure 1, adenosine is formed intracellularly or extracellularly by dephosphorylation of adenosine monophosphate (AMP) via the ATP pathway catalyzed by the enzyme 5'-nucleotidase. In addition to the ATP pathway, adenosine can also be formed intracellularly by the degradation of S-adenosyl homocysteine (SAH), and catalyzed by the enzyme SAH hydrolase pathway (Figure 1). The relative contribution of each metabolic pathway for the formation of adenosine varies according to the experimental conditions.[20] Extracellular cyclic AMP can also lead to the formation of adenosine.[21,22] In human blood, the uptake of adenosine is such that the half-life is under 10 sec.[23,24] Adenosine is removed through cellular uptake mechanisms in the tissues by either simple or facilitated diffusion, via a nucleoside transport system in the heart and by a Na-dependent active transport system in the brain. Adenosine is also degraded (deaminated) by the adenosine deaminase enzyme to inosine, which is mostly inactive; or adenosine is phosphorylated by adenosine kinase to AMP.[25,26] Inosine is further metabolized to hypoxanthine by enzyme nucleoside phosphorylase to hypoxanthine. Hypoxanthine is metabolized to xanthine which is further metabolized to uric acid by enzyme xanthine oxidase. During metabolic conversion of hypoxanthine to xanthine, by the enzyme xanthine oxidase, free radicals are generated, possibly resulting in the generation of free radicals during exercise, which has not received much attention. Free radical generation and lipid peroxidation during exercise has been reported in the heart tissue.[27,28] Uric acid, the final metabolic product of adenosine, is a good antioxidant and inhibits lipid peroxidation.[29] However, this pathway needs to be experimentally proved.

3. RELEASE OF ADENOSINE DURING EXERCISE

Exercise increases the intake of oxygen in various organs/tissues of the body, especially the skeletal muscles, heart, and brain with increased breakdown of

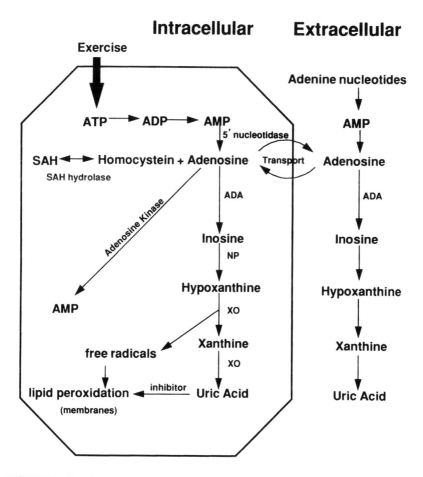

FIGURE 1. Exercise and metabolism of adenosine. ATP = adenosine triphosphate; ADP = adenosine diphosphate; AMP = adenosine monophosphate; SAH = S-adenocyl homocystein; ADA = adenosine deaminase; NP = nucleostide phosphorylase; XO = xanthine oxidase. (Modified from Lerman, B. B. and Belardinelli, L., *Circulation,* 83, 1499, 1991. With permission.)

ATP. Newby[30] reported that the production and release of adenosine are closely linked to energy balance. "If this balance is disturbed because of increased tissue work, as in the case of exercise, or because of a decrease in blood or oxygen supply, such as ischemia/hypoxia, then adenosine is released." Physiological stimuli that lower energy charge, such as exercise, hypoxia, and ischemia, greatly increase adenosine release.[31,32] The increased tissue work (during exercise) or decreased blood or oxygen supply (ischemia and hypoxia) triggers the release of adenosine and causes tissue to restore the energy balance by reducing oxygen demand and/or increasing oxygen availability (Figure 2). In the heart, adenosine can be released from hypoxic or ischemic myocardium.[21,33] Treadmill exercise increased adenosine about threefold in cardiac muscle.[34] The mechanisms responsible for the release of adenosine in the nervous tissue have also been

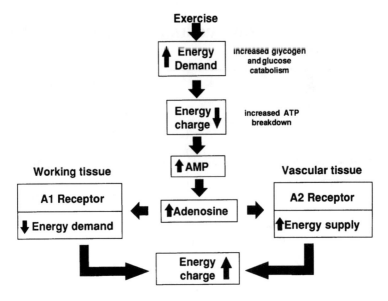

FIGURE 2. Role of adenosine in energy supply/demand during exercise. (Modified from Bruns, R. F., *Ann. N.Y. Acad. Sci.,* 603, 221, 1990. With permission.)

studied.[35,36] These studies have shown that potassium-induced depolarization and electrical stimulation enhanced the release of adenosine in both calcium-dependent and independent modes. The level of brain adenosine is elevated following increased energy consumption, such as during a seizure.[22] Exercise increases the energy consumption that could increase the release of adenosine in the brain; this hypothesis has not been experimentally proved.

4. ADENOSINE RECEPTORS: THEIR FUNCTION AND ROLE DURING EXERCISE

The responses to adenosine are mediated in cerebral and peripheral tissues by two major classes of receptors named A_1 and A_2.[37,38] The two receptor subtypes were originally defined in terms of their effects on adenylate cyclase and cyclic AMP levels, with A_1 receptors lowering cyclic AMP and A_2 receptors elevating cyclic AMP.[39,40] The interaction between adenosine receptors and adenylate cyclase has been known to be mediated by a nucleotide binding protein (G-protein).[41] Currently, these receptors are classified based on their agonist pharmacology.[42] In this respect, A_1 and A_2 nomenclature is based on ligand binding potency. The A_1 receptors are best characterized by 2-chloro-N^6-cyclopentyl adenosine (CCPA) binding whereas the A_2 receptors can be selectively labeled by 2[p-(2-carboxyethyl) phenetyl amino 5′-N-ethyl carboxamidoadenosine (CGS 21680).[38,41] Further subclasses have been proposed, including A_{1a}/A_{1b} and A_{2a}/A_{2b} to account for high and low affinity in binding studies.[36,43] A_1 and A_2 receptors appear to have distinct roles in protect-

TABLE 1
Agonists and Antagonists of Adenosine Receptors

Receptor	Agonists	Antagonists
A_1	CCPA = 2-chloro-N-cyclopentyl adenosine	CPT = 8-cyclopentyl theophylline
	CHA = N-cyclohexyl adenosine	CPX = 8-cyclopentyl-1,3-dipropyl xanthine
	PIA = N-phenylisopropyl adenosine	XAC = xanthine amine congener
	2-CADO = 2-chloroadenosine	PACPX = 1,3-dipropyl-8-(2-amino 4-chloro) phenyl xanthine
	NECA = 5-N-ethyl-carboxamido adenosine	Theophylline
	CV-1808 = 2-phenyl amino-adenosine	Caffeine
A_2	CGS21680 = 2 [p-(2-carboxyethyl) phenethyl amino]-5-N-ethyl carboxamido adenosine	CGS15943 = 9-chloro-2-(2-furyl) [1,2,4] triazolo [1,5-c] quinazolin-5-amine
	NECA = 5-N-ethyl-carboxamide adenosine	XAC = xanthine amine congener xanthine sulfonamide congener
	2-CADO = 2-chloroadenosine	PD115, 199 = 1,3-dipropyl-8-phenyl
	CV-1808 = 2-phenyl amino adenosine	CSC = 8-(3-chlorostynyl) caffeine
	PIA = N-phenyl isopropyl adenosine	8-PT = 8-phenyltheophylline
	CPA = cyclopentyl adenosine	Theophylline
A_3	APNEA = N^6-2-(4-amino phenyl) ethyladenosine	BW-A 522 = 3-(3-iodo-4-amino benzyl)-8-(4-oxyacetate)-1-propyl xanthine
	CHA = N-cyclohexyl adenosine	IBMX = 3-isobutyl-1-methyl xanthine
	PIA = N-phenyl isopropyl adenosine	Theophylline
	NECA = 5-N-ethyl carboxamido adenosine	
	2-CADO = 2-chloroadenosine	

ing against consequences of inadequate tissue oxygenation.[44] A_1 receptor responses bring about a decrease in oxygen demand, whereas A_2 receptor responses usually involve an increase in oxygen supply. A third subclass of adenosine receptor (A_3), present in the heart and nerve endings, has been proposed to mediate the electrophysiological effects of adenosine involving calcium fluxes, not coupled to adenylate cyclase but linked to calcium channels via G-protein.[45] However, as per the recent nomenclature and classification, true A_3 receptors present in mast cells and also in testes, mediate inhibition of adenylate cyclase and may couple with G_i-protein.[46,47] Our recent work shows that the adenosine released during exercise may enhance antioxidant enzyme activities through activation of A_3 receptors, thereby providing protection to the cell against oxidative injury caused by exercise.

An intracellular adenosine recognition site (P site) modulating adenylate cyclase has also been identified.[48] All receptor subtypes, except P site, can be blocked by methylxanthine, such as theophylline and caffeine. The agonists and antagonists of adenosine receptors are presented in Table 1. All known adenosine agonists are purine nucleosides,[49] whereas antagonists, with few exceptions, are imidazole [3,4d]-pyrimidines.[50] Adenosine receptor agonists may be effective as antihypertensive agents,[51] in the treatment of opiate

TABLE 2
Pharmacological Role of Adenosine

System of the Body	Effects
Cardiovascular system	Decreases heart rate
	Decreases heart force
	Coronary vasodilation
	Decreases blood pressure
	Inhibits platelet aggregation
	Inhibits lymphocyte proliferation
	Stimulates RBC production
	Stimulates angiogenesis
	Increases insulin-mediated glucose uptake
Central nervous system	Sedation
	Decreases locomotor activity
	Inhibits neurotransmitter release
	Decreases body temperature
	Increases sleep duration
	Induces hypnotic effects
	Anticonvulsant
	Analgesic
	Decreases neuronal firing
Renal system	Vasoconstrictor
	Decreases renin release
	Decreases glomerular filtration rate
Respiratory system	Stimulates respiration (peripheral)
	Decreases breathing (CNS)
	Induces bronchoconstriction
Metabolic system	Enhances glucose uptake into fat cells
	Inhibits lypolysis
	Stimulates hepatic and pancreatic glycogenolysis
Other systems	Relaxes gut smooth muscle
	Decreases neutrophil activation
	Anti-ischemic
	Inhibits superoxide anion production in granulocytes

withdrawal,[52] as modulators of immune competence[53] and renin release,[54] as antipsychotics,[55] and as hypnotics.[56] Adenosine receptor antagonists may be useful as central stimulants,[18] nootropics,[57] cardiotonics,[58] antistress agents,[59] antiasthmatics,[60] and in the treatment of respiratory disorders.[61]

5. PHYSIOLOGICAL AND PHARMACOLOGICAL EFFECTS OF ADENOSINE IN EXERCISE

The general pharmacological role of adenosine is summarized in Table 2. This section of the chapter describes the specific role of adenosine during exercise particularly in the heart, brain, and skeletal muscles.

5.1. HEART

Adenosine is an important regulator in cardiovascular physiology. It acts on sinoatrial and atrioventricular nodes causing bradycardia and heart block,[19] and displays a negative atrial contractility and ventricular automaticity[62] which are mediated by A_1 receptors. Adenosine is a potent vasodilator in the cardiovascular bed, as it increases coronary blood flow and reduces peripheral vascular resistance. These actions are mediated by A_2 receptors.[51,63] Adenosine infusion can decrease mean arterial pressure without affecting heart rate.[64] Adenosine reduces blood pressure through a combination of peripheral vasodilation and slowing of the heart rate, indicating involvement of both A_1 and A_2 receptors. The increased vasodilation of coronary arteries, coronary blood flow, myocardial oxygen supply and consumption, and cardiac work due to exercise may be compensated by adenosine-induced depression of cardiac pacemakers and atrioventricular node conduction, resulting in the reduction of cardiac work and decreased oxygen demand. Dipyridamole, an adenosine re-uptake inhibitor, increases the extracellular levels of adenosine[65] and produces coronary blood flow effects which approximate exercise.[66] Dipyridamole is also used in thallium 201 perfusion scintigraphy in the detection of coronary artery disease in patients unable to exercise.[67,68] The intravenous infusion of adenosine provoked angina-like chest pain in humans which was decreased by aminophylline, an antagonist of adenosine receptors.[69] In another study, Sylven et al.[70] have shown that intravascular doses of adenosine in humans caused pain and discomfort that preceded maximal blood flow. These studies revealed that adenosine acts as the source of pain or discomfort during acute exhaustive exercise, which is known to increase blood flow.[69,70]

5.2. BRAIN

Adenosine plays an important role in the regulation of cerebral blood flow when applied topically; it dilates blood vessels and increases cerebral blood flow. This action is mediated through A_2 receptors.[71] Cerebral blood flow has been shown to be influenced by adenosine during acute exercise.[14,72] Adenosine decreases spontaneous motor activity and produces a sedative effect through activation of A_2 receptors.[73] Adenosine is a potent modulator of neurotransmitter release, inhibiting the release of aspartate, glutamate, norepinephrine, GABA, dopamine, serotonin, and acetylcholine.[35,71] Adenosine has analgesic and anticonvulsant properties, increases sleep duration, and elicits a hypnotic state in mammals.[71,74] Adenosine modulates cyclic AMP formation, phosphatidyl inositol turnover, and calcium mobilization, in addition to regulating the potassium channel.[38,41]

5.3. MUSCLE AND OTHER TISSUES

A significant increase in tissue adenosine content in skeletal muscle after acute exercise has been demonstrated.[75,76] The effects of adenosine on skeletal muscle vasodilation are found to be dose-dependent, while isometric exercise increases the plasma adenosine concentration.[70] Increased adenosine levels also potentiate insulin-stimulated myocardial glucose uptake.[77] This process facilitates the myocardium to use more glucose for the generation of ATP at a faster rate as a result of exhaustive exercise. Adenosine has been reported to enhance the breakdown of glycogen in the perfused liver of rat, thereby augmenting glucose formation.[78] This allows maintenance of the energy supply to the tissue during exhaustive exercise. Adenosine is a vasoconstrictor in the kidney and has biphasic effects on renin release.[16,54] It stimulates respiration in man when given intravenously[79] by increasing carotid-body chemoceptor discharge.[80] Further studies have demonstrated that the increase in respiration is due to an increase in tidal volume, with the inspiratory flow rate increased and expiratory duration decreased during adenosine infusion.[81] Adenosine can cause respiratory depression via a central mechanism.[61] In addition, it has been demonstrated that adenosine increases heart rate, blood pressure, and plasma catecholamines via activation of the sympathoadrenal response.[82] Recently, Costa and Biaggioni[83] demonstrated that isometric exercise increases sympathetic nerve activity and blood pressure in humans that was mediated by adenosine.

The elevated levels of adenosine after each day of exercise may continue to exert influence on the body's adaptation to exercise, especially in skeletal muscles and the heart. Therefore, the role of adenosine in adaptive mechanisms has been implicated in the field of exercise training. Adenosine has been reported to enhance the process of angiogenesis (formation of new blood vessels) in normal as well as hypoxic conditions[84] which were abolished by antagonists of adenosine. Chronic dosing of dipyridamole, an adenosine re-uptake inhibitor, resulted in angiogenesis in the heart and skeletal muscle, further indicating the role of adenosine in angiogenesis.[85,86] These studies revealed that exercise training may provide a beneficial effect by augmenting the process of angiogenesis through enhanced adenosine production.

Adenosine is also involved in regulating production of erythropoietin. Erythropoietin is a hormone produced by the kidney that stimulates erythropoiesis (red blood cell production) in bone marrow. Elevated levels of adenosine enhance the production of erythropoietin in mice.[87,88] The adenosine antagonist, theophylline, has been shown to block adenosine-induced increases in erythropoietin production and to abolish erythropoietin production in normal individuals and in patients with erythrocytosis after renal transplants.[89] Thus, exercise training may be beneficial as it may increase the production of erythropoietin induced by adenosine.

6. ENDOGENOUS ACTIVATION OF ANTIOXIDANT ENZYMES BY ADENOSINE

We have already mentioned that exercise plays an important role in the breakdown of ATP and finally to adenosine, thereby increasing levels of adenosine in various tissues. Adenosine plays a cytoprotective role in ischemic reperfusion injury where free radicals and reactive oxygen species (ROS) are generated. Our laboratory had already studied exercise-generated free radicals and ascorbate radicals in heart tissue, and also the increased activity of antioxidant enzymes in the heart and brain regions. We thought that in both instances (1) free radicals are generated, (2) an increased level of adenosine occurs, and (3) increased activity of antioxidant enzyme also occurs. We hypothesized, therefore, that there might be a relationship between adenosine and antioxidant enzyme activity.

Based on this premise, we worked on the role of adenosine in the activation of antioxidant enzymes in *in vitro* systems using cell lines in the lab of one of our colleagues (Dr. Ramkumar) who has an immense interest in adenosine work. The potential harm of oxygen comes from its ability to be converted to ROS such as superoxide anion ($\bar{O}_2$), hydrogen peroxide (H_2O_2), singlet oxygen ($^1O_2$), hydroxyl radical ($\dot{O}H\cdot$), and lipid hydroperoxides (ROOH). A quantitative difference between the overproduction of ROS and the lack of coping mechanisms by the antioxidant system can cause many pathologic conditions, such as Parkinson's disease, ischemia reperfusion injury, cataract formation, aging process, arthritis, asthma, carcinogenesis, Down's syndrome, Alzheimer's disease, and other ailments. Detoxification of ROS is part of the antioxidant defense system which includes the following antioxidant enzymes: superoxide dismutase (SOD), catalase (CAT), glutathione peroxidase (GSH-Px); and an ancillary enzyme, glutathione reductase (GR). Numerous studies have demonstrated that the release of free radicals, and an incomplete response by an antioxidant system, may be a critical factor in the ischemic damage in myocardial infarction. Antioxidant enzymes are decreased in the elderly, a possible culprit for some of the increased ischemic injury or other diseases in older subjects. Adenosine serves a homeostatic and cytoprotective role in the body. During ischemia, the concentration of the nucleoside can increase almost eightfold, thereby playing a role of cytoprotection. Intracoronary infusion of adenosine during reperfusion, following a 90-min occlusion of the left anterior descending coronary artery, led to a significant decrease in infarct size.[90] This protection was mimicked by adenosine receptor agonists[91] and abolished by antagonists.[92] It seemed that adenosine played a beneficial role in reducing free radical formation during ischemia and in maintaining the integrity of lipid membranes by reducing lipid peroxidation.[93]

Recently, we have shown that adenosine mediates cytoprotection by activating the antioxidant enzyme activity in mast cells, cardiac myocyte, and endothelial cells via the activation of the A_3 adenosine receptor.[94] This receptor is predominantly present in mast cells and rat leukocytes.[46] The activation of antioxidant enzyme activities and GR, by adenosine agonist R-phenyl isopropyl adenosine (R-PIA), is shown in Figure 3. In these experiments, the effects of adenosine agonist on the antioxidant enzymes and GR activities were studied by eliminating the endogenously released adenosine with adenosine deaminase. The cells were treated with or without adenosine

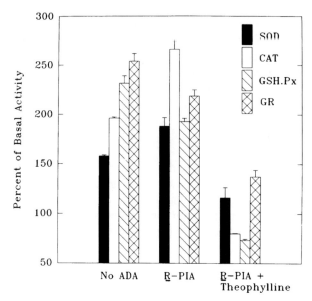

FIGURE 3.   Activation of the activities of antioxidant enzymes and glutathione reductase by adenosine agonist in RBL-2H3 cells. Values are mean ± SEM (n = 5). Significant (* p <0.05) increase in enzyme activity in the absence of adenosine deaminase group and in the presence of adenosine agonist R-phenyl isopropyl adenosine (R-PIA) group, compared to basal activity (100%) obtained in the presence of adenosine deaminase. (Adapted from Maggirwar, S. B., Dhanraj, D. N., Somani, S. M., and Ramkumar, V., *Biochem. Biophys. Res. Commun.,* 201, 508, 1994. With permission.)

deaminase (1 unit/ml) for 3 h. The antioxidant enzymes (SOD, CAT, GSH-Px) and GR activities were significantly decreased in RBL-2H3 cells with the adenosine deaminase treatment and the loss of adenosine. The untreated cells had much higher levels of antioxidant enzymes and GR activities, indicating that the cells normally secrete enough adenosine to maintain these enzymes in an activated state (Figure 3). In order to determine the role of the nonhydrolyzable adenosine agonist (R-PIA) in activation of antioxidant enzymes, the cells were pretreated with adenosine deaminase. The addition of R-PIA (10 μ*M)* increased the activity of these enzymes by two- to threefold, similar to levels obtained in the absence of adenosine deaminase (Figure 3). This activation was blocked by theophylline, an antagonist of the A_3 adenosine receptor in these cells (Figure 3). These results indicated that A_3 receptors were involved in the activation of antioxidant enzymes. R-PIA also activated antioxidant enzyme activity in other cell types such as human and bovine endothelial cells, rat myocytes, DDT MF-2 smooth muscle cells, and P815 mastocytoma cells, as shown in Table 2.[94] CAT and GR activities showed maximum increase, whereas SOD and GSH-Px showed moderate increases. It seems that adenosine and its agonist could act as an endogenous activator of antioxidant enzyme activity.

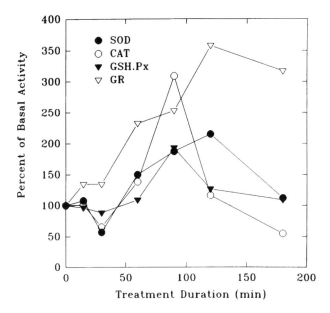

FIGURE 4. Time course of activation of antioxidant enzymes and glutathione reductase activities in RBL-2H3 cells. The values are plotted as a percent of leasal activity. (Adapted from Maggirwar, S. B., Dhanraj, D. N., Somani, S. M., and Ramkumar, V., *Biochem. Biophys. Res. Commun.*, 201, 508, 1994. With permission.)

The time course activation of enzymes and GR activities in RBL-2H3 cells showed the highest increase in enzyme activity within a 90 to 120 min period following the addition of 10 μM of R-PIA as shown in Figure 4. CAT and GSH-Px activities showed the highest increase within 90 min, whereas, SOD and GR activities increased to their highest level by 120 min. SOD, CAT, and GSH-Px returned to basal activity in 3 h, while GR remained elevated throughout this period. The higher activities of these enzymes were related to the concentration of the agonist. Pertussis toxin (1 μg/ml for 6 h), added to the RBL-2H3 cells, reduced the activation response to an agonist, indicating that activation is mediated via the G_i protein coupled with the A_3 adenosine receptors. Malondialdehyde is a by-product of lipid peroxidation; therefore, malondialdehyde was determined in RBL-2H$_3$ cells following different periods of treatment with agonist R-PIA to show the role of A_3 receptors in the inhibition of lipid peroxidation. Depletion of adenosine, by the addition of adenosine deaminase, increased the level of malondialdehyde over that of the no-adenosine-deaminase group, indicating the role of adenosine in mediating cytoprotection (Table 3). The addition of agonist R-PIA (10 μM) to these adenosine deaminase-treated cells decreased the levels of malondialdehyde to values that were obtained in the absence of adenosine. But this beneficial effect of agonist R-PIA was blocked by theophylline and pertussis toxin. This study suggests that the activation of antioxidant enzymes and glutathione reductase

TABLE 3

Regulation of Antioxidant Enzyme Activity by R-PIA in Different Cells

Percent of Basal Activity[a] (mean ± S.E.M.)

	SOD	CAT	GSH-Px	GR
Human endothelial cells	146 ± 3	175 ± 4	152 ± 1	137 ± 2
Bovine endothelial cells	132 ± 5	133 ± 1	131 ± 3	289 ± 9
DDT$_1$MF-2 cells	106 ± 2	237 ± 18	147 ± 1	127 ± 2
Rat cardiac myocytes	128 ± 2	257 ± 13	134 ± 1	279 ± 7
P815 Mastocytoma cells	129 ± 1	234 ± 10	139 ± 1	186 ± 4

[a]   Basal activity is defined as enzyme activity obtained in cells treated with adenosine deaminase
     alone.

Adapted from Maggirwar, S. B., Dhanraj, D. N., Somani, S. M., and Ramkumar, V., *Biochem.
Biophys. Res. Commun.*, 201, 508, 1994. With permission.

activity is mediated via the adenosine receptor G_i protein complex. It is quite
possible that the activation of antioxidant enzymes and GR with exercise
occurred through a similar pathway.[6] Therefore, the studies were performed by
exercising and administering the rat with agonist (RPLA) and antagonist
(theophylline) of adenosine A_3 receptor.

7. ADENOSINE AND ANTIOXIDANT ENZYMES IN EXERCISE

The above study has been the first to attempt to show that native antioxidant
enzymes are activated via A_3 adenosine cell surface receptors. Antioxidant
enzymes are also activated by single acute exercise and by exercise training.[28,95] The following questions then arise: are cell surface receptors involved
in the activation of antioxidant enzymes during exercise? Is the specific adenosine receptor activated by exercise which, in turn, activates antioxidant
enzymes and GR? To answer these questions, we extended the experiments to
study the effect of the administration of adenosine receptor agonist R-PIA and
antagonist (theophylline) on antioxidant enzymes, GR, and lipid peroxidation
in the heart of the rat. We also studied whether these enzyme activities and lipid
peroxidation are altered due to a combination of acute exercise and antagonist
or agonist. Our preliminary study shows that the acute exercise (100% VO_2
max) enhanced antioxidant enzyme activities in the rat heart (Table 4). This
increase in enzyme activity did not occur when theophylline was administered
to rats prior to exercise, indicating that theophylline blocked the activation of
antioxidant enzymes and GR, and increased the lipid peroxidation.

On the other hand, the administration of an agonist of A_3 adenosine receptor
R-PIA activated antioxidant enzyme activity similar to the administration of
acute exercise, indicating that the adenosine receptor is possibly involved in the

TABLE 4
Effect of A_3AR Activation on Lipid Peroxidation in RBL-2H3 Cells

Drug Treatment	Malondialdehyde (nmoles/mg protein)
ADA	2.34 ± 0.21
No ADA	1.25 ± 0.27[a]
ADA + R-PIA	1.52 ± 0.30[a]
ADA + R-PIA + theophylline	2.24 ± 0.12
Pertussis toxin	2.99 ± 0.06[a]
Pertussis toxin + R-PIA	3.03 ± 0.24[a]

[a] Statistically significant change (p <0.05) from values obtained with adenosine deaminase (ADA).

Adapted from Maggirwar, S. B., Dhanraj, D. N., Somani, S. M., and Ramkumar, V., *Biochem. Biophys. Res. Commun.,* 201, 508, 1994. With permission.

activation of antioxidant enzymes. Lipid peroxidation measured by malondialdehyde levels also decreased, as shown in Table 5. We did not carry out the experiment on the combined effect of exercise and R-PIA. However, the concurrent administration of agonist R-phenyl isopropyl adenosine and the antagonist (theophylline) reduced the antioxidant enzyme activity; the lipid peroxidation remained high in the rat heart (Table 5). The results of these experiments suggested that acute exercise stimulated the antioxidant enzyme activities in the rat heart which was blocked by theophylline, an antagonist of adenosine receptor. R-PIA, an agonist of the A_3 adenosine receptor, increased antioxidant enzyme activities in the heart of the sedentary control rat. How-

TABLE 5
Effect of Exercise, Adenosine Agonist (R-PIA), and Antagonist Theophylline (Th) and their Combination on Antioxidant Enzyme Activities in Rat Heart

		SOD	CAT	GSH-Px	GR
I.	Sendentary control	20.66 ± 0.70	11.66 ± 0.42	165.33 ± 6.1	2.52 ± 0.16
II.	AE (100% VO₂max)	30.63 ± 0.56[a]	25.82 ± 0.89[a]	209.77 ± 7.55[a]	4.09 ± 0.22[a]
III.	R-PIA	30.65 ± 0.88[a]	21.48 ± 0.71[a]	197.03 ± 6.51[a]	3.62 ± 0.14[a]
IV.	Th + AE	23.88 ± 1.70	11.03 ± 1.29	172.35 ± 8.22	2.81 ± 0.09
V.	Th + R-PIA	23.65 ± 1.17	13.40 ± 0.61	170.43 ± 9.12	2.71 ± 0.11
VI.	Th	20.63 ± 1.19	15.89 ± 1.77	166.45 ± 3.09	2.41 ± 0.14

[a] Represents the significant values (p <0.05).

Note: Each value represents mean S.E.M. (n = 4). Enzyme activity is expressed as U/mg protein.
R-PIA = R-phenyl isopropyl adenosine, AE = acute exercise, Th = theophylline.

ever, the concurrent administration of theophylline, and R-PIA, restored anti-oxidant enzyme activities to a normal level. Furthermore, the stimulation of antioxidant enzyme activities reduced the lipid peroxidation. Based on these preliminary results, we suggest that the stimulation of antioxidant enzyme activities, due to acute exercise, is mediated via the activation of the A_3 adenosine receptor. We have previously described the model scheme for adenosine receptor-mediated activation of antioxidant enzymes based on *in vitro* studies. It is possible that those steps are also followed during exercise; adenosine is released and activates adenosine receptor, thereby activating antioxidant enzymes. The activation of antioxidant enzymes can be blocked by the adenosine receptor antagonist, theophylline, during exercise (Figure 5).

8. FUTURE PERSPECTIVES

Adenosine and its agonists and antagonists are modulators of various mechanisms regulating the body's complex physiology. The recent work on A_3 receptors, through which adenosine enhances the activities of antioxidant enzymes, has opened a door for studying the interactions of agonists and antagonists of adenosine on antioxidant enzymes during exercise. The use of more selective agonists and antagonists of A_1, A_2, and A_3 receptors will provide a better understanding of the mechanisms responsible for the activation or inhibition of antioxidant enzymes during exercise. Exercise is known to enhance the production of nitric oxide (NO) in coronary vascular tissues. It is not known whether NO synthase inhibitors or activators would have antagonistic or synergistic effects on adenosine receptor-induced responses during exercise. Both adenosine and NO are produced during exercise. Therefore, the actions and interactions of both agents, through modulatory receptors on antioxidant enzymes during exercise, would be an important study in the future.

Recent evidence indicates that the biological activity of NO is limited by the intracellular superoxide anion ($\bar{O}_2$). NO reacts with $\bar{O}_2$ to form peroxynitrite anion radical ($ONO\bar{O}$) and protonated to give rise to a strong oxidant similar to hydroxyl radical ($\cdot OH$). Thus, the balance between these two radicals may decide whether the combined release of these radicals results in physiological effects. Whether NO is a beneficial scavenger or whether it represents a system to form toxic radicals in the heart and brain is not known. It is possible that NO can interact with the steps involved in the signal transduction pathway of the A_3 adenosine receptors which activates antioxidant enzymes during exercise because both adenosine and NO are produced during exercise and have common vasodilatory and free radical scavenging responses. Moreover, it is likely that Ca^{++}-dependent enzymes, such as protein kinase C and nitric oxide synthase, may contribute to the exercise-induced oxidative stress on cardiovascular and cerebrovascular systems. The use of calcium channel blockers, nucleoside transport blockers, protein kinase C, and NO synthase inhibitors will provide a better understanding of adenosine receptor-mediated electrophysiological responses in the heart and brain during exercise.

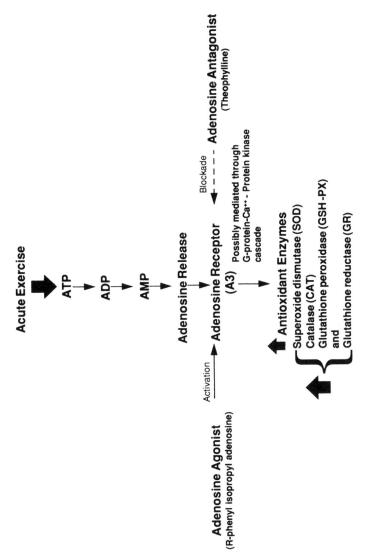

FIGURE 5. Possible scheme for activation of antioxidant enzymes during acute exercise.

184

Pharmacology In Exercise and Sports

TABLE 6
Effect of Exercise, Theophylline, and Adenosine Agonist (R-PIA) on Lipid Peroxidation (Malondialdehyde) in Rat Heart

		MDA nmoles[a]/mg Protein
I.	Sedentary control	2.69 ± 0.19
II.	AE (100% VO$_2$max)	1.58 ± 0.01
III.	R-PIA	1.53 ± 0.18
IV.	Theophylline + AE	2.53 ± 0.15
V.	Theophylline + R-PIA	2.35 ± 0.16
VI.	Theophylline	2.61 ± 0.12

[a] Mean + S.E.M.

9. SUMMARY

Recent evidence has emerged showing that adenosine is an important endogenous modulator of various physiological and pharmacological responses during exercise. Adenosine is produced in the tissues via an ATP pathway and is released during exercise due to enhanced tissue work, O_2 consumption, and ATP utilization. The vital actions of adenosine are mediated in cerebral and peripheral tissues by three major classes of receptors: A_1, A_2, and A_3 during exercise. The most important role of adenosine during exercise is the control of coronary, cerebral, and skeletal muscle blood flow by the vasodilation of blood vessels. Adenosine acts as the source of pain and discomfort during exhaustive exercise and increases sympathetic nerve activity and blood pressure in isometric exercise. Exercise training may provide beneficial effects, however, by augmenting the processes of angiogenesis and erythropoiesis which are induced by adenosine. Recent studies have demonstrated a beneficial role of adenosine in augmenting antioxidant enzyme activities and in reducing lipid peroxidation during exercise via the A_3 adenosine receptor. The interaction of selective agonists and antagonists which enhance athletic performance with the A_3 adenosine receptor-mediated effects on antioxidant enzymes would be an interesting study in the field of exercise research.

REFERENCES

1. **Stainsby, W. N. and Barclay, J. K.,** Exercise metabolism: O_2 deficit, steady level of O_2 uptake and O_2 uptake for recovery, *Med. Sci. Sports*, 2, 177, 1970.
2. **Jones, N. L., Heigenhauser, G. J. F., Kuksis, A., Matos, C. G., Sutton, J. R., and Toews, C. J.,** Fat metabolism in heavy exercise, *Clin. Sci.*, 59, 469, 1980.

3. **Butterfield, G. E.,** Whole body protein utilization in humans, *Med. Sci. Sports Exerc.,* 19, 157, 1987.

4. **Booth, F. W. and Thompson, D. B.,** Molecular and cellular adaptation of muscle in response to exercise: perspective of various models, *Physiol. Rev.,* 71, 541, 1991.

5. **Brooks, G. A., Wolfel, E. E., Groves, B. M., Bender, P. R., Butterfield, G. E., Cymerman, A., Mazzeo, R. S. Mutton, J. R., Wolfe, R. R., and Reeves, J. T.,** Muscle accounts for glucose disposal but not blood lactate appearance during exercise after acclimatization to 4,300 m, *J. Appl. Physiol.,* 72, 2435, 1992.

6. **Kiens, B., Essen-Gustavsson, B., Christensen. N. J., and Saltin, B.,** Skeletal muscle substrate utilization during submaximal exercise in man: effect of endurance training, *J. Physiol.,* 469, 459, 1993.

7. **Simpson, R. E. and Phillis, J. W.,** Adenosine in exercise adaptation, *Br. J. Sp. Med.,* 26, 54, 1992.

8. **Babu, S. R., Buckenmeyer, P., Knowlton, R. G., and Somani, S. M.,** Effect of physotigmine on plasma lactate and pyruvate in untrained/trained rats, *Pharmacol. Biochem. Behav.,* 42, 67, 1993.

9. **Buckenmeyer, P. J., Babu, S. R., Knowlton, R. G., and Somani, S. M.,** Effect of concurrent exercise and physotigmine on lactate and pyruvate in plasma, muscle and brain tissue of rats, *Pharmacol. Biochem. Behav.,* 47, 779, 1994.

10. **Sessa, W. C., Pritchard, K., Syedi, N., Wang, J., and Hintze, T. H.,** Chronic exercise in dogs increases coronary vascular nitric oxide production and endothelial cell nitric oxide synthase gene expression, *Circ. Res.,* 74, 349, 1993.

11. **Steffen, R. P., McKenzie, J. E., and Bockmann, E. L.,** Changes in dog gracilis muscle adenosine during exercise and acetate infusion, *Am. J. Physiol.,* 13, H387, 1983.

12. **Banister, E. W. and Cameron, B. J. C.,** Exercise-induced hyperammonemia: peripheral and central effects, *Int. J. Sports Med.,* 11, 129, 1990.

13. **Bacchus, A. M., Ely, S. W., Knabb, R. M., Rubio, R., and Berne, R. M.,** Adenosine and coronary blood flow in conscious dogs during normal physiological stimuli, *Am. J. Physiol.,* 243, 628, 1982.

14. **Phillis, J. W.,** Adenosine in the control of the cerebral circulation, *Cerebrovasc. Brain Metab. Rev.,* 1, 26, 1989.

15. **Proctor, K. G.,** Reduction of contraction-induced arteriolar vasodilation by adenosine deaminase or theophylline, *Am. J. Physiol.,* 247, H195, 1984.

16. **Osswald, H.,** Adenosine and renal function, in *Regulatory Function of Adenosine,* Berne, R. M., Rall, T. W., and Rubio, R., Eds., Nijhoff, Boston, 1983, 399.

17. **Born, G. V. R., Haslam, R. J., Goldman, M., and Lowe, R. D.,** Comparative effective- ness of adenosine analogues as inhibitor of blood-platelet aggregation and as vasodilators in man, *Nature,* 205, 678, 1965.

18. **Snyder, S. H.,** Adenosine as a neuromodulator, *Ann. Rev. Neurosci.,* 8, 103, 1985.

19. **Lerman, B. B. and Belardinelli, L.** Cardiac electrophysiology of adenosine, *Circulation,* 83, 1499, 1991.

20. **Lloyd, H. G. E, Deussen, A., Wupperman, H., and Schrader, J.,** The transmethylation pathways as a source for adenosine in the isolated guinea pig heart, *Biochem. J.,* 252, 489, 1988.

21. **Olsson, R. A., Snow, J. A., and Gentry, M. K.,** Adenosine metabolism in canine myocardial reactive hyperemia, *Circ. Res.,* 42, 358, 1978.

22. **Pons, F., Bruns, R. F., and Daly, J. W.,** Depolarization-evoked accumulation of cyclic AMP in brain slices: the requisite intermediate adenosine is not derived from hydrolysis of released ATP, *J. Neurochem.,* 34, 1319, 1980.

23. **Klabunde, R. E.,** Dipyridamole inhibition of adenosine metabolism in human blood, *Eur. J. Pharmacol.,* 93, 21, 1983.

24. **Ontyd, J. and Schrader, J.,** Measurement of adenosine, inosine and hypoxanthine in human plasma, *J. Chromatogr.,* 307, 404, 1984.
25. **Arch, J. R. S. and Newsholme, E. A.,** The control of the metabolism and the hormonal role of adenosine, *Essays Biochem.,* 14, 82, 1978.
26. **Wu, P. H. and Phillis, J. W.,** Uptake by central nervous tissue as a mechanism for the regulation of extracellular adenosine concentrations, *Neurochem. Int.,* 6, 613, 1984.
27. **Somani, S. M. and Arroyo, C. M.,** Endurance training generates ascorbate free radicals in rat heart, *Ind. J. Physiol. Pharmacol.,* in press, 1995.
28. **Somani, S. M., Frank, S., and Rybak, L. P.,** Responses of antioxidant system to acute and trained exercise in rat heart subcellular fractions, *Pharmacol. Biochem. Behav.,* 51, 627, 1995.
29. **Ames, B. N., Cathcart, R., Schwires, E., and Hochstein, P.,** Uric acid provides an antioxidant defense in humans against oxidant and radical-caused aging and cancer: A hypothesis, *Proc. Natl. Acad. Sci. U.S.A.,*78, 6858, 1981.
30. **Newby, A. C.,** Adenosine and the concept of "retaliatory metabolites," *Trends Biochem. Sci.,* 9, 42, 1984.
31. **Berne, R. M.,** The role of adenosine in the regulation of coronary blood flow, *Circ. Res.,* 47, 807, 1980.
32. **Sparks, H. V. and Bardenheuer, H.,** Regulation of adenosine formation by the heart, *Circ. Res.,* 58, 193, 1986.
33. **Rubio, R., Wiedmeier, V. T., and Berne, R. M.,** Relationship between coronary blood flow and adenosine production and release, *J. Mol. Cell. Cardiol.,* 6, 561, 1974.
34. **Watkinson, W. P., Foley, D. H., Rubio, R., and Berne, R. M.,** Myocardial adenosine formation with increased cardiac performance in the dog, *Am. J. Physiol.,* 236, H13, 1979.
35. **Stone, T. W., Newby, A. C., and Lloyd, H. G. E.,** *Adenosine and Adenosine Receptors,* Williams, M., Ed., Humana, Clifton, NJ, 1990, 173.
36. **Williams, M.,** *Adenosine and Adenosine Receptors,* Williams, M., Ed., Humana, Clifton, NJ, 1990, 501.
37. **Van Calker, D., Muller, M., and Hamprecht, B.,** Adenosine regulates via two different types of receptors, the accumulation of cyclic AMP in cultured brain cells, *J. Neurochem.,* 33, 999, 1979.
38. **Williams, M.,** Purine receptors in mammalian tissues: pharmacology and functional significance, *Ann. Rev. Pharmacol. Toxicol.,* 27, 315, 1987.
39. **Sattin, A. and Rall, T. W.,** The effect of adenosine and adenine nucleotides on the cyclic adenosine 3'5'-phosphate content of guinea pig cerebral cortex slices, *Mol. Pharamacol.,* 6, 13, 1970.
40. **Londos, C. D., Cooper, M. F., and Wolf, J.,** Subclasses of external adenosine receptors, *Proc. Natl. Acad. Sci. U.S.A.,* 77, 2551, 1980.
41. **Daval, J. L., Nehlig, A., and Nicolas, F.,** Physiological and pharmacological properties of adenosine: therapeutic implications, *Life Sci.,* 49, 1435, 1991.
42. **Hamprecht, B. and Van Calker, D.,** Nomenclature of adenosine receptors, *Trends Pharmacol. Sci.,* 6, 153, 1985.
43. **Gustafsson, L. E., Wiklund, C. U., Wiklund, M. P., and Stelius, L.,** *Adenosine Receptors in the Nervous System,* Ribeiro, J. A., Ed., Taylor & Francis, London, 1989, 194.
44. **Bruns, R. F.,** Adenosine receptors: roles and pharmacology, *Ann. N.Y. Acad. Sci.,* 603, 221, 1990.
45. **Ribeiro, J. A. and Sebastiao, A. M.,** Adenosine receptor and calcium: basis for proposing a third (A3) adenosine receptor, *Prog. Neurobiol.,* 26, 179, 1986.
46. **Ramkumar, V., Stiles, G. L., Beaven, M. A., and Ali, H.,** The A_3 adenosine receptor is the unique adenosine receptor which facilitates release of allergic mediators in mast cells, *J. Biol. Chem.,* 268, 16887, 1993.

47. **Fredholm, B. B., Abbracchio, M. P., Burnstock, G., Daly, J. W., Marden, T. K., Jacobson, K. A., Leff, P., and Williams, M.,** VI. Nomenclature and classification of purinoceptors, *Pharmacol. Rev.,* 46, 143, 1974.

48. **Haslam, R. J., Davidson, M. M. L., and Desjardins, T. V.,** Inhibition of adenylate cyclase by adenosine analogues in preparations of broken and intact human platelets. Evidence for the unidirectional control of platelet function by cyclic AMP, *Biochem. J.,* 176, 83, 1978.

49. **Daly, J. W.,** Adenosine receptors: target sites for drugs, *J. Med. Chem.,* 25, 197, 1982.

50. **Daly, J. W., Padgett, W., Shamin, M. T., Butts-Lamb, P., and Waters, J.,** 1,3-Dialkyl-8-(p- sulfophenyl) xanthines: potent water-soluble antagonists for A_1 and A_2 adenosine receptors, *J. Med. Chem.,* 28, 487, 1985.

51. **Evans, D. B., Schenden, J. A., and Bristol, J. A.,** Adenosine receptors mediating cardiac depression, *Life Sci.,* 30, 2425, 1982.

52. **Collier, H. O. J., Cuthbert, N. J., and Francis, D. L.,** Character and meaning of quasi-morphine withdrawal phenomena elicited by methyl-xanthines, *Fed. Proc.,* 40, 1513, 1981.

53. **Giblett, E. R.,** ADA and PNP deficiencies: How it all began, *Ann. N.Y. Acad. Sci.,* 45, 1, 1985.

54. **Itoh, S., Carretero, O. A., and Murray, R. D.,** Possible role of adenosine in the madula densa mechanism of renin release in rabbits, *J. Clin. Invest.,* 76, 1412, 1985.

55. **Heffner, T. G., Downs, D. A., Bristol, J. A., Bruns, R. F., et al.,** Antipsychotic-like effects of adenosine receptor agonists, *Pharmacologist,* 27, 293, 1985.

56. **Radulavacki, M., Virus, R. M., Djuricic-Nedelson, M., and Green, R. D.,** Adenosine analogs and sleep in rats, *J. Pharmacol. Exp. Ther.,* 228, 268, 1984.

57. **Hindmarch, I. and Subhan, Z.,** A preliminary investigation of "Albert 285" HWA 285 on psychomotor performance, mood and memory, *Drug Dev. Res.,* 5, 379, 1985.

58. **Lucchesi, B. R. and Patterson, E. S.,** Antiarrhythmic drugs, in *Cardiovascular Pharmacology,* Antonaccio, M., Ed., Raven, New York, 1984, 329.

59. **Geiger, J. D. and Glavin, G. B.,** Adenosine receptor activation in brain reduces stress-induced ulcer formation, *Eur. J. Pharmacol.,* 115, 185, 1985.

60. **Church, M. K. and Holgate, S. T.,** Adenosine and asthma, *Trends Pharmacol. Sci.,* 7, 49, 1986.

61. **Wessburg, P., Hedner, J., Hedner, T., Persson, B., and Jonason, J.,** Adenosine mechanisms in the regulation of breathing in the rat, *Eur. J. Pharmacol.,* 106, 59, 1985.

62. **Bellardinelli, L., West, A., Crampton, R., and Berne, R. M.,** Chronotropic and dromotropic effects of adenosine, in *Regulatory Function of Adenosine,* Berne, R. M., Rall, T. W., and Rubio, R., Eds., Nijhoff, Boston, 19, 377, 1983.

63. **Leung, E., Johnston, C. I., and Woodcock, E. A.,** An investigation of the receptors involved in the coronary vasodilatory effect of adenosine analogues, *Clin. Exp. Pharmacol. Physiol.,* 12, 515, 1985.

64. **Collis, M. G., Keddie, J. R., and Pettinger, S. J.,** 2-Chloroadenosine lowers blood pressure in the conscious dog without reflex tachycardia, *Br. J. Pharmacol.,* 80, 385, 1983.

65. **German, D. C., Kredich, N. M., and Bjornsson, T. D.,** Oral dipyridamole increases plasma adenosine levels in human beings, *Clin. Pharmacol. Ther.,* 45, 80, 1989.

66. **Brown, B. G., Josephson, M. A., Peterson, R. B., et al.,** Intravenous dipyridamole combined with isometric handgrip for near maximal acute increase in coronary flow in patients with coronary artery disease, *Am. J. Cardiol.,* 48, 1077, 1981.

67. **Josephson, M. A., Brown, B. G., Hecht, H. S., et al.,** Noninvasive detection and localization of coronary stenoses in patients: comparison of resting dipyridamole and exercise thallium-201 myocardial perfusion imaging, *Am. Heart J.,* 103, 1008, 1982.

68. **Verani, M. S., Mahmarian, J. J., Hixson, J. B., Boyce, T. M., and Staudacher, R. A.,** Diagnosis of coronary artery disease by controlled coronary vasodilation with adenosine and Thallium-201 scintigraphy in patients unable to exercise, *Circulation,* 82, 80, 1990.

69. **Crea, F., Pupita, G., Galassi, A. R., El-Tarhimi, H., Kaski, J. C., Davies, G., and Maseri, A.,** Role of adenosine in pathogenesis of anginal pain, *Circulation,* 81, 164, 1990.

70. **Sylven, C., Jonzon, B., Fredholm, B., and Kaijser, L.,** Adenosine injections into the brachial artery produces ischemia like pain or discomfort in the forearm, *Cardiovasc. Res.,* 22, 674, 1988.

71. **Dunwiddie, T. V.,** The physiological roles of adenosine in the central nervous system, *Int. Rev. Neurobiol.,* 27, 63, 1985.

72. **Phillis, J. W., Preston, G., and DeLong, R. E.,** Effects of anoxia on cerebral blood flow in the rat brain: evidence for a role of adenosine in autoregulation, *J. Cereb. Blood Flow Metab.,* 4, 586, 1984.

73. **Barraco, R. A., Coffin, V. L., Altman, H. J., and Phillis, J. W.,** Central effects of adenosine analogues on locomotor activity in mice and antagonism of caffeine, *Brain Res.,* 272, 392, 1983.

74. **Ahlijanian, M. K. and Takemori, A. E.,** Effects of phenylisopropyl adenosine (PIA) and caffeine on nociception and morphine-induced analgesia, tolerance and dependence in mice, *Eur. J. Pharmacol.,* 112, 171, 1985.

75. **Bockman, E. L., Steffen, R. P., McKenzie, J. E., Yachnis, A. T., and Haddy, F. J.,** Adenosine and active hyperemia on dog gracilis muscle, *Fed. Proc.,* 41, 1680, 1982.

76. **Phair, R. D. and Sparks, H. V.,** Adenosine content of skeletal muscle during active hyperemia and ischemic contraction, *Am. J. Physiol.,* 237, H1, 1979.

77. **Law, W. R. and Raymond, R. M.,** Adenosine potentiates insulin-stimulated myocardial glucose uptake *in vivo, Am. J. Physiol.,* 254, H970, 1988.

78. **Buxton, D. B., Fisher, R. A., Robertson, S. M., and Olsen, M. S.,** Stimulation of glycogenolysis and vasoconstriction by adenosine and adenosine analogues in the perfused rat liver, *Biochem. J.,* 248, 35, 1987.

79. **Watt, A. H. and Routledge, P. A.,** Adenosine stimulates respiration in man, *Br. J. Pharmacol.,* 20, 503, 1985.

80. **McQueen, D. S. and Ribeiro, T. A.,** Effect of adenosine on carotid chemoreceptor activity in the cat, *Br. J. Pharmacol.,* 74, 129, 1981.

81. **Reid, P. G., Watt, A. H., Routledge, P. A., and Smith, A. P.,** Intravenous infusion of adenosine but not inosine stimulates respiration in man, *Br. J. Clin. Pharmacol.,* 23, 331, 1987.

82. **Biaggioni, I., Onrot, J., Hollister, A. S., and Robertson, D.,** Cardiovascular effects of adenosine infusion in man and their modulation by dipyridamole, *Life Sci.,* 39, 2229, 1986.

83. **Costa, F. and Biaggioni, I.,** Role of adenosine in the sympathetic activation produced by isometric exercise in humans, *J. Clin. Invest.,* 93, 1654, 1994.

84. **Dusseau, J. W. and Hutchins, P. M.,** Hypoxia-induced angiogenesis in chick chorioallantoic membranes: a role for adenosine, *Res. Physiol.,* 71, 33, 1988.

85. **Mattfeldt, T. and Mall, G.,** Dipyridamole-induced capillary endothelial cell proliferation in the rat heart-a morphometric investigations, *Cardiovas. Res.,* 17, 229, 1983.

86. **Tornling, G.,** Capillary neoformation in the heart of dipyridamole-treated rats, *Acta Pathol. Microbiol. Immunol. Scand.,* 90, 269, 1982.

87. **Schooley, J. C. and Mahlmann, L. J.,** Adenosine, AMP, cyclic AMP, theophylline and the action and production of erythropoietin, *Proc. Soc. Exp. Biol. Med.,* 150, 215, 1975.

88. **Ueno, M., Brookins, J., Beckman, B., and Fisher, J. W.,** A_1 and A_2 adenosine receptor regulation of erythropoietin production, *Life Sci.,* 43, 229, 1988.

89. **Bakris, G. L., Sauter, E. R., Hussey, J. L., et al.,** Effects of theophylline on erythropoietin production in normal subjects and in patients with erythrocytosis after renal transplantation, *N. Engl. J. Med.,* 323, 86, 1990.

90. **Olafsson, B., Forman, M. B., Puett, D. W., Pou, A., Cates, C. U., Friesinger, G. C., and Virmani, R.,** Reduction of reperfusion injury in canine preparation by intracoronary adenosine: importance of the endothelium and the no-reflow phenomenon, *Circulation,* 76, 1135, 1987.

91. **Liu, G. S., Thornton, J. D., Van Winkle, D. M., Stanley, A. W. H., Olsson, R. A., and Downey, J. M.,** Protection against infarction afforded by preconditioning is mediated by A_1 adenosine receptors in rabbit heart, *Circulation,* 84, 350, 1991.

92. **Downey, J. M., Liu, G. S., and Thorton, J. D.,** Adenosine and the antiinfarct effects of preconditioning, *Cardiovasc. Res.,* 27, 3, 1993.

93. **Fredholm, B. B.,** Methods used to study the involvement of adenosine in the regulation of lipolysis, in *Methods in Pharmacology,* Paton, D. M., Ed., Plenum Press, New York, 1985, 337.

94. **Maggirwar, S. B., Dhanraj, D. N., Somani, S. M., and Ramkumar, V.,** Adenosine acts as an endogenous activator of the cellular antioxidant defense system, *Biochem. Biophys. Res. Commun.,* 201, 508, 1994.

95. **Somani, S. M., Ravi, R., and Rybak, L. P.,** Effect of exercise training on antioxidant system in brain regions of rat, *Pharmacol. Biochem. Behav.,* 50, 635, 1995.

Chapter 8

ENDOTHELIUM-DERIVED NITRIC OXIDE AND CONTROL OF BLOOD FLOW DURING EXERCISE

Richard M. McAllister, Michael D. Delp, and M. Harold Laughlin

CONTENTS

1. INTRODUCTION

There are large increases in blood flows to cardiac and active skeletal muscle during the adjustment from rest to exercise.[1] To this end, extensive dilation of arterial vasculature in these two tissues occurs during exercise. The roles of various regulators that act directly on vascular smooth muscle to induce vasorelaxation have been the subject of several excellent reviews.[2,3]

0-8493-8540-1/96/$0.00+$.50
© 1996 by CRC Press, Inc.

Less well characterized have been the roles of various endothelium-derived substances that may be released during exercise and cause vasodilation. The purpose of this chapter, then, is to discuss the importance of endothelium-derived relaxing factors (EDRFs) in the dilation of the coronary and skeletal muscle vascular beds associated with exercise. The focus of this chapter will be on one specific EDRF, nitric oxide, since it has been most intensively investigated. We will also examine exercise training-induced changes in vascular control exerted by nitric oxide.

1.1. ANATOMY OF THE VASCULAR WALL

The wall of an arterial blood vessel consists of three principal layers (working from lumen outward), the intima, the media, and the adventitia.[4] The intima is comprised of a single layer of endothelial cells and a basal lamina. The media is composed primarily of smooth muscle cells, with the number of layers of such cells ranging from ~25 (in large arteries) to 1 or 2 (in arterioles). The outermost layer of the vascular wall is the adventitia, consisting largely of collagenous tissue.

1.2. DISCOVERY AND CHARACTERIZATION OF EDNO

Prior to 1980, the endothelium was thought to be relatively passive, serving primarily as a smooth surface over which elements of the blood could pass. In 1980, however, Furchgott and Zawadzky[5] published a paper which launched a flurry of investigative activity that continues unabated today. In that paper, the authors described experiments that were designed to solve an apparent paradox. Acetylcholine, an agent that was known to be a vasodilator in intact animals, caused vasoconstriction when administered to isolated blood vessels. Furchgott and Zawadzky, in experiments conducted on isolated segments of rabbit thoracic aorta, determined that acetylcholine was a vasodilator of isolated vessels if vascular endothelium was undisturbed. If, however, endothelium was deliberately removed (denuded), acetylcholine became a vasoconstrictor. These investigators concluded that acetylcholine induces vasorelaxation via release of a substance from the endothelium (subsequently termed EDRF) that acts upon underlying vascular smooth muscle to cause vasorelaxation.

Since the discovery of EDRF in 1980 by Furchgott and Zawadzky, there has been a plethora of research activity concerning this vasodilator.[6] Indeed, it has been determined that there are several EDRFs, including nitric oxide, the prostaglandin PGI_2, and an endothelium-derived hyperpolarizing factor. Of these factors, endothelium-derived nitric oxide (EDNO) has received the most attention.

Figure 1 is a highly simplified schematic illustration of experimental findings pertinent to the role of EDNO in exercise-induced vasodilation. Two general classes of stimuli have been found to elicit release of EDNO. First, pharmacological stimuli such as norepinephrine, acetylcholine, and bradykinin, via putative specific endothelial cell receptors, lead to EDNO release. Second, physical stimuli such as shear stress (recall that endothelium is the

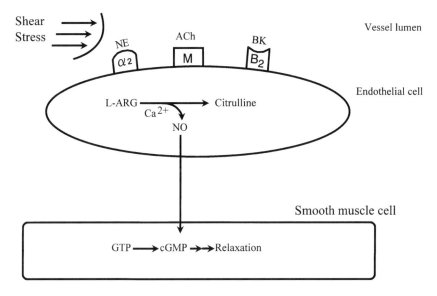

FIGURE 1. Schematic illustration of release of endothelium-derived nitric oxide (NO) and resultant vasorelaxation. Norepinephrine (NE), acetylcholine (ACh), and bradykinin (BK) are examples of pharmacological stimuli that induce NO release subsequent to interaction with putative α_2-adrenergic, muscarinic (M), and bradykinin (subclass 2; B_2) receptors, respectively, located on endothelial cell membrane. Shear stress is an example of a physical stimulus that, like pharmacological stimuli, elevates endothelial cell calcium (Ca^{2+}) levels. The enzyme nitric oxide synthase, for which Ca^{2+} is an essential cofactor, catalyzes conversion of L-arginine (L-ARG) to citrulline and NO. NO is thought to diffuse to adjacent vascular smooth muscle, where it activates the enzyme guanylate cyclase. Guanylate cyclase catalyzes conversion of GTP to cGMP, ultimately relaxing vascular smooth muscle. (References 6–8 used in constructing this schematic illustration.)

innermost layer of the vascular wall and, therefore, in direct contact with flowing blood) also lead to release of EDNO. This latter class of stimuli is probably most germane to consideration of the role of EDNO in exercise-induced vasodilation. Both of these general classes of stimuli have been found to increase intraendothelial cell calcium levels. This divalent cation is an essential cofactor for the constitutive enzyme nitric oxide synthase, which catalyzes conversion of the amino acid arginine (L-stereoisomer) to citrulline. Nitric oxide formed in this reaction is thought to diffuse to underlying vascular smooth muscle cells, where it in turn activates the enzyme guanylate cyclase. This enzyme catalyzes formation of cyclic guanosine monophosphate (GMP) from guanosine triphosphate (GTP). Guanylate cyclase can also be directly activated by such agents as nitroglycerin and sodium nitroprusside. Elevated cGMP levels in vascular smooth muscle cells result in vasorelaxation and, consequently, dilation of arterial vasculature. Importantly, a variety of L-arginine analogs that competitively inhibit nitric oxide synthase have been developed. Use of these analogs has permitted investigation into the role of EDNO in vascular control.

2. CORONARY BLOOD FLOW

2.1. ACUTE EXERCISE

One vascular bed that experiences a large increase in blood flow during exercise is the coronary circulation. Increased blood flow (and hence oxygen delivery) through this bed is necessary to meet the increased myocardial oxygen demands associated with exercise (i.e., increased heart rate, contractility, etc.). While the roles of regulators of coronary vascular tone such as vasodilator metabolites (e.g., adenosine) and the sympathetic nervous system have been extensively investigated,[2] the possible role of EDNO has only recently been studied and is not yet well understood. Nonetheless, the vascular endothelium releases EDNO in response to several stimuli that increase in magnitude during exercise, including neurohumoral agents such as catecholamines[7] and shear stress,[8] and thus it is an attractive hypothesis that EDNO is involved in exercise-induced coronary hyperemia.[9]

In order to appreciate results of these investigations, however, a brief review of functional anatomy of the coronary circulation is in order.

2.1.1. Functional Anatomy of the Coronary Circulation

In large mammals, diameters of coronary arterial vessels range from ~2 to 3 mm for the large, conduit-type coronary arteries to <100 μm (as small as 15 to 20 μm) for small coronary arterioles immediately proximal to capillaries. Most vascular resistance (~90%) in the coronary circulation resides on the arterial side. Under resting conditions, about 50% of coronary vascular resistance is proximal to the 100-μm diameter segments.[10] During coronary vasodilation, this changes such that the vast majority of coronary resistance occurs in the small (i.e., <100 μm) vessels.[10] It is important to bear in mind this shift in locus of coronary resistance in interpreting findings from experiments designed to determine if EDNO is involved in exercise-induced vasodilation (see below).

2.1.2. Studies of a Possible Role for EDNO in Acute Exercise

Most studies conducted to date have, due to technical limitations, examined only the large, conduit-type coronary arteries in attempting to elucidate a role for EDNO in the coronary blood flow response to acute exercise. Generally, the experimental approach utilized has been to eliminate the coronary vascular endothelium in some manner, and then to compare the coronary blood flow response to acute exercise with that under normal (i.e., endothelium-intact) conditions.

One manner in which coronary endothelium has been effectively eliminated is through the use of inhibitors of nitric oxide synthase. Hintze and colleagues[11] used one such inhibitor, nitro-L-arginine (NLA), to determine the importance of EDNO in regulating coronary blood flow in dogs, both at rest and during moderate exercise (treadmill running). At rest, blood flows to most myocardial regions (determined using the radiolabeled microsphere method) were reduced by treatment with NLA. During exercise, however, blood flows to those same regions were normal in the presence of NLA despite increases in calculated values for vascular resistance. These results were consistent with those of an earlier study by the same group.[12] In that study, NLA was also used to inhibit EDNO release in dogs during treadmill running. Blood flow through the left circumflex artery was determined using a Doppler flow probe. Blood flow during exercise was normal in spite of the presence of NLA. Interestingly, diameter of the circumflex artery, determined using implanted sonomicrometer crystals on that artery, increased during exercise without NLA present by ~4%. This exercise-induced dilation was prevented with NLA; indeed, it was converted to a constriction of about the same magnitude. The lack of effect of this constriction of the conduit-type circumflex artery on resultant blood flow is probably related to the minimal resistance to blood flow offered by large coronary arteries.[10] Since both studies of Hintze and colleagues documented near-complete blockade of nitric oxide synthase, these studies appear to indicate that EDNO is not involved in the acute exercise-induced increase in coronary blood flow. A similar conclusion was arrived at by Bache and coworkers.[13] Using the same inhibitor of nitric oxide synthase as Hintze and colleagues (NLA), they measured blood flow through the left anterior descending coronary artery of dogs during a progressive treadmill running protocol. The coronary arterial blood flow response to exercise (nearly doubled over resting levels at the highest exercise intensity) was normal with NLA present. Again, documentation of effective nitric oxide synthase blockade, coupled with the experimental findings, seemed to indicate that EDNO is not involved in coronary hyperemia associated with acute exercise.

A different approach to eliminating the coronary vascular endothelium was used by Berdeaux and associates.[14] These investigators used modified balloon angioplasty to denude a segment (~5 mm in length) of the left circumflex coronary artery in dogs. Similar to the study of Hintze and colleagues described above,[12] circumflex arterial diameter and blood flow were measured using sonomicrometer crystals and a Doppler flow probe, respectively. Responses to treadmill running at several intensities were then determined. The blood flow response to exercise remained normal after denudation of arterial endothelium. In a manner reminiscent of the study of Hintze's group,[12] the normal exercise-induced increase in circumflex artery diameter (~5%) reversed following denudation, becoming a ~5% constriction during exercise. In addition to confirming the findings of Hintze and colleagues, this study is important because it utilized a *direct* approach to completely eliminate EDNO from participation in the adjustment to acute exercise. The above-mentioned studies[11-13] that used inhibitors of nitric oxide synthase to eliminate EDNO formation were limited in that they failed to completely inhibit nitric oxide synthesis (i.e., some residual EDNO formation was present).

In summary, the limited number of studies conducted to date examining the role of EDNO in the increase of coronary blood flow during acute exercise do not point to an important contribution of nitric oxide as a vasodilator. These findings are perplexing. Studies performed on isolated coronary arterioles (<100 μm in diameter) that likely determine, in large part, coronary vascular resistance during exercise,[10] have shown that these coronary microvessels are sensitive to flow.[15] Coronary arterioles with intact endothelium exhibited vasodilation in response to increases in flow. Denudation of these vessels abolished this flow sensitivity.[15] Increased flow is clearly a stimulus present during exercise. As suggested by Bache and associates,[13] this discordance between intact animal-type studies and isolated vessel studies may indicate that other vasodilator mechanisms compensate for experimentally-inhibited EDNO-mediated dilation of coronary vasculature in intact animals. Alternatively, flow-induced vasodilator reserve may be completely utilized at resting coronary blood flow levels, and as a result further increases in flow induced by exercise do not produce additional EDNO release. Further studies will be required to test these suggestions.

2.1.3. Atherosclerosis and EDNO Involvement in Acute Exercise

Unlike the studies cited above performed in normal coronary circulations, results from studies in the setting of diseased coronary arteries (i.e., atherosclerosis) seem to point to an obligatory role for EDNO in the adjustment to acute exercise. Endothelium-dependent coronary vasodilation is impaired in patients with atherosclerotic coronary vasculature.[16] In a study involving dogs with an experimental stenosis of the left anterior descending coronary artery, a nitric oxide synthase inhibitor blunted exercise-induced increases in blood flow to myocardium served by this artery.[17] Stenosis of the left anterior descending artery reduced the increase in blood flow during exercise by ~50%; addition of nitric oxide synthase inhibition further reduced blood flow by about one-third. Thus, in the setting of myocardial hypoperfusion, EDNO appears to assume an important role in regulating coronary blood flow during exercise. These findings corroborated earlier findings from isolated coronary arterioles (<100 μm-diameter) from swine with coronary atherosclerosis, which exhibited greatly diminished (or absent) responses to pharmacologic and physical (i.e., flow) stimuli for EDNO production.[18]

2.2. CHRONIC EXERCISE

In spite of the findings reported above, seemingly indicating that EDNO does not play a significant role in the acute exercise-induced increase in coronary blood flow, investigators have nonetheless hypothesized that chronic exercise (i.e., exercise training) modifies EDNO-induced coronary vasodilation. This is an attractive hypothesis for several reasons:

1. Exercise training has been shown to increase blood flow capacity of the coronary circulation.[19,20] A training-induced increase in EDNO-mediated vasodilation could contribute to this phenomenon.

2. Intrinsic vasomotor reactivity of the media (i.e., smooth muscle) of the vascular wall has been found to be altered with exercise training in several animal models, such that a relative vasodilation is favored in the trained state.[21] Adaptations at the cellular/molecular level involving vascular smooth muscle management of calcium appear to contribute significantly to these findings.[22] These adaptations have recently been found to also occur in humans. It has been reported that conduit-type coronary arteries of highly-trained humans exhibit a vasodilatory response to nitroglycerin approximately twofold greater than that for sedentary individuals.[23]

3. A series of studies by Miller and colleagues[24-26] have shown that chronic increases in canine femoral arterial blood flow, achieved through the creation of a femoral arteriovenous fistula, results in enhanced vasodilator responses to endothelium-dependent agents. This enhancement of endothelium-dependent vasodilation has been determined to be due to increased release of EDNO.[25] Exercise training could be viewed as an intermittent version of the model of Miller and co-workers.

Thus, it seems reasonable to hypothesize that exercise training could result in enhanced EDNO release during acute exercise and, as a result, assume an important role in mediating increased coronary blood flow. While there are no studies available yet that have determined the contribution of EDNO to coronary vasodilation during exercise, pre- and posttraining, some findings concerning the impact of training on endothelium-dependent dilation have been reported. This question has been examined at various levels of the coronary circulation.

2.2.1. Conduit-Type Coronary Arteries

Due to their accessibility, the large (2 to 3 mm in diameter) coronary arteries have been most extensively studied. Hintze and associates[12] determined left circumflex arterial diameter and blood flow responses to acetylcholine (an endothelium-dependent vasodilator) and arterial occlusion, before and after a brief period (1 week) of exercise training. Circumflex arterial diameter increased in response to both acetylcholine administration and arterial occlusion (after release of occlusion), and these responses were markedly enhanced in dogs that had undergone the brief training program. In spite of these enhanced responses of arterial diameter, blood flow through the circumflex artery was unchanged in these dogs. As mentioned earlier in this review, the minimal contribution of large, conduit-type arteries to coronary resistance under these circumstances probably explains why enhanced dilation of these vessels does not improve blood flow.[10] On the other hand, studies of isolated arterial segments of large coronary vessels from both swine[27] and dogs[28] have failed to show training-induced augmentation of vasodilatory responses to a number of endothelium-dependent agents. These differing findings are difficult to reconcile, but it should be noted that the time point during training at which vascular responses were studied is much earlier in the study of Hintze and colleagues[12] than for the latter two studies involving longer-term (>10 week) training. This difference in experimental design may account for differing findings.

2.2.2. Near-Resistance and Resistance Coronary Arteries

Studies of isolated vessels from the coronary microcirculation of sedentary and trained swine have also been conducted. Preliminary results from experiments using near-resistance-type (i.e., ~150 to 250 μm in diameter) arteries suggest that the vasodilatory response to bradykinin is enhanced by training.[29] This enhancement is quite marked in resistance-type (i.e., <150 μm in diameter) arterioles.[30] The sensitivity to bradykinin was reported to be ~20-fold greater in arterioles from trained animals, an effect that is illustrated in Figure 2A by a leftward shift of the concentration-response curve for trained animals. This difference between sedentary and trained animals was eliminated by using a nitric oxide synthase inhibitor, as illustrated in Figure 2B. This suggests that the enhanced vasodilatory response of arterioles from trained animals to bradykinin is due to augmented generation of EDNO by nitric oxide synthase (see below). The dilatory response to sodium nitroprusside, an agent acting directly on vascular smooth muscle, was not changed by training, indicating that heightened sensitivity to bradykinin was not due to an improved relaxation response to EDNO. Preliminary results also suggest that an enhanced endothelium-dependent dilatory response to flow in these small arterioles occurs with exercise training.[27]

2.2.3. Mechanisms Involved in Training-Induced Adaptations

What may account for this enhancement of endothelium-dependent dilation in various-sized coronary arteries? A strong candidate is up-regulation of nitric oxide synthase expression. The augmented circumflex arterial dilation following training reported by Hintze and co-workers[12] has subsequently been shown to be associated with increased nitrite production by preparations of circumflex arterial tissue.[31] Nitrite production is an index of nitric oxide synthase activity. Laughlin and associates[32] have reported preliminary findings consistent with those of Hintze and colleagues. Exercise-trained animals were found to express higher levels of nitric oxide synthase in both coronary near-resistance arteries and resistance arterioles, coincident with enhanced vasodilatory responses of these vessels to bradykinin (see above).[30] Hintze and colleagues have reported increased transcription of the gene for nitric oxide synthase in trained animals.[31] This finding, however, was limited in that it was not localized to coronary vasculature, but rather the aorta of trained animals. It is tempting to speculate that increased transcription of nitric oxide synthase also occurs during training in coronary vessels, which would account for the findings of Laughlin and associates.[32] These findings regarding nitric oxide synthase expression are also consistent with findings from studies involving endothelial cells exposed to periods of increased shear stress in culture. These studies show

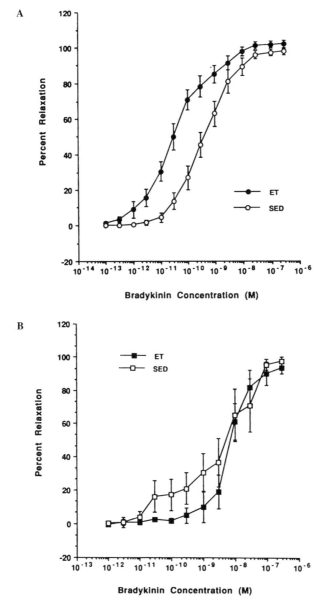

FIGURE 2. Bradykinin-induced dilation of porcine coronary resistance arterioles from endothelin-induced constriction. Values are mean ± SE, expressed as percentage of dilation induced by sodium nitroprusside (100 μ*M)* following endothelin-induced constriction. SED, sedentary; ET, exercise trained. (A) Responses in absence of inhibitor of nitric oxide synthase. $n = 16$ each for SED and ET. Note large shift to left of curve for ET, indicating greater sensitivity to bradykinin in arterioles from trained animals. (B) Responses in presence of N^G-monomethyl-L-arginine (3 m*M),* inhibitor of nitric oxide synthase. $n = 8$ and 6 for SED and ET, respectively. Note that difference between SED and ET shown in A is eliminated after inhibition of nitric oxide synthase, suggesting that training-induced difference in A is due to greater generation of endothelium-derived nitric oxide in arterioles from trained animals. (Reproduced from Muller et al., *Circulation,* 89, 2308, 1994. With permission.)

that chronically increased shear stress up-regulates expression of several en-dothelial macromolecules.[33] These intriguing findings may account for en-hanced endothelium-dependent coronary vasodilation in the trained state. Whether these changes are translated into an enhanced coronary blood flow response to acute exercise remains to be determined.

3. SKELETAL MUSCLE BLOOD FLOW

Current evidence indicates that EDNO is an important regulator of vascular tone in skeletal muscle at rest, and may act to enhance the hyperemic response to contractile activity. Recent studies also indicate that chronic muscle contrac-tile activity, such as that which occurs during endurance exercise training, can result in enhanced EDNO-mediated vasodilation. In the following sections we will highlight studies examining the role of EDNO in the regulation of vascular tone in skeletal muscle at rest and during exercise, and potential mechanisms through which exercise training may modify endothelium-dependent vasodila-tion.

3.1. ACUTE EXERCISE

Unlike vessels in the chronically active myocardium, there is a high degree of tone in skeletal muscle vasculature at rest. The consensus from studies examining the role of EDNO as a regulator of basal vascular tone in skeletal muscle is that it is an important modulator.[11,34-41] For example, using an isolated feline hindlimb preparation, Ekelund and Mellander[35] reported that inhibition of EDNO formation in resting muscle resulted in a ~100% increase in vascular resistance. The change in vascular resistance, however, was not uniform through-out the vascular tree. There was a ~140% increase in resistance in larger-bore resistance arteries (i.e., >25 μm in diameter), but only a ~20% increase in resistance in arterioles (i.e., <25 μm diameter). Regional variations in the basal release of EDNO have also been reported by Hester and co-workers.[36] These investigators found that inhibition of EDNO formation decreased diameter of first-order arterioles in resting hamster cremaster muscle, but had no effect on diameter of either second- or third-order arterioles.

The contribution of EDNO to the exercise-induced dilatory response in active skeletal muscle vasculature is presently unclear. Persson and colleagues[38] reported that the peak hyperemic response in contracting rabbit tenuissimus muscle was unaffected by inhibition of EDNO formation by N^G-monomethyl-L-arginine (L-NMMA), and Ekelund and co-workers[42] found that reductions in vascular resistance of cat gastrocnemius muscle during contractions were similar in the absence and presence of L-NMMA. In addition, forearm blood flow during wrist flexion exercise in humans has been reported to be unaffected by the presence of L-NMMA.[41] These studies suggest that exercise-induced dilation of skeletal muscle vasculature is either not endothelium-dependent or involves an endothelium-derived dilator substance other than EDNO. Alterna-tively, other vasodilatory mechanisms may compensate for elimination of an

EDNO-mediated dilatory influence. This conclusion is remarkably similar to that arrived at for the coronary circulation (see above).

Recently published work involving whole-body dynamic exercise, however, suggests that this conclusion may be incorrect. In a study designed to determine whether EDNO modulates regional skeletal muscle blood flow and vascular resistance in dogs during moderately intense treadmill running, Hintze and associates[11] found that although vascular resistance was increased in most muscles sampled following inhibition of EDNO formation (by NLA), only one of those muscles suffered reduced blood flow. Considering the limited number of muscles sampled and the variability of response among muscles, it is difficult to exclude the possibility that EDNO is functionally important in modulating the hyperemic response in skeletal muscle during whole-body exercise. Significantly, Hirai and co-workers[43] have reported that inhibition of EDNO formation in rats attenuated expected increases in blood flow elicited by moderate-intensity treadmill running in a majority of an array of hindlimb muscles. Attenuation of exercise-induced hyperemia was linearly related to fiber composition of the muscles, such that muscles with the highest content of slow-twitch oxidative (Type I) and fast-twitch oxidative/glycolytic (Type IIA) fibers suffered the greatest reductions in blood flow. Additionally, Hester and colleagues[36] found that contraction-induced dilation of first- and second-order arterioles in rat cremaster muscle was diminished in the presence of an EDNO formation inhibitor. Dilation of third-order arterioles, however, was unaffected. Collectively, these recent studies suggest that EDNO may play a role in exercise-induced hyperemia, but that the magnitude of its involvement depends on muscle fiber type composition and/or size of resistance vessel involved.

A potential mechanism through which the endothelium may participate in regulation of muscle perfusion during exercise is increased shear stress.[8,44,45] When muscles become active at the onset of exercise, local release of vasodilatory metabolites, mechanical propulsion of blood via the "muscle pump" effect, and/or withdrawal of sympathetic neural tone may serve as initiating stimuli for inducing dilation of skeletal muscle vasculature and thereby permitting increased blood flow to active muscle.[46] This acceleration of blood through resistance arterial vessels serves to increase shear stress along the intraluminal wall.[45] Endothelial cells, due to their location, sense this increased shear stress and respond by releasing EDNO,[8] resulting in further vasodilation and augmented perfusion of active skeletal muscle.[45] In this manner, EDNO may act as an amplifier of vasodilation induced by other mechanisms.

3.2. CHRONIC EXERCISE

Repeatedly challenging the cardiovascular system to deliver requisite oxygen and other nutrients to active skeletal muscle (i.e., exercise training) results in adaptations of this system that enhance muscle perfusion during an acute bout of exercise.[47-49] Training-induced vascular adaptations could result from structural changes (i.e., vascular remodeling, growth, and angiogenesis), adaptations in control of vascular tone, or a combination of these two possibilities.[50]

3.2.1. Adaptations to Exercise Training

Adaptive alterations in intrinsic responsiveness of vascular endothelial cells offer one of several classes of potential mechanisms through which vascular control could be modified by exercise training. Using thoracic aortic ring segments from rats, Hashimoto[51] was the first investigator to test the hypothesis that training induces adaptations in endothelium-mediated dilation. He reported no differences between sedentary and trained rats for either sensitivity or maximal responsiveness of aortic rings to the endothelium-dependent vasodilator acetylcholine. Unfortunately, no independent documentation of the effectiveness of the training program was provided; thus, the lack of change in endothelium-dependent dilation may have been due to an absence of a sufficient training stimulus.

Contrary to the findings of Hashimoto,[51] other investigators have reported that exercise training of both normal[52] and hypothyroid[53] rats enhances sensitivity and maximal responsiveness of aortic rings to acetylcholine (Figure 3A). There were, however, no differences in the dilatory responses of aortic rings to sodium nitroprusside, an agent that is not dependent upon the endothelium for its vasodilatory action (Figure 3B). The latter finding indicates that a change in smooth muscle-mediated dilation is not responsible for the enhanced response to the endothelium-dependent dilator acetylcholine. In addition, inhibition of nitric oxide synthase (i.e., EDNO formation) completely obliterated the difference between sedentary and trained animals in maximal acetylcholine-induced vasorelaxation of aortic rings.[52] These data suggest that training-induced enhancement of endothelium-dependent vasodilation is mediated through mechanisms responsible for EDNO formation. Efficacy of the training regimen used in these studies was independently documented.[52,53] Training-induced adaptations in vascular endothelium have also been observed in rabbits.[54] These investigators reported that thoracic aortae and pulmonary arteries from trained rabbits were more sensitive to acetylcholine than were vessels from sedentary animals. Importantly, vasorelaxation induced by sodium nitroprusside was not changed by training. This report also provided independent documentation of training efficacy.

Shorter-term exercise training has also been shown to induce adaptations in endothelium-dependent dilation in rats. Sun and co-workers[55] reported that arteriolar dilatory responses to acetylcholine and L-arginine were greater in gracilis muscles from rats trained for 2 to 4 weeks compared with those from sedentary animals; there were no differences in sodium nitroprusside-induced dilation. Short-term training has not, however, consistently elicited adaptations in endothelium-mediated vasorelaxation. Green and colleagues[56] reported that 4 weeks of training in humans did not alter the blood flow response (in the forearm muscle group trained) to either endothelium-dependent or independent vasodilators. These data indicate that the stimulus(i) present during chronic

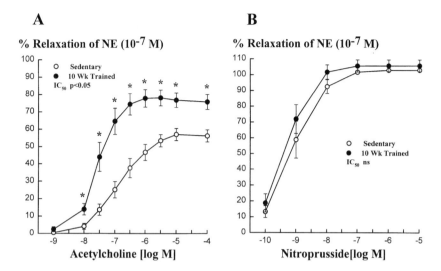

FIGURE 3.   (A) Acetylcholine-induced relaxation of rat abdominal aortic vascular rings from norepinephrine (100 nM)-induced isometric contraction. Values are mean ± SE, in percentage of developed tension induced by norepinephrine administration. *Significantly different between groups (p <0.05). IC$_{50}$, acetylcholine concentration at which rings exhibit 50% relaxation. Note enhanced response of vascular rings from trained animals. (B) Sodium nitroprusside-induced relaxation of same vascular rings from norepinephrine (100 nM)-induced isometric contraction. Note similarity of responses of rings from sedentary and trained animals, suggesting that training-induced enhancement of endothelium-dependent relaxation in A is due to increased release of endothelium-derived relaxing factor(s), rather than increased sensitivity of underlying vascular smooth muscle to those factors. (Reproduced from Delp et al., *J. Appl. Physiol.*, 61, 440, 1990. With permission.)

exercise that induce(s) endothelial adaptations may need to be present for longer durations (i.e., 10 weeks or more), as was true for the studies of Chen and Li[54] and Delp and colleagues[52,53] described above.

Training-induced endothelial adaptations not only enhance vasorelaxation, but also appear to diminish norepinephrine-induced vasoconstriction. For example, we found that aortic vessel rings from both euthyroid[52] and hypothyroid[53] exercise-trained rats were less sensitive to vasoconstrictor effects of norepinephrine than were vessels from euthyroid and hypothyroid sedentary controls, respectively. Removal of the endothelial cell layer abolished the reduced sensitivity to norepinephrine in vessel rings from trained animals (Figure 4A).[52] Furthermore, vasoconstrictor responses to the α_1-adrenergic agonist phenylephrine were not altered by exercise training (Figure 4B).[52] These data indicate that altered responsiveness to norepinephrine observed in aortic segments from trained animals is due to an endothelium-dependent mechanism involving α_2-adrenergic receptors.[7] Thus, binding of norepinephrine to endothelial cell α_2-adrenergic receptors may induce greater release of EDNO or other EDRFs, which could serve to oppose norepinephrine-induced vasoconstriction.

A

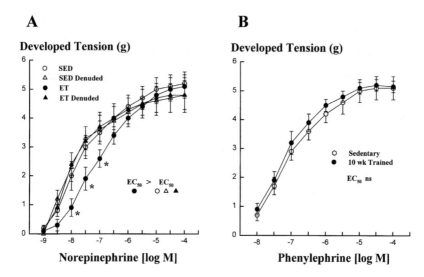

B

FIGURE 4. Modulation of norepinephrine-induced contractile responses by endothelium-derived relaxing factors(s). (A) Effects of endothelium removal on isometric contractile responses of rat abdominal aortic vascular rings to norepinephrine. Values are mean ± SE, in grams of developed tension. SED, sedentary; ET, trained. *Significantly different from responses of other three groups (SED, SED Denuded, ET Denuded). EC_{50}, norepinephrine concentration at which 50% of contractile response exhibited. Note shift to right of curve for ET, indicating lesser contractile response in vascular rings from ET animals. Also note that denuding rings of endothelium eliminates this effect of training. (B) Isometric contractile responses of rat abdominal aortic rings to phenylephrine, α_1-adrenergic receptor-specific agonist. Note similarity of responses for vascular rings from SED and ET animals. This suggests that lesser contractile response of ET shown in A is due to enhanced α_2-adrenergic receptor-mediated release of endothelial-derived relaxing factors in trained state. See text for details. (Reproduced from Delp et al., *J. Appl. Physiol.*, 61, 440, 1990. With permission.)

In addition to an inhibitory effect that enhanced release of EDNO may have on norepinephrine-induced smooth muscle contraction, evidence suggests that the endothelium may also inhibit release of norepinephrine from adrenergic nerves.[57,58] Therefore, it is conceivable that adaptations of the endothelium induced by exercise training could alter vascular control mechanisms in several ways, resulting in greater relative vasodilation. These include a direct dilatory effect through enhanced release of EDNO, and indirect effects via decreasing vascular sensitivity to norepinephrine and inhibiting adrenergic neuronal release of norepinephrine.

3.2.2. Mechanisms Involved in Training-Induced Adaptations

The stimulus produced by exercise that induces adaptation of the endothelium could be physical (e.g., increased blood flow, mechanical compression) and/or chemical (e.g., metabolites, catecholamines, other vasoactive substances).[50] Increased blood flow and the corresponding increase in vascular wall shear stress have been shown to be potent stimuli for adaptation of the endothelium. For example, Miller and co-workers[24-26] demonstrated that chronic

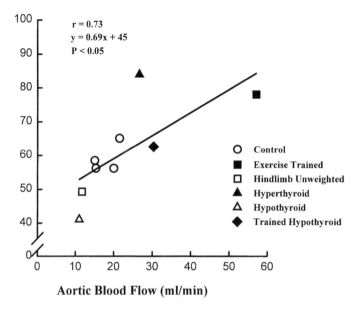

FIGURE 5. Influence of chronic blood flow levels on endothelium-dependent vasorelaxation. Values are means. Peak acetylcholine (ACh)-induced relaxation from norepinephrine (100 n*M*)-induced contraction of rat abdominal aortic vascular rings is plotted vs. estimated abdominal aortic blood flow. Regression analysis indicates significant relationship between peak endothelium-dependent relaxation and chronic levels of blood flow, suggesting that chronically-elevated blood flow through a vessel induces endothelial adaptations that enhance relaxation of vascular smooth muscle. Values for abdominal aortic blood flow are from References 47 and 59 to 62, values for peak ACh-induced relaxation are from References 52, 53, 63, and 64.

increases in blood flow in canine femoral arteries, via arteriovenous fistulas, resulted in augmented endothelium-dependent relaxation. Using exercise training,[47,59] hindlimb unloading,[60] hypothyroidism,[61] and hyperthyroidism[62] to alter blood flow through the abdominal aorta of rats, we have found that there is a significant relationship between acetylcholine-induced, endothelium-dependent relaxation[52,53,63,64] and aortic blood flow (Figure 5). This suggests that changes in blood flow during exercise training may stimulate adaptations in the endothelium. However, changes in blood flow only account for ~50% of the variability associated with changes in acetylcholine-induced relaxation. This suggests that other factors associated with exercise, such as increases in metabolite concentrations, altered mechanical forces, and changes in neurohumoral milieu, may also be important stimuli for endothelial adaptations to exercise training. As for the specific adaptation(s) induced by these factors, increased expression of nitric oxide synthase is a strong candidate, as described above for the coronary circulation. Increased blood flow associated with repeated bouts of exercise has been shown to increase transcription of the gene for nitric oxide synthase in the aorta.[31] It is tempting to speculate that a similar adaptation to exercise training occurs in skeletal muscle vasculature, but experiments confirming this possibility have not yet been performed.

4. SUMMARY

There is currently considerable interest in the role of EDNO in regulating vascular tone and, consequently, blood flow. Investigation into its possible role in exercise-induced dilation of the coronary and skeletal muscle vascular beds has only recently been initiated. While studies appear to minimize the importance of EDNO in regulation of coronary blood flow during exercise, a significant role for EDNO in the exercise-induced increase in skeletal muscle blood flow seems likely. Exercise training has been shown to increase the *potential* for endothelium-induced dilation of vessels from both of these vascular beds. Whether this increase in vasodilator potential is actually utilized during whole-body exercise in the trained state remains to be determined.

ACKNOWLEDGMENTS

Work cited from the authors' laboratory was supported by National Institutes of Health (MHL), University of Missouri Committee on Research (RMM), and American Heart Association-Missouri Affiliate (RMM).

REFERENCES

1. **Rowell, L. B.,** *Human Circulation Regulation During Physical Stress,* Oxford University Press, New York, 1986, chap. 9.
2. **Feigl, E. O.,** Coronary physiology, *Physiol. Rev.,* 63, 1, 1983.
3. **Shepherd, J. T.,** Circulation to skeletal muscle, in *Handbook of Physiology, Section 2: The Cardiovascular System, Vol. III. Peripheral Circulation and Organ Blood Flow,* Shepherd, J. T. and Abboud, F. M., Eds., American Physiological Society, Bethesda, MD, 1983, chap. 11.
4. **Rhodin, J. A. G.,** Architecture of the vessel wall, in *Handbook of Physiology, Section 2: The Cardiovascular System, Vol. II. Vascular Smooth Muscle,* Bohr, D. F., Somlyo, A. P., and Sparks, H. V., Jr., Eds., American Physiological Society, Bethesda, MD, 1980, chap. 1.
5. **Furchgott, R. F. and Zawadzky, J. V.,** The obligatory role of endothelial cells in the relaxation of arterial smooth muscle by acetylcholine, *Nature,* 288, 373, 1980.
6. **Moncada, S., Palmer, R. M. J., and Higgs, E. A.,** Nitric oxide: physiology, pathophysiology, and pharmacology, *Pharmacol. Rev.,* 43, 109, 1991.
7. **Vanhoutte, P. M. and Miller, V. M.,** Alpha$_2$-adrenoceptors and endothelium-derived relaxing factor, *Am. J. Med.,* 87, 3C-1S, 1989.
8. **Davies, P. F. and Tripathi, S. C.,** Mechanical stress mechanisms and the cell: An endothelial paradigm, *Circ. Res.,* 72, 239, 1993.
9. **Loscalzo, J. and Vita, J. A.,** Ischemia, hyperemia, exercise, and nitric oxide: Complex physiology and complex molecular adaptations, *Circulation,* 90, 2556, 1994.

10. **Chilian, W. M., Eastham, C. L., and Marcus, M. L.,** Microvascular distribution of coronary vascular resistance in beating left ventricle, *Am. J. Physiol. (Heart Circ. Physiol.),* 251(20), H779, 1986.
11. **Shen, W., Lundborg, M., Wang, J., Stewart, J. M., Xu, X., Ochoa, M., and Hintze, T. H.,** Role of EDRF in the regulation of regional blood flow and vascular resistance at rest and during exercise in concious dogs, *J. Appl. Physiol.,* 77, 165, 1994.
12. **Wang, J., Wolin, M. S., and Hintze, T. H.,** Chronic exercise enhances endothelium-mediated dilation of epicardial coronary artery in concious dogs, *Circ. Res.,* 73, 829, 1993.
13. **Altman, J. D., Kinn, J., Duncker, D. J., and Bache, R. J.,** Effect of inhibition of nitric oxide formation on coronary blood flow during exercise in the dog, *Cardiovasc. Res.,* 28, 119, 1994.
14. **Berdeaux, A., Ghaleh, B., Dubois-Randé, J. L., Vigué, B., Drieu La Rochelle, C., Hittinger, L., and Giudicelli, J. F.,** Role of vascular endothelium in exercise-induced dilation of large epicardial coronary arteries in concious dogs, *Circulation*, 89, 2799, 1994.
15. **Kuo, L., Davis, M. J., and Chilian, W. M.,** Endothelium-dependent, flow-induced dilation of isolated coronary arterioles, *Am. J. Physiol. (Heart Circ. Physiol.),* 259(28), H1063, 1990.
16. **Meredith, I. T., Yeung, A. C., Weidinger, F. F., Anderson, T. J., Uehata, A., Ryan, T. J., Selwyn, A. P., and Ganz, P.,** Role of impaired endothelium-dependent vasodilation in ischemic manifestations of coronary artery disease, *Circulation,* 87(Suppl. V), V-56, 1993.
17. **Duncker, D. J. and Bache, R. J.,** Inhibition of nitric oxide production aggravates myocardial hypoperfusion during exercise in the presence of a coronary artery stenosis, *Circ. Res.,* 74, 629, 1994.
18. **Kuo, L., Davis, M. J., Cannon, S., and Chilian, W. M.,** Pathophysiological consequences of atherosclerosis extend into the coronary microcirculation: restoration of endothelium-dependent responses by L-arginine, *Circ. Res.,* 70, 465, 1992.
19. **Laughlin, M. H.,** Effects of exercise training on coronary transport capacity, *J. Appl. Physiol.,* 58, 468, 1985.
20. **Laughlin, M. H., Overholser, K. A., and Bhatte, M.,** Exercise training increases coronary transport reserve in miniature swine, *J. Appl. Physiol.,* 67, 1140, 1989.
21. **Laughlin, M. H. and McAllister, R. M.,** Exercise training-induced coronary vascular adaptation, *J. Appl. Physiol.,* 73, 2209, 1992.
22. **Underwood, F. B., Laughlin, M. H., and Sturek, M.,** Altered control of calcium in coronary smooth muscle cells by exercise training, *Med. Sci. Sports Exerc.,* 26, 1230, 1994.
23. **Haskell, W. L., Sims, C., Myll, J., Bortz, W. M., St. Goar, F. G., and Alderman, E. L.,** Coronary artery size and dilating capacity in ultradistance runners, *Circulation,* 87, 1076, 1993.
24. **Miller, V. M., Aarhus, L. L., and Vanhoutte, P. M.,** Modulation of endothelium-dependent responses by chronic alterations of blood flow, *Am. J. Physiol. (Heart Circ. Physiol.),* 251(20), H520, 1986.
25. **Miller, V. M. and Vanhoutte, P. M.,** Enhanced release of endothelium-derived factor(s) by chronic increases in blood flow, *Am. J. Physiol. (Heart Circ. Physiol.),* 255(24), H446, 1988.
26. **Miller, V. M. and Burnett, J. C., Jr.,** Modulation of NO and endothelin by chronic increases in blood flow in canine femoral arteries, *Am. J. Physiol. (Heart Circ. Physiol.),* 263(32), H103, 1992.
27. **Laughlin, M. H., Oltman, C. L., Muller, J. M., Myers, P. R., and Parker, J. L.,** Adaptation of coronary circulation to exercise training, in *Cardiovascular Response to Exercise,* Fletcher, G. F., Ed., Futura Publishing, Mount Kisco, NY, 1994, chap. 10.
28. **Rogers, P. J., Miller, T. D., Bauer, B. A., Brum, J. M., Bove, A. A., and Vanhoutte, P. M.,** Exercise training and responsiveness of isolated coronary arteries, *J. Appl. Physiol.,* 71, 2346, 1991.

29. **Parker, J. L., Oltman, C. L., Muller, J. M., Myers, P. R., Adams, H. R., and Laughlin, M. H.,** Effects of exercise training on regulation of tone in coronary arteries and arterioles, *Med. Sci. Sports Exerc.,* 26, 1252, 1994.

30. **Muller, J. M., Myers, P. R., and Laughlin, M. H.,** Vasodilator responses of coronary resistance arteries of exercise-trained pigs, *Circulation,* 89, 2308, 1994.

31. **Sessa, W. C., Pritchard, K., Seyedi, N., Wang, J., and Hintze, T. H.,** Chronic exercise in dogs increases coronary vascular nitric oxide production and endothelial cell nitric oxide synthase gene expression, *Circ. Res.,* 74, 349, 1994.

32. **Laughlin, M. H., Amann, J. F., Thorne, P., and Pollock, J. S.,** Up-regulation of nitric oxide synthase in coronary resistance arteries isolated from exercise-trained pigs, *Circulation,* 90(Suppl. I), I-429, 1994.

33. **Mills, I., Cohen, C. R., and Sumpio, B. E.,** Cyclic strain and vascular cell biology, in *Hemodynamic Forces and Vascular Cell Biology,* Sumpio, B. E., Ed., R. G. Landes, Austin, TX, 1993, chap. 5.

34. **Broczkowski, J., Vicaut, E., Danialou, G., and Aubler, M.,** Role of nitric oxide and prostaglandins in the regulation of diaphragmatic arteriolar tone in the rat, *J. Appl. Physiol.,* 77, 590, 1994.

35. **Ekelund, U. and Mellander, S.,** Role of endothelium-derived nitric oxide in the regulation of tonus in large-bore arterial resistance vessels, arterioles and veins in cat skeletal muscle, *Acta Physiol. Scand.,* 140, 301, 1990.

36. **Hester, R. L., Eraslan, A., and Saito, Y.,** Differences in EDNO contribution to arteriolar diameters at rest and during functional dilation in striated muscle, *Am. J. Physiol. (Heart Circ. Physiol.),* 265(34), H146, 1993.

37. **Kaley, G., Koller, A., Rodenburg, J. M., Messina, E. J., and Wolin, M. S.,** Regulation of arteriolar tone and responses via L-arginine pathway in skeletal muscle, *Am. J. Physiol. (Heart Circ. Physiol.),* 262(31), H987, 1992.

38. **Persson, M. G., Gustafsson, L. E., Wiklund, N. P., Hedqvist, P., and Moncada, S.,** Endogenous nitric oxide as a modulator of rabbit skeletal muscle microcirculation *in vivo, Br. J. Pharmacol.,* 100, 463, 1990.

39. **Sun, D., Messina, E. J., Koller, A., Wolin, M. S., and Kaley, G.,** Endothelium-dependent dilation to L-arginine in isolated rat skeletal muscle arterioles, *Am. J. Physiol. (Heart Circ. Physiol.),* 262(31), H1211, 1992.

40. **Vallance, P., Collier, J., and Moncada, S.,** Effects of endothelium-derived nitric oxide on peripheral arteriolar tone in man, *Lancet,* 2, 997, 1989.

41. **Wilson, J. R. and Kapoor, S. C.,** Contribution of endothelium-derived relaxing factor to exercise-induced vasodilation in humans, *J. Appl. Physiol.,* 75, 2740, 1993.

42. **Ekelund, U., Bjornberg, J., Grande, P.-O., Albert, U., and Mellander, S.,** Myogenic vascular regulation in skeletal muscle *in vivo* is not dependent on endothelium-derived nitric oxide, *Acta Physiol. Scand.,* 144, 199, 1992.

43. **Hirai, T., Visneski, M. D., Kearns, K. J., Zelis, R., and Musch, T. I.,** Effects of NO synthase inhibition on the muscular blood flow response to treadmill exercise in rats, *J. Appl. Physiol.,* 77, 1288, 1994.

44. **Koller, A. and Kaley, G.,** Endothelium regulates skeletal muscle microcirculation by a blood flow velocity-sensing mechanism, *Am. J. Physiol. (Heart Circ. Physiol.),* 258(27), H916, 1990.

45. **Koller, A. and Kaley, G.,** Endothelial regulation of wall shear stress and blood flow in skeletal muscle microcirculation, *Am. J. Physiol. (Heart Circ. Physiol.),* 260(29), H862, 1991.

46. **Laughlin, M. H. and Armstrong, R. B.,** Muscle blood flow during locomotory exercise, *Exerc. Sport Sci. Rev.,* 13, 95, 1985.

47. **Armstrong, R. B. and Laughlin, M. H.,** Exercise blood flow patterns within and among rat muscles after training, *Am. J. Physiol. (Heart Circ. Physiol.),* 246(15), H59, 1984.

48. **Musch, T. I., Haidet, G. C., Ordway, G. A., Longhurst, J. C., and Mitchell, J. H.,** Training effects on regional blood flow response to maximal exercise in foxhounds, *J. Appl. Physiol.,* 62, 1724, 1987.

49. **Musch, T. I., Terrel, J. A., and Hilty, M. R.,** Effects of high-intensity sprint training on skeletal muscle blood flow in rats, *J. Appl. Physiol.,* 71, 1387, 1991.

50. **Laughlin, M. H., McAllister, R. M., and Delp, M. D.,** Physical activity and the microcirculation in cardiac and skeletal muscle, in *Physical Activity, Fitness, and Health: International Proceedings and Consensus Statement,* Bouchard, C., Shephard, R. J., and Stephens, T., Eds., Human Kinetics Publishers, Champaign, IL, 1994, chap. 18.

51. **Hashimoto, M.,** Effects of exercise on plasma lipoprotein levels and endothelium-dependent vasodilation in young and old rats, *Eur. J. Appl. Physiol.,* 61, 440, 1990.

52. **Delp, M. D., McAllister, R. M., and Laughlin, M. H.,** Exercise training alters endothelium-dependent vasoreactivity of rat abdominal aorta, *J. Appl. Physiol.,* 75, 1354, 1993.

53. **Delp, M. D., McAllister, R. M., and Laughlin, M. H.,** Exercise training alters aortic vascular reactivity in hypothyroid rats, *Am. J. Physiol. (Heart Circ. Physiol.),* 268(37), H1428, 1995.

54. **Chen, H. and Li, H.,** Physical conditioning can modulate endothelium-dependent vasorelaxation in rabbits, *Arterioscler. Thromb.,* 13, 852, 1993.

55. **Sun, D., Huang, A., Koller, A., and Kaley, G.,** Short-term daily exercise activity enhances endothelial NO synthesis in skeletal muscle arterioles of rats, *J. Appl. Physiol.,* 76, 2241, 1994.

56. **Green, D. J., Cable, N. T., Fox, C., Rankin, J. M., and Taylor, R. R.,** Modification of forearm resistance vessels by training in young men, *J. Appl. Physiol.,* 77, 1829, 1994.

57. **Tesfamariam, B., Weisbrod, R. M., and Cohen, R. A.,** Endothelium inhibits responses of rabbit carotid artery to adrenergic nerve stimulation, *Am. J. Physiol. (Heart Circ. Physiol.),* 253(22), H792, 1987.

58. **Cohen, R. A. and Weisbrod, R. B.,** Endothelium inhibits norepinephrine release from adrenergic nerves of rabbit carotid artery, *Am. J. Physiol. (Heart Circ. Physiol.),* 254(23), H871, 1988.

59. **McAllister, R. M., Delp, M. D., and Laughlin, M. H.,** Effects of training on muscle blood flow response to exercise in hypothyroid rats, *Physiologist,* 35, 183, 1992.

60. **McDonald, D. S., Delp, M. D., and Fitts, R. H.,** Effect of hindlimb unweighting on tissue blood flow in the rat, *J. Appl. Physiol.,* 72, 2210, 1992.

61. **McAllister, R. M., Delp, M. D., and Laughlin, M. H.,** Blunted high oxidative muscle blood flow response to exercise in hypothyroid rats, *Med. Sci. Sports Exerc.,* 24, S117, 1992.

62. **McAllister, R. M., Sansone, J. C., Jr., and Laughlin, M. H.,** Effects of hyperthyroidism on muscle blood flow during exercise in rats, *Am. J. Physiol. (Heart Circ. Physiol.),* 268(37), H330, 1995.

63. **Delp, M. D., Holder-Binkley, T., Laughlin, M. H., and Hasser, E. M.,** Vasoconstrictor properties of rat aorta are diminished by hindlimb unweighting, *J. Appl. Physiol.,* 75, 2620, 1993.

64. **Delp, M. D., McAllister, R. M., Grossenburg, V., and Laughlin, M. H.,** Hyperthyroidism enhances endothelium-mediated vasodilator responses in rat aortae, *FASEB J.,* 7, A776, 1993.

Chapter 9

EFFECT OF EXERCISE ON PLATELET PHYSIOLOGY AND PHARMACOLOGY

Gundu H. R. Rao

CONTENTS

1. INTRODUCTION

Morbidity and mortality related to cardiovascular and cerebrovascular diseases, such as thrombosis and stroke, rank one and three respectively in the U.S.[1] Atherosclerosis, a benign chronic complex disease, predisposes individuals to acute events like thrombosis, hemorrhage, and stroke. When a blood clot blocks a coronary artery, it initiates ischemia and coronary thrombosis, whereas hemorrhage and blocking of cerebral blood vessels results in stroke.

Many factors contribute to the pathogenesis of atherosclerosis. Some of the known risk factors include alterations in the level of blood lipids, hormones, fibrinogen, glucose, and plasminogen activator inhibitor; activity of blood cells such as platelets, endothelial cells, neutrophils and monocytes, glucose intolerance, insulin resistance, central abdominal obesity, body fat distribution, smoking, hypertension, and physical activity.[1] Therefore, there is considerable interest in the prevention or reversal of atherosclerosis by reducing the risk factors associated with cardiovascular diseases.

0-8493-8540-1/96/$0.00+$.50
© 1996 by CRC Press, Inc.

Platelets play an important role in the pathogenesis of atherosclerosis, thrombosis, and stroke. Platelet activation is a prerequisite for the formation of a hemostatic plug and arrest of bleeding.[2] However, hyperactivation of platelets may initiate complications leading to events associated with cardiovascular diseases. Platelet activation is a natural response to the vascular injury, however, their role in various cardiovascular diseases is due to their pathological manifestations.

Physical activity in the form of exercise has been recommended by various commissions, task forces, peer groups, physicians, and social service organizations.[3-5] These recommendations are made in order to prevent or reduce some of the leading risk factors for coronary artery disease such as hypertension, increases in blood cholesterol, alterations in circulating levels of hormones, glucose, fibrinogen, and vasoactive metabolites. Although vigorous exercise is beneficial, it may be harmful to individuals with various disorders if appropriate precautions are not taken. Moreover, many factors contribute to the pathogenesis of cardiovascular diseases and studies done so far have not been able to measure the beneficial effects of physical exercise in the prevention of development of risk factors for coronary artery disease. In this article, we provide a brief overview on the effect of exercise on platelet physiology and pharmacology and on some of the factors that modulate their functional responses. Readers are urged to refer to in-depth reviews for additional information on physiology and pharmacology of platelet activation mechanisms.

2. PHYSIOLOGY OF PLATELET ACTIVATION

Platelets in native blood circulate as nonadhesive, discrete disks. Four well-defined stages of activation are recognized: development of stickiness, change in shape, contraction, secretion, and irreversible aggregation.[1] The degree of activation platelets achieve depends on the strength of the stimulus and the information available in the interactive domains of the cell matrix components. When exposed to laminin, platelets form focal adhesions, whereas they spread on the fibronectin-covered surface. Collagen-coated surfaces induce adhesion, aggregation, and secretion of granule contents. The exact biochemical mechanisms involved in development of stickiness and changes in shape are not clear. The major biochemical events associated with ligand binding, signal transduction, formation of second messengers, calcium mobilization, contraction, secretion, and irreversible aggregation have been described.[2,7]

Soluble physiological agonists known to activate platelets include adenosine diphosphate, epinephrine, thromboxane A_2, thrombin and platelet activating factor. These agonists interact at specific receptor sites on the platelet plasma membrane and initiate activating signals. Epinephrine, thrombin, and thromboxane seem to induce signal transduction via membrane spanning GTP-binding protein-coupled receptors. Various types of collagen and other cell matrix components interact with platelets at discrete domains rich in glycoproteins (GP) called integrins. GPIIb/IIIa is a promiscuous integrin receptor which

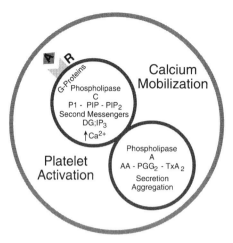

FIGURE 1. Agonist-mediated calcium mobilization and platelet activation. Agonist receptor interaction and signal transduction initiates the metabolism of two specific substrates, (1) phosphatidylinositol 4,5-bisphosphate (PIP$_2$), (2) arachidonic acid (AA). Activation of these two signalling pathways leads to the formation of second messengers, diacylglycerol (DG), inositol 1, 4,5-trisphosphate (IP$_3$), prostaglandin endoperoxides (PGG$_2$/PGH$_2$) and thromboxane (TxA$_2$). These second messengers play a critical role in signal transduction, activation of effector enzymes, calcium mobilization, expression of binding sites for adhesion molecules, actin assembly, contraction, secretion of granule contents, and irreversible aggregation of platelets.

serves as the binding site for fibrinogen, fibronectin, and laminin. Collagen interacts with several domains including an integrin receptor, GPIa/IIa. In addition to specific receptors for soluble agonists and integrin receptors for macromolecules, platelets also have nonintegrin receptors such as GPIb, GPIV, and GPV.

Receptor-mediated activation and signal transduction via GTP-binding proteins leads to the activation of effector intracellular enzymes such as phospholipase C (PLC), phospholipase D, phospholipase A$_2$, and formation of second messengers (Figure 1). Activation of phospholipase C results in the hydrolysis of phosphatidyl inositol 4,5-bisphosphate (PIP$_2$) and formation of the second messengers, inositol 1,4,5-triphosphate (IP$_3$) and 1,2-diacylglycerol (DG). Diacylglycerol induces translocation of protein kinase C isozymes. Inositol triphosphate mobilizes ionized calcium from internal membrane stores. Activation of phospholipase A$_2$ leads to the liberation of arachidonic acid and formation of prostaglandin (PG), endoperoxides (PGG$_2$/PGH$_2$) and thromboxane A$_2$ (TxA$_2$) (Figure 2). Thromboxane is a potent vasoconstrictor and platelet agonist. It exits the cell, binds to a specific receptor on the plasma membrane of platelets and, initiates activation of PLC-dependent hydrolysis of PIP$_2$. In the vascular tissues prostaglandin endoperoxides are transformed into a potent vasodilator, prostacyclin. Formation of second messengers such as DG, IP$_3$ and TxA$_2$ and elevation of cytosolic calcium facilitates granule mobilization, contraction and secretion.[2]

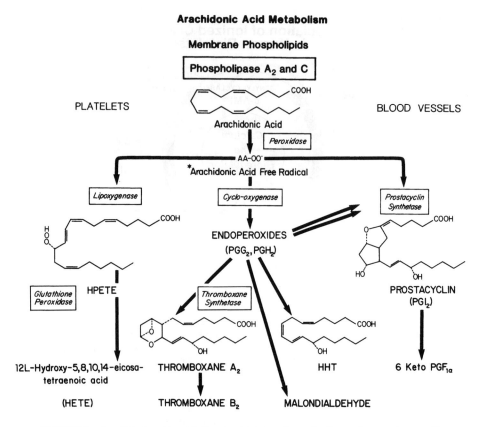

FIGURE 2. Arachidonic acid metabolism in platelets and vascular tissues. Increase in cytosolic free calcium levels stimulate phospholipase A_2 activity and promote the liberation of free arachidonic acid (AA) from membrane phospolipids. Free AA is converted by cyclooxygenase to prostaglandin endoperoxides, (PGG_2/PGH_2). These transient metabolites are further transformed to thromboxane. This metabolic pathway also generates malondialdehyde, the common lipid peroxide found in circulating blood.

Ionized calcium is the primary regulator (Figure 3). The availability and levels of this cation are modulated by second messengers cyclic adenosine monophosphate (cAMP) and cyclic guanosine monophosphate (cGMP). Agonists induce activation of effector enzymes and promote formation of second messengers that are capable of facilitating calcium mobilization. Antagonists communicate with effector enzymes (adenylyl cyclase, guanylyl cyclase) that produce second messengers cAMP and cGMP which are capable of lowering availability of ionized calcium. Availability of free calcium and assembly of filamentous actin dictates various phases and relative degree of platelet activation.

3. PHARMACOLOGY OF ANTIPLATELET DRUGS

Major pharmacological approaches revolve around prevention of the release of arachidonic acid, blocking conversion of the fatty acid by cyclooxygenase

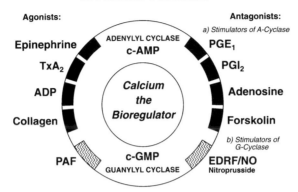

FIGURE 3. Modulation of cytosolic calcium by agonists and antagonists. Ionized calcium is the primary bioregulator. Resting platelets have low levels of ionized calcium (>100 nM). Ligands listed on the left side of the figure interact with specific receptors on the plasma membrane and cause platelet activation. Agonist-mediated signals stimulate effector intracellular enzymes such as phospholipase C, phospholipase D, or phospholipase A_2 and facilitate the formation of second messengers. One of these second messengers, inositol 1,4,5-trisphosphate, has been shown to mobilize free calcium from internal membrane stores, whereas antagonists (listed on the right side) stimulate adenylyl cyclase (A cyclase) and guanylyl cyclase (G-cyclase) and generate second messengers cAMP and cGMP, respectively. These molecules play an important role in the regulation of cytosolic calcium levels. Availability and the level of ionized calcium dictate the state of assembled actin and degree of platelet activation.

or interfere with the availability and rise in ionized cytosolic calcium[4] (Figure 4). Some of the known drugs that modulate platelet function include inhibitors of arachidonic acid metabolism (nonsteroidal antiinflammatory drugs, aspirin, indomethacin, etc.), drugs that alter membrane phospholipid composition (omega 3 fatty acids), stimulators of adenylyl cyclase (PGE_1, PGI_2, PGD_2, forskolin), guanylyl cyclase (nitric oxide, nitroglycerine, and nitroprusside) and calcium channel blockers (verapamil, nifedipine, diltiazem).[8]

Current research on the pharmacology of platelet activation inhibitory drugs is focused on the development of newer antithrombotic agents such as antibodies, fab-fragments, inhibitory peptides, and receptor antagonists.[9-13] Since platelets have multiple mechanisms for achieving activation, it would be rather difficult to develop a compound that is capable of causing complete inhibition of all activation signals. For instance, the intracellular calcium chelator, Quin 2, buffers cytosolic calcium and prevents agonist-mediated aggregation and secretion. However, Quin 2-loaded platelets still undergo shape change, develop stickiness, and adhere to exposed surfaces.

Strategies for the development of effective, safe antiplatelet drugs are based on our current understanding of thrombogenic and platelet activation mechanisms.[12,13] These strategies include interruption of platelet adhesion, specific receptor, integrin- or nonintegrin-dependent platelet interactions, inactivation of circulating and thrombus-bound thrombin, targeting antithrombotic and

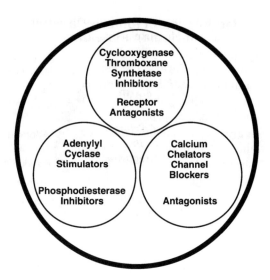

FIGURE 4. Major pharmacological approaches for the design of antiplatelet drugs. Major pharmacological approaches for designing antiplatelet drugs focused on preventing the formation of arachidonate metabolites and blocking secretion of granule contents. Some of the known anti-platelet drugs include cyclooxygenase/thromboxane synthetase inhibitors, specific receptor an-tagonists, stimulators of adenylyl and guanylyl cyclases, calcium chelators, calcium channel blockers, and antagonists.

fibrinolytic drugs to preformed thrombus, and modification of vascular wall or artificial surface thrombogenicity. In developing effective strategies, it is im-portant to evaluate the associated hemorrhagic risks.

Platelet adhesion involves binding of glycoprotein receptors to elements of the subendothelial extracellular matrix components such as collagen, von Willebrand factor (vWF), fibronectin, laminin, vitronectin, and thrombospondin. These adhesive proteins interact with platelet membrane glycoproteins, GPIb-IX, GPIIb/IIIa, GPIa/IIa, GPIc-IIa, and GPIV. Interactions between GPIb-IX and vWF support recruitment of platelets under high shear, whereas GPIIb/IIIa, under low shear, binds fibrinogen which is present in plasma in large quantities. Arginine-glycine-aspartic acid (RGD) serves as the integrin recognition se-quence in the adhesive proteins. The structural feature that is common in these peptides is the presence of aspartate residue. There is considerable interest in developing antibodies and inhibitory peptides to prevent platelet interaction with adhesive proteins and subendothelial matrix components. Monoclonal antibody 7E3 binds to GPIIb/IIIa and blocks the subsequent binding of adhesive proteins. In a preliminary phase I trial, patients with unstable angina have been treated with this antibody effectively.[14] Snake venoms contain peptides called disintegrins which also bind integrin receptors. Barbourin, a disintegrin peptide, is highly specific for preventing GPIIb/IIIa interaction with fibrinogen. A cyclic peptide directed against GPIIb/IIIa called "intergrelin" has been used to treat patients in phase I and phase II clinical trials.[14-19]

Thrombin is one of the most important modulators of platelet activation and recruitment. It can activate platelets at concentrations lower than that required to convert fibrinogen to fibrin. It can also activate platelets through ADP and TxA_2-mediated pathways. Therefore, there is considerable interest in developing antithrombin drugs. In addition to well-known agents like heparin capable of neutralizing thrombin action, recombinant hirudin, a 65 amino acid cysteine-rich polypeptide, has also been used effectively to antagonize the action of thrombin. Tripeptide D-Phe-Pro-Arg effectively blocks thrombin-mediated platelet activation, whereas the synthetic antithrombin D-Phe-Pro-Arg chloromethyl ketone (PPACK) irreversibly inactivates soluble thrombin as well as thrombus-bound thrombin.[20] All antithrombins tested so far interrupt platelet activation and platelet and fibrin deposition in a dose-dependent manner.

4. FACTORS MODULATING PLATELET FUNCTION

Several factors in blood contribute to the modulation of *in vivo* platelet responses. Hyperactivation of platelets may initiate a cascade of responses associated with thrombogenesis, whereas compromised platelet function may contribute to the pathogenesis of hemorrhagic conditions. Some of the major contributors to a procoagulant or thrombogenic state include altered hematocrit, hemorrheology, fibrinogen levels, various factors associated with coagulation cascade, vWF, protein c, protein s, lipid composition of serum blood cells, tissue plasminogen activator (TPA), TPA-inhibitor, prothrombin, antithrombin, catecholamines, platelet count, and platelet size.[1,2] Alterations in the levels or absence of these factors may lead to compromised hemostasis and result in hemorrhage.

Influence of exercise on hemostatic parameters such as fibrinolysis, factor vii, ristocetin cofactor, fibrinogen, antithrombin III, protein c, and plasminogen inhibitor levels have been documented.[21] However, little is known as to how exercise specifically influences the various factors that modulate platelet responses.

5. EFFECT OF EXERCISE ON PLATELET FUNCTION IN RACING ANIMALS

The majority of thoroughbred racing dogs (greyhounds) have platelets that do not respond with aggregation in response to catecholamines such as epinephrine and norepinephrine.[22] In addition, these platelets do not aggregate when stirred with arachidonate, although they synthesize normal amounts of cyclic endoperoxides (PGG_2/PGH_2) and thromboxane A_2. Contrary to this observation, approximately 30% of mongrels have platelets that do respond to arachidonate stimulation and aggregate irreversibly. However, epinephrine exposure restores the sensitivity of refractory canine platelets to the action of arachidonate.[22,23] We termed this phenomenon "membrane modulation." This novel mechanism is mediated via stimulation of alpha adrenergic receptors and restores the sensitivity of drug-induced refractory platelets to the action of physiologic agonists.[24] Although the majority of dogs have platelets that do not aggregate in response to epinephrine or thromboxane when tested individually *in vitro,* during exercise, these modulators are available *in vivo* to act synergistically. Therefore, canine platelets may perform normal functions in circulation during vigorous exercise. It is reasonable to speculate that racing dogs by and large will not encounter exercise-induced pulmonary hemorrhage or arterial thrombosis.

In an elegant study, Eidt et al.[25] monitored coronary blood flow in dogs with coronary artery stenoses and endothelial injury and demonstrated that treadmill exercise promotes cyclic alterations in the flow of blood. Based on their results using specific antagonists for sertonin, thromboxane, and catecholamines, they concluded that thromboxane and serotonin derived from activated platelets play an important role in the exercise-mediated cyclic flow variations in this model. However, in the absence of appropriate controls, the contribution of stenosis and endothelial injury to alterations observed in flow cannot be ruled out completely.

Exercise-induced pulmonary hemorrhage occurs frequently in racing horses. Based on endoscopic examination, it has been estimated that the incidence of bleeding in racing animals is between 45 to 80%.[26-30] The mechanisms responsible for this acquired coagulation defect is not clear. Studies done in our laboratory included analysis of biochemical constituents, evaluation of response of platelets to the action of physiological agonists, evaluation of ultrastructural features, and their interaction with the vascular surfaces.

Platelets from well-characterized bleeder horses and nonbleeder horses were used for this study.[26] Blood for these studies was drawn from resting horses. No significant differences could be demonstrated in the biochemistry, physiology or functional response of platelets from these two groups of horses.[27] However, in these studies no attempts were made to test the effect of exercise on the physiology and pharmacology of equine platelets.

In a separate study, Johnstone et al.[28] evaluated hemostatic parameters at rest and after moderate exercise in horses. They found that platelet function as assessed by the response of platelets from affected horses to agonists such as ADP, collagen, and platelet activating factor, were reduced. Similar to studies done in dogs, it has been shown that exercise induces elevation of circulating catecholamines in horses. Little is known about the hormonal levels in the affected horses and normal horses during various phases of exercise. Furosemide is used as a prophylactic treatment for preventing exercise-induced hemorrhage.[30] Olsen et al.[30] used a cyclooxygenase inhibitor, phenylbutazone, and demonstrated that inhibition of cyclooxygenase metabolites partially reversed the decrease in mean atrial pressure or pulmonary artery pressure. Cyclooxygenase inhibitors prevent the formation of both vasodilatory prostacyclin as well as vasoconstrictory metabolite thromboxane. Therefore, the observed effects may or may not be due to the effect of this drug on platelets. In addition, the observed effects may very well be due to the known vasodilatory effect of furosemide.

Recent studies in our laboratory have demonstrated that equine platelets do not respond with aggregation when exposed to epinephrine, norepinephrine, and arachidonate. Equine platelets, when challenged with arachidonate, synthesize normal amounts of TxA_2. Unlike canine platelets, the mechanism of membrane modulation mediated by alpha adrenergic receptor modulation fails to restore the sensitivity of platelets to the action of prostaglandin endoperoxides and TxA_2, and, therefore, equine platelets are relatively less responsive compared to that of platelets from humans and dogs.

Exercise will induce synthesis of normal amounts of prostacyclin (PGI_2), a potent vasodilator and platelet antagonist from vascular tissues. This alteration in the pharmacological modulation of platelet function by PGI_2/TxA_2 will further compromise platelet function and its ability to participate in the normal hemostatic process. Lack of platelet response to agonists such as epinephrine and TxA_2 and increased availability of circulating prostacyclin may initiate the exercise-induced pulmonary hemorrhage in racing horses. It looks as though nature has provided the animals with platelets that are relatively less responsive to the action of agonists. In the case of racing dogs, probably the most ideal athlete, the functional response of the platelets is fine-tuned to perform the usual role of maintaining the vascular tone and normal hemostasis. However, in the case of some racing thoroughbreds, this balance between various modulators of platelet function is shifted and the animals are, perhaps, predisposed for exercise-induced bleeding diathesis.

6. EFFECT OF EXERCISE ON PLATELET FUNCTION IN NORMAL INDIVIDUALS AND ENDURANCE-TRAINED SUBJECTS

Sporadic reports have appeared on the effect of exercise on various parameters of hemostasis, such as coagulation factors, platelet function, and fibrinolytic cascade. However, standardized definitive data on the effect of exercise on various biochemical events associated with hemostasis are not available. Earlier studies have shown that blood drawn after exercise clots better than blood drawn at rest. However, hypercoagulability as measured by activated partial thromboplastin time is observed postmaximumal exercise or after a marathon run more than after submaximal treadmill exercise (85% predicted heart rate). Whether or not platelet activation is involved in this exercise-induced alteration is not clear. Little change in other coagulation proteins have been reported as a result of exercise.[21]

Several studies have reported an increase in platelet count with exercise. However, it is not clear whether increased platelet count is a risk factor for the development of thrombotic episodes. Studies aimed at predicting *in vivo* platelet activation based on circulating level of platelet-released products have produced conflicting data. No data are available on exercise-induced activation of platelets using state of the art methods aimed at detecting activation-dependent molecules such as P-selectin (GMP-140), fibrinogen, or expression of activation-dependent platelet-bound epitope of glycoprotein IIb/IIIa. Several studies have demonstrated elevated levels of catecholamines during and immediately after exercise.[31] Similarly, the circulating levels of free fatty acids and proaggregatory metabolites TxA_2 as measured by plasma TxB_2 levels, increase during exercise. Plasma levels of endothelium derived vasodilatory metabolite prostacyclin also has been reported to be elevated during exercise.[31-34] However, no conclusive data are available on the levels of endothelium-derived relaxing factor (EDRF) or nitric oxide (NO) or endothelium-derived contracting factor (endothelin) during or immediately following exercise. Although not much is known about the influence of endothelin, a potent vasoconstrictor on platelet function, inhibitory influence of NO on platelet responses is well documented.[8] Therefore, if the level of NO increases during exercise as do the levels of PGI_2, then these products of endothelium will adversely affect platelet responses to the action of agonists. Several studies have demonstrated that during exercise, production of vascular PGI_2 increases. Under normal conditions, exercise-mediated production of PGI_2 down-regulates platelet function. However, some studies report that sensitivity of platelets to prostacyclin is compromised after vigorous exercise.

Exercise conditioning and endurance training modifies the exercise-induced alterations observed in normal unconditioned individuals.[35-41] A study by Carter et al.[41] demonstrated an association of increased bleeding time concurrent with reduced thromboxane production and elevated prostacyclin levels. However, these alterations were undetectable after exhaustive exercise of long duration. Therefore, in endurance trained individuals, like in the animal "models," there is a shift in the *in vivo* pharmacological modulators toward achieving restrained platelet activity and normal hemostasis.

7. EFFECT OF EXERCISE ON CIRCULATING LEVELS OF CATECHOLAMINES

Catecholamines play an important role in inducing platelet activation. Epinephrine is not only a platelet agonist, but is a potent synergist for the action of all other physiological agonists.[24] In addition, epinephrine also influences the formation of eicosanoids by liberating arachidonic acid from cell membranes. Free arachidonic acid is converted by platelets and vascular tissue to vasoactive metabolites TxA_2 and PGI_2, respectively.

An epidemiological study reported a correlation in deaths due to coronary artery disease and circadian rhythm, with an increase in cardiovascular deaths 3 to 4 h after arising. In a separate study, circulating levels of epinephrine were higher and platelets were active and stickier in the morning hours. Activated platelets serve as promoters of thrombin generation and facilitate formation of blood clots.

Platelets are not only stimulated by epinephrine, but also serve as storage sites for biogenic amines.[36] Anxiety and aerobic fitness seem to affect adrenoreceptor function. It has been shown that fitness positively influences platelet epinephrine accumulation and high trait anxiety interferes with this relationship. In a study aimed at determining the influence of exercise on platelet adrenoreceptors using yohimbine (an alpha adrenergic receptor antagonist) binding to determine receptor density, it was shown that maximal binding (B_{max}) and dissociation constant (KD) were significantly lower in endurance-trained individuals (148 fmol/10^9 cells; KD 0.92 nmol) than in nonendurance-trained individuals (284 fmol, KD = 1 to 79 nmol). In addition, studies have shown that sensitivity of platelets to epinephrine was reduced in endurance-trained subjects.[37] Using similar binding studies in a separate study, it was shown that trained athletes had a 45% increase in adrenergic receptors on platelets (338 ± 39 sites) than those of sedentary individuals (235 ± 25).[35]

In spite of the fact that this study demonstrated significantly increased numbers of alpha adrenergic receptors per platelet in endurance-trained individuals, the dissociation constant for the amines tested remained unchanged in the two groups studied (endurance trained vs. sedentary). Results of these studies and those reported by others suggest that short-term *in vivo* regulation of platelets may be modulated by changes in the affinity of receptors for a drug, whereas long-term changes in sensitivity may be mediated by alterations in the number of receptors. Available data fails to explain why the alpha adrenergic receptors are up-regulated (in terms of numbers) in endurance-trained individuals. It is also not clear how platelets from these well-conditioned individuals are down-regulated in terms of their *ex vivo* response to the action of agonists. However, physical fitness and endurance training seem to positively influence the response of platelets to catecholamines and their uptake and storage.[35-40]

Ability to do physical work decreases on ascent to high altitude. In an elegant study named "Operation Everest," researchers demonstrated that postexercise concentrations of plasma catecholamines were lower at high altitude compared with those at sea level.[39] Availability of free catecholamines is related to a variety of variables that exert their effect rather than one simple cause. In a recent study aimed at the elucidation of mechanisms responsible for increased incidence of essential hypertension among blacks, it was shown that at rest blacks had lower levels of norepinephrine (1275 pg/ml) than whites (1556 pg/ml), whereas they had higher epinephrine (306 pg/ml) levels than whites (216 pg/ml) at the highest work load.[40]

8. EFFECT OF EXERCISE ON PRODUCTION OF PROSTACYCLIN AND THROMBOXANE

Vasoactive metabolites of arachidonic acid, prostacyclin, and thromboxane modulate the platelet function by regulation of the primary messenger, ionized calcium.[2] Prostacyclin stimulates adenylyl cyclase and generates second messenger cyclic adenosine monophosphate (cAMP). This messenger modulates the level and availability of ionized calcium in platelets, whereas TxA_2 generated by platelets lowers the cAMP levels and facilitates the availability of ionized calcium.

Exercise at a heart rate equal to 30% VO_2max for 15 min increases the volume of bleeding per given duration of time from a mean of 133 µl at rest to 218 µl following exercise.[32] This exercise-induced alteration is accompanied by increase in circulating levels of thromboxane (6.4 to 11.5 nmol/l). However, the largest increases in bleeding time were associated with greater increase of vasodilatory PGI_2 availability (2.92 to 6.16 pg/min^{-1}). In this study, it was shown that a cyclooxygenase inhibitor, aspirin, which blocked the production of both PGI_2 and TxA_2, did not exert any additional effect on bleeding time. Acute low-level exercise resulted in increased bleeding time, whereas exhaustive exercise of long duration or long distance running did not cause significant changes in the bleeding time.[41]

In this study, the individuals who had increased bleeding time also had the greatest amounts of the vasodilatory metabolite, prostacyclin. Increased availability of this potent platelet antagonist may, therefore, have influenced the bleeding time in this group of individuals. Lack of any significant influence on exercise-mediated increase in bleeding time by aspirin suggests that the arachidonic metabolites may have a limited role in modulating the bleeding time. These results agree with our earlier studies in which we demonstrated that the platelet interaction with exposed subendothelium is not inhibited by aspirin.[36] Although platelets of cows and horses do not respond to thromboxanes, they support normal hemostasis in these animals. It is reasonable to speculate that marathon runners in this study had a fine-tuned balance between vasoactive metabolites PGI_2/TxA_2 and they exhibited normal hemostatic response.

Studies suggest that moderate ethanol ingestion and regular physical exercise offer some beneficial cardiovascular effects. Little is known about what should be the optimum intake of ethanol, the strength of ethanol, and the time of the day it offers its maximal beneficial effect. In a study to evaluate the effect of ethanol and exercise on platelet function, it was found that acute ethanol ingestion followed by exercise did not result in platelet hyperactivity.[42] Exercise alone decreased TxA_2 release and lowered the sensitivity of platelets to ADP. Fasting-mediated increase in plasma free fatty acids were enhanced by exercise. Exercise-induced increase in fatty acid release was lowered by ethanol ingestion as well as carbohydrate intake. Increased availability of free fatty acids may also have contributed to enhanced levels of PGI_2 and TxA_2 following exercise.

9. EFFECT OF EXERCISE ON PLATELET FUNCTION IN PATIENTS WITH VARIOUS DISORDERS

Platelet function is altered in various disease states such as asthma, hypertension, diabetes, and various complications associated with cardiovascular and cerebrovascular disease. Several factors contribute to the pathogenesis of vascular diseases. Known factors include hypertension, smoking, diabetes, cholesterol, triglycerides, obesity, and sedentary habits. Following the diagnosis of hypertension, diabetes, or coronary artery disease, patients are encouraged to increase their physical activity to reduce the risk factors associated with these diseases. In some patients with bronchial asthma, bronchoconstriction occurs following exercise, a phenomenon called exercise-induced asthma (EIA).[43-47] The exact mechanism involved in precipitating this state is unclear. However, in some cases, platelet activation has been shown to occur during EIA. Some studies have suggested that thromboxane A_2 may cause bronchial contraction,[43] whereas others have suggested a role for a mast cell-derived metabolite, prostaglandin D_2 (PGD_2).[44] Thromboxane A_2 is a major metabolite produced by platelets and is a potent agonist as well as vasoconstrictor. On the other hand, PGD_2 is a stimulator of platelet adenyl cyclase and therefore a potent antagonist. However, the researchers working on EIA suggest that PGD_2 works in the bronchial tissue via thromboxane receptors. Using a thromboxane receptor antagonist GR32191,[44] Finnery et al.[45] failed to demonstrate a role for PGD_2 in precipitating EIA. In a separate study, Magnussen et al.[44] induced EIA by nasal inhalation of PGD_2 in patients. They evaluated the effect of a specific thromboxane receptor antagonist, BAYU 3405 on EIA. They concluded from their results that PGD_2 had no major role in EIA. Thromboxane is a potent vasoconstrictor for bronchial smooth muscle, vascular smooth muscle, a proaggregatory metabolite and a chemotactic compound for leukocytes. In a novel study, Hushino and Fukushima[43] used a thromboxane synthetase inhibitor OKY-046 to alter the ratio of vascular PGI_2 to platelet TxA_2. Inhibition of thromboxane synthesis from platelets spares the cyclic endoperoxides from platelets and it is believed that these transient metabolites are used by vascular cells to synthesize vasodilatory PGI_2. In this study, the inhibitory effect of OKY-046 (oral 200 mg, 4 times a day) on treadmill exercise-induced asthma is attributed to the inhibition of TxA_2 and facilitation of PGI_2 synthesis.

Free fatty acids as well as various blood lipids that are susceptible for oxidation, generate lipid peroxides.[40-43] These lipid peroxides as well as free radicals could induce inhibition of nitric oxide synthetase as well as prostacyclin synthetase and reduce the availability of vasodilatory metabolites (Figure 5). In addition, lipid peroxides and free radicals will deplete platelet glutathione and alter arachidonic acid metabolism in favor of thromboxane generation. As a result of increased thromboxane synthesis, platelets release vasoconstrictory compounds such as serotonin, epinephrine and histamine (Figure 6).

It is well known that oxygen consumption by working muscle increases severalfold during strenuous exercise. Increased availablity and consumption of oxygen leads to formation of excess free radicals. Even in highly trained athletes, increased plasma lipid peroxides can be demonstrated following vigorous exercise. Little is known about the influence of exercise on the formation of lipid peroxides, free radicals, their influence on endothelial cell, platelet function, and the beneficial effect, if any, of prior consumption of antioxidants.

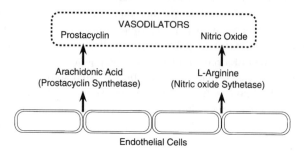

**Contribution of Endothelial Dysfunction to Vascular
Hypertension, Arterial Occlusion, Restenosis and Thrombosis**

Lipid Hydroperoxides and Oxidized Lipoproteins
Lower Endogenous Vasodilators

VASODILATORS
Prostacyclin   Nitric Oxide

Arachidonic Acid   L-Arginine
(Prostacyclin Synthetase)   (Nitric oxide Sythetase)

Endothelial Cells

FIGURE 5.   Contribution of endothelial dysfunction to vascular hypertension, arterial occlusion
and thrombosis. Endothelial cell dysfunction may contribute significantly to altered signaling.
Lipid hydroperoxides and oxidized lipoproteins may inhibit prostacyclin synthetase as well as
nitric oxide synthetase. Such inhibition may lead to lowered production of vasodilators, prostacyclin,
and nitric oxide.

Several studies have suggested alterations in the production of vascular
PGI_2 and platelet TxA_2 in diabetic patients. Koivisito et al.[54] followed the
effects of short- and long-term exercise on PGI_2/TxA_2 synthesis in Type 1
diabetic subjects. Their study demonstrated that during 40 min of cycling
exercise, the urinary excretion of 6 ketoPGF$_{1\alpha}$ (metabolite of PGI_2) increased
5.8-fold more in the control subjects than in patients. Serum TxB_2 increased
both in control and diabetic subjects. Similarly, urinary TxB_2 excretion was

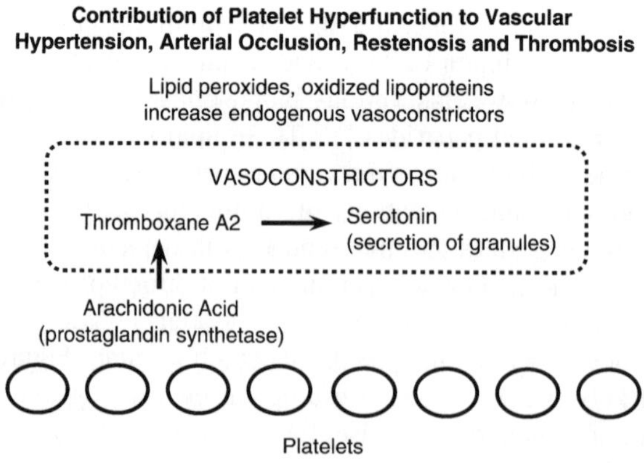

**Contribution of Platelet Hyperfunction to Vascular
Hypertension, Arterial Occlusion, Restenosis and Thrombosis**

Lipid peroxides, oxidized lipoproteins
increase endogenous vasoconstrictors

VASOCONSTRICTORS

Thromboxane A2   ⟶   Serotonin
(secretion of granules)

Arachidonic Acid
(prostaglandin synthetase)

Platelets

FIGURE 6.   Contribution of platelet hyperfunction to vascular hypertension, arterial occlusion,
restenosis, and thrombosis. Platelet hyperfunction may contribute significantly to altered cell
signaling. Lipid peroxides and oxidized lipoproteins may deplete platelet glutathione stores.
Platelets with lowered glutathione levels produce more thromboxane than those with normal levels
of protective antioxidants.

unaltered in both the groups during long-term exercise (a cross-country ski race). They concluded that diabetic patients have normal PGI_2 and TxA_2 synthesis in a resting state and diminished PGI_2 response to both acute and prolonged exercise.

There is considerable speculation that altered synthesis of PGI_2/TxA_2 and activation of platelets may occur during exercise in patients with angina pectoris. Twenty patients with stable angina pectoris were subjected to treadmill exercise and the blood samples analyzed for PGI_2/TxA_2 metabolites.[55] Platelet response to collagen was also evaluated. After exercise, plasma TxB_2 levels increased significantly. Platelet sensitivity to PGI_2 decreased in the patients, but increased in the control subjects. Although impaired sensitivity of platelets has been reported for PGI_2 in patients with angina pectoris, no data are available on the response of platelets to the other endothelium-derived vasodilatory metabolite, NO.

Several studies have examined the effect of exercise-induced myocardial ischemia on platelet function. It has been shown that serum TxB_2 level is increased in patients positive for ischemia as well as those who were negative for this condition (255 ± 150 to 314 ± 190 ng/ml, positive group; 240 ± 139 to 370 ± 169 ng/ml, negative group).[56] During vigorous exercise, there is usually an increase in circulating catecholamines, free fatty acids, potassium, and lactate.[57] Some studies have shown that exercise training of patients with coronary artery disease (CAD) will reduce the levels of catecholamines as it does in endurance-trained athletes. In a study aimed at evaluating the effect of exercise training on these parameters, it was found that norepinephrine levels were reduced at submaximal work but increased at the higher work load.[57] However, exercise training increased potassium levels and decreased free fatty acids. The use of a hot tub or sauna after exercise is widely enjoyed as a means of relaxation. Little is known of the effect of hot tub use following exercise on cardiovascular physiology, especially platelet function in patients with CAD.[58] Several studies have been done on the use of sauna by patients with CAD. The majority of Finnish CAD patients use sauna regularly within a year following myocardial infarction (MI) and no significant increase in heart attacks have been reported, suggesting a lack of any adverse influence on platelet function.[58]

What is the ideal exercise that one should recommend for patients with hypertension, diabetes, obesity, stable angina, and those with various phases of CAD? Exercise testing in the recovery phase after an MI has been extensively studied. Exercise test variables as markers of high risk have been described. Some of the known markers include development of angina during exercise, ST (EKG deflection due to ventricular contraction) segment-depression, and compromised hemodynamic response.[59-65] Although it is generally believed that the treadmill test is of limited value in identifying high risk patients, negative predictability (89% accuracy) identifies a group of patients with low risk.[61] Several studies have followed the effect of exercise on platelet activation. In spite of extensive studies done using exercise, modern techniques to determine exercise-induced platelet activation have not been applied.[63] The use of fluorescent antibodies for the detection of activation-dependent expression of adhesive molecules, and immunogenic epitopes will provide new and useful information regarding the state of platelet activation in these patients with various disorders. Although not much is known on the effect of exercise on platelet activity in patients with various cardiovascular disorders, it is widely accepted that exercise testing after MI to establish prognosis of the disease as well as a preventive protocol for lowering mortality and morbidity has a prominent role.[64]

When considering the effect of exercise on platelet physiology and pharmacology, it is important to keep in mind that *in vivo* function of these cells is modulated by a variety of factors operating at the blood vascular interface.[2,8] Just the shear stress, for instance, can raise the intracellular calcium levels in both endothelial cells and the platelets causing activation of these cells. Once they are activated, release of biologically active compounds will initiate a series of events aimed at generating either inhibitory or activation signals. Other blood cells, as well as a variety of factors available in circulation, play a role in the normal homeostasis of the microenvironment. However, when exercise-induced alterations occur in this microenvironment, it will be difficult to predict the effect of such changes on the physiology and pharmacology of one blood cell, without understanding how the other blood components modulate the physiology of the cell in question. For instance, if erythrocytes release ATP, it is hydrolyzed to ADP, a metabolite which is a potent stimulant of platelets. Similarly, many cells can generate platelet activation factor, also a powerful endogenous mediator of platelet activation. Release of hormones such as epinephrine or norepinephrine can initiate platelet activation or potentiate the response of other agonists. Smoking, which increases circulating fibrinogen levels will also increase the availability of platelet activating factor. Release of adhesion molecules and expression of these molecules will bring different cells into close contact. Platelets release a granule protein called p-selectin (GMP-140) which facilitates platelet neutrophil interaction. Similarly, platelet endothelial cell adhesion molecule (PECAM) brings these cells into proximity of each other. Even interaction of parasites, for example in erythrocytes (malaria), exposes a membrane receptor (CD 36, GPIV) which promotes platelet erythrocyte interaction. Therefore, when considering the effect of exercise on platelet physiology and pharmacology, it is essential to consider the effect of exercise not only on platelets, but on those factors that stimulate platelet activation as well.

10. PHARMACOLOGICAL INTERVENTIONS OF EXERCISE-INDUCED PLATELET ACTIVATION

Pharmacological approaches aimed at preventing *in vivo* platelet activation mainly focused on developing compounds capable of inhibiting the secretion of granule contents and the development of irreversible aggregation.[8] Some of the well known antiplatelet drugs include nonsteroidal agents such as aspirin and indomethacin, vasodilators (PGE_1, PGD_2, PGI_2) and calcium antagonists (Diltiazem, Nifedipine, Verapamil).

Although the majority of these compounds inhibit agonist-mediated secretion and irreversible aggregation, they do not prevent platelet interactions with the damaged vascular tissues or exposed cell matrix components such as collagen, fibronectin, and laminin. Patients taking potent antiplatelet drugs such as aspirin may develop myocardial ischemia or infarction following vigorous exercise since aspirin does not totally inhibit platelet function and therefore, cannot offer protection from platelet activation-mediated complications. It is therefore essential to closely monitor exercise-induced platelet activation in patients even if they are on antiplatelet drugs.

Several drugs have been evaluated to prevent or reduce the ill effects of exercise induced platelet activation.[66-87] Bopindolol, a nonselective beta-blocker has been shown to decrease bicycle exercise-induced platelet activation in male hypertensive patients.[80] The compound had a dual effect on platelet response. It counteracted the exercise-induced decrease in sensitivity to PGI_2 and it decreased the exercise-induced increase in serum TxB_2 levels.

In a separate study, it was shown that 8 weeks of isradipine (1.2 mg twice daily; a calcium antagonist) ingested by male hypertensives, lowered the serum levels of TxB_2, BTG and inhibited the *ex vivo* response of platelets to ADP.[81] These observations tend to support a concept that treatment of hypertension with a compound that lowers blood pressure and inhibits platelet activation may be of clinical benefit. Similar studies done with normotensive individuals with low-dose daily aspirin or some other compound that will reduce the availability of TxA_2 and serotonin, may offer considerable protection from exercise-induced platelet activation.

Patients with myocardial infarction are advised to perform moderate exercise. In a study aimed at preventing exercise-induced platelet activation, the effects of an antiplatelet drug were evaluated. Patients were given ticlopidine (500 mg daily) for 15 days. Blood samples were obtained to evaluate platelet function after 3 min vigorous exercise.[82] Exercise produced significant platelet activation. Ticlopidine ingestion significantly reduced *ex vivo* response of platelets to the action of agonists such as ADP, collagen, and AA as well as circulating aggregates both at rest and after the exercise tests.

Much of what is known about the effect of exercise on platelet physiology and pharmacology is derived from studies in adult men. Little is known about the influence of exercise on platelet responses in women or children. Major clinical trials enroll very few or no female or child subjects, despite the fact that cardiovascular disease is one of the leading causes of mortality in women. Some of the risk factors for CAD are the same for both men and women, but a few are unique to women. A strong relationship between the use of oral contraceptives and incidence of CAD has been reported. It has been estimated that morbidity and mortality due to MI in women is greater than that in men, although it occurs 10 to 20 years later in their lives. In view of the fact that women have greater risk for CAD, studies should be initiated to evaluate the effect of exercise on the factors that stimulate *in vivo* platelet responses.

In conclusion, exercise, whether it is acute or trained, induces activation of platelets in untrained as well as endurance-trained individuals. The exact mechanism that mediates exercise-induced platelet activation is not clear. An increase in blood pressure from enhanced heart rate, the availability of proaggregatory compounds such as catecholamines, ADP, and platelet activating factor (PAF) may serve as contributing factors. Imbalance in the production of vasoactive metabolites will also adversely affect the *in vivo* platelet response. In addition, the sensitivity of platelets to these metabolites will also determine the extent of activation that occurs during exercise. Beta-blockers, calcium antagonists, ticlopidine and thromboxane synthetase inhibitors have been tested for their ability to prevent exercise-mediated platelet activation.[80-87] A variety of compounds in addition to the known antiplatelet drugs retard or restrain the activity of platelets. Antioxidants such as butylated hydroxyanisole (BHA), butylated hydroxytoluene (BHT), ascorbic acid, vitamin E, and polyenoic acids (eicosapentanoic acid, EPA, docosahexanoic acid, DHA) also influence *in vivo* platelet response.

Future studies should include investigations on exercise-induced alterations in such altered physiological states as hypertension, pregnancy, and stress. There is considerable data to suggest that the observed hypertension in some pregnant women is due to platelet activation and increased production and release of vasoconstrictory compounds such as thromboxane and serotonin. Some studies have shown the beneficial effects of low-dose aspirin in preventing pregnancy-mediated hypertension.[88-93] Further clinical studies are needed to establish the exact dose of aspirin to obtain beneficial effects of this drug without any adverse effect on the development and health of the fetus. Similarly, clinical trials have to be done to identify a subpopulation of individuals who suffer from hypertension as a result of increased platelet activation and vasoconstrictory metabolites, so appropriate preventive protocols can be offered to such individuals before they are started on an exercise program.

No definitive data are available on what would be the ideal preventive protocol, and who should take such preventive measures to obtain maximum protection from any ill effects related to exercise-mediated complications induced by platelet activation. Considering the immense popularity that sports enjoy in the industrialized world, further intensive studies are warranted to generate new and useful information on how to maximize the beneficial effects of vigorous exercise.

ACKNOWLEDGMENTS

The author wishes to thank Mss. Julie Y. Lee and Janet D. Peller, and Dr. James G. White for their technical assistance, and Mss. Brenda Wernick and Susan Schwarze for their help in the preparation of the manuscript.

This work was supported by NIH grants HL11880 and HL49556 and a grant from the University of Minnesota Center for Interfacial Engineering.

REFERENCES

1. **Rao, G. H. R., Rao, A. S. C., and White, J. G.,** Aspirin in ischemic heart disease — an overview, *Ind. Heart J.,* 45, 73, 1993.
2. **Rao, G. H. R.,** Physiology of blood platelet activation, *Ind. J. Physio. Pharmacol.,* 37, 263, 1994.
3. **American College of Cardiology/American Heart Association,** Guidelines for exercise testing. A report of the American College of Cardiology/American Heart Association. Task force on association of diagnostic and therapeutic cardiovascular procedures (subcommittee on exercise testing), *J. Am. Coll. Cardiol.,* 8, 725, 1986.
4. **American College of Cardiology/American Heart Association,** Guidelines for the early management of patients with acute myocardial infarction. A report of the American College of Cardiology/American Heart Association task force on assessment of diagnostic and therapeutic cardiovascular procedures (subcommittee to develop guidelines for the early management of patients with acute myocardial infarction), *J. Am. Coll. Cardiol.,* 16, 249, 1990.
5. **Stevenson, R., Umachandran, V., Ranjadayalam, K., Wilkinson, P., Marchant, B., and Timmis, A. S.,** Reassessment of treadmill stress testing for risk stratification in patients with acute myocardial infarction treated by thrombolysis, *Br. Heart J.,* 70, 415, 1993.
6. **White, J. G.,** Platelet membrane ultrastructure and its changes during platelet activation, in *Platelet Membrane Receptors, Molecular Biology and Pathology,* Jamieson, G.A., Ed., Alan R. Liss, New York, 1988.
7. **Seiss, W.,** Molecular mechanisms of platelet activation, *Physiol. Rev.,* 69, 58, 1989.
8. **Rao, G. H. R.,** Pharmacology of platelet activation inhibitory drugs, *Ind. J. Physiol. Pharmacol.,* 38, 69, 1994.
9. **Sherman, D. G., Dyken, M. L., Fischer, M., Gent, M., Harrison, M., and Hart, R. G.,** Antithrombotic therapy for cerebrovascular disease, *Chest,* 102, 5295, 1992.
10. **Cairns, J. A., Hirsh, J., Lewis, H. D., Resnekov, L., and Theroux, P.,** Antithrombotic agents in coronary artery disease, *Chest,* 102, 4565, 1992.
11. **Fuster, V., Dyken, M. L., Vokonas, P. S., and Hennekens, C.,** Aspirin as a therapeutic agent in cardiovascular disease, *Circulation,* 87, 659, 1993.
12. **Leung, L., Charo, I. F., and Califf, R. M.,** Newer approaches to antithrombotic therapy, *Educ. Prog. Am. Soc. Hematol.,* 95, 1993.
13. **Herman, J. R., Herman, W. R. M., Vos, J., and Serrays, P. W.,** Pharmacological approaches to the prevention of restenosis following angioplasty. The search for the holy grail? Part I, *Drugs,* 46, 18, 1993.
14. **Simoons, M. L., Jan de Boer, M., Brand van den, J. B. M. M., Van Miltenburg, A. J. M., Hoorntje, J. C. A., Heyndrickx, G. R., van der Wieken, R. L., De Bono, D., Rutsch, W., Schaible, T. F., Weisman, H. F., Klootwijk, P., Nijssen, K. M., Stibbe, J., De Feyter, P. J., and the European Cooperative Study Group,** Randomized trial of a GPIIb/IIIa platelet receptor blocker in refractory unstable angina, *Circulation,* 89: 596, 1994.
15. **Kleinman, N. S., Ohman, M. E., Califf, R. M., George, B. S., Kereiakes, D., Aguirre, F., Bates, E., Schaible, T., and Topel, E. J.,** Profound inhibition of platelet aggregation with monoclonal antibody 7E3Fab following thrombolytic therapy: results of the TAMI 8 pilot study, *J. Am. Coll. Cardiol.,* 22, 381, 1993.

16. **Ellis, S. G., Tcheng, J. E., Navetta, F. I., Muller, D. W., Weisman, H. F., Smith, C., Anderson, K. M., Califf, R. M., and Topol, E. J.,** Safety and antiplatelet effect of murine monoclonal antibody 7E3Fab directed against platelet glycoprotein IIb/IIIa in patients undergoing elective coronary angioplasty, *Cor. Art. Dis.,* 4, 167, 1993.

17. **Tcheng, J. E., Kleinman, N. S., Miller, M. J., Sane, D. S., Wang, A. L., and Weisman, H. F.,** Chimeric antiplatelet GPIIb/IIIa receptor antibody (C-7E3) in elective PTCA: safety and platelet function inhibition, *Circulation,* 84(Suppl. 11), 11-590 2344(Abstr.), 1992.

18. **Bernardi, M. M., Califf, R. M., Kleiman, N., Ellis, S. G., and Topol, E. J., (for the TAMI Study Group),** Prolonged bleeding times do not predict hemorrhagic events in patients receiving the 7E3 glycoprotein in IIb/IIIa platelet antibody, *Circulation,* 86(Suppl. 1), 1-260 1035(Abstr.), 1992.

19. **Topol, E. J. and Plow, E. F.,** Clinical trials of platelet receptor inhibitors, *Thromb. Haemost.,* 70, 94, 1993.

20. **Mavaganore, J. M.,** Thrombin, thrombin inhibitors and the arterial thrombotic process, *Thromb. Haemost.,* 70, 208, 1993.

21. **Bourey, R. E. and Santoro, S. A.,** Interactions of exercise, coagulation, platelets and fibrinolysis — a brief review, *Med. Sci. Sports Exerc.,* 20, 439, 1988.

22. **Johnson, G. J., Leiss, L. A., Rao, G. H. R., and White, J. G.,** Arachidonate-induced platelet aggregation in the dog, *Thromb. Res.,* 14, 147, 1979.

23. **Johnson, G. J., Rao, G. H. R., Leiss, L. A., and White, J. G.,** Effects of agents which alter cyclic AMP on arachidonate-induced platelet aggregation in the dog, *Blood,* 55, 722, 1980.

24. **Rao, G. H. R. and White, J. G.,** Epinephrine-induced platelet membrane modulation, in *The Platelet Amine Storage Granules,* Meyer, K. M. and Barnes, C. D., Eds., CRC Press, Boca Raton, FL, 1992, 117.

25. **Eidt, J. F., Ashton, J., Golino, P., McNatt, J., Buja, L. M., and Willerson, J. J.,** Treadmill exercise promotes cyclic alterations in coronary blood flow in dogs with coronary artery stenosis and endothelial injury, *J. Clin. Invest.,* 84, 517, 1989.

26. **White, J. G., Matlack, C., Mundschenk, D., and Rao, G. H. R.,** Platelet studies in normal and a bleeder horse, *First Int. Symp. Equine Hematol.,* 1975, p. 209.

27. **Weiss, D. J., McClay, C. B., Smith, C. M., Rao, G. H. R., and White, J. G.,** Platelet function in the racing thoroughbred, implications for exercise-induced pulmonary hemorrhage, *Vet. Clin. Pathol.,* 19, 35, 1990.

28. **Johnstone, I. B., Viel, L., Crane, S., and Whiting, J.,** Hemostatic studies in racing standard bred horses with exercise-induced pulmonary hemorrhage, hemostatic parameters at rest and after moderate exercise, *Can. J. Vet. Res.,* 55, 101, 1991.

29. **Donaldson, L. L.,** A review of pathophysiology of exercise-induced pulmonary hemorrhage in the equine athlete, *Vet. Res. Comm.,* 15, 211, 1991.

30. **Olsen, S. C., Coyne, C. P., Lowe, B. S., Pelletier, N., Raub, E. M., and Erickson, H. H.,** Influence of cyclooxygenase inhibitors on furosemide-induced hemodynamic effects on exercise in horses, *Am. J. Vet. Res.,* 53, 1562, 1992.

31. **Krock, L. P. and Hartung, G. H.,** Influence of postexercise activity on plasma catecholamines, blood pressure and heart rate in normal subjects, *Clin. Auto. Res.,* 2, 89, 1992.

32. **Schonweter, D. J., Gerrard, J. M., and Dyck, D. G.,** Type A behavior and alcohol consumption, effect on resting and postexercise bleeding time thromboxane and prostacyclin metabolites, *Prost. Leukot. Essent. Fatty Acids,* 48, 143, 1993.

33. **Piret, A., Niset, G., Depiesse, E., Wyna, W., Boeynaems, J., Poortmans, J., and Degre, S.,** Increased platelet aggregability and prostacyclin biosynthesis induced by intense physical exercise, *Thromb. Res.,* 57, 685, 1990.

34. **Wilson, J. R. and Kapoor, S. C.,** Contribution of prostaglandins to exercise-induced vasodilation in humans, *Am. J. Physiol.,* 265, H171, 1993.

35. **Lockette, W., McCurdy, R., Smith, S., and Carretero, O.,** Endurance training and human A_2-adrenergic receptors on platelets, *Med. Sci. Sports Exerc.,* 19, 7, 1987.

36. **Rao, G. H. R. and White J. G.,** Epinephreine-induced platelet membrane modulation, in *The Platelet Amine Storage Granule,* Meyers, K. M. and Barnes, C. D., Eds., CRC Press, Boca Raton, FL, 1992, chap. 6.

37. **Lehman, M., Hasler, H., Bergdolt, E., and Keul, J.,** Alpha 2 andrenoreceptor density on platelets and adrenaline-induced platelet aggregation in endurance-trained subjects, *Int. J. Sports Med.,* 7, 172, 1980.

38. **Yoshizumi, M., Nakaya, Y., Hibino, T., Nomura, M., Minakuchi, K., Kitagawa, T., Katoh, I., Ohuchi, K., and Oka, M.,** Changes in plasma free and sulfaconjugated catecholamines before and after acute physical exercise, experimental and clinical studies, *Life Sci.,* 51, 227, 1992.

39. **Young, P. M., Sutton, J. R., Green, H. J., Reeves, J. T., Rock, P. B., Houston, C. S., and Cymerman, A.,** Operation Everest II, metabolic and hormonal responses to increment exercise to exhaustion, *J. Appl. Physiol.,* 73, 2574, 1992.

40. **Walker, A. J., Bassett, D. R., Duey, J. W., Howley, E. T., Bond, V., Torok, D. J., and Macuso, P.,** Cardiovascular and plasma catecholamine responses to exercise in blacks and whites, *Hypertension,* 20, 542, 1992.

41. **Carter, J. W., Ready, E. Z., Singhroy, S., Duta, E., and Gerrard, J. M.,** The effects of exercise on bleeding time and local production of prostacyclin and thromboxane, *J. Appl. Physiol.,* 59, 355, 1989.

42. **Numminen, H., Hillbon, M., Vapaatalo, H., Seppala, E., Laustiola, K., Benthin, G., Mauuronen, A., and Kaste, M.,** Effects of exercise and ethanol ingestion on platelet thromboxane release in healthy men, *Metabolism,* 40, 695, 1991.

43. **Hushino, M. and Fukushima, Y.,** Effect of OKY-046 (thromboxane A_2 synthetase inhibitor) on exercise-induced asthma, *J. Asthma,* 28, 19, 1991.

44. **Magnussen, H., Boerger, S., Templin, K., and Baunack, A. R.,** Effects of a thromboxane-receptor antagonist BAYu3405, on prostaglandin D_2 and exercise-induced bronchoconstriction, *J. Allergy Clin. Immunol.,* 89, 1119, 1992.

45. **Finnery, J. P., Twentyman, O. P., Harris, A., Palmer, J. B. D., and Holgate, S. T.,** Effect of GR32191, a potent thromboxane receptor antagonist on exercise induced bronchoconstriction in asthma, *Thorax,* 46, 190, 1991.

46. **Manning, P. J., Watson, R. M., and Byrne, P. M.,** Exercise-induced refractoriness in asthmatic subjects involves leukotines and prostaglandin independent mechanisms, *Am. Rev. Respir. Dis.,* 148, 1950, 1993.

47. **Sakane, T., Kato, M., and Ozawa, T.,** Role of prostaglandins in exercise-induced asthma, *Adv. Physiol. Sci.,* 10, 369 1980.

48. **Fitscha, P., Virgolini, I., Rauscha, F., and Sinzinger, H.,** Effects of isradipine on platelet function in hypertension at rest and during exercise, *Am. J. Hyperten.,* 4, 1785, 1991.

49. **Maxwell, S. R. J., Jakeman, P., Thomason, H., Leguen, C., and Thorpe, G. H. G.,** Changes in plasma antioxidant status during eccentric exercise and the effect of vitamin supplementation, *Free Rad. Res. Comm.,* 19, 191, 1993.

50. **Sumida, S., Tanaka, K., Kitao, H., and Nakadomo, F.,** Exercise-induced lipid peroxidation and leakage of enzymes before and after vitamin E supplementation, *Int. J. Biochem.,* 21, 835, 1987.

51. **Dillard, C. J., Litov, R. E., Savin, W. M., Dumelin, J. E., and Tappel, A. L.,** Effects of exercise, vitamin E and ozone on pulmonary function and lipid peroxidation, *J. Appl. Physiol.,* 45, 927, 1978.

52. **Kanaley, J. A., Cryer, P. E., and Jensen, M. D.,** Fatty acid kinetic responses to exercise, effects of obesity, body fat distribution and energy restricted diet, *J. Clin. Invest.,* 92, 255, 1993.

53. **Taylor, P. A. and War, A.,** Women, high-density lipoprotein cholesterol and exercise, *Arch. Intern. Med.,* 153, 1178, 1993.

54. **Koivisito, V. A., Jantunen, M., Sane, T., Helve, E., Pelkonen, R., Viinikka, L., and Ylikorkala, O.,** Stimulation of prostacyclin synthesis by physical exercise in type 1 diabetes, *Diabetic Care,* 12, 609, 1989.

55. **Trovati, M., Anfossi, G., DeFacis, R., Mularoni, R., Massucco, P., Cavalot, F., and Burzacca, S.,** Moderate exercise increases platelet function in type 1 diabetic patients without severe angiopathy and in good control, *Diabetic Care,* 15, 1742, 1992.

56. **McGill, M., McGuiness, J., Lloyd, J., and Ardlie, N.,** Platelet function and exercise-induced myocardial ischaemia in coronary heart disease patients, *Thromb. Res.,* 15, 147, 1989.

57. **MacGowan, G. A., Casey, M., Stirling, R., Brett, M., Kinsella, A., and Horgan, J. H.,** Exercise-related potassium and free fatty acid level changes in coronary artery disease, responses after intensity training, *Chest,* 103, 728, 1993.

58. **Alyson, T., Miller, T. D., Squires, R. W., and Gerald, T. G.,** Cardiovascular responses to immersion in a hot tub in comparison with exercise in male subjects with coronary artery disease, *Mayo. Clin. Proc.,* 68, 19, 1993.

59. **Schuler, G., Hambrecht, R., Schliere, G., Niebauer, J., Hauer, K., Neumann, J., Hoberg, M. D., Drinkmann, A., Bacher, F., Grunze, M., and Kubler, W.,** Regular physical exercise and low-fat diet, effects on progression of coronary artery disease, *Circulation,* 86, 1, 1992.

60. **Cross, S. J., Lee, H. S., Kenmure, A., Walton, S., and Jennings, K.,** First myocardial infarction in the under 60 year old, the role of exercise testing and symptoms in detecting whom to catheterize, *Br. Heart J.,* 70, 428, 1993.

61. **Stevenson, R., Umachandran, V., Ranjadayalan, K., Wilkinson, P., Merchant, B., and Timmis, A. D.,** Reassessment of treadmill stress testing for risk stratification in patients with acute myocardial infarction treated by thrombolysis, *Br. Hem. J.,* 70, 415, 1993.

62. **Murray, R. G.,** Which patients should have exercise testing after myocardial infarction treated by thrombolysis, *Br. Heart J.,* 70, 399, 1993.

63. **Yamazaki, H., Koyabashi, J., and Shimamoto, T.,** Enhancement of ADP-induced platelet aggregation by exercise test in coronary patients and its prevention by pyridinolcarbamate, *Thromb. Diath. Heaemorh.,* 24, 438, 1970.

64. **Sano, J., Motomaya, T., and Yamazaki, H.,** Platelet release reaction in vivo in patients with ischemic heart disease after isometric exercise and its prevention with Iypyridemole, *Thromb. Haemost.,* 42, 1589, 1979.

65. **Frishman, W. H., Weksler, B., Christodoulou, J. P., Smither, C., and Killip, T.,** Reversal of abnormal platelet aggregability and change in exercise tolerance in patients with angina pectoris following oral propranolol, *Circulation,* 50, 887, 1974.

66. **Green, L. H., Seroppiman, E., and Handin, R. I.,** Platelet activation during exercise induced myocardial ischemia, *N. Engl. J. Med.,* 302, 193, 1980.

67. **Kumpris, A. G., Luchi, R. J., Waddell, C. C., and Miller, R. R.,** Production of circulating platelet aggregates by exercise in coronary patients, *Circulation,* 61, 62, 1980.

68. **Morris, J. N., Pollard, R., Everitt, M. G., and Chave, S. P. W.,** Vigorous exercise in leisure time, protection against CHD, *Lancet,* 2, 1207, 1980.

69. **Gallino, A., Haberli, A., Straub, P. W., Steinbrunn, W. S., Turina, M., and Rothlin, M. E.,** Does exercise-induced myocardial ischaemia cause enhanced platelet activation and fibrin formation in patients with stable angina and sever coronary artery disease?, *Eur. Heart J.,* 8, 736, 1987.

70. **Hamm, C. W., Lorenz, R. L., Bleifeld, W., Kupper, W., Wober, W., and Weber, P. C.,** Biochemical evidence of platelet activation in patients with persistent angina, *J. Am. Col. Cardiol.,* 10, 998, 1987.

71. **Sinzinger, H. and Virgolini, I.,** Effects of exercise on parameters of blood coagulation, platelet function and the prostaglandin system, *Sports Med.,* 6, 238, 1988.

72. **Wennmalm, A., Edlund, A., Sevastik, B., and Fitzgerald, G. A.,** Excretion of thromboxane A_2 and prostacyclin metabolites during treadmill exercise in patients with intermittent claudication, *Clin. Physiol.,* 8, 243, 1988.

73. **Kurita, A., Taekase, B., Uehata, A., Sataomura, K., Sugawara, H., Kondo, S., Arakawa, K., Shibuya, K., and Nakamura, H.,** The role of prostacyclin during exercise in patients with chronic angina pectoris, *Jpn. Heart J.,* 29, 401, 1988.

74. **Lassila, R. and Laustiola, K. E.,** Physical exercise provokes platelet desensitization in men who smoke cigarettes — involvement of sympathoadrenergetic mechanisms. A study of monozygotic twin pairs discordant for smoking, *Thromb. Res.,* 51, 145, 1988.

75. **Kishi, Y., Numano, F., and Oniki, G.,** Altered sensitivity to prostacyclin may be involved in the exercise-induced activation of platelets in patients with ischemic heart disease, *Prost. Clin. Res.,* 181, 1989.

76. **Davis, R. B., Boyd, D. G., McKinney, M. E., and Jones C. C.,** Effects of exercise and exercise conditioning on blood platelet function, *Med. Sci. Sports Exerc.,* 22, 49, 1990.

77. **Wennmalm, A., Nowak, J., and Bjuro, T.,** Excretion of thromboxane A_2 and prostacyclin metabolites before and after exercise testing in patients with and without ischemic heart disease, *Circulation,* 8, 243, 1988.

78. **Naesh, O., Hindberg, J., Trap, Jensen, J., and Lund, J. O.,** Postexercise platelet-activation-aggregation and release in reaction to dynamic exercise, *Clin. Physiol.,* 10, 221, 1990.

79. **Kishi, Y., Ashikaga, T., and Numan, F.,** Inhibition of platelet aggregation by prostacyclin is attenuated after exercise in patients with angina pectoris, *Am. Heart J.,* 123, 291, 1992.

80. **Virgolini, I., Fitscha, P., Rauscha, F., and Sinzinger, H.,** Effects of bopindolol on platelet function in hypertension at rest and during exercise, *Prost. Leukot. Essent. Fatty Acids,* 40, 125, 1990.

81. **Fitscha, P., Virgolini, I., Rauscha, F., and Sinzinger, H.,** Effects of isradipine on platelet function in hypertension at rest and during exercise, *Am. J. Hyperten.,* 4, 1785, 1991.

82. **Tullio, D., Valerio, A., Ottaviano, M. A., Diguliemo, L., Accettura, P., Caraceni, C. E., and Sclocco, T.,** Effects of ticlopidine on platelet function at rest and after exercise in patients with previous myocardial infarction. An acute crossover double-blind study, *Minerva Med.,* 81, 87, 1990.

83. **Sengelov, H. and Winther, K.,** Effects of felodipine, a new calcium channel antagonist, on platelet function and fibrinolytic activity at rest and after exercise, *Eur. J. Clin. Pharmacol.,* 37, 453, 1989.

84. **Ohnishi, A., Ishizaki, T., Echizen, H., Yasuda, K., Fujiwara, H., and Tanaka, T.,** Effects of sustained thromboxane synthetase induced changes in eicosanoid production, catecholamine concentaration and platelet aggregation in humans, *Clin. Pharamcol. Ther.,* 51, 454, 1992.

85. **Bourey, R. E. and Santoro, S. A.,** Interactions of exercise, coagulation, platelets and fibrinolysis — a brief series, *Med. Sci. Sports Exerc.,* 20, 439, 1988.

86. **Prisco, D., Francalanci, I., Fillippini, M., and Hagi, M. I.,** Physical exercise and hemostasis, *Int. J. Clin. Lab. Res.,* 24, 125, 1994.

87. **Kuhn, F. E. and Rackley, C. E.,** Coronary artery disease in women, *Arch. Int. Med.,* 153, 2626, 1993.

88. **Fitzgerald, D. J., Entman, S. S., Mulloy, K., and Fitzgerald, G. A.,** Decreased prostacyclin biosynthesis preceding the clinical manifestation of pregnancy-induced hypertension, *Circulation,* 75, 956, 1987.

89. **Fitzgerald, D. J., Mayo, G., Gatella, F., Entman, S. S., and Fitzgerald, G. A.,** Increased thromboxane biosynthesis in normal pregnancy is mainly derived from platelets, *Am. J. Obstet. Gynecol.,* 157, 325, 1987.

90. **Fitzgerald, D. J., Rocki, W., Murray, R., Mayo, G., and Fitzgerald, G. A.,** Thromboxane A_2 synthesis in pregnancy-induced hypertension, *Lancet,* 335, 751, 1990.

91. **Zahradnik, H. P., Schafer, W., Wetzka, B., and Breckwoldt, M.,** Hypertensive disorders in pregnancy. The role of eicosanoids, *Eicosanoids,* 4, 123, 1991.

92. **Fitzgerald, G. A., Price, P., Rocki, W., and Fitzgerald, D. J.,** Thromboxane A_2 in pregnancy-induced hypertension, *Issues Nephrosci.,* 1, 3, 1991.

93. **Louden, K. A.,** The use of low dose aspirin in pregnancy, *Clin. Pharmacokinet.,* 23, 90, 1992.

Chapter 10

EXERCISE, DRUGS, AND THE CARDIOVASCULAR SYSTEM

Stuart Frank

CONTENTS

1. EPIDEMIOLOGIC CONSIDERATIONS

1.1. GENERAL HEALTH AND FITNESS

The role of exercise in maintaining good health and fitness has become clearly established and widely accepted in our society. The mechanisms by which these benefits are implemented are still controversial and are probably multifactorial. Definitive evidence that exercise is beneficial both in terms of

0-8493-8540-1/96/$0.00+$.50
© 1996 by CRC Press, Inc.

general good health and fitness but more specifically with regard to cardiovascular health and mortality is still not available.

Exercise has become a fundamental part of the nonpharmacologic treatment as well as prevention of a vast array of medical problems from obesity to diabetes and arthritis. Regular exercise has become an aggressive part of most school curricula. Exercise during pregnancy is encouraged, workplace exercise programs are flourishing, middle-aged men and women are starting regular exercise programs, and modified exercise protocols have been established for the elderly and for the disabled. Health clubs multiply and our entire society has accepted this phenomenon. Unfortunately, little consideration has been given to the costs, the complications and the consequences, no less the benefits.

Nevertheless, a number of prestigious organizations such as the American Heart Association, the American College of Cardiology,[1] the National Heart Lung and Blood Institute,[2] the British Joint Working Party,[3] and the U.S. Department of Health and Human Services[4] recommend that individuals without specific contraindications engage in regular physical activity. The benefits associated with exercise, an improvement in the state of well-being associated with its low cost and relative freedom from complications makes this a reasonably prudent recommendation. Based on observational studies and meta-analysis of these studies,[2] physical inactivity has been determined to be an independent risk factor for coronary heart disease.

Many individuals who participate in either structured or informal exercise programs take medications either for treatment of an acute short-term illness or chronically, for treatment of a vast array of medical illnesses. Little consideration is given to what effects medications may have on the exercise or what the effects of exercise are on the metabolism, the kinetics, and specifically the effectiveness of these medications in controlling disease.

This paper will review the interactions of exercise and the cardiovascular drugs given to these patients, the effects of the drugs on their ability to exercise, as well as the effects of the exercise on the drugs. This review will be confined to studies on human subjects except where only animal studies are available to evaluate important issues.

1.2. EXERCISE AND CARDIAC PATIENTS

Evaluation of the effects of physical activity on any of a variety of complex physiologic phenomena in humans is complicated with potential intrinsic and extrinsic confounders that need to be taken into account, both in evaluating the results of previous studies as well as in the design of future studies (Table 1). These include:

- Subjects who enter into regular exercise programs tend to be healthier than those who pursue a more sedentary lifestyle.
- The drop-out rate in subjects assigned to exercise is usually in excess of 30% and in some studies as high as 50% with higher attrition in subgroups with one or multiple risk factors,[5] and estimates of regular exercise among control subjects are in the range of 30%.

TABLE 1
Confounding Factors in Exercise Studies

Self selection process: inclusion of healthier subjects in exercise studies and exclusion of
  sicker subjects
High attrition in exercise group and unregulated exercise in control subjects
Uncontrolled modifications of other risk factors in exercise groups
Relatively transient benefits of exercise
Documentation of exercise status prior to study not determined
Subjective changes with exercise alter perception of benefits
Inadequate numbers of subjects for reliable statistical analysis
Less than optimal levels of exercise

- Although most studies attempt to control for associated risk factors prior to initiation of exercise, lifestyle modifications that often accompany fitness programs can neither be controlled nor corrected for.
- The benefits of exercise treatment are relatively transient and discontinuation of treatment generally allows the system to revert to its pretreatment status. The benefits of exercise are hard to demonstrate in as little as a few days after the exercise is interrupted or terminated, and certainly after a few weeks or a few months. Regular exercise has been shown, for example, to consistently increase the HDL cholesterol,[6] but blood levels revert to their baseline, preexercise state in as little as 5 to 7 days after discontinuation of regular physical activity.
- Historical documentation of activity prior to and during an exercise program is difficult to assess in an unsupervised study group. In addition, quantification of extra exercise activity can potentially confound results unless such things as occupation, socioeconomic status, and usual leisure activity are taken into account and controlled.
- Subjects who engage in regular physical activity tend to generally feel better, their sense of well-being is improved, they become more optimistic and less depressed, require less medication, and have greater physical capacity.[7-9]
- Many exercise programs register more patients in the exercise group than in the control group and some studies have inadequate numbers of control subjects for reliable statistical analysis.[10]
- Some studies and exercise programs require less than recommended or optimal levels of exercise.[11]

These potentially confounding factors are summarized in Table 1.

Most exercise studies to date are well conducted and consistent with the concept that regular vigorous physical activity decreases the incidence and severity of coronary heart disease, as well as a number of associated parameters. However, there are major and irreconcilable inconsistencies in some of these studies. These limitations are too serious and too systematic to accept the results without some reservations. "It must be emphasized that firm evidence establishing that physical conditioning will decrease coronary heart disease

TABLE 2

Benefits of Exercise

Decreased incidence of fatal recurrent infarctions[2,15]
Decreased severity of atherosclerosis[2]
Increased HDL cholesterol[21,22]
Increased exercise tolerance and less myocardial ischemia[2]
Decreased cardiac mortality after MI[27]
Decreased risk MI[28]
Lowered systolic and diastolic BP[29-31]
Lowered peripheral resistance in acute exercise[33]
Improved glucose tolerance[35]
Increased fibrinolytic activity[36]
Favorable effect on fibrinogen and blood viscosity[37]

No Benefits of Exercise

No change incidence recurrent nonfatal MI[2,15,27]
No change morbidity/mortality in secondary prevention studies[10]
No effect on total cholesterol, VLDL, triglycerides or LDL cholesterol[20]

Conflicting Data

Incidence sudden cardiac death[12]
Total mortality after first MI[12]
Incidence recurrent MI[25-27]
Decreased excess risk of MI during strenuous exercise[13,14,19]

and cardiovascular mortality is lacking and experiments to establish such may never be possible."[12]

1.3. EXERCISE AND MORTALITY AND CORONARY HEART DISEASE

Individuals who exercise regularly have a decreased incidence of sudden death[12] (Table 2), but in some studies there is an increased incidence particularly in previously sedentary individuals. Some of these deaths occur during or shortly after exercise.[13,14] Regular physical activity and organized rehabilitation programs reduce mortality and fatal recurrent myocardial infarction (MI) by about 25% over a 3-year period, but have no effect on the incidence of nonfatal recurrent MI.[2,15,16] Sudden death is assumed to be coronary heart disease with a complication of an acute myocardial infarction in older people,[17] but the most common cause of sudden unexpected death in young people, including competitive athletes, is hypertrophic cardiomyopathy.[18] The risk of myocardial infarction during heavy physical exertion or up to 1 h after exertion has been shown to be two to six times greater than during sedentary activity.[19] The excess risk with strenuous physical activity was limited to persons who did not exercise regularly. There was little or no excess risk for those who exercised at least four to five times per week.

The total mortality after a first myocardial infarction and possibly in the next 2 years is decreased in patients who engage in regular vigorous physical conditioning for at least 4 h/week. Other studies however, have suggested that in patients with known coronary heart disease, there may be a slight increase in mortality with exercise. This might be due to exercise-induced arrhythmias, lack of training, and an unfavorable oxygen supply-and-demand relationship.[12] The effect of exercise on morbidity and mortality are less well demonstrated and less impressive in patients with established coronary heart disease than in subjects with no clinically apparent heart disease.[10] In patients with known coronary heart disease, the reduction in mortality with exercise was not statistically significant, although the trends which favor exercise are impressive.

1.4.   EXERCISE AND SERUM LIPIDS

In the National Exercise and Heart Disease Project, long-term moderate physical exercise had no effect on the total serum cholesterol, the HDL cholesterol, the LDL cholesterol or the triglycerides.[20] However, since the improvement in serum lipids has been well documented in several other cross-sectional studies, it was felt that the level of exercise in this study was not sufficient to significantly alter the serum lipids.

The relationship of exercise and HDL cholesterol was studied in male runners and in an inactive control group.[21] The exercise group who ran more than 12 miles/week, had higher HDL cholesterol, lower serum lipids, and a leaner body mass than sedentary controls. Additional studies in women examining the relation of exercise, alcohol, and serum lipids demonstrated that exercise was a more significant determinant of HDL than alcohol in premenopausal women.[22] Women who exercised had a higher HDL_2 than sedentary controls.

Other studies have confirmed the increase in HDL cholesterol with physical activity, which in turn results in a decrease in coronary heart disease incidence.[23] The increase in HDL may be the result of a decrease in body fat rather than exercise, but the resulting decrease in coronary heart disease remains unchanged.[24]

1.5.   EXERCISE AND PREVENTION OF CORONARY HEART DISEASE

In the Ontario Exercise Heart Collaborative Study,[25] a high-intensity exercise program did not prevent the recurrence of myocardial infarction. The incidence of subsequent myocardial infarction was similar in patients participating in high-intensity exercise as well as light-intensity exercise. Other studies,[26] however, demonstrate that less physically fit men are twice as likely to have a subsequent myocardial infarction compared to physically trained men. A meta-analysis of available trials published in 1989[27] showed a significant benefit of exercise on both total and cardiac mortality, but a nonsignificant increase in recurrent infarction.

Most recently, a study of 1053 men aged 52 to 60 years demonstrated that subjects who were in the upper one-third of physical activity had a relative hazard of first myocardial infarction of 0.31 compared to the lowest tercile.[28] Those who were able to achieve the highest O_2 uptake had a relative risk of subsequent myocardial infarction one-fourth that of the least conditioned. After adjusting for protective variables they concluded that "men who engaged in more than two hours of conditioning physical activity a week had a risk 60% lower than that of the least active men."

1.6. EXERCISE AND HYPERTENSION

Regular aerobic exercise lowers both systolic and diastolic blood pressure, but the effects are small and thought to be in the range of 10 mm systolic and 5 mm diastolic.[29] In a review of 22 studies evaluating the effect of exercise on blood pressure, the average reduction was approximately 6 to 7 mm for both the systolic and diastolic pressure.[30] This decrease in blood pressure was independent of weight loss. The better designed studies reported smaller reductions in blood pressure than the poorer designed studies. Longitudinal studies have shown an inverse relationship between physical activity and blood pressure.[31]

Aerobic exercise has been shown to decrease blood pressure as well as prevent hypertension, and decrease mortality in hypertensive patients and those with increased coronary risk.[32] Acute exercise decreased the peripheral resistance and lowered the blood pressure for at least 1 h postexercise in both trained and untrained subjects[33] despite persistent sympathetic discharge after exercise.[34] The reason for the fall in peripheral resistance may be due to circulating vasodilators, but the exact mechanism has not yet been determined.

The mechanisms by which exercise lowers blood pressure are multiple. In addition to a decrease in circulating catecholamines such as norepinephrine, there is a decrease in the Na/K ratio, a decrease in endogenous oubain-like substances, and a decrease in erythrocyte mean corpuscular volume. Mean arterial pressure may also be depressed by elevations in circulating plasma prostaglandin E, serum taurine, and changes in urinary dopamine excretion.[29]

1.7. EXERCISE AND OTHER FACTORS

Regular physical activity improves glucose tolerance, but it has not been convincingly demonstrated that decreasing elevated blood glucose significantly lowers cardiovascular mortality.[35] Exercise produces a favorable effect on fibrinogen and blood viscosity[37] and results in an increase in fibrinolytic activity.[36]

The benefits, lack of benefit, and conflicting data are summarized in Table 2.

2. EXERCISE CHARACTERISTICS

The degree of cardiovascular conditioning which can be expected as a result of physical activity depends to a large degree on whether the exercise is regular or sporadic[38] (Table 3). The effect of a wide variety of cardiovascular drugs on

TABLE 3
Exercise Prescription

Minimal Benefits	Optimal Benefits
Irregular exercise	Regular exercise
Three times per week	$\geq$ 5–6 times per week
$\leq$ 20 minutes	$\geq$ 20–30 minutes
50–60% maximum heart rate	80–90% Maximum heart rate
Isometric exercise	Isotonic exercise
	14–20 kcal/kg/week or 2000 kcal/week

exercise performance and exercise physiology as well as the effects of the exercise on drug metabolism and kinetics is also dependent on the regularity of the exercise, and whether the exercise is chronic (trained) or acute (brief). Many healthy individuals, as well as patients with heart disease, engage in exercise to improve the state of their cardiovascular fitness. Unfortunately, the great majority of these patients pursue an exercise program that is intermittent and sporadic, or in some instances seasonal. It is less likely that these exercise schedules produce any significant benefits in terms of cardiovascular conditioning. The effects of many of the cardiovascular drugs on exercise performance and physiology have been evaluated in both acute and chronic exercise, but similar studies are difficult to assess with confidence in subjects engaging in irregular physical activity.

Generally accepted guidelines for healthy individuals which result in a significant improvement in aerobic capacity or in VO_2max suggest a minimum of three exercise sessions per week[2] and a maximal benefit probably achieved with at least five sessions per week.[38]

Many studies have demonstrated that a decrease in cardiovascular risk may be achieved in sedentary patients with a moderate intensity exercise program.[39,40] The intensity of exercise, the duration and the necessary frequency of exercise to accomplish this change in cardiovascular risk has not been established.[38] Recommendations of the American Heart Association's "Optimal Risk Factor Management in the Patient After Coronary Revascularization" suggest "level walking at a brisk pace for at least 1.5 to 2 miles a day, three times a week as a minimum (preferably daily)," or "vigorous enough to make the patient breath hard and/or sweat, performed at least three times a week, is a useful rule of thumb."[2] It is not clear if more sustained or more intense exercise provides additional protection. The threshold for vigorous exercise in primary prevention of myocardial infarction and deaths from coronary heart disease, based on longitudinal data from studies in the U.S., Great Britain, and Norway, is 4.5 to 6 times the basic oxygen requirements of the body in the inactive state, or metabolic equivalents,[2] assumed to be 3.5 ml O_2/kg/min. Current prudent and widely accepted recommendations require at least 20 to 30 min of sustained physical activity for significant cardiovascular conditioning[38] with measurable benefits not to be expected for at least 4 to 6 weeks.[41]

The benefits of exercise in terms of cardiovascular conditioning are largely confined to isotonic exercise.[42] Isometric exercise such as weight lifting, pushing, and pulling is effective in improving muscle strength and increasing muscle mass, but has little beneficial effect on the cardiovascular system and may be harmful to patients with hypertension. Isometric exercise often produces alarming increases in blood pressure by a reflex mechanism.[42]

Isometric handgrip causes an abnormal response in patients with coronary heart disease due to impaired regional left ventricular performance. Isometric exercise results in an increase in systemic vascular resistance which causes an increase in arterial pressure, heart rate, cardiac output, left ventricular filling pressure, and heart size.[43]

Cardiovascular performance is improved by isotonic exercise that is aerobic or of the endurance type.[44] Rhythmic, repetitive movements that can be continued for prolonged periods, and activities that use large muscle groups simultaneously such as walking, running, bicycle riding, or swimming are most appropriate and provide maximum cardiovascular conditioning. Athletic activities which are interrupted and involve surges of effort interspersed with pauses or periods of rest, such as tennis, squash, or volleyball and occupational activities such as shoveling, carpentry or lifting, no matter how vigorous, tend to be less efficient and less valuable in improving cardiovascular conditioning.

The exercise prescription that provides minimal and optimal benefits is summarized in Table 3.

3. RELATIONSHIP OF EXERCISE TO DRUG ADMINISTRATION

Most patients with cardiac disease receive drugs chronically or for extended periods of time, e.g., antihypertensive, antianginal, or antiarrhythmia drugs. The interrelation of these drugs with physical activity and cardiovascular performance is often critical to their appropriate utilization, optimal effects, and avoidance of toxicity. Multiple factors may be important in designing appropriate drug schedules in patients who exercise, particularly in those taking multiple drugs simultaneously.

Physical activity may have significant effects on the metabolism of some cardiovascular drugs. Circulatory changes that occur with exercise have significant effects on cardiac output and result in major changes in blood flow distribution[45,46] (Table 4). Cardiac output increases five- to sixfold, from 5.5 l/min at rest to as much as 30 l/min in a conditioned athlete during maximal effort. The blood flow to skeletal muscles increases markedly from 3.6 ml/100 g muscle/min to 90 ml/100 g muscle/min during maximal exercise, a 25-fold increase.[47] Blood flow is shunted away from the gastrointestinal tract and absorption of drugs taken prior to exercise is likely to be significantly impaired or unpredictable.

There may be unpredictable variations in absorption and distribution of drugs depending on whether they are administered prior to or after exercise.

TABLE 4
Circulatory Changes with Exercise[45,46]

	Blood Flow at Rest (1/min)	% Cardiac Output at Rest	Blood Flow Max Exercise 1/min	% Cardiac Output Max Exercise
Splanchnic bed including liver	1.5	22	0.25	1
Skeletal muscles	1.1	20	22	88
Kidneys	1.2	21	0.25	1
Cerebrum	0.75	13	0.75	3
Skin	0.5	9	0.75	3
Coronaries	0.25	4	1.0	4
Other organs	0.6	11	—	—
TOTAL	5.8	25		

This is potentially a greater problem with prolonged bouts of exercise when circulatory changes may persist long enough to change the pharmacokinetic variables. Clinically, the time of administration of drugs in relation to exercise may be more problematic in patients who exercise on alternate days or exercise irregularly, which may result in day-to-day variation in drug effects.

The relation of exercise to drug effect may be critically dependent on the route of drug administration. Absorption of drugs given transdermally is dependent on the membrane or vehicle separating the drug from the skin, the area over which it is administered, the degree of lipid solubility, cutaneous blood flow, occlusive dressings, and the use of oily vehicles which enhance absorption.[48] Cutaneous blood flow is changed markedly during exercise. Skin blood flow initially decreases during exercise but then increases as body temperature rises and continues to increase, depending on the duration and intensity of exercise[49]. Cutaneous blood flow decreases when exercise approaches its maximum and skin vessels constrict.

Drugs administered by the intramuscular route are subject to great variation in the rate of absorption if given prior to exercise. Skeletal muscle blood flow increases enormously during exercise (Table 4).

Acute mild exercise accelerates transit of material through the gastrointestinal tract.[50] Propranolol accelerated the transit rate equal to the increase with mild exercise, but the effects of both exercise and propranolol together were not determined.

4. EXERCISE AND SPECIFIC CARDIOVASCULAR DRUGS

4.1. ANGIOTENSIN CONVERTING ENZYME (ACE) INHIBITORS

The clinical effect of the ACE inhibitors as a group are all quite similar, and the major differences are related to their metabolism and duration of action.

The renin-angiotensin-aldosterone axis is activated in patients with congestive heart failure and circulating levels of all three substances are elevated.[51] ACE inhibitors block the enzymatic conversion of inactive angiotensin I to the potent vasoconstrictor angiotensin II. This results in decreased circulating levels of angiotensin II and markedly elevated levels of plasma renin activity.

In patients with congestive heart failure, ACE inhibitors result in a decrease in both left and right ventricular filling pressure, an increase in cardiac output, no change in the heart rate, and no change in systemic arterial pressure.[52] There is no significant change in the hemodynamic response to exercise. Studies in normotensive athletes[53] showed that maximal aerobic performance and isokinetic strength were not altered by chronic captopril administration.

Large, well-controlled long-range studies have shown that ACE inhibitors enhance a sense of well being in patients with congestive heart failure. There is marked symptomatic improvement, less frequent clinical deterioration requiring hospitalization, a consistent decrease in cardiac dimensions and a sustained improvement in exercise tolerance[54] (Table 5) which extends to patients with mild as well as severe congestive heart failure.[55]

The effects of captopril on the renin-angiotensin system during exercise were evaluated.[56] Exercise stimulates the release of renin, an effect increased after captopril administration. It was found that captopril did not modify the exercise capacity of untrained subjects. Angiotensin II is significantly increased with exercise despite captopril. There was no change in microalbuminuria with prolonged physical effort.

Quinapril improved the exercise capacity at all grades of heart failure,[57] an effect which is probably generalizable to all ACE inhibitors. Fosinopril decreased both systolic and diastolic blood pressure during exercise with a slight prolongation of exercise time.[58] This drug produced a sustained 24 h decrease in blood pressure which was present during exercise, without altering the normal diurnal variation, without producing excess hypotension at the time of maximal hypotensive effect, and with slight improvement in exercise tolerance. Temocapril lowered the blood pressure at rest without a significant change in the heart rate or cardiac output, and with no change in the hemodynamic response to exercise.[59] Chronic ACE inhibitors but not acute therapy increased blood flow to exercising muscles and improved oxygen consumption possibly due to the inhibitory effect on the renin-angiotensin system and beneficial remodeling of the vessel wall.[60] The beneficial effects of adding ACE inhibitors to diuretics and digoxin have been demonstrated as judged by significant improvement in exercise tolerance.[61]

4.2. VASODILATORS

Dipyridamole and adenosine are now widely used as effective alternatives to evaluate myocardial ischemia in patients unable to exercise.[62] Both drugs are utilized in conjunction with radionuclide scintigraphy, and dipyridamole is

TABLE 5
Drug Effects with Exercise

	Improves	Worsens	No Change
ACE inhibitors	Exercise tolerance Exercise capacity in CHF Exercise time Systolic and diastolic BP Blood flow to exercising muscles Oxygen consumption		Maximal aerobic performance Isokinetic strength Diurnal variation BP Heart rate
Beta-blockers	Systolic and diastolic BP Heart rate Exercise tolerance in angina Peripheral resistance in drugs with ISA Silent myocardial ischemia Normalizes beta-2-adrenoreceptor adenylate-cyclase cAMP system Exercise induced arrhythmias Platelet aggregability	Exercise tolerance Peripheral resistance Exercise capacity LV filling pressure Increased fall in glucose	
Calcium channel blockers	Mean exercise time in patients with angina ST segment abnormalities Metabolic equivalent score Number of anginal attacks Nitroglycerine consumption Sytstolic and diastolic BP External workload		
Diuretics		Maximal exercise capacity Duration of prolonged submaximal exercise	
Inotropic drugs	Exercise capacity Exercise duration		
Anti-arrhythmia drug (amiodarone)	Heart rate at rest and maximal heart rate Exercise tolerance	Peak PA Pressure Systemic arterial pressure	LV filling pressure Maximal cardiac output
Nitroglycerine			Exercise tolerance in patients with CHF on digoxin and ACEI

used with stress echocardiography. Both drugs are used to evaluate the coronary flow reserve by dilating the precapillary and arteriolar capillary beds. There is a decreased responsiveness in vessels with a limited coronary flow reserve which results in a relative flow reduction and a defect on perfusion scintigraphy.[63] The diagnostic accuracy is approximately similar to exercise perfusion scintigraphy. The increase in myocardial oxygen consumption and cardiac output with these drugs is not as great as the increase in coronary blood flow. The sensitivity and specificity of pharmacologic imaging utilizing either radionuclide scintigraphy or echocardiography is equivalent to exercise thallium imaging. Echocardiography is totally dependent on the induction of ischemia,[64] whereas scintigraphy induces nonischemic perfusion heterogeneity which may provide more useful data in some patients.[63] Adenosine is similar in many respects to dipyridamole, but has unique advantages both clinically and when used with single photon emission computed tomography with a higher sensitivity.[65]

4.3. β-ADRENERGIC BLOCKING DRUGS

The relationship of exercise and the β-adrenergic blocking drugs is complex and dependent to some degree on sympathetic tone, systolic and diastolic function, and the selectivity of the β-adrenergic blocking drug. Clinically, these drugs slow the heart rate, lower the blood pressure, exert a negative inotropic effect, decrease exercise tolerance with resultant fatigue, and initially produce peripheral vasoconstriction. Recent studies have provided some insight into the mechanisms responsible for some of these changes.

The effects of β-adrenergic blocking drugs and diuretics make these drugs relatively contraindicated in hypertensive patients and are not first choice drugs in hypertensive patients who are physically active. β-blocking drugs reduce exercise capacity, but the β-1 selective blockers have less pronounced effects than the nonselective β-blockers.[66] The β-1 selective blockers may be advantageous in patients with systolic hypertension and those with myocardial ischemia during exercise since they effectively lower systolic blood pressure and decrease the heart rate during exercise.[66] The extent of blood pressure lowering with regular exercise is relatively limited and usually not adequate to normalize blood pressure in patients with moderate or severe hypertension.

The plasma concentration of atenolol was not changed by either 10 min exercise at 50% maximal aerobic power or exhaustive exercise at 70% maximal aerobic power, but the plasma concentration of propranolol and the calcium channel blocker verapamil were significantly increased.[67] This study concluded that exercise led to a reduction in the volume of distribution (V_d) of propranolol during prolonged exercise, but not at 10 min exercise. The V_d was reduced with 10 min exercise, and no change in V_d during exercise could be shown with atenolol. These changes in V_d with propranolol and verapamil may contribute to preventing an increase in half-life of these drugs with prolonged physical exercise.

The relationship of left ventricular systolic function and heart rate to serum l-propranolol concentrations was determined during exercise.[68] The concentration effect relationship for l-propranolol and its negative inotropic effect differ from its negative chronotropic effect.

The effect of submaximal exercise on the pharmacokinetics of low-dose intravenous propranolol was studied.[69] The effect of exercise on the pharmacokinetics of propranolol, a flow-limited drug, is marked but variable, suggesting significant clinical unpredictability in patients taking the drug regularly who exercise intermittently.

K^+ efflux and re-uptake during exercise was examined in healthy subjects before and after propranolol administration. Serum K^+ increased in the femoral vein from 4.3 to 6.8 mmol/l at exhaustion before and after propranolol administration, but endurance was reduced after drug administration, indicative of a more rapid rise in K^+.[70] The higher K^+ after oral propranolol is mainly due to impaired redistribution outside the exercising muscles, and may, in part, be responsible for the excessive fatigue associated with these drugs. Labetolol, a combined action β-blocker, reduced the exercise-induced increase in serum K^+ in contrast with other β-blocking drugs which characteristically augment the K^+ increase caused by exercise.[71]

Labetolol, a combined action β-blocking drug has been shown to increase exercise tolerance in patients with angina.[72] Carvedilol, a new β-blocker without intrinsic sympathomimetic activity, has a peripheral vasodilating action due to α-1-adrenoreceptor blockade and decreases peripheral vascular resistance in contrast to propranolol which increases peripheral vascular resistance and decreases cardiac output. Carvedilol combines the positive effects of α-1 and β-blockade. The negative properties of each are neutralized by each other. It improves exercise tolerance in patients with angina, and reduces episodes of silent myocardial ischemia and improves myocardial function with an increase in ejection fraction.[72]

Increasing evidence points to abnormalities of diastolic function as the cause of exercise intolerance in patients with congestive heart failure.[73] The left ventricular filling pressure, an indicator of diastolic function, is more closely correlated with measures of effort tolerance as manifested by dyspnea or fatigue than the ejection fraction which relates to systolic function. Drugs which increase left ventricular filling pressure such as β-blockers are more likely to decrease exercise capacity, and this combined with their demonstrated negative inotropic effects with effect on systolic function usually causes clinical deterioration.

The treatment of heart failure with β-blocking drugs has been studied but remains controversial. In a number of recent uncontrolled clinical trials in patients with dilated cardiomyopathy and mild to moderate heart failure, low-dose β-blockers have been shown to improve some hemodynamic parameters and relieve symptoms.[74] The benefit is thought to be related to the gradual up-regulation of the depressed myocardial β-receptors seen in patients with congestive heart failure. There is conflicting data on the improvement in exercise tolerance in patients with heart failure treated with β-adrenergic blocking drugs.[74] The possible mechanism for these effects remains speculative.[75] The up-regulation of myocardial β-receptors allows the myocardium to become more responsive to increasing doses of β-agonists. In addition, β-blockers reduce neurohormonal activation and may have a beneficial effect on survival.

The effect of β-adrenergic antagonists with and without intrinsic sympatho-mimetic activity on the regulation of lymphocytic β-adrenoreceptors during physical exercise was studied.[76] Administration of β-blockers is associated with a subnormal up-regulation of the lymphocytic β-adrenoreceptors and changes in their functions which are not modified by the intrinsic sympatho-mimetic activity of the drug. At this time, β-blockers should be considered investigational in patients with heart failure and graduated low doses may improve exercise tolerance in selected patients with dilated cardiomyopathy and heart failure.

β-adrenoreceptors on lymphocytes are increased after exercise in normal subjects but not in patients with hypertension.[77] Dynamic exercise caused no significant change in receptor density or affinity nor in cAMP levels. After acute β-blockade, the rise in mean arterial blood pressure was significantly reduced, the β-adrenoreceptor density increased, but affinity was unchanged. Baseline and stimulated-cAMP levels increased significantly, suggesting that in primary hypertension the regulation of the β-2-adrenoreceptor-adenylate-cyclase-cAMP system is impaired with exercise and can be normalized with β-blockade.

Exercise or catecholamine-induced ventricular tachycardia may be sup-pressed with β-adrenergic blocking drugs.[78] Many of the effects of catechola-mines are mediated through β-adrenoreceptors located on cell membranes. The catecholamines are bound to β-adrenoreceptors resulting in an increase in intracellular cAMP which in turn activates protein kinase A, an enzyme which phosphorylates a number of other intracellular enzymes, influencing cellular metabolism and function.[79] These studies led to the following conclusions: (a) high aerobic capacity is associated with an increased density and ability of lymphocytic β-adrenoreceptors to respond to catecholamines, (b) both short- and long-term physical exercise induce a rapid up-regulation and more effec-tive functioning of lymphocytic β-adrenoreceptors, (c) administration of β-blocking drugs is associated with a submaximal exercise-induced up-regula-tion and decreased functioning of the lymphocytic β-adrenoreceptors, and (d) the exercise provoked up-regulation and improved functioning of β-adrenoreceptors is blunted in patients with heart failure.

Treatment with β-blockers significantly decreased the predictive accuracy of dipyridamole echocardiography in demonstrating myocardial ischemia.[80] It is not clear whether this change is primarily related to the negative inotropic and chronotropic effects of the drug as well as the concomitant increase in filling pressure and decrease in ejection fraction with increased fatigue and dyspnea, or the multiple other effects of these drugs on a cellular level as noted above. Recent studies have shown that metoprolol prevents an increase in platelet aggregability and a decrease in intracellular cAMP during stress testing in patients with stable angina pectoris.[81]

It is thought that the impaired endurance exercise capacity after administration of a β-adrenoreceptor blocker may be due to inhibition of adipose tissue lipolysis. Recent studies[82] demonstrated inhibition of lipolysis after propranolol administration, causing a shift from fat to carbohydrate combustion. The effect of selective and nonselective β-blockade on glucose turnover was evaluated in type I diabetes during moderate exercise.[83] It was concluded that the greater fall in glucose with exercise after β-blockade was due to a direct effect of β-2-blockade on muscles, increasing the exercise-induced rise in glucose disappearance rate. This reinforces the use of β-1-blocking drugs when necessary in patients with type I diabetes.

Autonomic control and reflex activity in the elderly decreases; these changes resemble the effects of β-adrenoreceptor blockade.[84] There is a decrease in intrinsic β-adrenoreceptor sensitivity with age and increasing sympathetic and parasympathetic dysfunction with a loss of compensatory adjustments to cardiovascular control. The treatment of hypertension in the elderly with β-blockers suggests that the increased cardiac output with exercise depends more on increased intracardiac volume and diastolic function than on the sympathetic modulation of heart rate. This constraint is superimposed on a background of altered drug pharmacokinetic and pharmacodynamics in the elderly.

Gordon and Duncan[85] succinctly summarized the effects of β-blockade on exercise physiology. Among their conclusions: (a) patients treated with β-blockers achieve the expected improvement in cardiorespiratory fitness irrespective of the type of drug used, (b) β-1-selective blockers are preferable to nonselective drugs for the treatment of hypertension in patients who exercise, although β-1-selective drugs can significantly impair exercise tolerance in some hypertensive patients, (c) intrinsic sympathomimetic activity confers no advantage during exercise training, (d) exercise training prescriptions for patients receiving β-blockers should be individualized within traditional guidelines and should be based on results of testing while patients are on drugs, (e) the adverse effects of β-blockers on lipoprotein metabolism are partly mitigated by exercise training, and (f) nonselective β-blockers may increase the predisposition to exertional hyperthermia and appropriate precautions are necessary.

4.4. CALCIUM CHANNEL BLOCKERS

Although there are significant chemical and pharmacological differences in the group of drugs identified as calcium channel blockers, the circulatory, hemodynamic and clinical effects are generalizable with some notable differences.

The calcium channel blockers increase the mean exercise time in patients with chronic stable angina.[86,87] ST segment depression was reduced and the metabolic equivalent score at peak exercise was significantly improved. All these effects were sustained on long-term administration.[86] Increased workload was accomplished with a decreased number of anginal attacks and decreased nitroglycerin consumption.[87] Both systolic and diastolic blood pressure at maximal effort was reduced and the external workload reached at the anaerobic threshold, but not at maximal effort, was increased.[88]

4.5. DIURETICS

Single-dose and short-term treatment with diuretics adversely affect maximal exercise capacity and the duration of prolonged submaximal exercise.[89] There are insufficient data to establish the effect of long-term diuretic therapy on exercise.

4.6. INOTROPIC DRUGS

An improvement in hemodynamics with inotropic drugs did not enhance oxygen consumption,[60] suggesting an intrinsic abnormality of exercising muscle which prevent acute improvement in VO_2. Digoxin is superior to placebo in improving exercise capacity, cardiac hemodynamics, increasing ejection fraction, and preventing congestive heart failure deterioration.[90, 91] The benefits are similar to the angiotensin converting enzyme inhibitors, but improved survival is seen with the ACE inhibitors only.[92] The increased mortality seen with the newer oral inotropic agents has made digoxin the only useful inotropic drug available in clinical practice.

Xamoterol was found to be superior to digoxin in increasing exercise duration, but this may be due to its β-1-adrenoreceptor antagonistic activity with antianginal effects, but the mortality with xamoterol was significantly higher at 13 weeks.[93] Studies have shown a significant increase in exercise time in patients given milrinone, digoxin, or both,[94] but an increased mortality in the milrinone group. Ibopamine, a dopamine derivative improved, exercise performance equivalent to digoxin.[95]

Flosequinan, a fluroquinolone derivative is a peripheral venous and arterial dilator and may have a positive inotropic effect. Several large multicenter trials demonstrated that a dose of 100 mg/day improved symptoms and exercise tolerance in patients with chronic congestive heart failure with or without additional ACE inhibitors therapy.[96]

4.7. ANTIARRHYTHMIA DRUGS

Amiodarone, an antiarrhythmia drug with predominant class III effects was given to 10 patients with hypertrophic cardiomyopathy, and the effect on exercise response was measured during maximal supine and symptom-limited erect treadmill exercise before and after 6 weeks of treatment.[97] There was a significant decrease in resting and maximal heart rate during erect exercise. Despite an increase in peak pulmonary artery and systemic arterial blood pressure during exercise, there was no difference in left ventricular filling pressure or maximal cardiac output. In another placebo controlled double-blind trial of 34 patients,[98] amiodarone (200 mg/day) significantly increased exercise tolerance.

4.8. NITROGLYCERINE

The organic nitrates are an effective treatment for patients with angina pectoris. There is substantial evidence that significant attenuation of the antianginal effect occurs with sustained treatment designed to provide antianginal efficacy throughout a 24-h period. Intermittent treatment designed to provide a nitrate-free interval improves exercise duration and clinical angina,[99] and appropriate dosing schedules can provide optimal exercise tolerance throughout the day.

Nitrates did not improve exercise tolerance in patients with mild to moderate heart failure who are already being treated with captopril and diuretics.[100]

4.9. SEROTONIN

The effects of serotonin or 5 hydroxy-tryptamine (5-HT) on human physiology are unusually complex. Studies have demonstrated a wide variety of pharmacologic activity, but a great deal of variability in its action between species, in animals of the same species, and successive tests on individuals. This variability is due to the fact that many of the actions of 5-HT are reflex mediated and due to the presence of tachyphylaxis with repeated injections. The actions of 5-HT on the cardiovascular system are uniquely complex. It may cause either vasoconstriction or vasodilatation, may activate pressor or depressor reflexes, and may increase or decrease the cardiac output. Administration of 5-HT causes direct vasoconstriction, particularly of the splanchnic and renal blood vessels, the cerebral blood vessels, the pulmonary, placental, umbilical, and uterine arteries, and at low doses, vasodilatation in the skeletal muscles.

5-HT has positive inotropic and chronotropic effects *in vitro,* but *in vivo* the direct cardiac activity is modified by autonomic reflexes due to changes in the blood pressure and complicating direct action on the baroreceptors, chemoreceptors, and vagal endings in the coronary bed. The effects on 5-HT on the blood pressure is even more unpredictable, but generally three phases can be recognized; a very brief hypotensive phase is followed by a short pressor phase and then a more prolonged depressor phase. These complex, direct, and often competing actions modified by reflex activity *in vivo* are further complicated when additional physiologic variables such as exercise are introduced.

It has been suggested that 5-HT is the neurotransmitter responsible for the sense of tiredness or fatigue and is responsible for sleep in both humans and experimental animals.[101] Recent studies have shown that sustained dynamic exercise results in a significant decrease in plasma branched-chain amino acids, no change in total tryptophan, a precursor of 5-HT, (free and bound), and a 2.4-fold increase in free tryptophan.[102] It is postulated that increased levels of tryptophan increased the synthesis of 5-HT which may be responsible, in part, for the sense of physical and mental fatigue associated with prolonged exercise.

L-tryptophan was administered to volunteers to study its effect on endurance and the sensation of effort.[103] Total exercise time was significantly greater in the group receiving L-tryptophan compared with placebo. A lower rate of perceived exertion was seen in the tryptophan group, although the differences were not statistically significant. Since 5-HT affects nociception, it is postulated that the increased exercise time and total workload performed could be due to an increase in pain tolerance.

Platelet 5-HT and plasma catecholamines were measured in ten healthy subjects undergoing tilt test, cold pressor test, treadmill testing, and isometric handgrip exercise.[104] A responder group had a significant decrease in 5-HT platelet content and nonresponders had no significant change. Increase in plasma catecholamines were higher in the responders, suggesting that some subjects were more susceptible to adrenergic stimuli, and that elevated circulating catecholamines may induce platelet activation and 5-HT release, and that this might induce a vasodilator response modulating sympathetic tone.

4.10. CATECHOLAMINES

Secretion of catecholamines during exercise initiates mobilization of glucose and free fatty acids which in turn stimulates other endocrine glands and cells, including the anterior and posterior pituitary, adrenal cortex, thyroid, parathyroid, liver, pancreas, and kidney.[105] Interpretation of the effects of acute exercise on this hormonal cascade is difficult because of the multiple factors which need to be controlled. These include changes in plasma volume and clearance rate, the timing and method of blood sampling, diurnal variations, the design of the exercise protocol, the age, sex, fitness level, training history, diet, emotional status, and menstrual status of the subject. Endurance training elicits adaptations that are tissue specific and are designed to improve the ability to maintain exercise energetics.[106] In evaluating the sympathoadrenal response to exercise, it is important to evaluate specific variables such as rates of turnover, synthesis, removal, and activity of key enzymes related to catecholamine metabolism.

Binding of catecholamines to β-adrenoreceptors increases the concentration of intracellular cAMP. This activates protein kinase A, which phosphorylates other intracellular enzymes, which in turn influence cell metabolism and function.[107] Studies on the physiologic adjustments to acute and prolonged physical exercise have demonstrated the following: "1) High aerobic capacity is associated with an increased density and ability of lymphocytic β-adrenoreceptors to respond to catecholamines. 2) Both short and long term physical exercise induce a rapid up-regulation and more effective functioning of lymphocytic β-adrenoreceptors. 3) Administration of β-blocking drugs is associated with a subnormal exercise induced up-regulation and decreased functioning of the lymphocytic β-adrenoreceptors. 4) The exercise provoked up-regulation and improved functioning of β-adrenoreceptors is blunted in heart failure patients."[107]

The neurohumoral and hemodynamic responses to dynamic exercise are altered in patients with chronic congestive heart failure. Plasma norepinephrine

(NE) is normally augmented as a function of peak oxygen consumption (VO_2) during exercise, but this occurs with higher levels of exercise with peak VO_2 greater than 50%. Patients with congestive heart failure show a greater than normal augmentation of plasma NE with exercise,[108] but a relative attenuation of the sympathetic response to exercise when the data are expressed as a percent of peak VO_2. The increase in both plasma NE and renin activity with exercise in patients with congestive heart failure is not due to a decrease in blood flow to skeletal muscles. Cardiac transplant patients have reduced exercise tolerance and an abnormal cardiovascular response to exercise with high plasma NE. β-blockade resulted in higher NE levels[109] and an adverse response to exercise.

The role of epinephrine (EPI) as a modulator of NE release was investigated at rest and during supine bicycle exercise.[110] Infusions of EPI at rest resulted in an increase in plasma arterial NE, an increase in whole body NE spillover to arterial plasma, and a trend toward an increase in whole-body NE clearance. Exercise was associated with a significant increase in peripheral NE concentrations and in cardiac and whole-body NE spillover. Infusions of high- and low-dose NE were given to a subject to test the influence of aerobic physical training on the pressor response to infused NE.[111] Aerobic fitness was associated with a highly significant reduction in pressor response during both low- and high-dose NE. Platelet catecholamines and plasma EPI were not reliably associated with fitness. The influence of physical training on responses to intravenous infusions of phenylephrine and isoproterenol were evaluated in well-trained runners and sedentary controls.[112] The results show that exercise conditioning enhances the β-adrenergic vasodilator and α-adrenergic vasopressor responses.

Plasma NE and EPI levels increase with intensity and duration of exercise.[113] Decreased catacholamine clearance is responsible for a small part of this increase. An increase in sympathetic nervous system activity has been suggested as a factor in the increased incidence of coronary heart disease in obesity.[114] This was evaluated in healthy obese subjects randomized to weight reduction or endurance exercise training. Neither group had a significant change in resting plasma NE or EPI levels, but NE appearance rate declined after weight loss, but not with exercise training, suggesting that dietary weight loss is more effective than exercise training in reducing the sympathetic nervous system activity in obesity. Other investigators found that obese subjects have a decreased thermogenic response to sympathomimetic stimulation and cold exposure, which improved only slightly with endurance exercise training.[115]

It has been suggested that changes in natural killer cell activity in response to physical activity were mediated by increased EPI concentrations.[116] These studies demonstrated that increased plasma EPI during physical stress causes a redistribution of mononuclear subpopulations that results in altered functions of natural killer cells.

4.11. OTHER DRUGS RELEVANT TO THE CARDIOVASCULAR SYSTEM

Pentoxyfylline, a drug which improves the flow properties of blood by decreasing its viscosity and improving erythrocyte flexibility was compared to a program of physical training in subjects with peripheral arterial occlusive disease.[117] The subjects treated with pentoxyfylline had a greater walking capacity and shorter half recovery time compared with patients treated with physical therapy alone. Pentoxyfylline inhibited free radical production and decreased the percentage of granulocytes expressing adhesion receptors.

Thrombolytic drugs (alteplace, streptokinase, anistreplace, urokinase) are administered intravenously over a brief period, and only a few studies evaluating the effect of these drugs on exercise capacity or exercise physiology, or the effect of exercise on the drug, have been completed. There have been studies evaluating the effect of these drugs on exercise capacity after they have been given, predischarge, but the performance is not influenced by the drug as much as the effect of the drug on the coronary circulation.[118]

Tissue plasminogen activator (TPA) increases with exercise, but studies have shown that 50% of the increase is due to stimulated release of TPA by epinephrine.[119] The levels of plasminogen activators were measured at rest, after exercise and after administration of propranolol.[120] TPA activity and extrinsic plasminogen activity significantly increased with exercise. Intrinsic activity was not significantly changed. Premedication with propranolol significantly decreased the exercise response increase in total and extrinsic plasminogen activators with no effect on intrinsic activity.

Plasma atrial naturietic peptide (ANP) levels increased during exercise and then gradually decreased.[121] Prior administration of propranolol for 3 days markedly elevated ANP levels before, during and after exercise. There was a concomitant rise in hematocrit and a positive correlation with ANP, suggesting that ANP may be a factor in producing the hemoconcentration associated with exercise.

Generally, drugs that decrease peripheral vascular resistance have little or no effect on exercise capacity,[121] but there are very few studies and only meager data available examining this relationship. Left ventricular dysfunction correlates poorly with exercise capacity and clinical symptoms. This suggests that changes in the peripheral circulation with reduced perfusion in the exercising muscles are critical factors in determining the functional state and exercise capacity of patients with congestive heart failure.[60]

The effects of some of the cardiovascular drugs on exercise is summarized in Table 5.

5. CONCLUSIONS AND RECOMMENDATIONS

1. The evidence that exercise and regular physical activity is beneficial is persuasive, but definitive studies demonstrating a decrease in coronary

heart disease, sudden death, decreased mortality, incidence of infarction and reinfarction, and primary and secondary prevention of coronary heart disease are not available. Studies that demonstrate the effect of exercise on a variety of cardiovascular endpoints may not be realistic, ethical, or feasible. Previous studies should be interpreted cautiously in view of the multiple factors which need to be controlled to assure scientific validity and to avoid bias.

2. There are currently no adequate comprehensive and definitive studies to evaluate the effect of exercise on drug metabolism and pharmacokinetics. Additional studies to evaluate the complex interrelationship of exercise and drug pharmacokinetics is necessary, particularly for those drugs that are given to cardiac patients who engage in physical activity on an irregular or unpredictable schedule and who take multiple drugs. These studies are particularly important and may be clinically warranted in patients taking β-adrenoreceptor blocking drugs, ACE inhibitors, inotropic agents, and diuretics in various combinations, and particularly those patients with chronic congestive heart failure whose neurohormonal system is activated and peripheral resistance may be a critical factor.

3. Previous studies on the effects of drugs on exercise physiology and cardiovascular hemodynamics should be interpreted cautiously because of the multiple factors that could potentially bias or confound these results. Current available information suggests that the effects of most cardiovascular drugs on exercise performance is relatively small and not a clinically significant factor. Some drugs in particular, β-adrenoreceptor blocking drugs and diuretics, should be avoided in patients who are physically active and should be modified or discontinued in patients who start regular physical activity. β-1-selective drugs are preferred in physically active patients when β-adrenergic-blockade is clinically necessary. ACE inhibitors, calcium channel blockers, α blockers, and central α agonists are recommended for treatment of patients with hypertension who are physically active.

4. The complex relations of drug administration and physical activity should be considered when designing appropriate drug schedules in patients who exercise, particularly in those taking multiple drugs simultaneously. Reasonable efforts should be made to assure that there is a consistent relationship between the time and route of administration, the interval between drug administration and exercise, and the regularity of exercise.

5. ACE inhibitors have a beneficial effect on physical activity. These drugs improve exercise tolerance, increase exercise time, and increase exercise capacity in congestive heart failure. ACE inhibitors lower systolic and diastolic blood pressure, increase blood flow to exercising muscles and improve oxygen consumption with no significant deleterious effect on exercise performance.

6. β blockers have a complex and largely detrimental effect on exercise tolerance. The β-adrenergic blocking drugs decrease systolic and diastolic blood pressure and lower the heart rate, which is instrumental in increasing exercise tolerance or angina. β-adrenergic blockers with intrinsic sympathomimetic activity increase peripheral resistance. β blockers decrease silent myocardial ischemia and normalize the β-2-adrenoreceptor adenylate cyclase cAMP system, decrease the tendency to exercise induced arrhythmias, and decrease platelet aggregability. The β-adrenergic blocking drugs, however, particularly those which are nonselective, decrease exercise tolerance, increase peripheral resistance, decrease exercise capacity, elevate the left ventricular filling pressure, and promote an increased fall in blood glucose.

7. Calcium channel blockers are generally well tolerated with exercise. The mean exercise time is increased in patients with angina. There are fewer ST abnormalities and improvement in the metabolic equivalent score, a decrease in the number of anginal attacks, and a decrease in nitroglycerine consumption. The calcium channel blockers lower systolic and diastolic blood pressure.

8. Diuretics decrease maximal exercise capacity and decrease the duration of prolonged submaximal exercise. Inotropic drugs, in particular digitalis, increase exercise capacity and exercise duration. Very few studies have been done on antiarrhythmia drugs, but amiodarone has been studied and has been found to have a mixed effect on patients who engage in physical activity.

9. The relation of exercise and serontonin is complex, variable, and not well studied. Preliminary data suggest that tryptophan or 5-HT is related to fatigue or sleep and pain tolerance, but the data are incomplete and conflicting.

10. Physical exertion increases the density and ability of β-adrenoreceptors to respond to catecholamines and up-regulate the β-adrenoreceptors. These effects are blunted by β-blockers and congestive heart failure. NE increases with exercise. In congestive heart failure the increase is augmented but with an attenuation of the sympathetic response.

REFERENCES

1. **American College of Cardiology, American Heart Association,** Guidelines for the early management of patients with acute myocardial infarction: A report of the ACC/AHA task force on assessment of diagnostic and therapeutic procedures (subcommittee to develop guidelines for the early management of patients with acute myocardial infarction), *J. Am. Coll. Cardiol.,* 16, 249, 1990.
2. **Lenfant, C.,** Task force on research in epidemiology and prevention of cardiovascular diseases, *Circulation,* 90, 2609, 1994.

3. Report of joint working party of the Royal College of Physicians and the British Cardiac Society, Prevention of coronary heart disease, *J. R. Coll. Phys.,* 10, 213, 1976

4. **Department of Health and Human Services (PHS),** Promoting health, preventing disease: objectives for the nation, U.S. Government Printing Office, Washington, D.C., 1980, 155.

5. **Oldridge, N. B., Donner, A. P., and Duck, C. W.,** Predictors of dropout from cardiac exercise rehabilitation, *Am. J. Cardiol.,* 51, 701, 1983.

6. **Wood, P. D. and Haskell, W. L.,** The effect of exercise on plasma high density lipoproteins, *Lipids,* 14, 417, 1979.

7. **Morgan, W. P.,** Affective beneficence of vigorous physical activity, *Med. Sci. Sports Exerc.,* 17, 94, 1985.

8. **Martinsen, E. W., Medhus, A., and Sandvik, L.,** Effects of aerobic exercise on depression: a controlled study, *Br. Med. J., 291,109, 1985.*

9. **Crews, D. J. and Landers, D. M.,** A meta-analytic review of aerobic fitness and reactivity to psychosocial stressors, *Med. Sci. Sports Exerc.,* 19(Suppl.), S114, 1987.

10. **Mayou, R. A.,** A controlled trial of early rehabilitation after myocardial infarction, *J. Cardiac Rehab.,* 3, 397, 1983.

11. **Shaw, L. W.,** Effects of a prescribed supervised exercise program on mortality and cardiovascular morbidity in patients after a myocardial infarction, *Am. J. Cardiol.,* 48, 39, 1981.

12. **Gotto, A. M. and Farmer, J. A.,** Risk factors for coronary artery disease, in *Heart Disease,* 3rd ed., Braunwald, E., Ed., W. B. Saunders, Philadelphia, 1988, 1176.

13. **Mittleman, M. A., Maclure, M., Tofler, G. H., et al.,** Triggering of acute myocardial infarction by heavy physical exertion, *N. Engl. J. Med.,* 329, 1677, 1993.

14. **Willich, S. N., Lewis, M., Löwel, H., et al.,** Physical exertion as a trigger of acute myocardial infarction, *N. Engl. J. Med.,* 329, 1684, 1993.

15. **Morris, J. N., Pollard, R., Everitt, M. G., et al.,** Vigorous exercise in leisure-time: protection agains coronary heart disease, *Lancet,* 2, 1207, 1980.

16. **Paffenbarger, R. S., Jr., Hale, W. E., Brand, R. J., et al.,** Work-energy level, personal characteristics, and fatal heart attack: a birth-cohort effect, *Am. J. Epidemiol.,* 105, 200, 1977.

17. **Thompson, P. D., Klocke, F. J., Levine, B. D., and Van Camp, S. P.,** Task force 5: coronary artery disease, *J. Am. Coll. Cardiol.,* 24, 888, 1994.

18. **Maron, B. J., Isner, J. M., and McKenna, W. J.,** Task force 3: hypertrophic cardiomyopathy, myocarditis and other myopericardial diseases and mitral valve prolapse, *J. Am. Coll. Cardiol.,* 24, 880, 1994.

19. **Curfman, G. D.,** Is exercise beneficial — or hazardous — to your heart?, *N. Engl. J. Med.,* 329, 1730, 1993.

20. **LaRosa, J. C., Cleary, P., and Muesing, R. A.,** Effect of long-term moderate physical exercise on plasma lipoproteins, The National Exercise and Heart Disease Project, *Arch. Intern. Med.,* 142, 2269, 1982.

21. **Hartung, G. H., Foreyt, J. P., Mitchell, J. G., et al.,** Effect of alcohol intake and exercise on plasma high-density lipoprotein cholesterol levels in runners and inactive men, *J. Am. Med. Assoc.,* 249, 747, 1983.

22. **Hartung, G. H., Reeves, R. S., Foreyt, J. P., et al.,** Effect of alcohol intake and exercise on plasma high-density lipoprotein cholesterol subfractions and apolipoprotein A-1 in women, *Am. J. Cardiol.,* 58, 148, 1986.

23. **Miller, N. E.,** Coronary atherosclerosis and plasma lipoproteins, *J. Cardiovasc. Pharmacol.,* 4(Suppl. 2), 190, 1982.

24. **Gordon, T., Castelli, W. P., Hjortland, M. C., et al.,** High-density lipoprotein as a protective factor against coronary heart disease, the Framingham study, *Am. J. Med.,* 62, 707, 1977.

25. **Rechnitzer, P. A., Cunningham, D. A., and Andrew, G. M.,** Relation of exercise to the recurrence rate of myocardial infarction in men, Ontario exercise-heart collaborative study, *Am. J. Cardiol.,* 51, 65, 1983.

26. **Peters, P. K., Cady, L. D., and Bischoff, D. B.,** Physical fitness and subsequent myocardial infarction in healthy workers, *J. Am. Med. Assoc.,* 249, 3052, 1983.
27. **Bobbio, M.,** Does post myocardial infarction rehabilitation prolong survival?, *G. Ital. Cardiol.,* 19, 1059, 1989.
28. **Lakka, T. A., et al.,** Moderately intense physical activity and "being fit" confer reduced rate of MI, *N. Engl. J. Med.,* 330, 1549, 1994.
29. **Arakawa, K.,** Hypertension and exercise, *Clin. Exp. Hyperten.,* 15(6), 1171, 1993.
30. **Arroll, B. and Beaglehole, R.,** Does physical activity lower blood pressure: a critical review of the clinical trials, *J. Clin. Epidemiol.,* 45(5), 439, 1992.
31. **Paffenbarger, R. S., Jr., Wing, A. L., Hyde, R. T., and Jung D. L.,** Physical activity and incidence of hypertension in college alumni, *Epidemiology,* 117, 245, 1983.
32. **Houston, M. C.,** Exercise and hypertension, maximizing the benefits in patients receiving drug therapy, *Postgrad. Med.,* 92(6), 139, 1992.
33. **Coats, A. J. S., Conway, J., Isea, J. E., et al.,** Systemic and forearm vascular resistance changes after upright bicycle exercise in man, *J Physiol. (London),* 413, 289, 1989.
34. **Coats, A. J. S., Adamopoulos, S., Radaelli, A., et al.,** Controlled trial of physical training in chronic heart failure: exercise performance, hemodynamic, ventilation, and autonomic function, *Circulation,* 85, 1, 1992.
35. **Garcia, M. J., McNamara, P. M., and Gordon, T.,** Morbidity and mortality of diabetics in the Framingham population, *Diabetes,* 23, 103, 1974.
36. **Williams, R. S., Lague, E. E., and Lewis, J. L.,** Physical conditioning augments the fibrinolytic response to venous occlusion in healthy adults, *N. Engl. J. Med.,* 302, 987, 1980.
37. **Stratton, J. R., Chandler, W. L., Schwartz, R. S., et al.,** Effects of physical conditioning on fibrinolytic variables and fibrinogen in young and old healthy adults, *Circulation,* 83, 1692, 1991.
38. **Pate, R. R., Pratt, M., Blair, S. N., et al.,** Physical activity and public health. A recommendation from the Centers for Disease Control and Prevention and the American College of Sports Medicine, *J. Am. Med. Assoc.,* 273, 402, 1995.
39. **Leon, A. S. and Connett, J.,** Physical activity and 10.5 year mortality in the Multiple Risk Factor Intervention Trial (MRFIT), *Int. J. Epidemiol.,* 20, 690, 1991.
40. **Thompson, P. D.,** The benefits and risks of exercise training in patients with chronic coronary artery disease, *J. Am. Med. Assoc.,* 259, 1537, 1988.
41. **Scheuer, J. and Tipton, C. M.,** Cardiovascular adaptions to physical training, *Ann. Rev. Physiol.,* 39, 221, 1977.
42. **Jennings, G., Nelson, L., Nestel, P., et al.,** The effects of changes in physical activity on major cardiovascular risk factors, hemodynamics, sympathetic function and glucose utilization in man: a controlled study of four levels of activity, *Circulation,* 73, 30, 1986.
43. **Matthews, D. A., Blomquist, C. G., Cohen, L. S., et al.,** Left ventricular function during isometric exercise (handgrip), *Am. Heart J.,* New York, 88, 686, 1974.
44. **Kattus, A.,** *Exercise Testing and Training of Individuals with Heart Disease or at High Risk for its Development: A Handbook for Physicians,* American Heart Association, New York, 1975.
45. **Honig, C. R.,** *Modern Cardiovascular Physiology,* Little, Brown and Company, Boston, 1981, 317.
46. **Shepherd, J. T. and Vanhoultz, P. M.,** *The Human Cardiovascular System,* Raven Press, New York, 1979, 325.
47. **Guyton, A. C.,** *Textbook of Medical Physiology,* 8th ed., W. B. Saunders, Philadelphia, 1991, 947.
48. **Wepierre, J. and Marty, J.-P.,** Percutaneous absorption of drugs, *Trends Pharmacol. Sci.,* 1, 23, 1979.
49. **Ruch, H. P. and Patton, T. C.,** *Physiology and Biophysics,* 12th ed., W. B. Saunders, Philadephia, 1974.
50. **Harris, A. and Martin, B. J.,** Effect of opiate and beta-adrenergic blockers on the gut transit response to mild exercise, *Int. J. Sports Med.,* 14(6), 320, 1993.

51. **Dzau, V. J., Colucci, W. S., Hollenberg, N. K., and Williams G. H.,** Relation of the renin-angiotensin-aldosterone system to clinical state in congestive heart failure, *Circulation,* 63, 645, 1981.

52. **Creager, M. A., Halperin, J. L., Bernard, D. B., et al.,** Acute regional circulatory and renal hemodynamic effects of converting enzyme inhibition in patients with congestive heart failure, *Circulation,* 64, 483, 1981.

53. **Carre, F., Handschuh, R., Beillot, J., et al.,** Effects of captopril chronic intake on the aerobic performance and muscle strength of normotensive trained subjects, *Int. J. Sports Med.,* 13(4), 308, 1992.

54. **Creager, M. A., Massie, B. M., Faxon, D. P., et al.,** Acute and long-term effects of enalapril on the cardiovascular response to exercise and exercise tolerance in patients with congestive heart failure, *J. Am. Coll. Cardiol.,* 6, 163, 1985.

55. **Kromer, E. P., Riegger, G. A. J., Liebau, G., and Kochsiek, K.,** Effectiveness of converting enzyme inhibition (elalapril) for mild congestive heart failure, *Am. J. Cardiol.,* 57, 459, 1986.

56. **Aldigier, J. C., Huang, H., Dalmay, F., et al.,** Angiotensin-converting enzyme inhibition does not suppress plasma angiotensin II increase during exercise in humans, *J. Cardiovasc. Pharmacol.,* 21(2), 289, 1993.

57. **Northridge, D. B. and Dargie, H. J.,** Quinapril in chronic heart failure, *Am. J. Hyperten.,* 3(11), 283S, 1990.

58. **Fortini, A., Cappelletti, C., Cecchi, L., and Laureano, R.,** Fosinopril in the treatment of hypertension: effects on 24 h ambulatory blood pressure and on blood pressure response to exercise, *J. Human Hyperten.,* 8(6), 469, 1994.

59. **Arita, M., Ueno, Y., Nakamura, C., et al.,** Effect of temocapril on haemodynamic and humoral responses to exercise in patients with mild essential hypertension, *Clin. Exp. Pharmacol. Physiol.,* 21(3), 195, 1994.

60. **Munzel T., Kurz, S., and Drexler, H.,** Are alterations of skeletal muscle ultrastructure in patients with heart failure reversible under treatment with ACE-inhibitors?, *Herz,* 18 (Suppl. 1), 400, 1993.

61. **Cleland, J. G. F., Dargie, H. J., Hodsman, G. P., et al.,** Captopril in heart failure: a double blind controlled trial, *Br. Heart J.,* 52, 530, 1984.

62. **Beleslin, B. D., Ostojic, M., Stepanovic, J., et. al.,** Stress echocardiography in the detection of myocardial ischemia. Head-to-head comparison of exercise, dobutamine, and dipyridamole tests, *Circulation,* 90(3), 1168, 1994.

63. **Botvinick, E. H. and Dae, M. W.,** Dipyridamole perfusion scintigraphy, *Semin. Nucl. Med.,* 21(3), 242, 1991.

64. **Bolognese, L., Sarasso, G., Bongo, A. S., et al.,** Stress testing in the period after infarction, *Circulation,* 83(Suppl. 5), III32, 1991.

65. **Iskandrian, A. S.,** Single-photon emission computed tomographic thallium imaging with adenosine, dipyridamole, and exercise, *Am. Heart J.,* 122, 279, 1991.

66. **van Baak, M. A.,** Hypertension, beta-adrenoceptor blocking agents and exercise, *Int. J. Sports Med.,* 15(3), 112, 1994.

67. **van Baak, M. A., Mooij, J. M., and Schiffers, P. M.,** Exercise and the pharmacokinetics of propranolol, verapamil and atenolol, *Eur. J. Clin. Pharmacol.,* 43(5), 547, 1992.

68. **Clifton, G. D., Pennell, A. T., and Harrison, M. R.,** Pharmacodynamics of propranolol on left ventricular function: assessment by Doppler echocardiography, *Clin. Pharmacol. Ther.,* 48(4), 431, 1990.

69. **Frank, S., Somani, S. M., and Kohnle, M.,** Effect of exercise on propranolol pharmacokinetics, *Eur. J. Clin. Pharmacol.,* 39(4), 391, 1990.

70. **Hallen, J., Gullestad, L., and Sejersted, O. M.,** K^+ shifts of skeletal muscle during stepwise bicycle exercise with and without beta-adrenoceptor blockade, *J. Physiol. (London),* 477, 149, 1994.

71. **Kantola, I., Kaila, T., and Erkkola, R.,** Acute exercise and drug-induced potassium shifts during pregnancy, *Ann. Chirurg. Gynaecol. Suppl.,* 208, 88, 1994.

72. **Prichard, B. N.,** Carvedilol in ischaemic heart disease, *Cardiology,* 82(Suppl.), 34, 1993.
73. **Packer, M.,** Abnormalities of diastolic function as a potential cause of exercise intolerance in chronic heart failure, *Circulation,* 81(Suppl. 2), III78, 1990.
74. **Waagstein, F.,** Beta blockers in heart failure, *Cardiology,* 82(Suppl. 3), 13, 1993.
75. **Eichhorn, E. J.,** The paradox of beta-adrenergic blockade for the management of congestive heart failure, *Am. J. Med.,* 92(5), 527, 1992.
76. **Maki, T., Naveri, H., Leinonen, H., et al.,** Effect of propranolol and pindolol on the up-regulation of lymphocytic beta adrenoceptors during acute submaximal physical exercise. A placebo-controlled double-blind study, *J. Cardiovasc. Pharmacol.,* 15(4), 544, 1990.
77. **Middeke, M., Reder, S., and Holzgreve, H.,** Regulation of the beta-adrenoceptor-cAMP-system during dynamic exercise in patients with primary hypertension after acute beta-blockade, *Blood Press.,* 3(3), 189, 1994.
78. **Brodsky, M., Doria, R., Allen, B., et al.,** New-onset ventricular tachycardia during pregnancy, *Am. Heart J.,* 123, 933, 1992.
79. **Maki, T., Kontula, K., and Harkonen, M.,** The beta-adrenergic system in man: physiological and pathophysiological response. Regulation of receptor density and functioning, *Scand. J. Clin. Lab. Invest.,* 201(Suppl.), 25, 1990.
80. **Beleslin, B. D., Ostojic, M., Stepanovic, J., et al.,** Stress echocardiography in the detection of myocardial ischemia. Head-to-head comparison of exercise, dobutamine, and dipyridamole tests, *Circulation,* 90(3), 1168, 1994.
81. **Winther, K. and Willich, S. N.,** Beta 1-blockade and acute coronary ischemia. Possible role of platelets, *Circulation,* 84(Suppl. 6), VI68, 1991.
82. **Wijnen, J. A., van Baak, M. A., de Haan, C., et al.,** Beta-blockade and lipolysis during endurance exercise, *Eur. J. Clin. Pharmacol.,* 42(2), 101, 1993.
83. **Benn, J. J., Brown, P. M., Beckwith, L. J., et al.,** Glucose turnover in type I diabetic subjects during exercise. Effect of selective and nonselective beta-blockade and insulin withdrawal, *Diabetes Care,* 15(11), 1721, 1992.
84. **Collins, K. J.,** Age-related changes in autonomic control: the use of beta blockers in the treatment of hypertension, *Cardiovasc. Drugs Ther.,* 4(Suppl. 6), 1257, 1991.
85. **Gordon, N. F. and Duncan, J. J.,** Effect of beta-blockers on exercise physiology: implications for exercise training, *Med. Sci. Sports Exerc.,* 23(6), 668, 1991.
86. **Navarro Estrada, J. L. and Oliveri, R.,** Long-term efficacy of amlodipine in patients with severe coronary artery disease, *J. Cardiovasc. Pharmacol.,* 22(Suppl. A), S24, 1993.
87. **Taylor, S. H.,** Usefulness of amlodipine for angina pectoris, *Am. J. Cardiol.,* 73,(3), 28A, 1994.
88. **Fariello, R., Boni, E., Corda, L., et al.,** Exercise-induced modifications in cardiorespiratory parameters of hypertensive patients treated with calcium antagonsists, *J. Hyperten.,* 9(3)(Suppl.), S67, 1991.
89. **Fagard, R., Staessen, J., Thijs, L., and Amery, A.,** Influence of antihypertensive drugs on exercise capacity, *Drugs,* 46(Suppl. 2), 32, 1993.
90. **Guyatt, G. H., Sullivan, M. J. J., Fallen, E. L., et al.,** A controlled trial of digoxin in congestive heart failure, *Am. J. Cardiol.,* 61, 371, 1988.
91. **Sullivan, M., Atwood, J. E., Myers, J., et al.,** Increased exercise capacity after digoxin administration in patients with heart failure, *J. Am. Coll. Cardiol.,* 13, 1138, 1989.
92. **Beaune, J.,** Comparison of enalapril vs digoxin for congestive heart failure, *Am. J. Cardiol.,* 63, 22D, 1989.
93. **The Xamoterol in Severe Heart Failure Study Group,** Xamoterol in severe heart failure, *Lancet,* 336, 1, 1990.
94. **DiBianco, R., Shabetal, R., Kostuk, W., et al.,** for the Milrinone Multicenter Trial Group, A comparison of oral milrinone, digoxin, and their combination in the treatment of patients with chronic heart failure, *N. Engl. J. Med.,* 320, 677, 1989.
95. **Alicandri, C., Fariello, R., Boni, E., et al.,** Ibopamine vs digoxin in chronic heart failure: a double-blind, crossover study, *J. Cardiovasc. Pharmacol.,* S77, 1989.

96. **Massie, B. M., et al.,** Can further benefit be achieved by adding a vasodilator to triple therapy in CHF: results of the flosequinan-ACE inhibitor trial (FACET)?, *Circulation,* 86, I, 645, 1992.

97. **Frenneaux, M. P., Counihan, P. J., Porter, A., et al.,** Effects of amiodarone on erect and supine exercise haemodynamics and exercise capacity in patients with hypertrophic cardiomyopathy, *Eur. Heart J.,* 13(5), 687, 1992.

98. **Hamer, A. W. F., Arkles, L. B., and Johns, J. A.,** Beneficial effects of low dose amiodarone in patients with congestive cardiac failure: a placebo-controlled trial, *J. Am. Coll. Cardiol.,* 14, 1768, 1989.

99. **Scheidt, S.,** Angina: evolution of the role of nitrates, *Am. Heart J.,* 120(3), 757, 1990.

100. **Wieshammer, S., Hetzel, M., Hetzel, J., et al.,** Lack of effect of nitrates on exercise tolerance in patients with mild to moderate heart failure caused by coronary disease already treated with captopril, *Br. Heart J.,* 70/1, 17, 1993.

101. **Young, S. N.,** The clinical psychopharmacology of tryptophan, in *Nutrition and the Brain,* Vol. 7, Wurtman, R. J. and Wurtman, J. J., Eds., Raven Press, New York, 1986, 49.

102. **Blomstrand, E., Celsing, F., and Newsholme, E. A.,** Changes in plasma concentrations of aromatic and branched-chain amino acids during sustained exercise in man and their possible role in fatigue, *Acta Physiol. Scand.,* 133, 115, 1988.

103. **Segura, R. and Ventura, J. L.,** Effect of L-tryptophan supplementation on exercise performance, *Int. J. Sports Med.,* 9(5), 301, 1988.

104. **Palermo, A., del Rosso, G., Costantini, C., Bertalero, P., Rizzi, S., and Libretti, A.,** Platelet content of serotonin and response to stress, *J. Hyperten.,* 4(1)(Suppl.), S43, 1986.

105. **Bunt, J. C.,** Hormonal alterations due to exercise, *Sports Med.,* 3(5), 331, 1986.

106. **Mazzeo, R. S.,** Catecholamine responses to acute and chronic exercise, *Med. Sci. Sports Exerc.,* 23(7), 839, 1991.

107. **Maki, T., Kontula, K., and Harkonen, M.,** The beta-adrenergic system in man: physiological and pathophysiological response. Regulation of receptor density and functioning, *Scand. J. Clin. Lab. Invest.,* 201, 25, 1990.

108. **Francis, G. S.,** Hemodynamic and neurohumoral responses to dynamic exercise: normal subjects versus patients with heart disease, *Circulation,* 76(6 Pt. 2), VI11, 1987.

109. **Kushwaha, S. S., Banner, N. R., Patel, N., et al.,** Effect of beta blockade on the neurohumoral and cardiopulmonary response to dynamic exercise in cardiac transplant recipients, *Br. Heart J.,* 71(5), 431, 1994.

110. **McCance, A. J. and Forfar, J. C.,** Cardiac and whole-body (3H) noradrenaline kinetics during adrenaline infusion in man, *Clin. Sci.,* 80(3), 227, 1991.

111. **Morrell, E. M., Cameron, O. G., Kandarian, S. C., et al.,** Aerobic physical training and alterations in pressor response during norepinephrine infusion: a controlled single-subject experiment, *Int. J. Sports Med.,* 11(1), 53, 1990.

112. **Svendenhag, J., Martinsson, A., Ekblom, B., and Hjemdahl, P.,** Altered cardiovascular responsiveness to adrenoceptor agonists in endurance-trained men, *J. Appl. Physiol.,* 70(2), 531, 1991.

113. **Kjaer, M., Secher, N. H., and Galbo, H.,** Physical stress and catecholamine release, *Baillieres Clin. Endocrinol. Metab.,* 1(2), 279, 1987.

114. **Schwartz, R. S., Jaeger, L. F., Veith, R. C., and Lakshminarayan, S.,** The effect of diet or exercise on plasma norepinephrine kinetics in moderately obese young men, *Int. J. Obesity,* 14(1), 1, 1990.

115. **Nielsen, B., Astrup, A., Samuelsen, P., Wengholt, H., and Christensen, N. J.,** Effect of physical training on thermogenic responses to cold and ephedrine in obesity, *Int. J. Obesity Relat. Metab. Disorders,* 17(7), 383, 1993.

116. **Kappel, M., Tvede, N., Galbo, H., et al.,** Evidence that the effect of physical exercise on NK cell activity is mediated by epinephrine, *J. Appl. Physiol.,* 70(6), 2530, 1991.

117. **Ciuffetti, G., Paltriccia, R., Lombardini, R., et al.,** Treating peripheral arterial occlusive disease: pentoxifylline vs. exercise, *Int. Angiol.,* 13(1), 33, 1994.

118. **Zhu, W. X., Gibbons, R. J., Bailey, K. R., and Gersh, B. J.,** Predischarge exercise radionuclide angiography in predicting multivessel coronary artery disease and subsequent cardiac events after thrombolytic therapy for acute myocardial infarction, *Am. J. Cardiol.,* 74(6), 554, 1994.
119. **Chandler, W. L., Veith, R. C., Fellingham, G. W., et al.,** Fibrinolytic response during exercise and epinephrine infusion in the same subjects, *J. Am. Coll. Cardiol.,* 19(7), 1412, 1992.
120. **el-Sayed, M. S.,** Extrinsic plasminogen activator response to exercise after a single dose of propranolol, *Med. Sci. Sports Exerc.,* 24(3), 327, 1992.
121. **Tsai, R. C., Yamaji, T., Ishibashi, M., et al.,** Role of atrial natriuretic peptide in hemoconcentration during exercise, *Am. J. Hyperten.,* 3(11), 833, 1990.

Chapter 11

EXERCISE, DRUGS, AND THE CHOLINERGIC SYSTEM

Satu M. Somani and Kazim Husain

CONTENTS

1. INTRODUCTION

Physical exercise is an influential factor on various physiological processes of the body. It causes a number of metabolic[1,2] and enzymatic changes in various tissues, especially in the muscles.[3-5] These changes depend upon the type of exercise being performed and also the intensity of the exercise.[6-8] In recent years, considerable information has accumulated pertaining to the exercise-induced changes in molecular and cellular mechanisms associated with metabolism of the muscles.[9,10] However, the neurotransmitter systems of the brain, which play an important role for human beings' ability to adapt to changes in their environment, have not received much attention from exercise researchers. The neurotransmitter acetylcholine, a component of the

0-8493-8540-1/96/$0.00+$.50
© 1996 by CRC Press, Inc.

cholinergic system, plays an essential role in neurotransmission at central and peripheral sites. Exercise may influence the synaptic and neuromuscular transmission by altering the metabolism of acetylcholine or by modifying the sensitivity of the cholinergic receptors. The changes in cholinergic systems may have functional implications for the performance of the brain regions and muscles during exercise. In order to determine the mechanisms controlling the cholinergic activity and its functional significance during exercise, the relationship must be established between exercise and the components of the cholinergic system in cerebral and peripheral tissues. Therefore, this chapter describes the effects of exercise on cholinergic systems.

The details of the cholinergic system are well explained and illustrated in text books of pharmacology; however, a brief description of the cholinergic system is given below. The cholinergic system consists primarily of synthetic (choline acetyltransferase) and degradative (acetylcholinesterase) enzyme of neurotransmitter-acetylcholine and its receptors, muscarinic and nicotinic.

The effects of exercise on acetylcholine metabolism can be studied indirectly to determine the changes in the activities of choline acetyltransferase (ChAT), and acetylcholinesterase (AChE) and choline uptake. Its physiological function, however, is demonstrated by the use of its specific receptor agonists and antagonists, and also the inhibitors of acetylcholinesterase. The cholinesterase inhibitors (carbamates and organophosphates) are being used extensively as pesticides in agriculture, chemical warfare agents, as pretreatment drugs against organophosphate intoxication, and in the treatment of glaucoma and Alzheimer's disease. Military personnel perform regular exercise, and farmers in fields also engage in strenuous work; thus, they may be exposed to these drugs or agents. The interactive effects of drugs and exercise affect the cholinergic system, which in turn is likely to influence an individual's performance. An extensive literature search on the mechanism of synaptic and neuromuscular transmission, regional distribution of acetylcholine, choline acetyltransferase, acetylcholinesterase, and acetylcholine receptors, reveals only a few studies have specifically examined the interaction of exercise and drugs with choline acetyltransferase and acetylcholinesterase.[8,11-16] The following review deals concisely with the interactions of acute exercise, exercise training, and drugs in relation to the components of the cerebral and peripheral cholinergic systems.

2. CHOLINERGIC SYSTEM

The central nervous system (CNS) plays a pivotal role in controlling the various activities of the body's tissues and organs. The CNS is comprised of the brain and the spinal cord, which are composed of specialized types of cells called neurons. Neurons are electrically excitable; they conduct impulses, and do not undergo cell division during an entire lifetime of an individual. There are two types of neurons: afferent (sensory) and efferent. Afferent neurons carry impulses from sense organs (ear and eye), or from receptors in tissues,

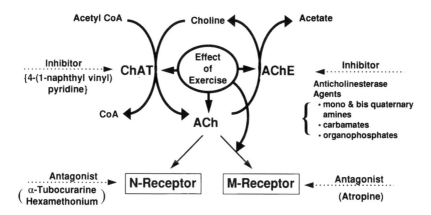

FIGURE 1. The components of cholinergic system and the exercise affecting the enzymes and acetylcholine. ACh = Acetylcholine; AChE = acetylcholinesterase; ChAT = choline acetyltransferase; N = nicotinic; M = muscarinic.

toward the CNS, and efferent neurons carry impulses from the CNS to the tissues, organs, and glands. Chemical transmissions of the impulses between the two neurons occur at synapses or junctions and are unidirectional. The chemicals involved in the transmission of impulses from one neuron to another are called neurotransmittters. These neurotransmitters are acetylcholine, norepinephrine, serotonin, dopamine, gamma aminobutyric acid, glutamate, and a few other amino acids. The synthesis, storage, release, and degradation of neurotransmitters are precisely regulated by an extensive enzymatic process. The synaptic and neuromuscular transmissions, that are mediated by neurotransmitter acetylcholine, are called cholinergic neurotransmissions, and the system is referred to as the cholinergic system.

The cholinergic system and associated components and functions are depicted in Figure 1. Acetylcholine is synthesized in the cytoplasm from choline and acetyl CoA through the catalytic action of enzyme choline acetyltransferase. Acetylcholine molecules bind together to activate an acetylcholine receptors (muscarinic or nicotinic). Eventually, all of ACh molecules diffuse and are hydrolyzed by enzyme acetylcholinesterase into choline and acetate, and choline is again transported into the nerve terminal for the resynthesis of ACh. Since the exercise causes a stress response, it is quite possible that ACh is released during exercise, thereby, changing other components of the cholinergic system. In addition, the existence of a variety of other noncholinergic functions may alter activities of the cholinergic enzymes during exercise.

2.1. ACETYLCHOLINE

Acetylcholine, a neurotransmitter, is a quaternary ammonium ester and produces negative inotropic (contractile force) and chronotropic (rate) effects and vasodilation on the cardiovascular system. It increases gastrointestinal mobility and secretory activity and stimulates the salivary, sweat, and lacrimal

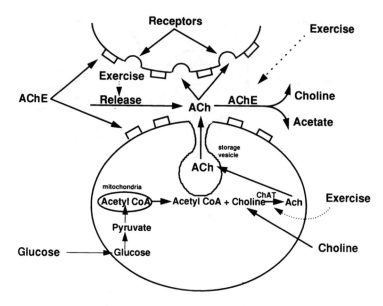

FIGURE 2. Influence of exercise on synthesis, release and degradation of acetylcholine. ACh = acetylcholine; ChAT = choline acetyltransferase; ChAT = choline acetyltransferase; AChE = acetylcholinesterase.

glands, in addition to contracting smooth muscle in the uterus, ureter, bladder, bronchioles, and irises. Acetylcholine is considered an excitatory neurotransmitter in the nervous system. Most ACh is synthesized in the cytoplasm from choline and acetyl CoA, the reaction being catalyzed by the enzyme choline acetyltransferase (ChAT). Acetyl CoA is synthesized in mitochondria, which are numerous in the nerve endings. Choline is transported by membrane carrier mechanisms from the extracellular fluid into the neuronal terminal. Acetylcholine is stored in vesicles and released due to an increase in Ca^{++} concentration. After release from the presynaptic terminal, ACh molecules bind to activate an acetylcholine receptor. All of the ACh released is diffused within range of AChE molecule. Acetylcholinesterase efficiently degrades ACh into choline and acetate and, thereby, terminates the ACh action. Choline is transported into the nerve terminal by carriers for the resynthesis of ACh. Synthesis, release, and degradation of ACh are shown in Figure 2.

2.2. CHOLINE ACETYLTRANSFERASE

The choline acetyltransferase enzyme catalyzes the synthesis of acetylcholine using choline and acetyl CoA as a substrate. The enzyme protein is synthesized on the ribosomes of the nerve cell body and is transported to the axon terminals by axoplasmic flow. The synthesis of ACh occurs mainly in the synaptic nerve terminals. ChAT enzyme activity is inhibited by its inhibitor 4-(1-naphthyl-vinyl) pyridine.[17] The distribution of ChAT in cellular and subcellular regions has been reviewed.[18,19] ChAT activity does not restrict the rate of

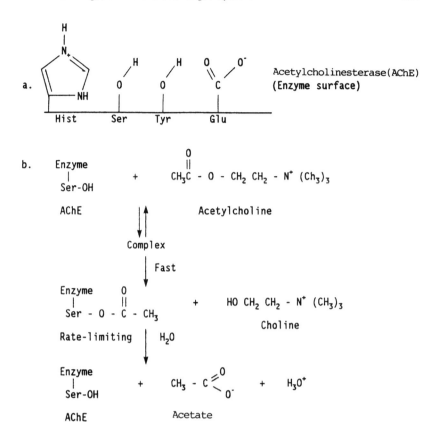

FIGURE 3. Mechanism of hydrolysis of acetylcholine by acetylcholinesterase. (a) Groups present on the active sites of acetylcholinesterase; (b) enzyme-substrate complex formation and subsequent hydrolysis of acetylcholine into choline and acetylated enzyme and finally acetate and free enzyme.

ACh synthesis. In addition, activity is likely to be 25 times lower at substrate concentrations that are present in neurons.[20] Since calcium increases the output of acetyl CoA from brain mitochondria and also activates the uptake of choline into nerve endings, it is likely that the concentration of ChAT substrates during exercise may also be affected by an increased uptake of calcium in different brain regions.

2.3. CHOLINESTERASES

Cholinesterase enzymes catalyze the hydrolysis of acetylcholine and other choline esters. They have been classified on the basis of substrate specificity into two classes. Acetylcholinesterase, or true (specific) cholinesterase, efficiently hydrolyses acetylcholine, at cholinergic synapses, into choline and acetate. The mechanism of hydrolysis of acetylcholine by acetylcholinesterase is depicted in Figure 3. Esteratic sites of the enzyme contain hydroxyl groups of serine and binds with acetylcholine to form an enzyme-substrate complex.

This complex produces choline and acetylated enzymes at a faster rate and, finally, acetate and free enzymes are released. Other major classes of cholinesterases are called pseudo (nonspecific) cholinesterases, which hydrolyze butyrylcholine and propionylcholine. Acetylcholinesterase's crucial function in neurotransmission occurs in the nervous tissue, striated muscle, and red blood cells. Pseudocholinesterase is present in plasma, intestine, skin, and other tissues; its function, however, is largely unknown. The cholinesterases are inactivated by their inhibitors, which are grouped into three classes based on their structures. These groups are mono and bis quaternary amines, the carbamates, and organophosphates. Carbamates are reversible inhibitors of cholinesterase, whereas organophosphates are irreversible inhibitors of cholinesterase.

2.4. CHOLINERGIC RECEPTORS

Acetylcholine is released from cholinergic nerve endings of the brain and neuromuscular junctions. It interacts reversibly with the appropriate receptors (muscarinic) and (nicotinic) and activates them. Muscarinic receptors are present in smooth and cardiac muscle as well as exocrine glands while nicotinic receptors are located on post ganglionic neurons, adrenal medullary cells, and skeletal muscle cells. Muscarinic receptors are selectively activated by the agonist muscarine, and are blocked by the antagonist atropine; nicotinic receptors are activated by agonist nicotine and blocked by antagonist curare.

Muscarinic receptors are further classified into subclasses M_1, M_2, M_3, and M_4, and nicotinic receptors into N_1 and N_2, based on selective ligand binding studies.[21,22] It is possible that exercise and drugs may interact with the cholinergic receptors and modify the physiological functions of body's organs.

3. EFFECT OF EXERCISE ON CHOLINE ACETYLTRANSFERASE

3.1. IN CEREBRAL TISSUES

Alterations in the central cholinergic system due to physical exercise, especially those involving the biosynthetic enzyme of acetylcholine, ChAT, have been sparsely researched. In addition, few studies examine the changes in ChAT activity in brain regions due to exercise and other types of stresses. Table 1 summarizes the changes in ChAT activity in cerebral tissues due to exercise. In rats exposed to repeated immobilization stress, ChAT activity diminished (33%) in brain basal ganglia of rats exposed to repeated immobilization stress;[23] ChAT activity decreased in cortex (59%), hypothalamus (48%), hippocampus (30%), and mid-brain (38%) of rats after acute immobilization stress.[24] Conversely, ChAT activity increased in the rat cerebral cortex (16%) after acute and repeated electroshock.[25] After exposure to immobilization, ChAT activity has been reported unchanged in different brain regions: brain stem, striatum, hippocampus, and hypothalamus.[26,27] Chronic exposure of rats to cold conditions and other stressors has enhanced ChAT activity in basal

TABLE 1
Effect of Exercise and Other Stresses on Choline Acetyltransferase Activity in Cerebral and Peripheral Tissues of Rats

Type of Exercise	Tissues	% Change in Activity[a]	Ref.
Exercise training	Brain stem	−27	Somani et al.[14]
	Cerebral cortex	−16	
	Corpus striatum	No change	
	Hippocampus	−22	
Chronic cold stress	Basal ganglia	+15	Kita et al.[28]
	Hypothalamus	+12	
Chronic cold stress	Medulla	+50	Wahba and Soliman[24]
Acute cold stress	Hippocampus	+18	Fatranska et al.[30]
Repeated immobilization stress	Basal ganglia	−33	Gottesfeld et al.[23]
Acute immobilization stress	Cerebral cortex	−59	Wahba and Soliman[24]
	Hypothalamus	−48	
	Hippocampus	−30	
	Mid-brain	−38	
Chronic stress	Medulla	+63	Lin and Li[29]
Immobilization stress	Brain stem	No change	Gilad and McCarty[26]
	Striatum	No change	
	Hypothalamus	No change	
	Hippocampus	No change	
Acute electric shock stress	Cerebral cortex	+16	Longoni et al.[25]
Acute immobilization and cold stress	Adrenal gland	+46	Wahba and Soliman[24]
Chronic immobilization stress	Adrenal gland	No change	Wahba and Soliman[24]
Repeated cold stress	Duodenum	No change	Kita et al.[28]
Exercise	Adrenal gland	−28	Tumer et al.[38]
Exercise training	EDL muscle	−32	Babu et al.[11]
	Soleus muscle	+24	

[a]   +, Increase; −, decrease.

ganglia (15%) and hypothalamus (12%),[28] and in medulla (50[24] and 63%[29]). Acute exposure of rats to cold stress resulted in an increase in ChAT activity (18%) in the hippocampus.[30] It is concluded from the above studies that acute and chronic stresses differentially altered the ChAT activity in the brain regions, thereby regulating the synthesis of the neurotransmitter and altered sensitivity of the cholinergic system.

Recently, Somani et al.[14] have studied the effect of exercise training on the changes in the biosynthetic enzyme for ACh in different brain regions of rats. They report that changes were differentially expressed within subregions of the brain during exercise training. These investigators showed that ChAT activity did not change in the corpus striatum, and activity decreased in the cerebral cortex due to exercise training. Choline acetyltransferase activity decreased (27%) in the brain stem due to exercise training, thereby indicating that ChAT activity of this region is more sensitive to exercise than others. In addition, ChAT activity decreased (22%) in hippocampus after exercise training.[14]

Somani et al.[14] suggest that the biosynthetic enzymes for ACh in brain regions involved with control of motor, autonomic, and cognitive functions are affected by exercise training in a regionally selective pattern. For example, the only brain region in that ChAT activity responded to exercise training was the brain stem, a region that is involved in maintaining critical autonomic functions related to the cardiopulmonary system, and where ACh has potent actions. These data are consistent with the hypothesis which states that the responsiveness of the brain regions to the physical stressors is a function of the level of ongoing cholinergic transmission, and that elevations in ACh levels may have long-term effects on ChAT activity through a negative feedback mechanism.

The marked differences in ACh levels (up to two- to threefold) observed in the regional distribution of ChAT were consistent with the known cholinergic innervation to the stress examined.[31] ChAT activity in the cerebral cortex is not affected by exercise, possibly suggesting the relative sparing of cholinergic systems in higher association centers that are involved with cognitive function. The cholinergic system in corpus striatum, which is normally involved in motor control, is essentially unaffected by exercise. However, cholinergic parameters in various regions of the brain react differently to altered stress conditions, such as electric shock, cold, and swimming.[32,33] Since regional differences in cholinergic activities were also observed during exercise training, this study supports such a concept.

The brain stem regulates respiratory and cardiovascular functions. Exercise training alone increases blood pressure and heart rate[34] and regulates ChAT activity.[35] Increases in medullary tissue concentrations of ACh by ChE inhibitors, also elevate pressure and respiration.[36] It is plausible that when tissue levels of ACh increase, ChAT activity is down-regulated as a compensatory mechanism to normalize cholinergic transmission and, hence, blood pressure. Chronically elevated ACh concentrations eventually down-regulate ChAT, and AChE activities to normalize cholinergic transmissions, whereas acute exercise initially increases tissue ACh levels by enhancing biosynthesis without affecting degradation. It is suggested that acute stress or exercise may enhance the sensitivity of the cholinergic system, whereas chronic exercise or stress decreases the sensitivity of the cholinergic system.

3.2. IN PERIPHERAL TISSUES

The components of the cholinergic system are present in peripheral (nonnervous) tissues and muscle as well as glands, and are innervated with cholinergic fibers.[37] Since exercise stress evokes a number of metabolic and enzymatic changes in peripheral tissues, the cholinergic enzymes are also altered in peripheral tissues. Acute immobilization, and cold stress have been shown to increase ChAT activity (46%) in the adrenal gland of rats, whereas no change has been observed with chronic cold stress.[24] In addition, Kita et al.[28] have reported no change in ChAT activity in rat duodenum after repeated cold stress. Exercise decreased ChAT activity in the adrenal gland of young rats.[38]

Muscle characteristics are influenced by the neurotransmitter ACh, a neurogenic substance conveyed by axoplasmic transport, and muscle electromechanical activity.[39] These regulatory factors are affected by changes in motor activity. The experimentally induced enhancement of neuromuscular use or disuse invariably leads to dramatic modifications in the muscle metabolism, contractile properties, and neuromuscular transmission-related molecules.[39,40] Acetylcholine receptors, ChAT, and AChE have received much research attention because of their usefulness as sensitive indicators of normal nerve–muscle interactions.[39]

Trained exercise induces several ultrastructural and protein metabolic changes in exercised skeletal muscle.[41,42] Endurance training decreases ChAT activity (32%) in extensor digitorum longus (EDL), whereas in slow twitch soleus, it increased 24%.[11] This finding is explained by considering the animal locomotion and the type of muscles involved. Fast twitch muscles are active primarily during locomotion, whereas slow twitch (soleus) muscles are active while the animals are at rest.[43,44] Such active involvement of fast twitch EDL during exercise may lead to a decrease in ChAT activity.

4. EFFECT OF EXERCISE ON CHOLINESTERASES

4.1. IN CEREBRAL TISSUES

Acute and repeated exercise and other stressors have had marked effects on the acetylcholinesterase activity of various brain regions and peripheral tissues (Table 2). Increased levels of AChE activity have been observed in the cortex, thalamus, and hypothalamus of rats given electric foot shock stress.[45] Convulsions induced with a single electroconvulsive shock resulted in a transient increase in AChE activity in the cortex and striatum, and a sustained decrease in the hippocampus and mid-brain of the rats.[46] Acetylcholinesterase activity was increased by acute immobilization stress in cerebrum (100%) and in the cerebellum (40%). The lesser stimulation of cerebellum AChE activity, when compared to that in the cerebrum, is due to the presence of relatively small amounts of cerebellar cholinergic innervation.[47] Acute and chronic immobilization stress induced an increase in the AChE activity of the hypothalamus and brain stem.[48]

Acute stress (in the form of vehicle injection) produced a decrease in the cortical and hippocampal soluble AChE activity; whereas, chronic mild stress in the form of repeated handling (vehicle injection) increased soluble AChE activity in the mid-brain and decreased total AChE activity in the cortex and hippocampus in rats.[49] Kita et al.[28] reported that repeated exposure of rats to cold stress caused an enhancement of AChE activity in basal ganglia and the

TABLE 2
Effect of Exercise on Acetylcholinesterase Activity in Cerebral and Peripheral Tissues of Rats and Humans

Species	Type of Exercise	Tissues	% Change in Activity[a]	Ref.
Rat	Exercise training	Brain stem	−19	Somani et al.[14]
		Cerebral cortex	−16	
		Corpus striatum	−6	
		Hippocampus	−6	
Rat	Exercise training	Brain	−3 to −9	Somani and Dube[13]
Rat	Acute exercise	Cerebral cortex	−17	Husain and Somani[15]
	(100% VO$_2$max)	Cerebellum	−6	
		Corpus striatum	−40	
		Hypothalamus	−4	
		Medulla	−23	
Rat	Acute exercise	Brain	−3 to −12	Dube et al.[12]
	(80% VO$_2$max)			Somani and Dube[13]
Rat	Acute exercise	Brain	−8 to −13	Dube et al.[8]
	(50, 80, 100% VO$_2$max)			
Rat	Acute exercise	Brain	+3	Pedzikiewicz et al.[50]
Rat	Acute immobilization	Cerebrum	+100	Tsakiris and
	stress	Cerebellum	+40	Kontopoulos[47]
Rat	Repeated cold stress	Basal ganglia	+31	Kita et al.[28]
		Hypothalamus	+13	
Rat	Acute cold stress	Hippocampus	+29	Fatranska et al.[30]
		Hypothalamus	−25	
Mice	Acute handling stress	Cerebral cortex	−24	Appleyard et al.[49]
		Hippocampus	−39 to −49	
		Mid-brain	−41	
Rat	Repeated cold stress	Duodenum	−8	Kita et al.[28]
Rat	Acute exercise	Serum	+36	Pawlowska et al.[7]
Rat	Acute exercise	Plasma	+55	Husain and Somani[15]
	(100% VO$_2$max)			
Rat	Acute exercise (50,	RBC	+8 to +16	Dube et al.[8]
	80, 100% VO$_2$max)	Heart	−13 to −18	
		Diaphragm	No change	
		Muscle	No change	
Rat	Acute exercise	RBC	+12	Dube et al.[12]
	(80% VO$_2$max)		+14	Somani and Dube[13]
		Heart	−13	Dube et al.[12]
			−5 to −11	Somani and Dube[13]
Rat	Exercise training	RBC	−34	Somani and Dube[13]
		Heart	−15 to −25	
		Diaphragm	−15 to −22	
		Muscle	−11 to −21	
Rat	Exercise training	Extensor	−21 to −43	Babu et al.[11]
		digitosum		
		longus muscle		
		Soleus muscle	−27 to −45	
Rat	Exercise training	Fast muscle	+420	Gisiger et al.[55]
Human	Exercise training	RBC	+8	Spodaryk et al.[52]

[a] +, Increase; −, decrease.

hypothalamus. Dube et al.[8] reported that different intensities of acute exercise (50, 80, and 100% VO_2max) produced slight decreases in brain AChE activity (8 to 13%) in rats. This finding is in agreement with Ryhanen et al.,[16] and is contrary to the findings of Pedzikiewicz et al.,[50] who have shown a slight increase (3%) in brain ChE activity after single exercise. Holmstedt[51] reports that physical exercise accelerates the nerve action in the CNS, resulting in an increased amount of acetylcholine in the nerve endings, and hence increasing ChE inhibition. Recently, Husain and Somani[15] have reported that acute exercise (100% VO_2max) decreased AChE activity in the striatum (40%), medulla (23%), and cerebral cortex (17%) without any change in the hypothalamus and cerebellum of rats. Somani et al.[14] have studied the effect of exercise training on the changes in the AChE activity in cerebral tissues. They reported that these changes are differentially expressed within subregions of the brain. These investigators show that AChE activity decreased 19% in the brain stem, 16% in cerebral cortex, 6% in striatum and hippocampus.

The marked differences (up to two- to ninefold) observed in the regional distribution of AChE are consistent with the known cholinergic innervation to the brain regions that have been previously examined.[31] Under normal conditions, tissue levels of ACh are regulated by its net synthesis and degradation by ChAT and AChE, respectively. Immediately following AChE inhibition, tissue levels of ACh increase and thereby initiate processes that decrease AChE activity. Chronically elevated ACh concentrations eventually down-regulate AChE activity to normalize cholinergic transmissions, whereas acute exercise initially increases tissue ACh levels by enhancing biosynthesis without affecting degradation. This phenomenon does not appear to be expressed in the striatum, hippocampus, or cortex. However, chronically elevated levels of ACh still down-regulate AChE activity. It is concluded that acute exercise decreases AChE activity in the area of the brain which possesses high AChE activity and controls motor function, thereby enhancing the sensitivity of the cholinergic system. Conversely, exercise training decreases the sensitivity in the brain region that contains less AChE activity and regulates the cardiopulmonary system.

4.2. IN PERIPHERAL TISSUES

Peripheral tissues, especially muscle and glands, are connected by cholinergic fibers and contain cholinesterase enzymes. It is quite possible that during physical exercise, or other stresses, enzyme activity is altered. The changes in ChE activity after exercise and stress in tissues are summarized in Table 2. Chronic cold stress to rats has been shown to increase blood butyry cholinesterase (BuChE) activity and decrease the ChE activity in the lung,[16] whereas ChE activity decreased (8%) in the duodenum.[28] Acute physical exercise for 1 and 2 h increased cholinesterase activity (36%) in the blood serum of rats.[7]

Spodaryk et al.[52] have studied the influence of physical training on blood AChE activity in athletes and report that in the reticulocytes and young erythrocytes of endurance-trained athletes, AChE activity was higher than in the control group. Acute exercise produces a slight elevation of ChE activity in red blood cells (RBC).[8,12,13] Changes in ChE activity were in agreement with the earlier work[7] which shows a significant increase in ChE activity in blood serum after acute physical exercise in rats. The increase in erythrocyte ChE with acute exercise may be due to a secondary effect of hypoxia,[7] and hemoconcentration may result from a plasma shift[53] during exercise. Surprisingly, the increase in the intensity of exercise from 40% VO_2max to 100% VO_2max did not show a corresponding increase in ChE activity; rather, we observed a slight decrease in ChE activity (8%) at 100% VO_2max, and (16%) at 50% VO_2max. This may be due to excitement, anxiety, and stress in the rats during the initial period of exercise (50% VO_2max); subsequently, there may be a cholinergic acclimatization at higher intensities of exercise corresponding to treadmill exercise for 20 and 30 min, respectively. Recently, Husain and Somani[15] demonstrated a 55% increase in plasma cholinesterase activity after 30 min of acute exercise (100% VO_2max) in rats. Acute exercise at 50 to 100% VO_2max for 10 to 30 min decreased ChE activity in the heart (5 to 18%) without affecting ChE activity in the diaphragm and muscle.[8,12,13] However, Tipton et al.[54] found no significant change in myocardial ChE activity after trained exercise. Contrary to acute exercises, exercise training decreased ChE activity in RBC (24 to 34%), in the heart (15 to 25%), in the diaphragm (15 to 22%), and in the muscle (11 to 21%).[13] Babu et al.[11] studied the effect of exercise training on AChE activity in fast extensor digitorum longus (EDL) and slow soleus muscles of rat. The data presented in Table 2 shows that AChE activity had decreased in both EDL muscle (43%) and soleus muscle (45%) 20 min after the exercise training; whereas the AChE activity decreased in EDL muscle (21%) and coleus muscle (27%) 24 h after exercise training. This is contrary to Fernandez and Donoso's findings who reported an increase in G_4 form AChE in fast twitch muscle due to exercise.[39] Similarly, a profound increase in G_4 form AChE in fast twitch muscle (420%) of rat after exercise training has been reported recently.[55] Dettebarn[56] has reported the distinctive difference in AChE activity in fast and slow muscles after reinnervation in rats. Recent studies have revealed that AChE shows remarkable plasticity in response to chronic enhancement of neuromuscular activity during exercise training. Acetylcholinesterase adaptation is highly specific in that it selectively affects the tetrameric AChE molecular form G_4. The changes in the G_4 form of AChE are independent of the concurrent adaptations to exercise training in the muscles' oxidative capacity.[39] It has been proposed that muscle G_4 participates in the regulation of motor endplate excitability by degrading ACh molecules that diffuse out of the synaptic cleft. G_4 prevents the accumulation of ACh molecules around the endplates during exercise and causes desensitization of nicotinic receptors. Therefore, the adaptations in neuromuscular transmission in mouse EDL muscle is brought about by profound increase in G_4 form of AChE during exercise training.[55] Babu et al.[11] studied the total AChE instead of molecular forms and, moreover, the treadmill exercise differed from the protocol followed by the above authors whose exercise protocol consisted of

TABLE 3
Effect of Repeated Dose of Physostigmine (70 μg/kg, i.m.) Daily for 2 Weeks and Trained Exercise for 2 Weeks on Choline Acetyltransferase (ChAT) Activity (% of control), in Different Brain Regions of Rats

Group	Treatment	Corpus Striatum	Cerebral Cortex	Brain Stem	Hippocampus
II	Trained exercise	98.1 ± 4.0	84.04 ± 2.2	72.8* ± 2.2	77.8 ± 2.2
III	Subacute Phy				
IIIa	Sacrificed 20 min after Phy	76.3* ± 0.7	95.6 ± 8.5	81.1* ± 7.0	85.5 ± 6.2
IIIb	Sacrificed 24 h after Phy	88.7* ± 2.9	89.0 ± 3.4	78.0* ± 3.2	75.9 ± 4.2
IV	Subacute Phy + acute exercise				
IVa	Sacrificed 20 min after Phy	95.1* ± 1.2	95.3 ± 4.6	84.3 ± 8.2	74.9 ± 1.3
IVb	Sacrificed 24 h after Phy	68.5* ± 0.3	92.5 ± 4.6	81.8* ± 3.5	72.1* ± 3.2
V	Subacute Phy + trained exercise				
Va	Sacrificed 20 min after Phy	91.9* ± 3.3	82.4 ± 10.7	80.1* ± 6.4	75.3 ± 3.5
Vb	Sacrificed 24 h after Phy	88.5* ± 0.2	79.4* ± 2.3	81.1* ± 1.2	73.3* ± 2.1

*Significant at $p < 0.05$.

Adapted from Somani et al., *Pharmacol. Biochem. Behav.,* 39, 337, 1991. With permission.

1 to 2 h of exercise with a speed of 30 to 35 m/min once or twice a day, whereas our protocol included 20 min of exercise at progressive speeds only once a day. The difference in exercise protocols may alter the enzyme activity. Total AChE activity decreased, even when the molecular forms (G_4 form) showed an increase, thereby indicating the overall decrease of AChE. It is concluded that acute exercise increased ChE activity in the blood, whereas exercise training decreased ChE activity. Therefore, blood ChE may be used as a biochemical indicator to differentiate acute exercise and exercise training.

5. INTERACTION OF DRUGS AND EXERCISE ON CHOLINE ACETYLTRANSFERASE

The interaction of various drugs and exercise in man and animals has been widely reported.[57,58] However, few reports are available regarding the interaction of exercise on the disposition and pharmacodynamics of drugs.[59-61] The various forms of physical exercise do not alter the processes of drug absorption to the same extent, thereby resulting in the varied pharmacodynamic action of drugs. The combined effect of physical exercise and drugs on the cholinergic system has not as yet been thoroughly studied.

Somani et al.[14] studied the interaction of a centrally acting anticholinesterase drug Physostigmine (Phy), exercise, and the ChAT activity in brain regions of rat as presented in Table 3. ChAT activity in corpus striatum

TABLE 4
Choline Acetyltransferase Activity (% of Control) in Fast (EDL) and Slow (Soleus) Muscles in Subacute Administration of Phy (70 µg/kg, i.m., Twice Daily for 2 Weeks) and/or Exercised (Once Daily for 2 Weeks) Rats

Group	Treatment	Time of Sacrifice After Treatment	Choline Acetyltransferase EDL	Soleus
I	Sedentary control	20 min	100%	100%
IIa	Exercise training	20 min	67.8 ± 2.1*	123.9 ± 4.9*
IIb	Exercise training	24 h	86.5 ± 3.2	109.1 ± 2.9
IIIa	Subacute Phy	20 min	89.6 ± 3.3	94.4 ± 4.9
IIIb	Subacute Phy	24 h	110.5 ± 6.0	116.4 ± 4.8
IVa	Subacute Phy +	20 min	96.7 ± 7.8	89.8 ± 11.1
IVb	Single acute exercise	24 h	105.1 ± 3.9	111.1 ± 8.9
Va	Subacute Phy +	20 min	65.3 ± 3.8*	98.4 ± 3.5
Vb	Exercise training	24 h	66.7 ± 5.6*	108.5 ± 7.2

Note: Values are mean ± SEM. Control value of ChAT in EDL 10.77 ± 0.23; soleus 8.81 ± 0.29 nmoles of ACh synthesized/mg protein/h*. Statistical significance at $p < 0.05$.

Adapted from Babu et al., *Pharmacol. Biochem. Behav.*, 45, 713, 1993. With permission.

decreased (24, 5, and 8%) due to subacute Phy plus acute exercise as well as Phy plus exercise training. This decrease suggests that corpus striatum is affected by chemical stressors, but even more so by the combination of chemical and physical stressors. The brain stem is the only region which showed inhibition of ChAT activity due to exercise. Subacute Phy also inhibited brain stem ChAT activity (19%) after 20 min, and (22%) after 24 h posttreatment. The hippocampus showed significant decreases in ChAT activity due to Phy plus exercise (28%), but not due to Phy alone. These results suggest that the brain regions involved with control of motor, autonomic, and cognitive functions are affected by subacute Phy and exercise. These data are consistent with the hypothesis that the brain region responsiveness to different stressors is a function of the level of ongoing cholinergic activity, and indicates that elevations in ACh levels may have long-term effects on the regulation of ChAT activity through a negative feedback mechanism.

The results of another recent study are shown in Table 4. Babu et al.[11] have studied the interaction of exercise and Phy to ChAT activity in different muscles of rats. Choline acetyltransferase activity decreased in rats by trained exercise in EDL muscle (32%) and Phy prolonged this effect even up to 24 h. Soleus muscles showed a small increase of ChAT due to exercise, but Phy plus exercise did not change the activity significantly. No recovery was observed in ChAT activity of EDL in Phy plus trained exercise group even after 24 h. Results suggest that Phy and exercise have significant effects on the synthetic

(ChAT) enzyme of acetylcholine in active EDL muscle. Exercise has prolonged the inhibitory effect of Phy on ChAT activity, both in active EDL and passive soleus muscles. This study shows that Phy plus exercise modified the functional activity of cholinergic system in EDL and soleus muscles.

6. INTERACTION OF DRUGS AND EXERCISE ON CHOLINESTERASES

The changes in AChE activity in different tissues of animals after acute exercise and exercise training have been discussed under the previous headings; however, the drugs which are known to inhibit AChE activity, such as physostigmine and other organophosphorus pesticides, will certainly be changed. A post-exercise stress-induced change in enzyme activities may serve as an adaptational phenomenon or may modify the actions of the drugs. The interaction of drug, exercise, and stress on AChE activity is depicted in Table 5. Ryhanen et al.[16] studied the relationship of cold stress, and cholinesterase inhibiting organophosphorus compounds, to cholinesterase activity in rats. They reported that cholinesterase in the liver of chronically cold-exposed rats (2 weeks) was more sensitive to diisopropyl fluorophosphate (DFP) inhibition when compared to acute cold exposed rats. Studies have been conducted on the effects of organophosphorous pesticides and exercise on cholinesterase enzymes in rats.[7] In such studies, parathione-methyl-induced inhibition of blood serum cholinesterase was less marked 1 h after its termination. The activity of cholinesterase, an enzyme produced in the liver, depends upon a number of endo- and exogenous factors. It may be assumed that increased ChE activity is a secondary effect of hypoxia and the labilization of lysosomal membrane of liver cells after acute exercise. The higher values of serum ChE activity after exercise attenuates the effect of organophosphorus pesticides on this enzyme; this phenomenon is transient.

Physostigmine is a centrally acting anticholinesterase drug used as a potential pretreatment drug for organophosphorus intoxication.[61] McMaster and Foster[62] have demonstrated that acute exercise increases behavioral sensitivity to Phy. Carbamate-induced decrease in performance has been shown to be restored with diazepam and atropine.[63] However, the combined effect of physical exercise and physostigmine on AChE activity in different tissues of rat has been extensively studied during the last 5 years by Somani and co-workers.[8,11-13] Matthew and co-workers[63,64] have studied the acute and chronic administration of physostigmine on ChE inhibition and performance (endurance) of exercising rats. Acute physostigmine administration in exercising rats resulted in a 50% inhibition of blood ChE and a reduction in endurance (performance), whereas chronic administration attenuated the decrease in ChE activity and the endurance of exercising rats. Similarly, actue administration of peripheral acting carbamate (pyridostigmine) resulted in decreased endurance and inhibition of ChE (40 to 60%), whereas chronic administration of this drug elicited a ChE inhibition of 40% without decreasing the performance of exercising rats.

TABLE 5

Effect of Exercise and Physostigmine (70 µg/kg i.m.) on Cholinesterase Activity in Different Tissues of Rat

Treatment	Tissues	% Change in Activity[a]	Ref.
Acute exercise	RBC	–5 to +16	Dube et al.[8]
		Dube et al.[12]	
Physostigmine		–16 to –27	
Acute exercise + physostigmine		–17 to –49	
Acute exercise	Heart	–5 to –18	
Physostigmine		–15 to –32	
Acute exercise + physostigmine		–5 to –27	
Acute exercise	Diaphragm	No change	
Physostigmine		–19 to –33	
Acute exercise + physostigmine		–17 to –30	
Acute exercise	Muscle	–6 to –9	
Physostigmine		–17 to –43	
Acute exercise + physostigmine		–31 to –46	
Acute exericse	Brain	–8 to –13	
Physostigmine		–15 to –34	
Acute exercise + physostigmine		–14 to –50	
Exercise training	RBC	–24 to –34	Somani and Dube[13]
Physostigmine		–21 to –33	
Acute exercise + physostigmine		–34 to –35	
Exercise training	Heart	–15 to –25	
Physostigmine		–11 to –31	
Exercise training + physostigmine		–42	
Exercise training	Diaphragm	–15 to –22	
Physostigmine		–34	
Exercise training + physostigmine		–50	
Exercise training	Muscle	–11 to –21	
Physostigmine		–17 to –36	
Exercise training + physostigmine		–22 to –42	
Exercise training	Brain	–3 to –9	
Physostigmine		–1 to –40	
Exercise training + physostigmine		–36 to –52	
Exercise training	Fast EDL muscle	–21 to –43	Babu et al.[11]
Physostigmine		–31 to –44	
Exercise training + physostigmine		–37 to –57	

TABLE 5 (Continued)

Treatment	Tissues	% Change in Activity[a]	Ref.
Exercise training	Slow soleus	−27 to −43	
Physostigmine	muscle	−33 to −43	
Exercise training + physostigmine		−34 to −71	

[a]   +, Increase; −, decrease.

These studies suggest that decreases in performance, caused by acute drug administration, may be attenuated through accommodation with chronic administration. These studies also indicate the interactive effect of exercise, drugs, and cholinergic systems in controlling the performance of exercising rats. Dube et al.[8] reported the interactive effects of physostigmine and exercise on cholinesterase activity in RBC and tissues of rat. The cholinesterase activity in red blood cells of exercised rats that were not exposed to physostigmine increased (16, 12, and 8% at 50, 80, and 100% VO_2max, respectively), while in other tissues the cholinesterase activity, in general, decreased slightly. In unexercised rats given physostigmine, the cholinesterase activity ranges were 73 to 79%, 66 to 68%, 68 to 74%, 67 to 81%, and 57 to 61% of controls from 10 to 30 min in RBC, brain, heart, diaphragm, and thigh muscle, respectively. In exercised rats exposed to physostigmine, the cholinesterase activity decreased (21 to 27%, 32 to 34%, 26 to 32%, 19 to 33%, and 39 to 43%) from 10 to 30 min in red blood cells, brain, heart, diaphragm, and thigh muscles, respectively. In exercised rats exposed to physostigmine, the cholinesterase activity decreased (46 to 49%, 42 to 50%, 23 to 27%, 17 to 29%, and 42 to 46%) from 10 to 30 min in red blood cells, brain, heart, diaphragm, and thigh muscles, respectively. These results indicate that in control rats not given physostigmine, different intensities of acute exercise affect the cholinesterase enzyme to a moderate degree in red blood cells and heart without affecting brain, diaphragm, and thigh muscles. Acute exercise modifies the effect of physostigmine by increasing the cholinesterase inhibition in red blood cells and brain without affecting other tissues.

Somani and Dube[13] report that the central and peripheral responses of rats were altered due to the interactive effect of acute exercise and endurance training in the presence of a chemical stressor such as physostigmine, an anticholinesterase drug. Acute exercise, as well as endurance training, produced a slight decrease in ChE activity of the brain (3 to 9%) at various time points. Acute exercise plus physostigmine showed an increase in ChE activity (30%) as compared to physostigmine alone (40%) at 15 min, which recovered to control level at 60 min. Endurance training plus physostigmine showed a further decrease in ChE activity (48% of control; at 15 min it recovered to 64%

of control at 60 min). It seems that endurance training delayed ChE recovery; however, there was almost complete recovery in rats given acute exercise plus physostigmine and slower recovery in endurance training plus physostigmine as compared to physostigmine alone at 60 min.

The rate of decarbamylation (kDa) was increased (81%) (0.025/min) by acute exercise and decreased (34%) (0.009/min) in the brain. The half-time ($T_{1/2}$) of the enzyme recovery was 60, 27.5, and 75 min in physostigmine, acute exercise plus physostigmine and endurance training plus physostigmine groups, respectively.[13]

Babu et al.[11] reported the interactive response of exercise and physostigmine on muscular AChE activity. Acetylcholinesterase activity was decreased in both fast twitch EDL and soleus muscles of endurance trained rats. Subacute Phy decreased ChAT (11 and 6%) in EDL and soleus at 20 min, but increased (10 and 16%) by 24 h. Acetylcholinesterase activity also decreased (44 and 43%) in EDL and soleus at 20 min, and remained depressed (32 and 33%) even after 24 h. Acetylcholinesterase activity in EDL and soleus decreased (37 and 68%) at 20 min in subacute Phy plus single acute exercise; however, AChE recovered to 88% of control in EDL and 50% of control in soleus at 24 h. Acetylcholinesterase activity decreased (58 and 71%) at 20 min in EDL and soleus, respectively. Acetylcholinesterase activity remained depressed at 62 and 65% of control even after 24 h in EDL and soleus muscle, respectively. Our results showed a constant decrease in AChE activity in both muscle groups at 20 min and did not recover even after 24 h.

Dube et al.[12] studied the interactive effect of Phy and concurrent acute exercise on ChE activity in the brain. Acute exercise resulted in a slight decrease in ChE activity in the brain (3 to 12% from 20 to 50 min). Phy decreased ChE activity 33, 23, and 15% at 20, 30, and 50 min, respectively. Phy plus concurrent acute exercise depressed the ChE activity 46 and 30% at 20 and 25 min respectively, but recovered to 85 to 86% of control within 50 min. There was an increase (67%) in the rate of decarbamylation of ChE enzymes in Phy plus concurrent acute exercise (0.0385 min^{-1}) in the brain. Somani et al.[14] demonstrated the interaction of exercise and Phy on AChE activity in different brain regions of rat. Acetylcholinesterase activity decreased in corpus striatum (18%) 20 min after subacute Phy-administration and subacute Phy plus acute exercise (19%), or trained exercise (22%). Acetylcholinesterase activity remained at 89, 87, and 90% of control in Phy-administered, Phy plus acute exercise, and Phy plus trained exercise, respectively, even after 24 h. In cerebral cortex, AChE activity decreased in endurance trained rats (16%) and in subacute Phy (9%), as shown in Table 5. However, AChE activity decreased 28 and 27% in subacute Phy plus acute exercise and in subacute Phy plus trained groups. Acetylcholinesterase activity recovered in all groups by 24 h after Phy administration. These results indicate that AChE activity in cerebral cortex was inhibited by Phy plus exercise (acute or trained) at 20 min of Phy administration and had recovered to control level by 24 h. Acetylcholinesterase activity decreased (18 to 39%) in the brain stem in all groups except in Phy plus acute exercise and Phy plus trained exercise rats sacrificed after 24 h. Acetyl-cholinesterase activity decreased to 19, 39, and 18% in trained exercise, subacute Phy sacrificed after 20 min and subacute Phy sacrificed after 24 h, respectively. The activity decreased 21% in subacute Phy plus acute exercise and 25% in Phy plus trained exercise 20 min after Phy administration. The activity decreased (22%) in rats sacrificed after 24 h of Phy administration. However, activity recovered to 93 and 90% of control in Phy plus acute exercise and Phy plus trained exercise rats sacrificed after 24 h, respectively. In hippocampus, AChE activity decreased 24, 31, and 28% in Phy-adminis-tered, Phy plus acute exercise, and Phy plus trained exercise rats sacrificed after 20 min, respectively.

The study indicated that Phy, exercise, or the combination of both decreased AChE activity in a regionally selective pattern. The data are consistent with the hypothesis that elevation in ACh levels down-regulates the ongoing cholin-ergic neurotransmission through a negative feedback mechanism.

7. EFFECT OF EXERCISE AND OTHER STRESSES ON ACETYLCHOLINE

Many processes intervene between the stressful stimulus and subsequent behavioral response. The data concerning changes that occur in the brain's cholinergic system during exercise and stress is considerably less than those concerning other biogenic amine systems. Acetylcholine is synthesized from choline, a precursor normally obtained from the diet. Choline is also incorpo-rated into cell membranes; the membranes serve as a choline source for ACh synthesis. The level of choline in the brain controls the rate of ACh synthesis. Therefore, the choline acetylcholine relationship is important during exercise because (1) reducing choline concentrations has been shown to reduce acetyl-choline release, and (2) reductions in plasma choline have been observed in marathon runners and in humans consuming a choline-free diet. These reduc-tions are associated with a slowing in impulse transmissions across muscles. Thus, the dietary control of ACh synthesis is possible due to the following reasons: choline readily enters into the brain, ChAT is not saturated with choline at physiological concentrations, and ACh does not "feed-back" to inhibit its own synthesis. Therefore, additional consumption of choline can generate more ACh. The level of choline has been shown to affect blood pressure, sleep, memory, pain, and mood. Thus, a proper diet may positively influence an athlete's performance and level of fatigue. It is suggested that cholinergic system activity undergoes regulation resulting from exercise-in-duced stress in order to maintain the body's homeostasis. This action may lead to changes in the ACh turnover rate (synthesis and/or degradation) which may alter the cholinergic enzyme activity.

Gilad et al.[66] demonstrated that the hippocampal cholinergic system is actively involved in stress response. Acute and chronic stress-induced changes in synaptic ACh release choline uptake (parameter of cholinergic system) have been studied in rat hippocampus.[67] Acute as well as chronic intermittent immobilization stress increased ACh release, whereas choline uptake increased after acute stress and decreased after chronic stress. Repeated cold stress has been shown to decrease the total ACh content in basal ganglia and hypothalamus and increase its amount in the duodenum of rat.[28,68] Similarly, cold stress resulted in a decrease of ACh levels in the hypothalamus and hippocampus of rat.[30] It has been assumed that the stores of ACh in the hippocampus of a rat that is exposed to stress may become depleted. However, Costa et al.[69] and Mizukawa et al.[70] failed to find any change in rat ACh after stress. After electric shock stress, the ACh concentration was found to be depleted in brain regions of rat[25,45] and brain of mice.[71] Following 2 h of mild restrain stress, choline uptake was increased in hippocampus, septum, and frontal cortex of rat.[72] The administration of chronic electric shock to rats has increased the ACh content in the medulla.[28]

Since exercise is considered physical stress, it is likely that it may also influence the ACh content in brain and other tissues. Swimming exercise in rats has been shown to deplete the ACh content in various brain regions such as hippocampus and cerebral cortex.[17,30] Conlay et al.[73] reported a decrease in the plasma choline levels of marathon runners. Recently, Conlay et al.[74] have shown that in trained athletes, running a 26 km marathon reduced plasma choline by 40% and decreased ACh release from the neuromuscular junctions in a similar magnitude. Since ACh is synthesized from choline, the reductions in plasma choline associated with strenuous exercise may reduce ACh release, and could thereby affect endurance, or performance, of the athlete.

8. EFFECT OF EXERCISE AND OTHER STRESSES ON CHOLINERGIC RECEPTORS

Both the peripheral and central cholinergic systems may play an important role in acute and chronic stress conditions as well as in exercise-induced stress. Acetylcholine released from the nerve endings and neuromuscular junctions binds with specific nicotinic and muscarinic receptors and exerts physiological responses in the body. Zerbib and Laborit[75] reported that restrain stress for 10 days induced hypersensitivity of the central cholinergic system in mice, whereas restrain stress for 30 days caused hyposensitivity of the central cholinergic system. Similarly, shock stress also increased the hypersensitivity of the central acetylcholine receptor site.[76] Gilad et al.[66] demonstrated that hippocampal muscarinic acetylcholine receptor binding increased in rats after chronic intermittent immobilization stress.

Information from animal and human studies has suggested the stress-induced hyperactivity of central muscarinic mechanisms.[77,78] Chronic immobilization stress increased muscarinic receptor binding capacity (135% of control) in hippocampal synaptosomes of rats.[67] Similarly, immobilization stress produced an increase in muscarinic cholinergic (mACh) binding sites in the septum, striatum, hippocampus, and pons plus medulla oblongata of rats.[79] In another study, Mizukawa et al.[70] have demonstrated that immobilization stress for 30 min produced increases in the concentration of mACh binding sites in the hippocampus of rat. The effect of acute exercise (swimming) for 15 min, on cholinergic muscarinic receptors in rat brain regions, has been studied by Estevez et al.[80] Results show that specific mACh binding decreased in the cerebral cortex (27%) and basal ganglia (14%), whereas it increased in cerebellum (41%). Chronic exercise has been reported to produce tolerance to muscarinic antagonists in rats.[81] These studies suggest that acute exercise or stress exerts rapid reversible and selective changes of cholinergic muscarinic receptors.

9. FUTURE PERSPECTIVES

Considerable research has focused on the role of acetylcholine in the regulation of cerebral and peripheral responses after acute and chronic exercise and other stresses. Evidence exists that a variety of drugs interact with exercise and the cholinergic system, especially the enzymes involved in the synthesis (choline acetyltransferase) and degradation (acetylcholinesterase) of acetylcholine enzymes. However, data regarding the intensity, frequency, and duration of exercise and the ACh turnover is lacking.

It will be interesting to study the effect of exercise and stress on ACh turnover. This study will help develop an understanding of the cholinergic mechanisms of cerebral and peripheral manifestations of exercise and stress. Acetylcholine interacts with muscarinic and nicotinic receptors and exerts physiological responses at central and peripheral sites. However, there has been few reports related to the effect of exercise or stress on cholinergic receptor sensitivity in cerebral and peripheral tissues. In the area of exercise and sports, the nicotinic receptors present on muscles will be more appropriate to study during muscular fatigue and acute exhaustive exercise. If the effects of exercise and stress are indeed mediated in some part by activation of central muscarinic mechanisms, centrally active anticholinergic drugs may be useful in the evaluation of sensitivity and vulnerability to exercise-induced central responses. Choline uptake by synaptosomes is also considered an important parameter of the cholinergic system. Acetylcholine is synthesized from choline and therefore the choline/acetylcholine relationship is important during exercise because it may influence exercise performance, responses to exercise or stress, decision-making abilities, and levels of fatigue. It will be important to study the choline uptake along with ACh turnover during acute as well as chronic exercise.

The organophosphorus compounds are pesticides, insecticides, and also potent chemical warfare agents, and they are irreversible inhibitors of cholinesterase. Military personnel perform regular exercises and they may also be exposed to either drugs or chemical warfare during war time. Exercise modifies the cholinesterase activity in the presence of ChE inhibitors and also alters the pharmacokinetics. Therefore, these studies would be useful in the development of an appropriate therapy regimen and pretreatment agent against organophosphorus intoxication.

10. SUMMARY

Recent studies have shown that exercise has potential influences on cholinergic systems of the body. Acetylcholine plays a pivotal role for human beings to react or adapt to changes exerted by exercise or stress. Acetylcholine as a neurotransmitter synthesized from choline and acetyl CoA by the enzyme choline acetyl transferase, releases and mediates synaptic and neuromuscular transmission. It interacts with cholinergic receptors (muscarinic and nicotinic) and is degraded by the enzyme acetylcholinesterase. Exercise preferentially decreases choline acetyl transferase activity in cerebral and peripheral tissues, whereas acetylcholinesterase activity is decreased in cerebral and peripheral tissues except for a significant increase in the blood after acute exercise. The responsiveness of the cerebral and peripheral tissues to exercise is a function of the levels of ongoing cholinergic activity; and elevations in acetylcholine levels, due to AChE inhibition, may have long-term effects on the regulation of enzyme activities through a negative feedback mechanism. The increased ChE activity in the blood revealed a secondary effect of hypoxia, leakage of the enzyme due to increased membrane permeability, and hemoconcentration due to plasma shifts during exercise. Acute exercise influences the release of ACh and exerts rapid reversible and selective changes of cholinergic muscarinic receptors. The interactive effect of exercise and drugs modifies the central and peripheral cholinergic systems; thus, the combination of exercise and drugs affect the endurance or performance of the athlete. This review also provides future direction for exercise and sports researchers to study the interactive effect of exercise and drugs on acetylcholine turnover and cholinergic (muscarinic and nicotinic) receptor sensitivity.

REFERENCES

1. **Babu, S. R., Buckenmeyer, P., Knowlton, R. G., and Somani, S. M.,** Effect of physostigmine on plasma lactate and pyruvate in untrained/trained rats, *Pharmacol. Biochem. Behav.,* 42, 67, 1992.
2. **Buckenmeyer, P. J., Babu, S. R., Knowlton, R. G., and Somani, S. M.,** Effect of concurrent exercise and physostigmine on lactate and pyruvate in plasma, muscle and brain tissue of rats, *Pharmacol. Biochem. Behav.,* 47, 779, 1994.
3. **Kovanen, B.,** Effects of aging and physical training on rat skeletal muscle, *Acta. Physiol. Scand.,* 135, 1, 1989.
4. **Rodnick, K. J., Reaven, G. M., Haskell, W. L., Sims, C. R., and Mondon, C. E.,** Variations in running activity and enzymatic adaptations in voluntary running rats, *J. Appl. Physiol.,* 66, 1250, 1989.

5. **Cartee, G. D.,** Aging skeletal muscle: response to exercise, *Exerc. Sport Sci. Rev.,* 22, 91, 1994.

6. **Holloszy, J. O. and Booth, W.,** Biochemical adaptations to endurance exercise in muscle, *Ann. Rev. Physiol.,* 38, 273, 1976.

7. **Pawlowska, D., Moniuszko-Jankoniuk, and Soltys, M.,** Parathion methyl effect on the activity of hydrolytic enzymes after single physical exercise in rats, *Pol. J. Pharmacol. Pharm.,* 37, 629, 1985.

8. **Dube, S. N., Somani, S. M., and Colliver, J. A.,** Interactive effects of physostigmine and exercise on cholinesterase activity in RBC and tissues of rat, *Arch. Int. Pharmacodyn. Ther.,* 307, 71, 1990.

9. **Booth, F. W. and Thompson, D. B.,** Molecular and cellular adaptation of muscle in response to exercise: perspective of various models, *Physiol. Rev.,* 71, 541, 1991.

10. **Kiens, B., Essen-Gustavsson, B., Christensen, N. J., and Saltin, B.,** Skeletal msucle substrate utilization during submaximal exercise in man: effect of endurance training, *J. Physiol.,* 469, 1993.

11. **Babu, S., Somani, S. M., and Dube, S. N.,** Effects of physostigmine on choline acetyltransferase and acetylcholinesterase activities in fast and slow muscles of rat, *Pharmacol. Biochem. Behav.,* 45, 713, 1993.

12. **Dube, S. N., Somani, S. M., and Babu, S. R.,** Concurrent acute exercise alters central and peripheral responses to physostigmine, *Pharmacol. Biochem. Behav.,* 46, 827, 1993.

13. **Somani, S. M. and Dube, S. N.,** Endurance training changes central and peripheral responses to physostigmine, *Pharmacol. Biochem. Behav.,* 41, 773, 1992.

14. **Somani, S. M., Babu, S. R., Arneric, S. P., and Dube, S. N.,** Effect of cholinesterase inhibitor and exercise on choline acetyltransferase and acetylcholinesterase activities in rat brain regions, *Pharmacol. Biochem. Behav.,* 39, 337, 1991.

15. **Husain, K. and Somani, S. M.,** Effect of acute exercise and ethanol on cholinesterase activity in blood and brain regions of rat, *Pharmacol. Biochem. Behav.,* 1995, submitted.

16. **Ryhanen, R., Kajovaara, M., Harri, M., Kaliste-Korhonen, E., and Hanninen, O.,** Physical exercise affects cholinesterases and organophosphate response, *Gen. Pharmacol.,* 19, 815, 1988.

17. **Kasa, P., Szapesy, C., Gulya, K., Bansaghy, K., and Rakonczay, Z.,** The effect of 4-(1-0-naphthyl vinyl) pyridine on the acetylcholine system and on the number of synaptic vesicles in the central nervous system of the rat, *Neurochem. Int.,* 4, 185, 1982.

18. **Satoh, K. and Fibiger, H. C.,** Distribution of central cholinergic neurons in the baboon (Papic papio). I. General morphology, *J. Comp. Neurol.,* 236, 197, 1985.

19. **Kimura, H. McGreer, P. L., and Peng, J. H.,** Choline acetyltransferase-containing neurons in the rat brain, in *Handbook of Chemical Neuroanatomy,* Bjorklund, A., Hokfelt, T., and Kuhar, M. J., Eds., Elsevier, Amsterdam, 1984, 51.

20. **Tucek, S.,** Problems in the organization and control of acetylcholine synthesis in brain neurons, *Prog. Biophys. Mol. Biol.,* 44, 1, 1984.

21. **Galzi, J. L., Ravah, F., Bessis, A., and Changeux, J. P.,** Functional architecture of the nicotine aacetylcholine receptor: from electric organ to brain, *Annu. Rev. Pharmacol. Toxicol.,* 31, 37, 1991.

22. **Hulme, E. C., Birdsall, N. J. M., and Buckley, N. J.,** Muscrinic receptor subtypes, *Annu. Rev. Pharmacol. Toxicol.,* 30, 633, 1990.

23. **Gottesfeld, Z., Kvetnansky, R., Kopin, I. J., and Jacobowitz, D. M.,** Effects of repeated immobilization stress on glutamate decarboxylase and choline acetyltransferase in discrete brain regions, *Brain Res.,* 152, 374, 1978.

24. **Wahba, Z. Z. and Soliman, K. F. A.,** Effect of stress on choline acetyltransferase activity of the brain and adrenal of the rat, *Experientia,* 48, 265, 1992.

25. **Longoni, R., Mulas, A., Oderfeld-Novak, B., Pepeu, I. M., and Pepeu. G.,** Effect of single and repeated electroshock applications on brain acetylcholine levels and choline acetyltransferase activity in the rat, *Neuropharmacology,* 15, 283, 1976.

26. **Gilad, G. M. and McCarty, R.,** Differences in cholinacetyltransferase but similarities in catecholamine biosynthetic enzymes in brains of two rat strains differing in their response to stress, *Brain Res.,* 206, 239, 1981.

27. **Tucek, S., Zelena, J., Ge, I., and Vyskocil, F.,** Choline acetyltransferase in transected nerves, denervated muscles and Schwann cells of the frog: correlation of biochemical, electron microscopical and electrophysiological observations, *Neuroscience,* 3, 709, 1978.

28. **Kita, T., Hata, T., Higashiguchi, T., Itah, E., and Kawabata, A.,** Changes of total acetylcholine content and the activity of related enzymes in SART (Repeated cold)-stress rat brain and duodenum, *Jpn. J. Pharmacol.,* 40, 1974, 1986.

29. **Lin, Q. and Li, P.,** Rostral medullary cholinergic mechanisms and chronic stress-induced hypertension, *J. Auto. Nerv. Sys.,* 31, 211, 1990.

30. **Fatranska, M., Budai, D., Oprsalova, L., and Kvetnansky, R.,** Acetylcholine and its enzymes in some brain areas of the rat under stress, *Brain Res.,* 424, 109, 1987.

31. **Eckstein, F. P., Baughman, R. W., and Quinn, J.,** An anatomical study of cholinergic innervation in rat cerebral cortex, *Neuroscience,* 25, 457, 1988.

32. **Fibiger, H. C.,** The organization and some projections of cholinergic neurons of the mammalian forebrain, *Brain Res. Rev.,* 4, 327, 1982.

33. **Godfrey, D. A., Park, J. L., and Ross, C. D.,** Choline acetyltransferase and acetylcholinesterase in centrifugal labyrinthine bundles of rats, *Hearing Res.,* 14, 93, 1984.

34. **Arneric, S. P., Giuliano, R., Ernsberger, P., Underwood, M. D., and Reis, D. J.,** Synthesis, release and receptor binding of acetylcholine in the C_1 area of the rostral ventrolateral medulla: contributions in regulating arterial pressure, *Brain Res.,* 511, 98, 1990.

35. **Roskoski, R., Jr., Mayer, H. E., and Schmid, P. G.,** Choline acetyltransferase activity in guinea-pig heart in vitro, *J. Neurochem.,* 23, 1197, 1974.

36. **Benarroch, E. E., Granata, A. R., Ruggiero, D. A., Park, O. H., and Reis, D. J.,** Neurons of C_1 area mediate cardiovascular response initiated from ventral medullary surface, *Am. J. Physiol.,* 250, R932, 1986.

37. **Ramasastry, B. V. and Sadavongvivad, C.,** Cholinergic systems in non-nervous tissues, *Pharmacol. Rev.,* 30, 65, 1978.

38. **Tumer, N., Hale, C., Lawler, J., and Strong, R.,** Modulation of tyrosin hydroxylase gene expression in the rat adrenal gland by exercise: effects of age, *Mol. Brain Res.,* 3, 51, 1992.

39. **Fernandez, H. L. and Donoso, A.,** Exercise selectively increases G4 AChE activity in fast twitch muscle, *J. Appl. Physiol.,* 65, 2245, 1988.

40. **Gupta, R. C., Misculis, K. E., and Dettbarn, W. D.,** Changes in the cholinergic system of the rat sciatic nerve and skeletal muscle following suspension-induced disuse, *Exp. Neurol.,* 89, 622, 1985.

41. **Dohm, G. L., Beecher, G. R., Hecker, A. L., Puente, F. R., Klain, G. J., and Askew, E. W.,** Changes in protein synthesis in rats in response to endurance training, *Life Sci.,* 21, 189, 1977.

42. **Howald, H.,** Training-induced morphological and functional changes in skeletal muscle, *Int. J. Sports Med.,* 3, 1, 1982.

43. **Smith, J. L., Edgerton, V. R., Betts, R., and Collatos, T. C.,** EMG slow and fast ankle extensors of cat during posture, locomotion and jumping, *J. Neurophysiol.,* 40, 503, 1977.

44. **Terjung, R. L.,** Muscle fiber involvement during training of different intensities and durations, *Am. J. Physiol.,* 230, 946, 1976.

45. **Singh, H. C., Singh, R. H., and Udupa, K. N.,** Electric shock-induced changes in free, bound and total acetylcholine and acetylcholinesterase in different brain regions of rats, *Indian J. Exp. Biol.,* 17, 304, 1979.

46. **Appleyard, M. E., Green, A. R., and Smith, A. D.,** Acetylcholinesterase activity in regions of the rat brain following a convulsion, *J. Neurochem.,* 46, 1749, 1986.

47. **Tsakiris, S. and Kontopoulos, A. N.,** Time changes in NA^+, K^+-ATPase, Mg^{++}-ATPase, and acetylcholinesterase activities in the rat cerebrum and cerebellum caused by stress, *Pharmacol. Biochem. Behav.,* 44, 339, 1993.

48. **Romero, E.,** Secretion of acetylcholinesterase from the central nervous system, Ph.D. thesis, Oxford University, 1981.

49. **Appleyard, M. E., Taylor, S. C., and Little, H. J.,** Acetylcholinesterase activity in regions of mouse brain following acute and chronic treatment with a benzodiazepine inverse agonist, *Br. J. Pharmacol.,* 101, 599, 1990.

50. **Pedzikiewicz, J., Piaskowska, E., and Pytas, M.,** Acetylcholinesterase (E.C.3.1.1.7) in the skeletal muscle and brain of rats after exercise and long term training, *Acta Physiol. Pol.,* 35, 469, 1984.

51. **Holmstedt, B.,** Distribution and determination of cholinesterase in mammals, *Bull. Wld. Hlth. Org.,* 44, 99, 1971.

52. **Spodaryk, K. K., Berger, L., and Hanke, S.,** Infusion of physical training on the functional changes of young and old red blood cells, *Mech. Agency Dev.,* 55, 199, 1990.

53. **Dill, D. B. and Costill, D. L.,** Calculation of percentage changes in volume of blood, plasma, and red cells in dehydration, *J. Appl. Physiol.,* 37, 247, 1974.

54. **Tipton, C. M., Barnard, R. J., and Tharp, G. D.,** Cholinesterase activity in trained and nontrained rats, *Int. Z. Angew. Physiol. Einschl. Arbeitsphysiol.,* 23, 34, 1966.

55. **Gisiger, V., Belisle, M., and Gardiner, P. F.,** Acetylcholinesterase adaptation to voluntary wheel running is proportional to the volume of activity in fast, but not slow, rat hind limb muscles, *Eur. J. Neurosci.,* 6, 673, 1994.

56. **Dettebarn, W. D.,** A distinct difference between slow and fast muscle in acetylcholinest-erase recovery after reinnervation in the rat, *Exp. Neur.,* 74, 33, 1981.

57. **Horvath, S.,** Review of energetics and blood flow in exercise, *Diabetes,* 28(Suppl.1), 33, 1979.

58. **Rowell, L. B.,** Human cardiovascular adjustments to exercise and thermal stress, *Physiol. Rev.,* 54, 75, 1974.

59. **Somani, S. M. and Dube, S. N.,** In vivo dose response relationship between physostigmine and cholinesterase activity in RBC and tissues of rats, *Life Sci.,* 44, 1907, 1989b.

60. **Somani, S. M., Babu, S. R., Buckenmyer, P., Dasilva, M., Dube, S. N., Fitzpatrick, L., Garcia, V., Klinger, K., Knowlton, R., McCoy, J., Rashid, A., Rybak, M., and Sunderam, S.,** Effect of exercise on pharmacokinetics and pharmacodynamics of physostigmine in rats, Report U.S. Army Med. Res. Dev. Commands, Fort Detrick, Frederick, MD, February 1991.

61. **Somani, S. M. and Dube, S. N.,** Physostigmine — an overview as pretreatment drug for organophosphate intoxication, *Int. J. Clin. Pharmacol. Ther. Toxicol.,* 27, 367, 1989.

62. **McMaster, S. B. and Foster, R. E.,** Behavioral and morphological studies of the interaction between exercise and physostigmine, U.S. Army Med. Res. Dev. Commands, *Sixth Ann. Chem. Def. Biosci. Rev.,* August, 629, 1987.

63. **Matthew, C. B., Hubbard, R. W., Fracesconi, R. P., and Thomas, G. J.,** Carbamate-induced performance and thermoregulatory decrements restored with diazepam and atro-pine, *Aviat. Space Environ. Med.,* 58, 1183, 1987.

64. **Matthew, C. B., Bowers, W. D., Francesconi, R. P., and Hubbard, R. W.,** Chronic physostigmine administration in the exercising rat, Report U.S. Army Med. Res. Dev. Command, Natick, MA, March, 1990.

65. **Thomas, G. J.,** Carbamates, atropine, and diazepam: effects on performance in the running rat, *Life Sci.,* 42, 1925, 1988.

66. **Gilad, G. M., Rabey, J. M., and Shenkman, L.,** Strain-dependent and stress-induced changes in rat hippocampalcholinergic system, *Brain Res.,* 267, 171, 1983.

67. **Finkelstein, Y., Kaffler, B., Rabey, J. M., and Gilad, G. M.,** Dynamics of cholinergic synaptic mechanisms in rat hippocampus after stress, *Brain Res.,* 343, 314, 1985.

68. **Hata, T., Kita, T., Higash, T., and Ichide, S.,** Total acetylcholine content and activities of choline acetyltransferase and acetylcholinesterase in brain and duodenum of SART stressed (repeated cold stressed) rat, *Jpn. J. Pharmacol.,* 41, 475, 1986.

69. **Costa, E., Tagliamonte, N., Brunello, N., and Cheney, D. L.,** Effects of stress on the metabolism of acetylcholine in the cholinergic pathways of extra pyramidal and limbic systems, in *Catecholamines and Stress: Recent Advances,* Usdin, E., Kvetnansky, R., and Kopin, I. J., Eds., Elsevier, New York, 1980, 59.

70. **Mizukawa, K., Takayama, H., Sato, H., Ota, Z., Haba, K., and Ogawa, N.,** Alteration of muscrinic cholinergic receptors in the hippocampal formation of stressed rat: in vitro quantitative autoradiographic analysis, *Brain Res.,* 478, 187, 1989.

71. **Cosgrove, K. A., Scudder, C. L., and Karczmar, A. C.,** Some aspects of acute quantitative shock on mouse whole brain levels of acetylcholine and choline, *Pharmacologist,* 15, 255, 1973.

72. **Gilad, G. M., Gilad, V. H., and Tizabi, Y.,** Aging and stress-induced changes in choline and glutamate uptake in hippocampus and septum of two rat strains differing in longevity and reactivity to stressors, *Int. J. Dev. Neurosci.,* 8, 709, 1990.

73. **Conlay, L. A., Wurtman, R. J., Blusztajn, J. K., Lopoz, G. I., Maher, T. J., and Evoniuk, G. B.,** Marathon running decreases plasma choline concentration, *N. Engl. J. Med.,* 315, 892, 1986.

74. **Conlay, L. A., Sabounjian, L. A., and Wurtman, R. J.,** Exercise and neuromodulators: choline and acetylcholine in marathon runners, *Int. J. Sports Med.,* 13, 5141, 1992.

75. **Zerbib, R. and Laborit, H.,** Chronic stress and memory: implication of the central cholinergic system, *Pharmacol. Biochem. Behav.,* 36, 897, 1990.

76. **Cherek, D. R., Laue, J. D., Freeman, M. E., and Smith, J. E.,** Receptor changes following shock avoidance, *Soc. Neurosci. Abstr.,* 6, 543, 1980.

77. **Dilsaver, S. C.,** Effects of stress on muscarinic mechanisms, *Neurosci. Biobehav. Rev.,* 12, 23, 1988.

78. **Janowsky, D. S. and Risch, S. C.,** Cholinomimetic and anticholinergic drugs used to investigate an acetylcholine hypothesis of affective disorders and stress, *Drug. Dev. Res.,* 4, 125, 1984.

79. **Takayama, H., Mizukawa, K., Ota, Z., and Ogawa, N.,** Regional responses of rat brain muscarinic cholinergic receptors to immobilization stress, *Brain Res.,* 436, 291, 1987.

80. **Estevez, E. E., Jerusalinsky, D., Medina, J. H., and Robertis, E. D.,** Cholinergic muscrinic receptors in rat cerebral cortex, basal ganglia and cerebellum undergo rapid and reversible changes after acute stress, *Neuroscience,* 13, 1353, 1984.

81. **McMaster, S. B. and Carney, J. M.,** Chronic exercise produces tolerance to muscarinic antagonists in rats, *Pharmacol. Biochem. Behav.,* 24, 865, 1986.

Chapter 12

NEUROENDOCRINE AND IMMUNOLOGICAL RESPONSES TO EXERCISE

John A. Smith

CONTENTS

1. ABSTRACT

Exercise can be varied in type, intensity, duration, and frequency. Many reports have established that exercise has intensity-dependent effects on the secretion of hormones into the circulation. Exercise also exerts both short- and

0-8493-8540-1/96/$0.00+$.50
© 1996 by CRC Press, Inc.

long-term effects on some immune parameters. Although exercise at moderate capacity enhances some aspects of immunity, work at high intensity is generally immunosuppressive. Emerging epidemiological evidence on the incidence of infection supports the immunological data. The mechanisms by which exercise-induced immunological changes are mediated are not known. Because a variety of hormones have been shown to be immunoregulatory, exercise-induced changes in immune function may be initiated via the neuroendocrine system. One way of testing this hypothesis is through pharmacological manipulation. A variety of drugs have been shown to, selectively, enhance or inhibit hormonal responses to single bouts of exercise. Although some drugs modulate immunological and inflammatory processes, pharmacological manipulation of exercise-induced immunological responses has received little attention. This chapter explores the relationship between exercise-induced immunological and neuroendocrine responses. Manipulation of these responses by specific drugs may enable the causative mechanisms to be characterized.

2. INTRODUCTION

Some human physiological systems can be stressed in a reproducible manner by exercise and/or pharmacological agents. Both these stressors can be varied in intensity, duration, frequency, and type. Although the effects of exercise on the secretion of many neuroendocrine mediators have been well characterized, the relationship between exercise and immunity has received limited scientific attention. In fact, exercise appears to be an addictive drug itself; this may be due to the *euphoria* induced by opioid secretion,[1] which can also influence immunity.[2]

At present, considerable evidence suggests that, while intensive training increases susceptibility to infection, moderate exercise enhances some immunological responses.[2] The mechanisms by which these paradoxical responses to exercise are produced are poorly understood, but neuroendocrine mediators appear to be involved.[2] Pharmacological manipulation of the exercise-induced responses is one strategy that may resolve exactly how exercise affects the immune system. This chapter will give an overview of research in these fields, primarily with human subjects. Emphasis is placed on drugs that modify exercise-induced neuroendocrine or immunological responses rather than those used in the clinical situation.

2.1. NEUROENDOCRINE SYSTEM
The neuroendocrine system incorporates a network of classical hormones and neurotransmitters which are secreted from both the endocrine glands and neurons. These mediators are, traditionally, thought to play regulatory roles in controlling metabolic, reproductive, and osmoregulatory processes. In response

to exercise, hormone responses primarily contribute to control of energy metabolism. However, many publications have reported that the immune system is also strongly influenced by neuroendocrine hormones.

The secretion of pituitary hormones, for example, is coordinated by a steady-state balance of hypothalamic release and inhibitory mediators. Because many of these agents have been purified and characterized, they have been used as drugs to treat endocrine dysfunction. Many hormones are secreted into the circulation in a pulsatile manner where amplitude and frequency varies considerably over a 24-h period. Diet and exercise exert strong independent influences on hormone secretion. The main focus here will be on neuroendocrine mediators that respond to exercise and/or influence immune function.

2.2. CELLULAR AND HUMORAL IMMUNITY

The immune system is a highly complex network of interacting cellular and humoral factors which protect the body against a myriad of infectious agents including viruses, bacteria, and fungi. Mechanisms mediating immunity can be divided functionally into innate (natural or nonspecific) and adaptive (specific) elements (Figure 1). The specific arm (T cells and B cells) recognizes foreign or nonself (antigenic) molecules exposed on the infectious agent or transformed host cells. While specific immune responses take at least 24 h to become effective (because of antigen processing by macrophages, T and B cell activation, and antibody synthesis), nonspecific immune processes such as phagocytosis by neutrophils are activated immediately upon contact with the infectious agent. Once an antigen is encountered by the adaptive arm, the response to a second challenge is rapid because memory T cells and antibodies persist in the body. This phenomenon has enabled vaccines to be developed against some infectious agents. Unfortunately, some immunological responses have pathological consequences because of allergic, inflammatory, or cytotoxic reactions against healthy body tissues.[3] Given the dynamic role of the immune system in maintaining homeostasis, it is not surprizing that the composition of the immune system is in a constant state of flux where some T cell subpopulations are long-lived while there is rapid turnover of B cells and neutrophils.[3]

Although changes in blood leukocyte counts has been used in the clinical laboratory for many years to determine immune status, many immunological functions can be assessed *in vitro*.[3] The ability of lymphocytes to proliferate upon antigenic stimulation is an essential component of the immune response. Likewise, phagocytic cells such as neutrophils must ingest (phagocytose) and kill infectious agents efficiently. These responses can both be assessed *in vitro*. Some of the major immunological measures are listed in Table 1. The effects of single episodes of exercise and consequences of athletic training on both enumerative and functional indicators of immunity have been examined in the field of exercise immunology (see Section 6).

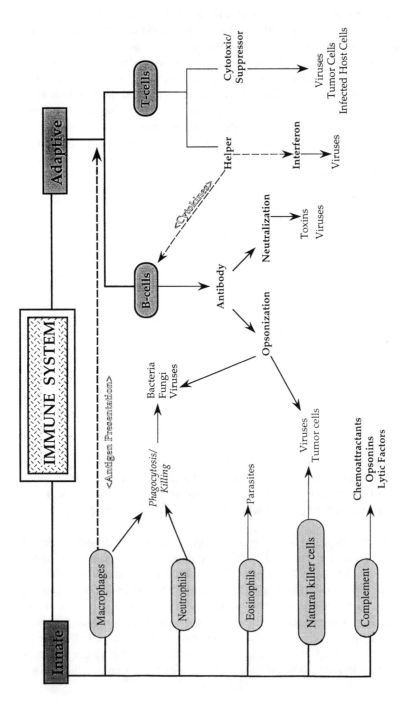

FIGURE 1. The innate and adaptive arms of the human immune system. Major components of the adaptive and innate arms of the immune system and their primary targets. Although each component can operate independently to some extent, there are significant interactions between some immune processes. Although not shown in detail, cytokines and other humoral mediators released from most types of immune cells play a major role in regulating the immune response.

TABLE 1
Some Measures of Immunological Status and Function

General	Differential blood leukocyte count
	Determination of blood lymphocyte subsets
	Activation status of leukocyte subpopulations
Phagocytes	Phagocytosis
	Killing
	Chemotaxis
	Production of reactive oxygen species
	Degranulation
Lymphocytes	Proliferation (mitogenesis)
	Mixed lymphocyte reaction
	Killer cell function
	Activation status
	Antibody production (*in vivo* or *in vitro*)
NK Cells	Cytotoxicity
	Activation status
Complement	Plasma concentrations of specific complement components
Immunoglobulins	Plasma and/or saliva concentrations
Delayed-type hypersensitivity skin test	*In vivo* measurement of cell-mediated immunity

2.3. THE NEUROENDOCRINE CONNECTION

Based on the strong interrelationships between the neuroendocrine and immune systems, we proposed that the positive effects of moderate exercise on some immunological responses may be due to the secretion of immunopotentiating hormones and cytokines into the circulation.[2] In contrast, intensive exercise may depress immunity because corticosteroids and catecholamines — which only increase in concentration in the blood after exercise intensity exceeds 60% of maximal oxygen uptake, $\dot{V}O_2$max — may override the influence of the positive mediators; this would result in a net suppressed response (Figure 2). Since this model was proposed in 1990, we have found some evidence to support the view that GH (growth hormone) may be responsible for exercise-induced priming of neutrophil microbicidal activity.[4] The role of cytokines is still unknown. Furthermore, this model could also be extended to other immune processes.

3. IMMUNOREGULATION

The immune response is regulated by a complex balance of stimulatory and inhibitory pathways that are controlled by humoral mediators which, in some cases, can be delivered by direct cell-to-cell contact. The immune system is not autonomous: cellular and humoral immune activities are influenced by soluble mediators secreted from the endocrine, nervous, and cardiovascular systems as well as by those produced by other immune cells (Figure 3).[5,6] These mediators include hormones, neurotransmitters, and cytokines, many of which are

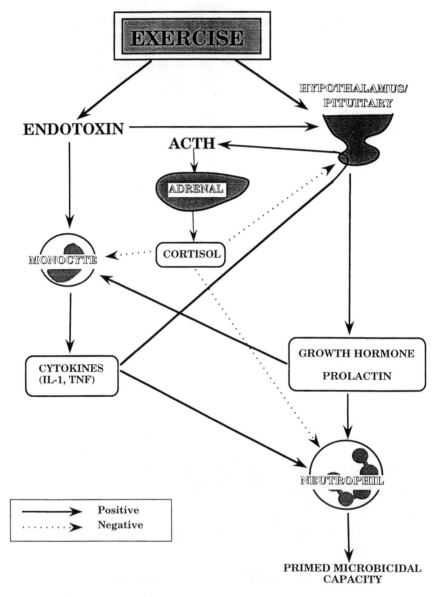

FIGURE 2. Proposed relationship between exercise, neuroendocrine/cytokine changes and the microbicidal activity of neutrophils. The diagram shows how moderate exercise may induce priming of neutrophil microbicidal capacity through immunostimulatory pituitary hormones and/ or an endotoxin-cytokine cascade. These mechanisms may work synergistically or independently of each other. Priming may be negated, however, by very intensive exercise, due to activation of the immunosuppressive arm of the pituitary-adrenal axis. The initial switch may be triggered by local hypothalamic/pituitary factors once exercise intensity reaches a critical threshold level. Immunosuppression may be manifested as a consequence of sustained ACTH and cortisol release caused by high concentrations of cytokines.

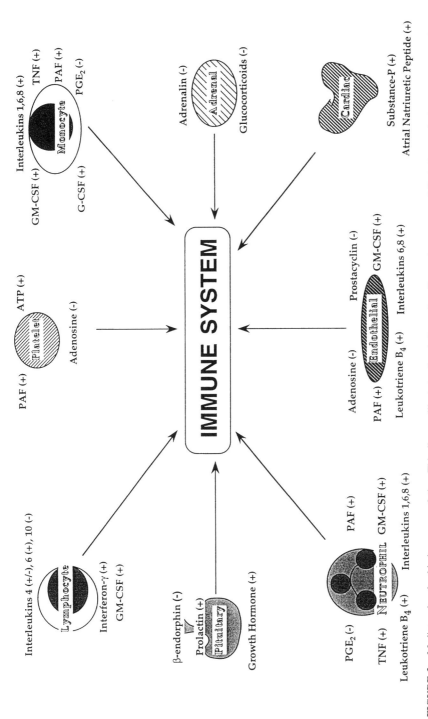

FIGURE 3. Mediators involved in immunoregulation. This diagram illustrates the plethora of mediators that can potentially influence the immune system. The major cellular sources of these mediators are also shown. (Compiled primarily from Reference 5.) See text for full explanation.

secreted in response to stress. Because immune cells can synthesize and release small amounts of most of these mediators, they can contribute to autocrine and paracrine amplification networks.[5] These observations have spawned the development of new disciplines such as psychoneuroimmunology and neuroimmunoendocrinology.[6]

3.1. CYTOKINES

Cytokines are produced and secreted in different combinations and at different rates by most immune cells.[5] These proteins have powerful and multiple overlapping (pleiotropic) actions on their target cells. In appropriate concentrations they can amplify or diminish a wide variety of immunological activities.[5] Cytokines are normally present in the bloodstream in trace amounts, except under pathological conditions, and may act locally at picomolar concentrations.[5] Cytokines have been shown to act both alone and/or synergistically to regulate the proliferation and activation of immune cells *in vitro,* but their exact functional roles *in vivo* are not known.

3.2. NEUROENDOCRINE MEDIATORS

Although corticosteroids (glucocorticoids) have long been known to be potent immunosuppressive agents, it is only recently that some pituitary hormones have been shown to be potent activators of some immune functions.[7] The importance of the pituitary gland in the immune response is shown by the detrimental effect of hypophysectomy on experimental animals and, conversely, the ability of hormone replacement therapy (HRT) to restore immunocompetence.[7] Hormones involved in immunoregulation include growth hormone (GH) and prolactin (PRL), which are immunostimulatory, and adrenocorticotropic hormone (ACTH), epinephrine, and cortisol, which are generally immunosuppressive.[2,7] The plasma concentrations of these hormones fluctuate throughout the day because of pulsatile secretion and rapid clearance, both of which are regulated by negative feedback. The bidirectional interactions of cytokines and neurotransmitters with neurons and immune cells, respectively, provide a means of indirect chemical communication between the neuroendocrine and immune systems.[6] Other mediators not classified as hormones, such as neurotransmitters and cytokines, also influence immune function (Figure 3).[5]

3.3. INTERACTIONS BETWEEN NEUROENDOCRINE AND IMMUNE SYSTEMS

The communications between the neuroendocrine and immune systems are bidirectional. These interactions also trigger behavioral changes associated with the stress response.[8] Immune cells possess receptors for many hormones associated classically with the neuroendocrine system (e.g., growth hormone, opioids) and they are able to synthesize and secrete small amounts of a variety of these hormones.[6,8] Leukocytes also synthesize and release regulatory factors such as somatostatin that may modulate hormone secretion from the immune system in a manner analogous to the regulation of pituitary hormone secretion by hypothalamic mediators.[9]

The physiological significance of cell communication at this level is not known, but leukocyte hormones may participate in the paracrine amplification of afferent pituitary signals in microenvironments such as infection sites.[8] Cells in these regions may secrete cytokines and other mediators that feed back to the pituitary gland and the brain.[8] Cytokines, for example, can stimulate parts of the brain, including the hypothalamus, to secrete corticotropin-releasing factor (CRF) which, in turn, triggers the secretion of ACTH from the pituitary gland. ACTH stimulates glucocorticoid secretion from the adrenal cortex. When glucocorticoids achieve a threshold plasma concentration, they inhibit most types of immunological processes and therefore complete the negative feed-back loop.[8]

In contrast to hormones of neuroendocrine origin, leukocyte hormones are not stored and therefore must be synthesized *de novo;* the quantities produced by immune cells are much smaller than those produced by neuroendocrine cells.[8] Because immune cells are mobile and can congregate at sites of infection, they can concentrate the hormone at distant targets.[5] While antigenic stimuli are not recognized directly by the central nervous or endocrine systems, leukocytes may convey information delivered by antigens, via humoral mediators, to these systems which triggers, in turn, a physiological and/or behavioral response.[8]

4. PHARMACOLOGICAL MANIPULATION OF NEUROENDOCRINE RESPONSES

Drugs have been developed to enhance or suppress nearly all types of endocrine responses. These drugs vary from agents that mimic endogenous regulatory factors (e.g., somatostatin to inhibit GH secretion) or factors that interfere in the pathways of hormone synthesis. Furthermore, the development of genetic engineering has enabled protein hormones to be synthesized in large amounts and used as drugs. Because deficiency of certain hormones is relatively common, HRT has become a powerful treatment of many endocrine disorders. However, excess concentrations of some hormones may lead to cancer. Examples of HRT include GH administration to treat short stature in GH-deficient infants, insulin to treat diabetes, and estrogon/progesterone replacement for postmenopausal women. Although HRT for these women can prevent osteoporosis, it may increase the risk of developing steroid-dependent breast cancer in the long term.[10]

Unfortunately, some hormone treatments can be abused. For example, GH is a powerful growth-promoting agent that is taken illegally by some athletes as a performance-enhancing drug.[11] In GH-deficient adults, aerobic fitness and exercise performance is enhanced by 6 months of GH treatment.[12] Like many glucoregulatory hormones, the secretion of GH is influenced by diet, circadian rhythm, and exercise under normal conditions. Many drugs also stimulate or

TABLE 2
Physiological and Pharmacological Manipulation of Growth Hormone Secretion[11]

Activators	Inhibitors
Physiological	
Exercise	
Fasting	Hyperglycemia
Sleep	
Psychological stress	
High Ambient Temperature	Low ambient temperature
Pharmacological	
Neuroendocrine Mediators	
GH-releasing hormone	Somatostatin
Estrogens	Progesterones
Glucagon	Corticosteroids
Vasopressin	
Epinephrine	
Serotonin	
Nutrients	
Arginine	Glucose
	Free fatty acids
	Water
	Some branched-chain amino acids
Other	
Apomorphine	Atropine
Atenolol	Chlorpromazine
Bromocriptine	Cyproheptadine
Clonidine	Imapramine
Levodopa	Isoproterenol
Metyrapone	Methysergide
Propranolol	Morphine
Pyridostigmine	Theophylline

inhibit GH release (Table 2).[11] Although GH promotes muscle hypertrophy, excess levels lead to disorders such as acromegaly and tumors.[13] Arginine is a potent stimulus of GH secretion: in fact, arginine is used widely in the clinical diagnosis of GH deficiency. This amino acid also boosts prolactin and insulin secretion, and inhibits somatostatin release within the hypothalmus.[14] It is not known whether the stimulatory effect of arginine on GH secretion is related to its role in nitric oxide metabolism. In the elderly, however, arginine does not stimulate GH secretion.[13] In comparison to pharmacological stimuli such as arginine, exercise is a much stronger stimulus of GH secretion.[15] Menstrual phase and status has no effect on the plasma concentration of GH either before or after exercise.[16] Blockage of β_1-receptors enhances the GH secretory response to GH-releasing hormone.[17] Furthermore, cortisol influences GH secretion because inhibition of cortisol synthesis with metyrapone boosts the secretion of GH in response to GH-releasing hormone.[18] It is not known whether exercise affects the efficacy of these therapies; this could be a fruitful area of investigation.

5. PHARMACOLOGICAL MANIPULATION OF IMMUNITY

Many immunosuppressive and antiinflammatory drugs are used to treat people with transplanted organs, or autoimmune, inflammatory, or allergic diseases. These drugs include cyclosporine and synthetic corticosteroids. However, their effects on various aspects of immunological and inflammatory diseases is beyond the scope of this chapter. The primary focus here will be enhancement of immune function. This is particularly important with the elderly (because immune competence declines with advancing age[19]) and people with conditions associated with immunodeficiency.

Because diet has such a strong influence on immunity,[19] it is not surprising that many of the drugs used to manipulate the immune system are micronutrients. Deficiency of certain vitamins, minerals, or essential fatty acids depresses immune function and increases the incidence of infection. Every micronutrient has a threshold level for optimal immune function: large fluctuations in either direction may compromise immunity.[19] Protein and/or calorie malnutrition also depresses most of the host defense mechanisms.[19] Given the independent effects of exercise and some micronutrients on immunity, exercise and dietary factors may have powerful synergistic effects. Exercise may, in fact, reverse the immunosuppressive effects of malnutrition.[20]

Many studies have shown that vitamin and/or mineral supplementation (even to healthy individuals) boosts immune competence when compared to unsupplemented controls. Multivitamin and mineral supplementation to a group of elderly people was associated with increased circulating T cell and NK cell numbers in the blood and enhanced lymphocyte mitogenesis, NK cell cytotoxicity, and IL-2 secretion from mononuclear cells stimulated *in vitro*; the antibody response to influenza vaccine was also boosted and the general incidence of infection was reduced.[21] In a double-blind placebo-controlled study with healthy elderly subjects, vitamin E supplementation improved delayed type hypersensitivity skin test reactions and enhanced the lymphocyte mitogenic response to phytohemagglutinin (PHA) but not concanavalin-A (Con-A); however IL-2 secretion from Con-A-stimulated cells was boosted.[22] Vitamin E may decrease the production of immunosuppressive prostaglandins and/or prevent lipid peroxidation.[22] Glutathione supplementation enhances the mitogenic responses of blood mononuclear cells and their production of IL-2.[23] Girls supplemented with vitamin A and zinc show improved lymphocyte responses to tuberculin, but not Con-A or tetanus toxoid.[24] As many of these drugs are antioxidants, they may amplify immune function by countering the deleterious effects of cytotoxic free radicals.

Trace metals are essential nutrients because of their role as cofactors in many metaloenzymes. Because of its strong influence on DNA synthesis and lymphocyte proliferation, zinc is essential for development, differentiation, and maturation of the immune system.[25] Zinc deficiency in humans is associated with thymic atrophy, and impaired lymphocyte mitogenesis and NK cell cytotoxicity.[19] Athletes have lower plasma concentrations of zinc, which may be due to high carbohydrate diets and/or loss through sweating and excretion.[26] Supplementation of a normal diet with zinc increases immunoglobulin-A concentration in saliva and T cell-dependent delayed-type hypersensitivity skin reactions to both bacterial and fungal antigens.[19] With mononuclear cells from elderly people, zinc supplementation of the culture medium decreases their sensitivity to the antiproliferative effect of prostaglandin E_2.[27] Iron deficiency — which is the most prevalent nutritional disorder in the Western Hemisphere — also compromises host defense. Although not common, copper deficiency also depresses immune function.[19] Because of their role (in the free form) in promoting free radical generation, excess intake of iron or copper can be toxic.

Depending on their degree of unsaturation and concentration, dietary lipids can be either immuno-potentiating or -suppressive. The Western diet tends to be high in fat, particularly saturated fatty acids. However, some fats such as omega-3 fatty acids are scarce in the normal diet, although fish oil is a rich source. High fat intake may increase the risk of mortality from cancer, perhaps as a result of impaired immunosurveillance. Lowering of dietary fat results in a substantial increase in NK cell cytotoxicity.[28] Some fatty acids are essential nutrients because of their importance in the synthesis of lipid mediators such as eicosanoids. As some eicosanoids are pro-inflammatory, decreased generation as a result of dietary changes may ameliorate autoimmune conditions. Supplementation of a normal Western diet with omega-3 fatty acids suppresses the synthesis of IL-1β, IL-1α, and TNF-α by endotoxin-stimulated mononuclear cells.[29] Prostaglandin production is also attenuated. Fish oil also enhances the immunosuppressive effects of cyclosporine and thus lowers the risk of transplanted organs to being rejected.[30]

While amino acids are essential for protein synthesis, some are also immunomodulatory agents. In addition to glucose, for example, glutamine appears to be an essential fuel for proliferating lymphocytes and monocytes (even cells in the quiescent state).[31] Although small, decreases in plasma glutamine concentration may play a role in the apparent immunodeficiency associated with overtraining.[31] Arginine also enhances a variety of immunological functions.[32] While the mechanism is not known, it could be related to its role in nitric oxide synthesis, because reactive nitrogen intermediates are involved in the synthesis of cytotoxic molecules in phagocytes.[5]

As well as influencing hormone secretion, some drugs also affect the expression of receptors on immune cells. Isoproterenol infusion, for example, mimics the effect of short-term exercise in increasing the number of β-adrenergic receptors expressed on the surface of mononuclear cells.[33] Further investigations of this type are required.

6. EXERCISE AND IMMUNITY

Although the health benefits of regular exercise (e.g., reduced susceptibility to cardiovascular disease) are well known, the relationship between exercise and immunity has only recently become a focus of intense research activity. This is surprising considering that anecdotal evidence linking these two phenomena has been cited in reports that date back to 1920.[2,3,34-36] At present, some reports suggest that moderate exercise may increase resistance to infection; beyond this point of moderation, however, the daily exercise undertaken by athletes during intensive training periods appears to depress immunity.[2,3,34-36] The mechanisms by which these paradoxical responses to exercise are produced are poorly understood.

Numerous anecdotal reports suggest that intensive training (and overtraining) is associated with increased susceptibility to common infections.[34-36] The psychological stress associated with intensive training and competition may exacerbate this tendency.[2,37] Exercising during illness may worsen the symptoms of the infection. Transient immunosuppression induced by intensive exercise or stress may create a window of opportunity for infectious agents to evade host defenses and establish infections.

6.1. EPIDEMIOLOGICAL EVIDENCE

Despite the dearth of wide-ranging epidemiological studies, several investigations have shown that, compared to untrained individuals, athletes in training show increased incidence of upper respiratory tract infections, infectious hepatitis, and aseptic meningitis.[34-36] The majority of infections that affect athletes are viral in origin, but fungal skin infections are also common. Highly-stressed individuals are also more susceptible to respiratory infections and to some cancers.[37,38] Moderate exercise programs and/or physically active jobs may, in contrast, reduce susceptibility to colon and breast cancers, upper respiratory tract infections, and the severity and duration of depression-related illness.[2,34-36,38]

Moderate training (26 to 30 miles/week of running) reduced the occurrence of self-reported infectious episodes compared with those experienced by individuals running less than 15 miles/week.[39] Highly-conditioned elderly women have lower incidence of upper respiratory tract infections than their sedentary counterparts.[35] In contrast, running more than 60 miles/week doubled the odds of acquiring an infectious episode compared to those running less than 20 miles/week.[39] This group also reported that running a 26-mile marathon at competition speed increased the odds of infection fivefold compared to a group who trained for the race but did not compete.[40] High training mileage is, in fact, a significant risk factor for upper respiratory tract infections.[36]

6.2. THE LEUKOCYTOSIS OF EXERCISE

Submaximal (aerobic) and maximal (anaerobic) exercise cause substantial but transient increases in circulating leukocyte (immune cell) numbers due to their release from marginated vascular pools and the bone marrow.[41] Blood leukocyte counts can remain significantly elevated for up to 8 h after prolonged moderate exercise, but they return to preexercise (resting) levels within 1 h after a brief episode of exercise at maximum capacity. The magnitude and period of the leukocytosis depends upon the intensity and duration of the workload; it is mediated by increased blood flow and the substantial elevations that occur in circulating catecholamines and cortisol.[41]

The increase in the relative proportions of lymphocytes and neutrophils contribute jointly to the leukocytosis induced by exercise; increased neutrophil numbers become predominant once cortisol release is activated.[41] In general, exercise of moderate and maximal intensities lowers both the T cell to B cell, and the CD4+ (helper) to CD8+ (suppressor/cytotoxic) T cell, ratios among the circulating cells that are transiently elevated.[34-36] The CD4+/CD8+ ratio is, in fact, reduced progressively as the intensity and duration of submaximal exercise increases.[42] Acute maximal exercise triggers the mobilization into the circulation of all classes of leukocytes in both trained and untrained human subjects while chronic bouts of submaximal exercise enhance neutrophil mobilization at the expense of lymphocytes.[43] Regular training status does not affect the magnitude of these acute responses to exercise, nor does it affect neutrophil and lymphocyte numbers in the circulation chronically.[41] The potential immunological consequences of these quite marked changes in circulating leukocyte numbers are not clear because they do not correlate positively with functional changes and may intersect with the circadian variations in leukocyte hemodynamics that also occur.[44]

6.3. EXERCISE AND FUNCTIONAL CHANGES IN IMMUNITY

The majority of studies that have attempted to assess the effects of exercise on cell-mediated immune responses have focused on lymphocytes and NK cells, but there are some recent reports in which neutrophil and macrophage functions have been examined.

Many independent investigations have reported transient reductions in the responsiveness of isolated lymphocytes to T and B cell mitogens after exercise at maximum intensity, while variable results have been documented for submaximal exercise.[34-36] This variability may be due to differences in the intensity and duration of the submaximal exercise protocols employed and/or failure to express the results on a per cell basis.[3] For example, exercise at maximum intensity and marathon running both cause significant reductions in NK cell cytotoxicity and lymphocyte proliferation while moderate exercise may boost these responses.[34-36,45-47] Prolonged submaximal exercise and brief maximal exercise both lower the concentrations of salivary immunoglobulin-A and various complement components, and neutrophil microbicidal activity.[34,45,48-50] Surprisingly, tissue macrophage phagocytic capacity has been

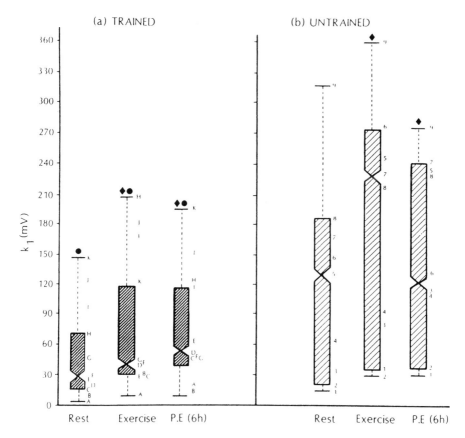

FIGURE 4. Interindividual variability in neutrophil microbicidal activity. This figure shows the large degree of interindividual variability in the neutrophil chemiluminescence responses to stimulation *in vitro* (immediately before and after an episode of moderate exercise, and 6 h post-exercise) in both trained and untrained human subjects. The individual responses (k_1) are identified by either upper case letters or numbers. (From Smith, J. A., Telford, R. D., Mason, I. B., and Weidemann, M. J., *Int. J. Sports Med.,* 11, 179, 1990. With permission.) See this reference for full explanation. Considerable interindividual variability in lymphocyte responses to mitogenic stimulation *in vitro* has also been reported.[3]

reported to increase immediately after a bout of exhaustive exercise but this may be associated with the roles that these cells have in remodeling damaged tissues.[51]

In contrast to intensive exercise, individual episodes of moderate exercise potentiate antibody-dependent cytotoxicity and neutrophil microbicidal activity, but have no significant effects on NK cell cytotoxicity or salivary immunoglobulin-A concentration.[2,34,36,48-50] Moderate exercise also triggers small increases in the serum concentrations of some immunoglobulin isotypes that are independent of changes in plasma volume.[35] The variable immunological responses to moderate exercise are not surprising considering that, even under normal (resting) conditions, there is considerable interindividual variation in functions such as neutrophil microbicidal activity[50] (Figure 4).

Several striking immunodeficiencies have been reported in cross-sectional studies of athletes undergoing intensive training programs. These include reductions in serum complement factors, salivary immunoglobulin-A, neutrophil microbicidal activity, and lymphocyte mitogenesis.[34-36,48,50,52] Intensive training does not alter the baseline concentrations of serum immunoglobulins, but falls have been reported in some athletes during periods of intense competition.[34] Few longitudinal studies have been undertaken, however, to determine at what stage of the training program these diminished responses become significant.

Moderate training, in contrast, produces significant chronic increases in the following parameters: lymphocyte mitogenesis *in vitro;*[46] NK cell activity,[35] serum immunoglobulins and salivary immunoglobulin-A.[35,52] The beneficial effects of regular training on NK cell activity were lost within 15 weeks, perhaps because the intensity of the exercise undertaken was no longer sufficient to induce the priming response, presumably because of adaptation to the higher fixed workload.[35] Moderate exercise increases NK cell cytotoxicity in elderly women[53] and, compared to their sedentary counterparts, trained elderly women have superior T cell and NK cell activities.[35]

Trauma causes similar defects to those produced by intensive endurance exercise in T cell, macrophage, and neutrophil function, which may explain the high infection rates observed in these individuals.[54] Transient perturbations of immune responses after intense exercise or trauma may be a protective response that prevents severe inflammatory damage to body tissues, particularly at injury sites. For instance, elevated concentrations of neutrophil elastase (which may damage body tissues) have been detected in plasma after prolonged running and cycling.[55]

These observations suggest that the intensity and duration of exercise may exert, via humoral mechanisms, a functional influence on cellular immunity. The depression of some immune cell functions in response to psychological and traumatic stress shows a remarkable similarity to that induced by intensive training. Impaired mitogenic responsiveness of lymphocytes and reductions in NK cell cytotoxicity have, for example, been reported following bereavement and in response to the psychological stress of college examinations.[2] The variability of the exercise effect may be due to the failure of some investigators to express their results in terms of a defined cell number (to take account of any coincidental leukocytosis) or to the tendency of others to restrict sampling times to the periods just before and immediately after exercise.[3] NK cell cytotoxicity, for example, may increase immediately after moderate to intense exercise, only to fall substantially below preexercise values 2 h later, with recovery to normal levels occurring over the next 21 h.[47] Some immune responses may also show endogenous diurnal fluctuations in their activities.[44]

Because of a favorable link with immunity, AIDS patients are now being prescribed exercise programs as part of their treatment and some long-term AIDS survivors have reported favorably on participation in exercise programs.[56,57] Moderate exercise also reduces the emotional distress and decrements in NK cell activity of the subjects that occur following notification of positive serologic status for HIV-1.[57] This may be due to increases in circulating CD4[+] cells triggered by exercise — which are similar to those induced by azidothymidine (AZT) — but without the deleterious side effects.[57]

7. EXERCISE AND IMMUNOREGULATION

The intensity and duration of exercise influences the extent to which many neuroendocrine hormones are released into the circulation.[58] The magnitude of these responses is substantially lower in trained subjects exercising at the same absolute workload as their untrained counterparts.[58] Training may, however, increase cellular responsiveness to some hormones such as insulin.[58] There may also be individual differences in the kinetics of hormone secretion in response to exercise that are independent of training status. Stress hormones such as GH, catecholamines, and cortisol are thought to be secreted in response to the direct metabolic and physiological demands of exercise. Circulating and marginated immune cells with receptors for these hormones are highly susceptible targets. With some hormones, the plasma concentrations peak immediately after a critical threshold is reached in workload intensity, but with some others (e.g., cortisol) this may not occur until several hours after the episode of exercise has ceased. There may also be a substantial lag time between the attainment of peak plasma concentration of a particular hormone and the appearance of a functional cellular response. Thus, several postexercise measurements should be made at least up to 24 h after the exercise test. Control measurements at each sampling point are required to rule out the effect diurnal variation.

7.1. IMMUNOPOTENTIATING MEDIATORS

Exercise-induced increases in the plasma concentrations of cytokines and neuroendocrine hormones have been reported widely. The release of cytokines into the circulation has been reported following submaximal and eccentric exercise[59] and strenuous running.[60] Endotoxin, a potent stimulus of cytokine secretion, has also been detected in plasma after an ultratriathlon.[61] Furthermore, mononuclear cells isolated from human subjects after exercise have been reported to secrete significantly greater quantities of cytokines than cells isolated before exercise when stimulated with endotoxin *in vitro*.[62] Sprenger and colleagues[63] have reported, in contrast, that cytokine concentrations do not change significantly in the plasma of well-trained runners after a 12-mile road race. They were able to demonstrate, however, quite significant increases in the concentrations of interferon-γ, tumor necrosis factor-α (TNF), IL-1β, IL-6, and soluble IL-2 receptors in the urine of exercised subjects, which they claimed to be indicative of enhanced production and/or release of these factors.[63] We also found no increase in circulating cytokines after 1 h of moderate exercise.[64] Furthermore, with the exception of IL-6, a similar workload was reported to cause no increase in plasma cytokines or mRNA in blood mononuclear cells.[65]

The systemic TNF response to endotoxin challenge is suppressed in rats after exhaustive exercise.[66] Additional work, using more sensitive assays is required to verify whether exercise-induced changes in the accumulation of cytokines, or their endogenous inhibitors, in plasma or urine are significant.

The GH response to exercise has been studied extensively. The circulating concentration of GH is elevated significantly after 30 min of exercise of moderate intensity and it rises progressively with increasing workload.[58,67] Although endurance training blunts the GH response to acute exercise, it amplifies the pulsatile secretion of GH which doubles the integrated (24-h) concentration.[68] Prolactin shares considerable structural and functional homology with GH.[6] Unlike GH, the plasma concentration of prolactin does not increase until the exercise intensity exceeds 50% $\dot{V}O_2$max and the magnitude of the increase is much smaller than that of GH.[58] Moderate exercise also activates the secretion of atrial natriuretic peptide (ANP) into the circulation.[69] This hormone (which regulates blood pressure and fluid electrolytes) responds almost instantly to exercise and is rapidly cleared from the blood as soon as exercise ceases.[69]

7.2. IMMUNOSUPPRESSIVE MEDIATORS

The immunostimulatory properties of GH and prolactin are antagonized by ACTH and glucocorticoids. ACTH — which stimulates cortisol release from the adrenal gland and is secreted concomitantly with β-endorphin — does not rise in the plasma until exercise intensity exceeds 60% $\dot{V}O_2$max.[70] This threshold must be exceeded before cortisol (the major human glucocorticoid) and opioid release are triggered. These increases are not affected significantly by prolongation of the workload because exercise at maximum intensity causes the plasma concentrations of ACTH and β-endorphin to rise within 30 to 60 sec.[70] As already discussed, some hormones have concentration-dependent effects on immune cell function. For example, a transient 15 min increase in NK cell cytotoxicity induced by prolonged submaximal exercise may be mediated by low concentrations of endorphins, whereas the postexercise decrease in this cellular response — sustained for 24 h — may be due to excessive release or slow catabolism of endorphins.[71]

Catecholamine secretion during exercise is also intensity-dependent. The rise in the plasma concentration of catecholamines is fivefold larger after maximal exercise than the small increase induced by moderate exercise. Norepinephrine secretion is triggered at much lower workloads than those required to raise epinephrine[72] and norepinephrine may, in turn, initiate GH release by activating hypothalamic GH-releasing hormone.[73]

Nearly all immunosuppressive responses induced by intense exercise correlate with increases in circulating cortisol, the plasma half-life of which is 60 to 90 min at rest.[2] Cortisol release is slower than that of catecholamines and ACTH, and may not peak until 30 min after exercise has ceased. Sustained cortisol secretion, such as the 200% increase observed after a marathon run,[41] may represent failure of this glucocorticoid to trigger, under these conditions, the feedback signals that shut down ACTH release.[74] While the plasma concentrations of opioids and epinephrine usually return to resting values 10 to 20 min after exercise, these hormones may also contribute to transient suppression of immune responses after intense exercise.[75] The return of their plasma concentrations to preexercise values may not coincide with the disappearance of their immunosuppressive effects. Increases in plasma histamine or prostaglandins after intense exercise may also contribute to suppressed immune responses.[47,76] Some of these changes may be prolonged and may require the recruitment of recently-matured cells from the bone marrow to reverse them. The effects of training on the rate of leukocyte division, differentiation, and release have not been investigated. Receptors to certain hormones may also be influenced by exercise. Vigorous exercise leads to uncoupling of neutrophil β_2-adrenergic receptors; this may be due to lactic acid accumulation.[77] There appears to be no other reports of exercise-induced changes in receptor expression or affinity for various cytokines or neuroendocrine mediators.

7.3. THE ACUTE-PHASE RESPONSE AND OVERTRAINING

The acute-phase response is a characteristic reaction to infection or trauma. Intense exercise also triggers a mild acute-phase response.[78] Physical training may generate a homeostatic shift that involves changes in the concentrations of inflammatory mediators and their endogenous inhibitors.[79] Ultramarathon running and triathlons induce substantial elevations in plasma C-reactive protein levels that peak 24 h after the race.[34-36] C-reactive protein synthesis may be triggered by either endotoxemia or muscle damage. Elite athletes show chronic elevations of some acute-phase proteins, including serum protease inhibitors (e.g., α_1-antitrypsin, C_1-inhibitor), yet training appears to progressively reduce the magnitude of the acute-phase response to regular episodes of acute exercise at the same intensity.[79] Attenuation of the production of C-reactive protein, which may act as a nonspecific opsonin, may increase the susceptibility of some individuals undergoing such an intense training program to bacterial infections.[79]

Psychological stress is also associated with elevated cortisol activity and impaired immune responses. Decreased phagocyte activity was observed as early as 1920 in emotionally-stressed people.[80] Stress caused by trauma, infection, pain, and fear also stimulates the secretion of cortisol.[81] These responses have functional consequences because psychological stress increases susceptibility to rhinovirus infections such as the common cold.[82] Because the neuroendocrine responses to intensive physical exertion and psychological stress bear striking similarities, it is not surprising that similar changes in the responses of immune cells also occur. In contrast, moderate training reduces the basal circulating concentration of β-endorphin and this correlates with greater emotional stability and reduced incidence of depression.[83]

Overtraining may induce immunosuppression through neuroendocrine dysfunction; thus immune and neuroendocrine factors may be useful in diagnosing overtraining.[84] At present, overtraining is suspected when a large fall in the testosterone/cortisol ratio, caused by increased cortisol, occurs.[84] Because this ratio may fluctuate diurnally, it is not universally accepted as a marker of overtraining. In overtrained athletes, catecholamines, and/or their metabolites, may also increase in the circulation and urine.[85] Overtraining research is, in general, hampered by small sample sizes and the present lack of reliable diagnostic markers. Profiles of immune and neuroendocrine parameters every 2 to 4 h over a 24-h period may provide more reliable results.

Perhaps the best example of endocrine dysfunction associated with training is athletes' amenorrhea.[86] This is a reversible condition that primarily affects female endurance runners. While the etiology is unknown, multiple factors including hypothalamic dysfunction, low body weight, and poor diet are thought to be involved. Chronically, the condition can lead to stress fractures, osteoporosis, and infertility.[86]

8. PHARMACOLOGICAL MANIPULATION OF EXERCISE-INDUCED NEUROENDOCRINE RESPONSES

A variety of drugs can be used to manipulate exercise-induced hormone responses. As discussed already, GH is one the most responsive hormones to exercise. Thus, it is not unexpected that a variety drugs can affect its secretion during exercise. Although basal hormone concentrations in plasma are not affected, administration of glucose, free fatty acids,[87] or branched-chain amino acids blunts GH and testosterone secretion in response to exercise.[88] This is not surprising considering the role of GH in mobilizing fatty acids for energy metabolism. In contrast, low blood glucose concentration (<3.3 mM) triggers the secretion of ACTH and cortisol during low-intensity exercise.[89] Maintenance of blood glucose also abolishes glucagon release and blunts epinephrine secretion as well as preventing the progressive decrease in insulin during exercise.[90] Even rehydration with water blocks the GH response to exercise in a hot environment.[91] Some drugs also amplify the GH response to exercise. Ingestion of the cholinergic agonist, pyridostigmine, doubled the integrated concentration of GH found in response to moderate exercise while the opioid receptor antagonist, naltrexone, had no effect.[92] Infusion of the β-blocker, propranolol, also amplifies the GH and cortisol responses to submaximal exercise.[93] These studies show that control of GH secretion during exercise is a complex process. In middle-aged rats, GH administration potentiates the positive effect of exercise on long bone formation.[94]

Numerous administration studies with energy substrates support the view that the primary role of exercise-induced hormonal responses is to control energy metabolism. Carbohydrate ingestion blunts the exercise-induced increase in the plasma glucagon/insulin ratio and cortisol concentration but does not affect catecholamine responses.[95] Although ingestion of glycerol (10%) increased plasma osmolality, it did not alter the secretion of fluid-regulating hormones during moderate exercise in the heat.[96] Steroids used as contraceptives in women block the secretion of cortisol, 17β-estradiol, and progesterone during intense exercise.[97] Progressive rehydration to individuals exercising in a hot environment blunted the exercised-induced increases in plasma ANP, vasopressin, ACTH, and cortisol concentrations.[69] Drinking a solution containing carbohydrates and electrolytes blunts the secretion of cortisol and vasopressin during a 2-h run.[98] Administration of phosphatidylserine to humans blunts the ACTH and cortisol responses to exercise, but it does not affect catecholamines, prolactin, or GH.[99]

Opioid- and β-antagonists have been used in many exercise studies. Compared to exercise alone, ingestion of the β-blocker, arotinolol, boosted the secretion of epinephrine and ANP substantially.[100] Other β-blockers also amplify the exercise-induced increases in ANP[101] epinephrine, cortisol, and prolactin while the secretion of renin and norepinephrine is attenuated.[102] Although the antihypertensive drug, cicletanine, had no effect,[103] naltrexone[104] or penbutanolol[105] administration blunt the ANP response to exercise. Enalapril increased the renin response to exercise by twofold and reduced aldosterone by 40%.[106] Compared to eumenorrheic women, amenorrheic women do not show an increase in the secretion of ACTH, β-endorphin, and cortisol in response to intense exercise; however, naltrexone treatment restores these suppressed responses.[107] Administration of the opioid antagonist, naloxone, increases the plasma concentrations of β-endorphin[108] and ACTH, but it has no effect on GH, prolactin, or thyroid-stimulating hormone[109] after exercise at maximum capacity.

Exercise can also alter the sensitivity of some endocrine glands to local mediators that control hormone secretion. The secretion of luteinizing hormone and testosterone induced by gonadotropin-releasing hormone treatment is enhanced after strenuous exercise.[110] In rats, the ACTH and corticosterone responses to acute exercise and IL-1β or CRF administration is blunted by training and this is associated with decreased prostaglandin E_2 secretion into the circulation.[111] One week of amino acid supplementation did not influence basal testosterone, GH, or cortisol concentrations in plasma; nor is the response to resistance exercise in adolescent males affected.[112] In many cases, blockage of receptors by antagonistic drugs (and thus hormone uptake by target cells) may explain why hormones accumulate in the circulation during exercise.

9. PHARMACOLOGICAL MANIPULATION OF EXERCISE-INDUCED IMMUNOLOGICAL RESPONSES

Although pharmacological manipulation of exercise-induced hormonal responses has been studied extensively, there are relatively few studies that have examined immunological parameters. The exception, perhaps, is exercise-induced asthma: a range of drugs has been used to treat this condition. In many cases, the underlying cause may be immunological.[113]

It has long been recognized that epinephrine infusion causes a similar mobilization of leukocytes from marginated tissue pools into the circulation as that caused by exercise.[41] Irrespective of whether exercise or epinephrine is used as a stimulus, the pattern of the changes in blood mononuclear cell subsets is the same; furthermore, in both cases, the proliferative response to PHA is not altered on a per cell basis.[114] Epinephrine may mediate the inhibitory effects on lymphocyte proliferation and IL-2 receptor expression *in vitro* found immediately after single episodes of maximal exercise because nonselective blockage of β-receptors prevents this.[115] At physiological concentrations, this hormone also suppresses NK cell cytotoxicity; this may be due to prostaglandin action.[75] Administration of indomethacin, an inhibitor of prostaglandin synthesis, to individuals undertaking maximal exercise abolishes the postexercise decrease in NK cell cytotoxicity.[47] Given the considerable redundancy in immunoregulatory mediators, however, other factors are likely to be involved. Opioid receptor blockade by naloxone in human volunteers attenuated the exercised-induced increase in NK cell cytotoxicity.[71] Vitamin C supplementation reduced the incidence of upper respiratory tract infections in a group of runners who completed a 60-mile ultramarathon.[116] Vitamin E attenuated the secretion of IL-1β from endotoxin-stimulated cells *in vitro* after a episode of eccentric exercise.[117]

Several studies have shown that some drugs do not affect immunological responses to exercise. Ingestion of β-blockers, either propranolol or atenolol, during 4 months of endurance training did not influence lymphocyte mitogenesis and NK cell activity.[46] As with any drug, most of these exercise-induced responses are likely to be dose-dependent. Thus, low dose ranges may explain some negative results.

10. CONCLUSIONS AND FUTURE DIRECTIONS

Because exercise can be varied in intensity, type, duration, and frequency, it is an ideal experimental stressor to examine physiological responses. Exercise clearly has intensity-dependent effects on the neuroendocrine system that are reproducible. Although less conclusive, the data suggest, in general, that the immune system appears to be altered in an intensity-dependent manner by exercise. Circumstantial evidence suggests that neuroendocrine responses may be a connecting link to the immunological changes triggered by exercise. Pharmacological manipulation is one strategy that may enable some of these mechanistic issues to be solved.

If the ideas presented in this review are confirmed, it may be possible to design suitable exercise regimes as part of a therapeutic program for immunodeficient individuals on the one hand, and to use immunological parameters to monitor the effects of intensive training on the health of athletes on the other. Although some drugs have been shown to enhance aspects of athletic performance, possibly through modulation of neuroendocrine responses, there is significant potential for adverse side effects. Given this caveat, it is important to note that no drug in current or prospective use holds as much promise for maintaining health, or athletic performance, as a regular well-designed exercise program.[118] Nevertheless, drugs remain a powerful tool for investigating the mechanisms involved in various physiological responses to exercise.

11. ACKNOWLEDGMENTS

I am grateful to my colleagues at the Australian Institute of Sport, Drs. David Pyne and David Martin, for their helpful comments on the manuscript.

REFERENCES

1. **Grossman, A., Bouloux, P., Price, P., Drury, P. L., Lam, K. S., et al.,** The role opioid peptides in the hormonal responses to acute exercise in man, *Clin. Sci.,* 67, 483, 1984.
2. **Smith, J. A. and Weidemann., M. J.,** The exercise and immunity paradox: a neuro-endocrine/cytokine hypothesis, *Med. Sci. Res.,* 18, 749, 1990.
3. **Smith, J. A.,** Guidelines, standards, and perspectives in exercise immunology. *Med. Sci. Sports Exerc.,* 27, 497, 1995.
4. **Smith, J. A., Gray, A. B., Pyne, D. B., Telford, R. D., and Weidemann, M. J.,** Mechanisms involved in exercise-induced priming (amplification) of neutrophil microbicidal activity, *Med. Sci. Sports Exerc.,* Suppl. 26, A191, 1994.
5. **Smith, J. A.,** Neutrophils, host defense and inflammation: a double-edged sword, *J. Leukoc. Biol.,* 56, 672, 1994.
6. **Blalock, J. E.,** Production of peptide hormones and neurotransmitters by the immune system, in *Neuroimmunoendocrinology,* 2nd ed., Blalock, J. E., Ed., Basel, Karger, 1992, as cited in *Chem. Immunol.,* 52, 1, 1992.
7. **Gala, R. R.,** Prolactin and growth hormone in the regulation of the immune system, *Proc. Soc. Exp. Biol. Med.,* 198, 513, 1991.
8. **Sternberg, E. M., Chrousos, G. P., Wilder, R. L., and Gold, P. W.,** The stress response and the regulation of inflammatory disease, *Ann. Intern. Med.,* 117, 854, 1992.
9. **Aguila, M. C., Dees, W. L., Haensly, W. E., and McCann, S. M.,** Evidence that somatostatin is localized and synthesized in lymphoid organs, *Proc. Natl. Acad. Sci. U.S.A.,* 88, 11485, 1991.
10. **Sitruk-Ware, R.,** Hormone therapy of menopause and risk of breast cancer: polemics and controversies, *Presse Med.,* 23, 38, 1994.
11. **Macintyre, J. G.,** Growth hormone and athletes, *Sports Med.,* 4, 129, 1987.
12. **Cuneo, R. C., Salomon, F., Wiles, M., Hesp, R., and Sonksen, P. H.,** Growth hormone treatment in growth hormone-deficient adults. II. Effects on exercise performance, *J. Appl. Physiol.,* 70, 695, 1991.
13. **Corpas, E., Harman, S. M., and Blackman, M. R.,** Human growth hormone and aging, *Endocrine Rev.,* 14, 20, 1993.
14. **Ghigo, E., Maccario, M., Arvat, E., Valetto, M. R., Valente, et al.,** Interactions of galanin and arginine on growth hormone, prolactin, and insulin secretion in man, *Metabolism,* 41, 85, 1992.
15. **Sutton, J. and Lazarus, L.,** Growth hormone in exercise: comparison of physiological and pharmacological stimuli, *J. Appl. Physiol.,* 41, 523, 1976.
16. **Kanaley, J. A., Boileau, R. A., Bahr, J. A., Misner, J. E., and Nelson, R. A.,** Substrate oxidation and GH responses to exercise are independent of menstrual phase and status, *Med. Sci. Sports Exerc.,* 24, 873, 1992.

17. **Mauras, N., Blizzard, R. M., Yhorner, M. O., and Rogal, A. D.,** Selective β_1-adrenergic receptor blockade with atenolol enhances growth hormone releasing hormone and mediated growth hormone release in man, *Metabolism,* 36, 369, 1987.

18. **Dinan, T. G., Thakore, J., and O'Keane, V.,** Lowering cortisol enhances growth hormone response to growth hormone releasing hormone in healthy subjects, *Acta Physiol. Scand.,* 151, 413, 1994.

19. **Chandra, R. K.,** 1990 McCollum Award Lecture. Nutrition and immunity: lessons from the past and new insights into the future, *Am. J. Clin. Nutr.,* 53, 1087, 1991.

20. **Filteau, S. M., Menzies, R. A., Kaido, T. J., O'Grady, M. P., Gelderd, J. B., and Hall, N. R.,** Effects of exercise on immune functions of undernourished mice, *Life Sci.,* 51, 565, 1992.

21. **Chandra, R. K.,** Effect of vitamin and trace-element supplementation on immune responses and infection in elderly subjects, *Lancet,* 340, 1124, 1992.

22. **Meydani, S. N., Barklund, M. P., Liu, S., Meydani, M., Miller, R. A., et al.,** Vitamin E supplementation enhances cell-mediated immunity in healthy elderly subjects, *Am. J. Clin. Nutr.,* 52, 557, 1990.

23. **Wu, D., Meydani, S. N., Sastre, J., Hayek, M., and Meydani, M.,** In vitro glutathione enhances interleukin-2 production and mitogenic response of peripheral blood mononuclear cells from young and old subjects, *J. Nutr.,* 124, 655, 1994.

24. **Kramer, T. R., Udomkesmalee, E., Dhanamitta, S., Sirisinha, S., Charoenkiatkul, S., et al.,** Lymphocyte responsiveness of children supplemented with vitamin A and zinc, *Am. J. Clin. Nutr.,* 58, 566, 1993.

25. **Singh, A., Failla, M. L., and Deuster, P. A.,** Exercise-induced changes in immune function: effects of zinc supplementation, *J. Appl. Physiol.,* 76, 2298, 1994.

26. **Tipton, K., Green, N. R., Haymes, E. M., and Waller, M.,** Zinc loss in sweat of athletes exercising in hot and neutral temperatures, *Int. J. Sports Nutr.,* 3, 261, 1993.

27. **Santos-Neto, L., Tosta, C. E., and Dorea, J. G.,** Zinc reverses the increased sensitivity of lymphocytes from aged subjects to the antiproliferative effect of prostaglandin E_2, *Clin. Imunol. Immunopathol.,* 64, 184, 1992.

28. **Hebert, J. R., Barone, R. J., Reddy, M. M., and Backlund, J. Y.,** Natural killer cell activity in a longitudinal dietary fat intervention trial, *Clin. Immunol. Immunopathol.,* 54, 103, 1990.

29. **Endres, S., Ghorbani, R., Kelley, V. E., Georgilis, K., Lonnemann, G., et al.,** The effect of dietary supplementation with n-3 polyunsaturated fatty acids on the synthesis of interleukin-1 and tumor necrosis factor by mononuclear cells, *N. Engl. J. Med.,* 320, 265, 1989.

30. **Homan van der Heide, J., Bilo, H. J. G., Donker, J. M., Wilmink, J. M., and Tegzess, A. M.,** Effect of dietary fish oil on renal function and rejection in cyclosporine-treated recipients of renal transplants, *N. Engl. J. Med.,* 329, 769, 1993.

31. **Parry-Billings, M., Budget, R., Koutedakis, Y., Blomstrand, E., Brooks, S., et al.,** Plasma amino acid concentrations in the overtraining syndrome: possible effects on the immune system, *Med. Sci. Sports Exerc.,* 24, 1353, 1992.

32. **Reynolds, J. V., Daly, J., Zhang, M. S., Evantash, E., Shou, J., et al.,** Immunomodulatory mechanisms of arginine, *Surgery,* 104, 142, 1988.

33. **Landmann, R.,** Beta-adrenergic receptors in human leukocyte subpopulations, *Eur. J. Clin. Invest.,* 22(Suppl. 1), 30, 1992.

34. **Mackinnon, L. T.,** *Exercise and Immunology,* Human Kinetics, New York, 1992.

35. **Nieman, D. C. and Nehlsen-Cannarella, S. L.,** The immune response to exercise, *Sem. Hematol.,* 31, 166, 1994.

36. **Heath, G. W., Macera, C. A., and Nieman, D. C.,** Exercise and upper respiratory tract infections: is there a relationship?, *Sports Med.,* 14, 353, 1992.

37. **Graham, N. M. H., Douglas, R. M., and Ryan, P.,** Stress and acute respiratory infection, *Am. J. Epidemiol.,* 124, 389, 1986.

38. **Shephard, R. J.,** Physical activity and cancer, *Int. J. Sports Med.,* 11, 413, 1990.

39. **Nieman, D. C., Johanssen, L. M., and Lee, J. W.,** Infectious episodes in runners before and after a road race, *J. Sports Med. Phys. Fitness,* 29, 289, 1989.

40. **Nieman, D. C., Johanssen, L. M., Lee, J. W., and Arabatzis, K.,** Infectious episodes in runners before and after the Los Angeles marathon, *J. Sports Med. Phys. Fitness,* 30, 316, 1990.

41. **McCarthy, D. A. and Dale, M. M.,** The leucocytosis of exercise, *Sports Med.,* 6, 333, 1988.

42. **Kendall, A., Hoffman-Goetz, L., Houston, M., MacNeil, B., and Arumugam, Y.,** Exercise and blood lymphocyte subset responses: intensity, duration and subject fitness effects, *J. Appl. Physiol.,* 69, 251, 1990.

43. **Ferry, A., Picard, F., Duvallet, A., Weill, B., and Rieu, M.,** Changes in blood leucocyte populations induced by acute maximal and chronic submaximal exercise, *Eur. J. Appl. Physiol.,* 59, 435, 1990.

44. **Levi, F. A., Canon, C., Touitou, T., Sulon, J., Mechkouri, M., et al.,** Circadian rhythms in circulating T lymphocyte subsets and plasma testosterone, total and free cortisol in five healthy men, *Clin. Exp. Immunol.,* 71, 329, 1988.

45. **Nehlsen-Cannarella, S. L., Nieman, D. C., Jessen, J., Chang, L., Gusewitch, G., et al.,** The effects of acute moderate exercise on lymphocyte function and serum immunoglobulin levels, *Int. J. Sports Med.,* 12, 391, 1991.

46. **Watson, R. R., Moriguchi, S., Jackson, J. C., Werner, L., Wilmore, J. H., and Freund, B. J.,** Modulation of cellular immune functions in humans by endurance exercise training during β-adrenergic blockade with atenolol or propanolol, *Med. Sci. Sports Exerc.,* 18, 95, 1986.

47. **Pederson, B. K.,** Influence of physical activity on the cellular immune system: mechanisms of action, *Int. J. Sports Med.,* 12(Suppl. 1), S23, 1991.

48. **Nieman, D. C., Tan, S.A., Lee, J. W., and Berk, L. S.,** Complement and immunoglobulin levels in athletes and sedentary controls, *Int. J. Sports Med.,* 10, 124, 1989.

49. **Pyne, D. B.,** Regulation of neutrophil function during exercise, *Sports Med.,* 17, 245, 1994.

50. **Smith, J. A., Telford, R. D., Mason, I. B., and Weidemann, M. J.,** Exercise, training and neutrophil microbicidal activity, *Int. J. Sports Med.,* 11, 179, 1990.

51. **Fehr, H. G., Lotzerich, H., and Michna, H.,** Human macrophage function and physical exercise: phagocytic and histochemical studies, *Eur. J. Appl. Physiol.,* 58, 613, 1989.

52. **McDowell, S. L., Chaloa, K., Housh, T. J., Tharp, G. D., and Johnson, G. O.,** The effect of exercise intensity and duration on salivary immunoglobulin A, *Eur. J. Appl. Physiol.,* 63, 108, 1991.

53. **Crist, D. M., Mackinnon, L. T., Thompson, R. F., Atterbom, H. A., and Egan, P. A.,** Physical exercise increases natural cellular-mediated tumor cytotoxicity in elderly women, *Gerontology,* 35, 66, 1989.

54. **Green, D. R. and Faist, E.,** Trauma and the immune response, *Immunol. Today,* 9, 253, 1988.

55. **Dufaux, B. and Order, U.,** Plasma elastase-α1-antitrypsin, neopterin, tumor necrosis factor and soluble interleukin-2 receptor after prolonged exercise, *Int. J. Sports Med.,* 10, 434, 1989.

56. **Solomon, G. F.,** Psychosocial factors, exercise, and immunity: athletes, elderly persons, and AIDS patients, *Int. J. Sports Med.,* 12(Suppl. 1), S50, 1991.

57. **LaPerriere, A., Fletcher, M. A., Antoni, M. H., Klimas, N., Ironson, G., and Schneiderman, N.,** Aerobic exercise training in an AIDS risk group, *Int. J. Sports Med.,* 12 (Suppl. 1), S53, 1991.

58. **Viru, A.,** Plasma hormones and physical exercise, *Int. J. Sports Med.,* 13, 201, 1992.

59. **Cannon, J. G., Evans, W. J., Hughes, V. A., Meredith, C. N., and Dinarello, C. A.,** Physiological mechanisms contributing to increased interleukin-1 secretion, *J. Appl. Physiol.,* 61, 1869, 1986.

60. **Espersen, G. T., Elbaek, A., Ernst, E., Toft, E., Kaalund, S., et al.,** Effect of physical exercise on cytokines and lymphocyte subpopulations in human peripheral blood, *Acta Pathol. Microbiol. Immunol. (Scand.),* 98, 395, 1990.

61. **Bosenberg, A. T., Brock-Utne, J. G., Gaffin, S. L., Wells, M. T. B., and Blake, G. T. W.,** Strenuous exercise causes systemic endotoxemia, *J. Appl. Physiol.,* 65, 106, 1988.

62. **Haahr, P. M., Pedersen, B. K., Fomsgaard, A., Tvede, N., Diamant, M., et al.,** Effect of physical exercise on in vitro production of interleukin 1, interleukin 6, tumour necrosis factor-α, interleukin 2 and interferon-γ, *Int. J. Sports Med.,* 12, 223, 1991.

63. **Sprenger, H., Jacobs, C., Nain, M., Gressner, A. M., Prinz, H., et al.,** Enhanced release of cytokines, interleukin-2 receptors, and neopterin after long distance running, *Clin. Immunol. Immunopathol.,* 63, 188, 1992.

64. **Smith, J. A., Telford, R. D., Baker, M. S., Hapel, A. J., and Weidemann, M. J.,** Cytokine immunoreactivity in plasma does not change after moderate endurance exercise, *J. Appl. Physiol.,* 73, 1396, 1992.

65. **Ullum, H., Haahr, P. M., Diamant, M., Palmø, Halkjaer, J., and Pedersen, B. K.,** Bicycle exercise enhances plasma IL-6 but does not change IL-1α, IL-1β, IL-6, or TNF-α pre-mRNA in BMNC, *J. Appl. Physiol.,* 77, 93, 1994.

66. **Bagby, G. J., Sawaya, D. E., Crouch, L. D., and Shepherd, R. E.,** Prior exercise suppresses the plasma tumor necrosis factor response to bacterial lipopolysaccharide, *J. Appl. Physiol.,* 77, 1542, 1994.

67. **Farrell, P. A., Garthwaite, T. L., and Gustafson, A. B.,** Plasma adrenocorticotropin and cortisol responses to submaximal and exhaustive exercise, *J. Appl. Physiol.,* 55, 441, 1983.

68. **Weltman, A., Weltman, J. Y., Schurrer, R., Evans, W. S., Veldhuis, J. D., and Rogal, A. D.,** Endurance training amplifies the pulsatile release of growth hormone: effects of training intensity, *J. Appl. Physiol.,* 72, 2188, 1992.

69. **Follenius, M., Candas, V., Bothorel, B., and Brandenberger, G.,** Effect of rehydration on atrial natriuretic peptide release during exercise in the heat, *J. Appl. Physiol.,* 66, 2521, 1989.

70. **Buono, M. J., Yeager, J. E., and Hodgdon, J. A.,** Plasma adrenocorticotropin and cortisol responses to brief high-intensity exercise in humans, *J. Appl. Physiol.,* 61, 1337, 1986.

71. **Fiatarone, M. A., Morley, J. E., Bloom, E. T., Benton, D., Makinodan, T., and Solomon, G. F.,** Endogenous opioids and the exercise-induced augmentation of natural killer cell activity, *J. Lab. Clin. Med.,* 112, 544, 1988.

72. **Deuster, P. A., Chrousos, G. P., Luger, A., DeBolt, J. E., and Bernier, L. L., et al.,** Hormonal and metabolic responses of untrained, moderately-trained, and highly-trained men to three exercise intensities, *Metabolism,* 38, 141, 1989.

73. **Malozowski, S., Hao, E., Ren, S. G., Genazzani, A. D., Kalogeras, K. T., and Merriam, G. R.,** Effects of inhibition of norepinephrine synthesis on spontaneous and growth hormone-releasing hormone-induced GH secretion in cynomolous macaques: evidence for increased hypothalamic somatostatin tone, *Neuroendocrinology,* 51, 455, 1990.

74. **Sapolsky, R. M., Armanini, M. P., Packan, D. R., Sutton, S. W., and Plotsky, P. M.,** Glucocorticoid feedback inhibition of adrenocorticotropic hormone secretagogue release, *Neuroendocrinology,* 51, 328, 1990.

75. **Kappel, M., Tvede, N., Galbo, H., Haahr, P. M., Kjaer, M., et al.,** Evidence that the effect of physical exercise on NK cell activity is mediated by epinephrine, *J. Appl. Physiol.,* 70, 2530, 1991.

76. **Dufaux, B., Order, U., and Liesen, H.,** Effect of short maximal physical exercise on coagulation, fibrinolysis, and complement system, *Int. J. Sports Med.,* 12(Suppl. 1), S38, 1991.

77. **Davies, O.,** Exercise-induced fall in coupling of human β₂-adrenergic receptors, *Metabolism,* 37, 916, 1988.

78. **Liesen, H., Dufaux, B., and Hollmann, W.,** Modifications of serum glycoproteins the days following a prolonged physical exercise and the influence of physical training, *Eur. J. Appl. Physiol.,* 37, 243, 1977.

79. **Dufaux, B., Order, U., Geyer, H., and Hollmann, W.,** C-Reactive protein serum concentrations in well-trained athletes, *Int. J. Sports Med.,* 5, 102, 1984.

80. **Khansari, D. N., Murgo, A. J., and Faith, R. E.,** Effects of stress on the immune system, *Immunol. Today,* 11, 170, 1990.

81. **Munck, A. and Guyre, P. M.,** Glucocorticoid hormones in stress: physiological and pharmacological actions, *News Physiol. Sci.,* 1, 69, 1986.

82. **Cohen, S., Tyrrell, D. A. J., and Smith, A. P.,** Psychological stress and susceptibility to the common cold, *N. Engl. J. Med.,* 325, 606, 1991.

83. **Lobstein, D. D., Rasmussen, C. L., Dunphy, G. E., and Dunphy, M. J.,** Beta-endorphin and components of depression as powerful discriminators between joggers and sedentary middle-aged men, *J. Psychosom. Res.,* 33, 293, 1989.

84. **Fry, R. W., Morton, A. R., and Keast, D.,** Overtraining in athletes: an update, *Sports Med.,* 12, 32, 1991.

85. **Hooper, S. L., Mackinnon, L. T., Gordon, R. D., and Bachmann, A. W.,** Hormonal responses of elite swimmers to overtraining, *Med. Sci. Sports Exerc.,* 25, 741, 1993.

86. **Warren, M. P.,** Amenorrhea in endurance runners, *J. Clin. Endocrinol. Metab.,* 75, 1393, 1992.

87. **Cappon, J. P., Ipp, E., Brasel, J. A., and Cooper, D. M.,** Acute effects of high-fat and high-glucose meals on the growth hormone response to exercise, *J. Clin. Endocrinol. Metab.,* 76, 2490, 1993.

88. **Carli, G., Bonifazi, M., Lodi, L., Lupo, C., Martelli, G., and Viti, A.,** Changes in the exercise-induced hormone response to branched chain amino acid administration, *Eur. J. Appl. Physiol.,* 64, 272, 1992.

89. **Tabata, I., Ogita, F., Miyachi, M., and Shibayama, H.,** Effect of low blood glucose on plasma CRF, ACTH, and cortisol during prolonged physical exercise, *J. Appl. Physiol.,* 71, 1807, 1991.

90. **Massicotte, D., Peronnette, F., Adopo, E., Brisson, G. R., and Hillaire-Marcel, C.,** Metabolic availability of oral glucose during exercise, *Metabolism,* 41, 1284, 1992.

91. **Saini, J., Bothorel, B., Brandenberger, G., Candas, V., and Follenius, M.,** Growth hormone and prolactin response to rehydration during exercise: effect of water and carbo-hydrate solutions, *Eur. J. Appl. Physiol.,* 61, 61, 1990.

92. **Thompson, D. L., Weltman, J. Y., Rogal, A. D., Metzger, D. L., Veldhuis, J. D., and Weltman, A.,** Cholinergic and opioid involvement in release of growth hormone during exercise and recovery, *J. Appl. Physiol.,* 1993.

93. **Jezova, D., Vigas, M., Klimes, I., and Jurcovicova, J.,** Adenopituitary hormone response to exercise combined with propranolol infusion in man, *Endocrinol. Exp.,* 17, 91, 1983.

94. **Yeh, J. H., Aloia, J. F., and Chen, M.,** Growth hormone administration potentiates the effect of treadmill exercise on long bone formation but not on the vertebrae in middle-aged rats, *Calif. Tissue Int.,* 54, 38, 1994.

95. **Mitchell, J. B., Costill, D. L., Houmard, J. A., Flynn, M. G., Fink, W. J., and Beltz, J. D.,** Influence of carbohydrate ingestion on counterregulatory hormones during prolonged exercise, *Int. J. Sports Med.,* 11, 33, 1990.

96. **Murray, R., Eddy, D. E., Paul, G. L., Seifert, J. G., and Halaby, G. A.,** Physiological responses to glycerol ingestion during exercise, *J. Appl. Physiol.,* 71, 144, 1991.

97. **Bonen, A., Haynes, F. W., and Graham, T. E.,** Substrate and hormonal responses to exercise in women using oral contraceptives, *J. Appl. Physiol.,* 70, 1917, 1991.

98. **Deuster, P. A., Singh, A., Hofmann, A., Moses, F. M., and Chrousos, G. C.,** Hormonal responses to ingesting water or a carbohydrate beverage during a 2 h run, *Med. Sci. Sports Exerc.,* 24, 72, 1992.

99. **Monteleone, P, Beinat, L., Tanzillo, C., Maj, M., and Kemali, D.,** Effects of phosphatidylserine on the neuroendocrine response to physical stress in humans, *Neuroen-docrinology,* 52, 243, 1990.

100. **Mori, T., Handa, K., Terao, Y., Kiyonaga, A., Shindo, M., Matsunaga, A., Sasaki, J., and Arakawa, K.,** Effects of arotinolol on exercise capacity and humoral factors during exercise in normal subjects, *Cardiovasc. Drugs Ther.,* 6, 387, 1992.

101. **Deray, G., Berlin, I., Maistre, G., Martinez, F., Legrand, et al.,** Beta-adrenoceptor blockade potentiates exercise-induced release of atrial natriuretic peptide, *Eur. J. Clin. Pharmacol.,* 38, 363, 1990.
102. **Gullestad, L., Dolva, L. O., Kjeldsen, S. E., Eide, I., and Kjekshus, J.,** Effect of beta blockade on hormonal responses during continuous and intermittent exercise, *Cardiovasc. Drugs Ther.,* 3, 63, 1989.
103. **Berlin, I., Deray, G., Maistre, G., Masson, F., Barthelemy, C., Legrand, J. C., and Jacobs, C.,** Cicletanine does not affect plasma atrial natriuretic peptide concentration in healthy subjects, *Eur. J. Clin. Pharmacol.,* 39, 593, 1990.
104. **Louisy, F., Guezennec, C. Y., Lartigue, M., Aldigier, J. C., and Galen, F. X.,** Influence of endogenous opioids on atrial natriuretic factor release during exercise in man, *Eur. J. Appl. Physiol.,* 59, 34, 1989.
105. **Verho, M., Farber, G., Kirsten, R., and Nelson, K.,** Effects of penbutanolol on plasma atrial natriuretic peptide and antidiuretic hormone levels before and after exercise: a double-blind comparison against placebo, *Pharmatherapeutica,* 5, 320, 1989.
106. **Mulligan, I. P., Frasrer, A. G., Tirlapur, V., Lewis, M. J., Newcombe, R. G., and Hendersen, A. H.,** A randomised cross-over study of enalapril in congestive heart failure: hemodynamic and hormonal effects during rest and exercise, *Eur. J. Clin. Pharmacol.,* 34, 323, 1988.
107. **Botticelli, G., Bacchi-Modena, A., Bresciani, D., Villa, P., Aguzzoli, L., et al.,** Effect of naltrexone treatment on the treadmill exercise-induced hormone release in amenorrheic women, *J. Endocrinol. Invest.,* 15, 839, 1992.
108. **Droste, C., Greenlee, M. W., Schreck, M., and Roskamm, H.,** Experimental pain thresholds and plasma beta endorphin levels during exercise, *Med. Sci. Sports Exerc.,* 23, 334, 1991.
109. **Bramnert, M. and Hokfelt, B.,** The influence of naloxone on exercise-induced increase in plasma pituitary hormones and the subjectively experienced level of exhaustion in healthy males, *Acta Endocrinol.,* 115, 125, 1987.
110. **Vasankari, T. J., Kujala, U. M., Taimela, S., and Huhtaniemi, I. T.,** Pituitary-gonadal response to gonadotropin-releasing hormone stimulation is enhanced in men after strenuous physical exercise, *Acta Endocrinol.,* 129, 9, 1993.
111. **Watanabe, T., Morimoto, A., Sakata, Y., Long, N. C., and Murakami, N.,** Prostaglandin E2 is involved in adrenocorticotropic hormone release during swimming exercise in rats, *J. Physiol.,* 433, 719, 1991.
112. **Fry, A. C., Kraemer, W. J., Stone, M. H., Warrn, B. J., Kearney, J. T., et al.,** Endocrine and performance responses to high volume training and amino acid supplementation in elite junior weightlifters, *Int. J. Sports Nutr.,* 3, 306, 1993.
113. **Keast, D. and Morton, A. R.,** Long-term exercise and immune functions, in *Exercise and Disease,* Watson, R. R. and Eisinger, M., Eds., CRC Press, Boca Raton, FL, 1992, 89.
114. **Tvede, N., Kappel, M., Halkjaer-Kristensen, J., Galbo, H., and Pedersen, B. K.,** The effect of light, moderate and severe bicycle exercise on lymphocyte subsets, natural and lymphokine activated killer cells, lymphocyte proliferative response and interleukin 2 production, *Int. J. Sports Med.,* 14, 275, 1993.
115. **Murray, D. R., Irwin, M., Rearden, C. A., Ziegler, M., Motulsky, H., and Maisel, A. S.,** Sympathetic and immune interactions during dynamic exercise: mediation via a beta 2-adrenergic-dependent mechanism, *Circulation,* 86, 203, 1992.
116. **Peters, E. M., Goetzsche, J. M., Grobbelaar, B., and Noakes, T. D.,** Vitamin C supplementation reduces the incidence of postrace symptoms of upper-respiratory-tract infection in ultra marathon runners, *Am. J. Clin. Nutr.,* 57, 170, 1993.
117. **Cannon, J. G., Meydani, S. N., Fielding, R. A., Fiatarone, M. A., Meydani, M., Farhangmehr, M., Orencole, S. F., Blumberg, J. B., and Evans, W. J.,** Acute phase response in exercise. II. Associations between vitamin E, cytokines, and muscle proteolysis, *Am. J. Physiol.,* 260, R1235, 1991.
118. **Bortz, W. M.,** Disuse and aging, *JAMA,* 248, 1203, 1982.

Chapter 13

SEDENTARY VS. AMBULATORY STATUS ON PHARMACOKINETICS AND PHARMACODYNAMIC EFFECTS OF DRUGS

Clinton N. Corder and Wallace R. Pratt

1. INTRODUCTION

In the past, bed rest was used for the treatment of many illnesses, including rheumatic fever, tuberculosis, and congestive heart failure. Bed rest continues to be required for the treatment of trauma victims, and other acutely ill patients admitted to the hospital. More recently the deleterious effects of bed rest have been recognized, and early mobilization of patients has been emphasized.[1] Bed rest will be used as interchangeable with sedentary in this review, while

0-8493-8540-1/96/$0.00+$.50
© 1996 by CRC Press, Inc.

ambulatory will include usual daily living of mild to moderate physical activity whether in sitting or standing positions.

If a patient who is on a regimen of maintenance medications becomes ill and is treated with bed rest, will the effectiveness of the patient's usual medications be changed, or will toxicity develop? Conversely, if the patient who is sedentary begins a long-term medication will dosage adjustments be necessary when the patient resumes his ambulatory activities? Our own survey of local hospitals indicates that there is no standing policy advising dosage adjustments in patients making the transition between their normal ambulatory status and sedentary activity. Likewise, standard reference works do not mention dosage adjustments for bed rest and our previous review confirmed the paucity of literature on the subject.[2-4] This would seem to imply that bed sedentary activity doesn't have any significant pharmacologic effects.

In reality, under some circumstances, sedentary state may make an important difference in the pharmacology of some medications. In this chapter we will touch upon some of the physiologic changes that occur during bed rest, emphasizing those aspects that may have an influence on drug pharmacokinetics and pharmacodynamics. Next we will review studies that have investigated the effect of bed rest on various medications. Finally we will draw some conclusions from these studies, and make some suggestions regarding further research in this area.

2. PHYSIOLOGIC CHANGES DURING SEDENTARY STATUS

2.1. MUSCULOSKELETAL

Sedentary status brings about numerous physiologic changes. The basal metabolic rate is decreased during the entire period of immobilization. Muscles at complete rest lose 10 to 15% of their strength each week. In healthy men, 10 days of bed rest results in a 15.1% decrease in maximal oxygen consumption during upright exercise. Negative nitrogen balance develops, with the average urine excretion of nitrogen reaching as low as 2 g/day. Bone loss also occurs during bed rest. Patients who have high rates of bone turnover, such as patients with Paget's disease and children, often develop hypercalcemia during prolonged immobilization. Calcium excretion in the urine increases during the first 1 to 2 months of bed rest, then plateaus or declines, but always stays higher than the calcium excretion of ambulatory individuals.[1,5]

2.2. CARDIOVASCULAR AND HEMATOLOGIC

The supine position is associated with marked shifts in blood flow. Upon lying down, about 11% of the blood volume is shifted away from the legs. Seventy-eight percent of this redirected flow goes to the thorax, and 20% to the head and neck. The increased blood volume in the thorax results in an increase in cardiac output from an average of 5 to 6 l/min while standing, to 7 to 8 l/min while lying. These changes in blood flow are maintained during prolonged bed rest. Also there is a loss of total body water during bed rest. Plasma volume is reduced 300 to 500 cc during the first week of bed rest. During prolonged recumbency, plasma volume may increase somewhat, but always stays below control values. Besides changes in body water, bed rest brings about a reduction in total blood volume. Typically males lose about 200 cc of red cell mass during a 35-day period of bed rest.[1,6] During standing, serum albumin concentration increases as plasma water moves into interstitial spaces because of increased hydrostatic pressure on the legs. This theoretically could acutely increase plasma levels of drugs that bind to albumin. Circulatory changes during bed rest may have important pharmacokinetic consequences. During bed rest, renal blood flow increases 15 to 20%, and hepatic blood flow also increases.[7,8] These changes may enhance the elimination of drugs excreted by these organs. Medications given by i.m. injection during bed rest are absorbed less quickly than they are during ambulation,[9-11] apparently because of the reduced blood flow in muscles in the resting state. Bed rest may affect the absorption of medications injected subcutaneously as well.

2.3. RESPIRATORY

The supine position produces changes in both breathing mechanics and lung volumes. Breathing in the upright position is largely due to movement of the rib cage.[12] In contrast, abdominal muscles produce most of the air flow while lying down. Lying down causes a reduction in all lung volumes except tidal volume. When healthy elderly subjects assume the supine position, the mean arterial tension declines from 85 to 77 mmHg, the pCO_2 falls, and the pH rises.[1] During prolonged bed rest the strength of respiratory muscles diminishes, producing a 25 to 50% reduction in respiratory capacity.[5]

2.4. GASTROINTESTINAL

During bed rest, there is decreased gastrointestinal peristalsis and sphincters are more constricted.[5] In elderly individuals, gastrointestinal transit time during bed rest has been shown to be increased compared to the ambulatory state.[13] These changes make constipation and fecal impaction a common complication of immobilization.[14,15] With slowly absorbed drugs, the longer gastrointestinal transit time could increase bioavailability.

If medications are taken lying down while a patient is at bed rest, gastrointestinal absorption of the drugs may be altered in another way: capsules taken while standing reach the stomach in 10 seconds in 90% of patients.[15] In contrast, if a capsule is swallowed while lying down, it reaches the stomach more slowly. In fact, in 40% of patients the capsule remains in the esophagus until it disintegrates. This may result in a delayed onset of action and a lower peak level of the medication.

2.5. ENDOCRINE

During bed rest, the diurnal cycles of insulin, growth hormone, cortisol, thyroid hormones, epinephrine, and aldosterone are altered.[14-16] Vernikos-Danellis

TABLE 1
Pharmacokinetic Changes: Sedentary vs. Ambulatory

Drug	Absorption		Elimination		
	T_{max}	C_{max}	$t_{1/2}$	Cl	Vd
Antibiotics:					
Amoxicillin[18]	+	−	+	+	+
Cefprozil[19]	+	−	−	NA	NA
Gentamycin[11]	+	−	NA	NA	NA
Penicillin i.m.[20]	+	−	+	+	+
Penicillin i.v.[21]	NA	NA	0	+	+
Streptomycin[10]	NA	−	NA	NA	NA
Sulfasymazine[2]	NA	−	−	NA	NA
Cardiovascular:					
Digoxin[23,24]	NA	+,−	NA	−	NA
Lidocaine[21]	NA	NA	0	0	0
Theophylline[24,25]	0	+,−	−	+	0
Other:					
Acetaminophen[26]	+	−	0	NA	NA
Antipyrine[27]	0	NA	NA	+	−
Insulin[28-30]	+	NA	NA	NA	NA

Note: Cl = Volume plasma cleared per unit time; T_{max} = time to max.; C_{max} = maximum plasma concentration; $t_{1/2}$ = time to eliminate half concentration from plasma corresponding to β phase; Vd = volume of distribution; + = sedentary greater than ambulatory; − = sedentary less than ambulatory; 0 = no effect; NA = no data.

et al.[16] found that after healthy males had been at bed rest for 56 days, the amplitude of the diurnal cortisol fluctuation was reduced, while thyroid hormone rhythms showed marked rephasing. These investigators also reported that the mean daily concentration of T_3 was increased during bed rest, although other researchers who studied healthy males during 17 days of bed rest found no change in the plasma concentrations of T_3 or T_4. Bed rest does not affect the metabolic clearance of thyroid hormones.[17]

3. EFFECT OF SEDENTARY STATUS ON SPECIFIC DRUGS

Bed rest brings about many changes that may potentially affect the disposition of a drug. The effect of bed rest on drug pharmacokinetics has not been widely studied. Table 1 summarizes the results of our findings on this topic.

3.1. ANTIBIOTICS
3.1.1. Amoxicillin
Oral dosing of amoxicillin during bed rest produced peak serum levels that were about two thirds of the peak levels observed in the same patients when

they were ambulatory.[18] This difference is caused by increased renal elimination of amoxicillin during bed rest, and is ostensibly the result of increased renal blood flow during bed rest. The apparent volume of distribution of amoxicillin was 1.05 l/kg during bed rest greater than 0.67 l/kg during ambulation and the $t_{1/2}$ elimination was 1.4 h vs. 1.22 h during ambulation. In addition, the rate of amoxicillin absorption was slower during bed rest. The mean time to reach the peak serum concentration was longer during bed rest 106 ± 6 min vs. 86 ± 16 min during ambulation, but these differences were not statistically significant.

3.1.2. Cefprozil (Cefzil®)

No significant differences in ambulatory vs. sedentary activity were found for oral cefprozil.[19] Although the time to maximum absorption was longer in the sedentary (1.5 h) vs. ambulatory (1.25 h) activity pattern.

3.1.3. Gentamycin

Absorption of gentamycin given i.m. in the sedentary position was reported to be slowed with a lower maximal serum concentration of gentamycin, but no actual data was presented.[11]

3.1.4. Penicillin

Penicillin and its derivatives have been studied the most. In 1966 Schmidt and Roholt[9] reported that i.m. penicillin injections produced higher maximum serum concentrations of penicillin, and the peak concentrations occurred more rapidly, when patients were ambulatory rather than bedridden. They also noted that more of the penicillin dose was recoverable in the urine when the patients were at bed rest, which they theorized was due to more rapid destruction of penicillin by the liver when the subjects were ambulatory. Levy[20] used the data of Schmidt and Roholt to perform a pharmacokinetics analysis. He discovered that the rate constant for metabolism (k_m) during immobilization was about half of the ambulatory value. He suspected this reduced k_m value was actually an artifact of changes in drug distribution during bed rest, rather than caused by impaired drug metabolism. In contrast, Kates et al.[21] studied the elimination of penicillin injected intravenously and found no difference in total body clearance, elimination half-life, or volume of distribution when their subjects were kept at bed rest or allowed to remain ambulatory. Perhaps this discrepancy in results is due to the difference in the duration of bed rest: the subjects in Schmidt and Roholt's experiments were kept at bed rest for 8 h, while those studied by Kates et al. remained at bed rest for 7 days.

3.1.5. Streptomycin

Similar observations have been made for i.m. injections of streptomycin[10] as was noted for penicillin. In three of the five subjects studied by Riches,[10] peak streptomycin serum levels were about twice as high when the i.m.

injection was given when the patient was ambulatory, compared to when the patient was at bed rest. Streptomycin side effects, including paresthesia around the mouth, vertigo, ataxia, and headache, were less common when the patients were at bed rest.

3.1.6. Sulfasymazine

Dettli and Spring[22] studied the effect of sleep on the elimination of sulfanilamide and sulfasymazine in patients kept at strict bed rest. A few of their subjects did not follow the study instructions completely and got out of bed early in the morning. As an incidental finding, these investigators noted that when a patient had left his bed, the elimination rate of sulfasymazine appeared to be very much slowed. For example, in one patient the serum half-life of sulfasymazine was 49.7 h when he stayed in bed, and 513.4 h when he got out of bed. In another patient the serum half-life was 53.6 h when he remained at bed rest, but on two occasions when he got out of bed, the serum concentration of sulfasymazine was higher at the end of the 12-h study period than it was at the beginning. These investigators speculated that the apparent marked reduction of sulfasymazine elimination when the patients became ambulatory was actually an artifact of fluid shifts that occur during the transition from lying to standing. They did not measure the amount of drug eliminated in the urine to confirm this explanation. A fall in urine pH normally occurs during sleep due to a decreased sensitivity of the respiratory center during sleep, and this may also have had an effect in this study.

3.2. CARDIOVASCULAR DRUGS
3.2.1. Digoxin

Pederson et al.[23] reported that plasma digoxin levels increased markedly during bed rest. They studied eight healthy men on a maintenance regimen of oral digoxin. During normal ambulatory activity, the mean plasma digoxin level was 0.64 ng/ml. After 2 h of total immobilization in the supine position, the mean digoxin level increased 163% to 1.04 ng/ml. The mean urinary digoxin excretion during bed rest and ambulation was virtually identical, but since the digoxin level was higher during bed rest, the mean renal digoxin clearance decreased from 168.4 ml/min during ambulation to 137.2 ml/min during bed rest. These researchers postulated that the increased digoxin level during bed rest was caused by decreased skeletal muscle binding of digoxin, which resulted in a shift of digoxin from skeletal muscles to plasma.

In contrast, a recent report of serum digoxin levels indicated no significant differences in the accuracy of the predicted pharmacokinetics consultations between a group of sedentary hospitalized and a group of ambulatory outpatients, although these were two different groups of patients.[24] The differences between the observed and pharmacokinetically predicted serum digoxin levels were 0.093 ± 0.055 in the activity pattern sedentary vs. 0.119 ± 0.07 ng/ml ambulatory activity.

3.2.2. Lidocaine

Ambulatory vs. sedentary pharmacokinetics of lidocaine given i.v. were similar.[21]

3.2.3. Theophylline

Schlaeffer et al.[25] studied the kinetics of orally administered theophylline during sedentary and ambulatory, i.e., exercise of similar intensity to that encountered with daily work or recreational activities. They found the theophylline serum half-life was reduced from 8.5 h during light exercise, to 6.4 h during rest. Similarly, theophylline clearance increased from 0.70 ml/min/kg during light exercise to 0.99 ml/min/kg during bed rest. They suggested that these changes in theophylline elimination were the result of decreased hepatic blood flow during exercise, and hence decreased theophylline metabolism by the liver. The differences in plasma theophylline levels were not great between the rest and light exercise experiments: immediately after light exercise the mean theophylline level was about 8 μg/ml, while the corresponding value for the rest experiment was about 7 μg/ml. In another study of sedentary hospitalized patients the differences between serum theophylline levels were 0.870 ± 0.526 μg/ml, and the differences were slightly elevated in the ambulatory state at 1.135 ± 0.0905 μg/ml.[24]

3.3. OTHER DRUGS

3.3.1. Acetaminophen

Channer and Robert[26] found that patients who took acetaminophen tablets while lying down had a lower initial absorption of the drug, and that peak levels were lower 5.92 ± 0.95 vs. 8.76 ± 1.17 μg/ml and delayed about 70 min, compared to subjects who took the medication while standing. Similarly the onset of action of a hypnotic medication was reported to be delayed about 30 min in those who took the medication lying down instead of standing up.[15]

3.3.2. Antipyrine (Phenazone)

Elfstrom and Lindgren[27] studied the pharmacokinetics of oral and intravenous antipyrine in 6 men during their ordinary work activities, and during 60 h of bed rest. The elimination rate constant increased from 0.062 h during normal activities, to 0.074 h during bed rest. Likewise, the total body clearance increased from 39.2 ml/h/kg during the ambulatory state to 44.1 ml/h/kg during bed rest. The apparent volume of distribution decreased from 0.628 l/kg while ambulatory to 0.594 l/kg while at bed rest. These differences, albeit small, were reported to be statistically significant. The authors proposed that the changes in the elimination of antipyrine, which is mainly excreted by the liver, were chiefly caused by increased hepatic blood flow during bed rest. No differences were found in the absorption of oral phenazone between bed rest and normal activity. The actual serum concentrations of phenazone were not reported in this study.

3.3.3. Insulin

The efficacy and sensitivity of insulin is subject to a number of variables including physical activity, status of the immune system, balance with other endocrine factors, and the formulation of insulin. Therefore, it is very difficult to delineate sedentary vs. ambulatory status on pharmacokinetics of insulin. However, it is well known clinically that insulin dosing may need frequent adjustment throughout the daily changes in physical status. The pharmacokinetics of insulin have been recently reviewed.[28] Patients at bed rest for as little as 7 days frequently develop glucose intolerance because of a considerable reduction of insulin's action on skeletal muscle.[29,30] Hildebrant et al.[31] found that I[125] labeled insulin injected subcutaneously was absorbed 19.2 to 43.6% slower when patients were lying down compared to when they were sitting; these differences in absorption were correlated with changes they measured in subcutaneous blood flow.

4. CONCLUSIONS

What can we conclude from the above studies? First of all, ambulatory activity usually enhances the absorption of i.m. injections a great deal.[9-11] Another point is that although the elimination of a drug may be so increased during sedentary state that the plasma concentration of the drug is significantly reduced,[18] it is hard to predict which drugs will be affected this way. For example penicillin and amoxicillin are both excreted mainly by the kidneys, but while bed rest has little effect on the renal elimination of penicillin,[20] the elimination of amoxicillin is made much faster.[18] The findings with digoxin[23] would suggest that in some cases changing between bed rest and the ambulatory state may alter the amount of drug that is tissue bound, resulting in a large change in the plasma concentration of a drug. Again, it is hard to forecast which drugs might show this type of behavior. Finally, the results with oral sulfasymazine[22] suggest that the plasma concentration of a highly protein-bound drug may be dramatically affected by fluid shifts that occur as a result of a change in posture from lying to standing. However, since the amount of sulfasymazine excreted in the urine was not measured, we can't be sure that these observations were not actually the result of reduced renal excretion of sulfasymazine. Consequently, these results warrant further study to verify this explanation.

The physiology of bed rest would suggest that since there is more renal and hepatic blood flow during bed rest,[7,8] the renal and hepatic excretion of drugs should be more rapid. However, this supposition was not well supported by the results of the drug studies cited above. While the renal excretion of amoxicillin[18] and the hepatic elimination of theophylline[25] increased during bed rest, the renal excretion of penicillin[20] was not affected by bed rest, and the renal clearance of digoxin[23] was reduced during bed rest.

Several of the findings of this review highlight the need for further research in this area: first of all, as we have seen for amoxicillin,[18] digoxin,[23] and sulfasymazine,[22] bed rest makes a large change in drug levels for some medications. Second, it is not possible to predict a priori which drug's pharmacokinetics will be markedly altered by bed rest. Finally, not many drugs have been studied; our literature review turned up only 11 drugs that had been investigated. Medications that would merit a high priority for such further research would include drugs that have a narrow therapeutic window and are also used for conditions in which patients often make transitions from an ambulatory status to bed rest.

Zidovudine (AZT), which is used to treat AIDS, would appear to be one worthy candidate for further study. With their intercurrent opportunistic infections, AIDS patients periodically become hospitalized and are put at bed rest. Zidovudine has a narrow therapeutic index, with its principal toxicities being neutropenia and anemia.[32] At a dose of 250 mg orally every 4 h, the highest recommended dose, 41% of patients had to discontinue therapy because of hematological toxicity.[33] Although the relationship between plasma levels of zidovudine and its effectiveness or toxicity has not been established,[32] *in vitro* the concentrations that produce the best antiviral effect are similar to concentrations that inhibit the formation of granulocyte-macrophage and red cell precursors.[34,35] Zidovudine has an elimination half-life of about 1 h.[36] It undergoes glucuronidation in the liver, followed by rapid excretion of the glucuronidated metabolite in the urine. Consequently, if bed rest should have much effect on either the hepatic metabolism of zidovudine or the renal excretion of the metabolite, the efficacy or toxicity of this medication could be significantly altered.

REFERENCES

1. **Harper, C. M. and Lyles, Y. M.,** Physiology and complications of bed rest, *J. Am. Geriatrics Soc.,* 36, 1047, 1988.
2. **Melmon, K. L., Morrell, H. F., Hoffman, B. B., and Nirenberg, D. W.,** *Clinical Pharmacology Basic Principles in Therapeutics,* McGraw-Hill, New York, 1992.
3. **Bennett, D. R.,** Editor-in-Chief, *Drug Evaluation Annal 1994,* American Medical Association, 1993.
4. **Somani, S. M., Gupta, S. K., Frank, S., and Corder, C. N.,** Effect of exercise disposition and pharmacokinetics of drugs, *Drug Dev. Res.,* 20, 251, 1990.
5. **Teassell, R. and Dittmer, D. K.,** Complication of immobilization and bed rest. II. Other complications, *Can. Fam. Phys.,* 39, 1440, 1993.
6. **Rubin, M.,** The physiology of bed rest, *Am. J. Nursing,* 88, 50, 1988.
7. **Selkurt, E. E.,** *Handbook of Physiology,* Vol. 2, Williams and Williams, Baltimore, 1993, 1457.
8. **Culbertson, J. W., Wildins, R. W., Ingelfinger, F. J., and Bradly, S. E.,** The effect of upright posture upon hepatic blood flow in normotensive and hypertensive subjects, *J. Clin. Invest.,* 30, 305, 1951.
9. **Schmidt, H. and Roholt, K.,** Penicillin serum concentrations in relation to exercise, *Acta Path. Microbial. Scand.,* 68, 396, 1966.

10. **Riches, H. R. C.,** Streptomycin reactions relation to exercise, *Lancet,* 1, 540, 1954.
11. **Leopold, G., Hameister, W., and Wahlig, H.,** The effect of bed rest and of physical activity on the blood level of gentamycin after intramuscular application, *Naunyn-Schiedebergs Arch. Pharmacol.,* Suppl. 282, R57, 1974.
12. **Tyler, M.,** The respiratory effects body positioning and immobilization, *Resp. Care,* 19, 472, 1984.
13. **Broklehurst, G. C. and Khan., M. Y.,** A study of faecal stasis in old age and the use of 'Dorbanex' in its prevention, *Geront. Clin.,* 11, 293, 1969.
14. **Broklehurst, J. C.,** Disorders of the lower bowel in old age, *Geriatrics,* 35, 47, 1980.
15. **Anonymous,** Don't take your medicine lying down!, *Drug Ther. Bull.,* 23, 73, 1985.
16. **Vernikos-Danellis, J., Leach, C. S., Winget, C. M., Rambaut, P. C., and Mack, P. B.,** Thyroid and adrenal cortical rhythmicity during bed rest, *J. Appl. Physiol.,* 33, 644, 1972.
17. **Balsam, A. and Leppo, L.,** Assessment of the degradation of thyroid hormones in man during bed rest, *J. Appl. Physiol.,* 38, 216, 1975.
18. **Robets, M. S. and Denton, M. J.,** Effect of posture and sleep on pharmacokinetics. I. Amoxycillin, *Eur. J. Clin. Pharmcol.,* 18, 175, 1980.
19. **Shyu, W., Gleason, C., and Barbhaiya, R.,** Effect of time of administration and posture on the pharmacokinetics of cefprozil, *Clin. Pharacokinet.,* 25, 237, 1993.
20. **Levy, G.,** Effect of bed rest on distribution and elimination of drugs, *J. Pharm. Sci.,* 56, 928, 1967.
21. **Kates, R. E., Harapat, S. R., Keefe, D. L. D., Goldwater, D., and Harrison, D. C.,** Influence of prolonged recumbency on drug disposition, *Clin. Pharmacol. Ther.,* 28, 624, 1980.
22. **Dettli, L. and Spring, P.,** Diurnal variations in the elimination rate of a sulfonamide in man, *Helv. Medica Acta,* 33(Suppl. 46), 134, 1966.
23. **Pederson, K. E., Madsen, J., Kjaer, K., Klitgaard, N. A., and Hvidt, S.,** Effects of physical activity and immobilization on plasma digoxin concentration and renal digoxin clearance, *Clin. Pharmacol. Ther.,* 34. 309, 1983.
24. **Gianini, D., Rich, D., and Jeffrey, L.,** Accuracy of pharmacokinetic estimates in ambulatory patients, *Am. J. Hosp. Pharm.,* 40, 49, 1983.
25. **Schlaeffer, F., Engelberg, I., Kaplaski, J., and Danon, A.,** Effect of exercise and environmental heat on theophylline kinetics, *Respiration,* 45, 438, 1984.
26. **Channer, K. S. and Robert, C. J. C.,** Effect of delayed esophageal transit on acetaminophen absorption, *Clin. Pharmacol. Ther.,* 37, 72, 1985.
27. **Elfstrom, J. and Lindgren, S.,** Influence of bed rest on the pharmacokinetics of phenazone, *Eur. J. Clin. Pharmacol.,* 13, 379, 1978.
28. **Brogden, R. N. and Heel, R. C.,** Human insulin, a review of its biological activity, pharmacokinetics, and therapeutics, and therapeutic use, *Drugs,* 34, 350, 1987.
29. **Stuart, C. A., Shangraw, R. E., Prince, M. J., Peters, E. J., and Wolfe, R. R.,** Bed-rest induced insulin resistance occurs primarily in muscle, *Metabolism,* 27, 802, 1988.
30. **Mikines, K. J., Richter, E. A., Flemming, D., and Galbo, H.,** Seven days of bed rest decrease insulin action on glucose uptake in leg and whole body, *J. Appl. Physiol.,* 70, 1245, 1991.
31. **Hildebrant, P., Birch, K., Sestoft, L., and Nielson, S. L.,** Orthostatic changes in subcutaneous blood flow and insulin absorptiom, *Diabetes Res. Clin. Exp.,* 2, 187, 1985.
32. **Collins, J. and Unadkat, J.,** Clinical pharmacokinetics of zidovudine an overview of current data, *Clin. Pharmacokinet.,* 17, 1, 1989.
33. **Collaborative AZT study Group,** Activity and tolerence of AZT, 4th Int. Conf. AIDS, Vol. 2, Stockholm, 1988, 169.
34. **Mitsuya, H., Weinhold, K., Furman, P., St. Clair, M., Nusinoff-Lehrman, S., et al.,** 3'-azido-3'-deoxythymidine (BW A5609U) an antiviral agent that inhibits the infectivity and cytopathic effect of human-lyphotrophic virus type III/lymphadenopathy-associated virus in vitro, *Proc. Natl. Acad. Sci. U.S.A.,* 82, 7096, 1985.

35. **Sommadossi, J. P. and Carlisle, R.,** Toxicity of 3'-azido-3'-deoxythymidine and 9-(1,3-dihidroxy-2-propoxymethyl) guanine for normal human hematopoietic progenitor cells in vivo, *Antimicrob. Agents Chemother.,* 31, 452, 1987.
36. **Cload, P. A.,** Review of the pharmacokinetics of zidovudine in man, *J. Infection,* 18(Suppl. 1), 15, 1989.

Chapter 14

PHARMACOLOGICAL ASPECTS OF YOGA

**Satu M. Somani, Satyanarayan G. Bhat, T. K. Bera, and
Mannfred A. Hollinger**

CONTENTS

1. INTRODUCTION

One of the most provocative forms of exercise that has received relatively little attention in Western scientific literature is yoga. This is true even though yoga is practiced by more than 3.5 million Americans. Yoga differs from most other types of physical exercises in that it also emphasizes contemporaneous meditation training. Through the centuries, yoga has evolved into a variety of methods in order to attain physical, mental, and spiritual health utilizing diet, body posturing, breathing control, and meditation. Many systems or schools of yoga exist which recommend their own particular technique(s) to achieve the same goal.

0-8493-8540-1/96/$0.00+$.50
© 1996 by CRC Press, Inc.

Some of the problems encountered in trying to assess pharmacological aspects of yoga include the fact that the literature is replete with anecdotal reports and poorly controlled studies. Nevertheless, a body of information does exist that has not been subjected to wide scrutiny. Therefore, despite these shortcomings, the authors believe that such data can be justifiably included in a book on the effect of exercise (a component of yoga) on pharmacological parameters in the hope that this information will serve to stimulate rigorous research in this area.

Drugs are, of course, frequently used to control the symptoms of various disorders. However, drug therapy has certain inherent disadvantages, such as side effects. Any modality that can minimize the use of drugs has, therefore, potential benefits. It has been suggested that yoga may offer a supplemental or even an alternative management system in the treatment of certain disease states. Unfortunately, as mentioned above, few rigorously controlled studies have been carried out to test this hypothesis.

In this chapter, pharmacological aspects relating to the practice of yoga will be discussed which pertain primarily to the use of yoga as a therapeutic adjuvant in the treatment of certain diseases. The diseases focused upon include diabetes, coronary heart disease, asthma, and certain psychological disorders. This chapter will also attempt to identify the limitations of research carried out on yoga exercises and drug use, as well as suggesting future areas for research. For the interested reader, there have been several books published on yoga terminology, exercises, and techniques.[1-8] These books are recommended to readers who are particularly interested in more general aspects relating to the practice of yoga.

2. CONCEPT OF YOGA EXERCISE AND MEDITATION

The concepts underlying yoga can be found in the Vedas, the oldest literature known to mankind. The origin of yoga has been traced to approximately 2000 BC, during the Indus Valley Civilization. Yoga is a Sanskrit word meaning yoke or "union." Yoga exercises, therefore, attempt to involve both the body and mind.

3. RATIONALE OF YOGA EXERCISE AS AN ADJUVANT THERAPY

Anand[9] has recently reviewed the role of yoga in the medical sciences. It has been suggested that several disease states may be improved by the physical and mental components of yoga. One of these is diabetes mellitus.

3.1. DIABETES MELLITUS

Diabetes is a major health problem that can lead to several degenerative illnesses. Treatment of diabetes may include diet, insulin, or hypoglycemic agents or exercise. Insulin-dependent diabetes mellitus (IDDM) patients do not secrete insulin, thereby requiring exogenous administration of insulin. In noninsulin-dependent diabetes mellitus (NIDDM) patients, treatment strategy depends on the severity of the patient's hyperglycemia and symptomatology. Treatment may include dietary management of caloric intake, increased exercise, and the use of hypoglycemic agents such as sulfonylureas. Since the long-term use of hypoglycemic drugs can produce adverse effects, anything minimizing their use would be beneficial. A number of studies (Table 1; References 10–16) support the assertion that yoga is beneficial in managing diabetes. Palliative effects reported include reduction in sulfonylurea, biguanides, and insulin dose, decreased body weight, increased glucose tolerance, and decreased blood sugar. It is not known if variations between the studies in the type of yoga practiced is significant. It is also not clear from these studies if other variables were adequately controlled. Therefore, direct conclusions can be speculative at best.

3.1.1. Yogic Practices in Controlling Diabetes

Yoga exercises include dietary regulation, muscle stretching, breathing exercises, and behavioral modifications. Dietary regulation may be particularly important since caloric management is essential in successfully controlling diabetes. Yoga practice emphasizes a diet of natural food that contains complex carbohydrates and high fiber. These ingredients would tend to assist in controlling glucose levels and improve insulin sensitivity. In addition, yoga exercise discourages overeating; the recommended diet is to fill one half of the stomach with solid food, one fourth with liquid, and the remaining one fourth is to be kept empty.[17,18] Because of the importance of controlling obesity, particularly in NIDDM, the principles underlying a yogic diet would appear to be consistent with diabetes management guidelines. Yogic dietary practices have been reported useful in controlling obesity and lowering drug dosage necessary to reduce blood cholesterol and manage hyperglycemia.[10,19-24]

3.2. CORONARY HEART DISEASE

Coronary heart disease has increased in recent years in both developed and developing countries. Considering the high impact of coronary heart disease on morbidity, mortality, and the substantially high cost of treatment (drugs, bypass surgery), alternative management methods may deserve consideration. Some research findings suggest that yogic exercises may be helpful in the treatment of coronary heart disease.[10,25-27]

3.2.1. Causes for Coronary Heart Disease

Both genetic and environmental factors may play an important role in the genesis of coronary heart disease.[10,27,28] The important risk factors for coronary heart disease include high blood pressure, high blood cholesterol, elevated blood triglycerides, intake of diets rich in cholesterol and saturated fat, obesity, smoking, chronic stress, type A personality and diabetes. Some risk factors injure the lining of the coronary arteries. The repair process involves the body's ability to deposit cholesterol, collagen, and platelets that lead to atherosclerosis. Elevated blood cholesterol and saturated fat is also associated with a

TABLE 1
Effect of Yoga Exercise in Controlling Diabetes

Type of Yoga Exercise	Number of Diabetic Patients in the Study	Duration of Yoga Exercise		Effect of Yoga Exercise	Ref.
Kriyas, asanas, and pranayamas	149	45–70 min/day for 40 days	↓ ↓ ←→ ↑	Blood sugar Use of hypoglycemic drug BMI Glucose tolerance	Jain et al.[12]
Pranayama savasana	35	30 min/day	↓ ↓ ↑	Insulin dose Oral hypoglycemic drug Glucose tolerance	Sahay et al.[13]
Various asanas	52	45 min/day	↓ ↓ ↓ ↓	Insulin dose in juvenile diabetes Oral hypoglycemic drug Body weight Blood cholesterol	Divakar et al.[14]
Various asanas pranayama savasana	7	40 min/day for 6 months	↓ ↓ ↓	BSL (Blood Sugar Level) Body weight Oral hypoglycemic drug energetic feeling	Shembekar and Kate[15]
Various asanas pramayamas kriyas and meditation	9	6 months	↓ ↓ ↑ ↑	BSL after 3 weeks Oral hypoglycemic drug and insulin dose Body weight slightly Glucose tolerance	Gore[11]
Various kriyas sukshma vyama asanas	123	90 min/day for 4 years	↑ ←→ ↓ ↓	In 64% of subjects 36% of subjects Insulin dose from 40–70 units/day to 20–90 units/day in 40 days Oral hypoglycemic drugs	Rugmini and Sinha[16]
Various asanas, nauli, and other yoga exercises	20	6 months	↓ ↓ ↓ ↓ ↑	Oral hypoglycemic drug In BSL Acetylcholine Catecholamine Glucose tolerance	Udupa[10]

Note: Symbols represent: ↑, improvement; ↓, decrease or reduction; ←→, no change.

reduction in the number of HDL cholesterol receptors. As a result, removal of cholesterol from the blood decreases, thereby leading to further increases in blood cholesterol levels.

3.2.2. Role of Yogic Exercise in Reducing the Risk of Coronary Disease

Several research reports suggest that yogic exercises may effectively influence some risk factors associated with coronary artery disease.[10,26,27] Blackwell et al.,[29] for example, has reported in a limited uncontrolled study that 2 of 7 patients with essential hypertension "treated" with transcendental meditation (TM) for 6 months showed a decrease in blood pressure. Baride and Sancheti[30] have also reported a significant decrease in pulse rate (from 85.6 to 75.1), but not in blood pressure or body weight, during a course of yoga practice in 24 subjects. Control of high blood pressure (BP) is important in reducing coronary heart disease. Various yogic relaxation techniques have been reported to be useful in controlling high BP.[26,30-32,34] Such findings have obvious implications towards possibly reducing the need for pharmacological management of BP and would appear to warrant confirmation.

Stancak and co-workers[34,35] have studied cardiovascular and respiratory changes during yogic breathing exercise. During Kapalabhati (KB) yogic exercise, an increase in heart rate, systolic and diastolic blood pressures and a decrease in respiratory frequency was observed. The authors suggest that the increase in heart rate during KB may be due to a decrease in cardiac vagal tone or, alternatively, due to a decrease of baroreceptor-cardiac reflex sensitivity secondary to changes in respiratory pattern. These studies suggest perhaps, that KB may influence respiratory and cardiovascular rhythmicities. In any event, this increase in cardiac activity is not typical of yoga exercise (see below).

For yoga practitioners, simple, easily digestible, natural foods without spices are suggested.[17,18,36] This diet helps to control obesity, and maintain body weight. Fresh fruits and vegetables, sprouts and other natural foods can supply the body with sufficient vitamins and minerals and provide fiber necessary for proper absorption and digestion. Diets rich in animal products, animal fats, are risk factors for coronary heart diseases and are not recommended in yogic diets. Therefore, as with diabetes, possible beneficial effects from yoga may be more related to dietary change, as well as body posturing and meditation.

3.3. HYPERTENSION

The heart works like a pump by contraction and relaxation of the muscle. During contraction of the heart, the pressure exerted on the arteries is known as systolic pressure. When the heart relaxes, the pressure drops; yet there is pressure remaining with arteries, this is called diastolic pressure. Normally, systolic blood pressure is approximately 120 mmHg and diastolic pressure is approximately 80 mmHg. When arterial blood pressure becomes elevated (above 140/90 mmHg), the condition is called hypertension. Hypertension is considered to be the result of genetic and environmental factors.

3.3.1. Causes

Psychogenic attributes in concert with cholesterol, salt, lack of adequate rest and relaxation have all been identified as contributing factors in the development of hypertension. Although not all obese people are hypertensive, hypertension is frequently linked with obesity and stress. Salt intake and alcohol consumption are also major risk factors for this health problem.

TABLE 2
Effect of Yoga Exercise in Controlling Hypertension

Type of Yoga Practice	No. of Subjects	Duration	Effect on Blood Pressure (mmHg)	Ref.
Yoga relaxation technique Transcendental meditation Control Gr simply relaxes by themselves	34	30 min twice a week for 6 weeks	↓ Systolic BP Yoga group 26.1 Control group 8.9 ↓ Diastolic BP Yoga group 15.2 Control group 4.2	Patel and North[38]
Relaxation training to yoga group Control simple rest	20	30 min/day for 3 months	↓ Systolic BP Yoga 20.4 ± 11.4 Control 0.5 ± 14.5 ↓ Diastolic BP Yoga 14.2 ± 7.5 Control 2.1 ± 6.2 ↓ Hypertensive drug dose 41.9% (range 33–100%) in yoga group only ↑ Dose (5.5%) in control	Patel[32]
Transcendental meditation	7	6 months	↓ In BP ↓ Anxiety hypertensives	Blackwell et al.[29]
Savasana	25	6 months to 3 years	↓ In systolic BP ↓ In diastolic BP ↓ Hypertensive drug dose 47.6% ↑ BP when yoga was stopped	Sunder et al.[37]

Note: ↓, Reduction in; ↑, increase in; ←→, no change.

3.3.2. Yoga and Hypertension

Most mild and moderate cases of hypertension can be controlled without drugs. Severe hypertension, however, usually requires pharmacological intervention. The available drugs for the treatment of hypertension include β-blockers, sympatholytics, calcium channel blockers, and ACE inhibitors. Considering the disadvantages and limitations of drugs, experimental reports suggesting that yoga may offer an alternative strategy for the treatment of hypertension may have clinical significance. A summary of the effect of yoga on hypertension is presented in Table 2. In each of the cases cited, at least some of the subjects in the yoga groups displayed lowered systolic and diastolic pressure with a concomitant reduction in the dosage of antihypertension medication. These preliminary observations may therefore, have clinical significance.

Stress-related hypertension can be influenced by progressive muscle relaxation. In this regard, yogic exercises have been utilized to achieve this end.[32,37] Muscle tonicity improves[39] which, in turn, can modify states of anxiety, thus reducing stress associated hypertension.[40] Yoga relaxation reduces oxygen consumption, carbon-dioxide elimination, respiratory rate, and minute ventilation, while the respiratory quotient remains unchanged. Cardiac output and heart rate are typically reduced, and in hypertensive individuals blood pressure may be reduced.[32] Whether yoga practice increases parasympathetic activity or decreases sympathetic activity is not clear.

In a hypertensive state, breathing tends to become fast and irregular. The practice of yoga provides slow and calming rhythmic breathing. Proper training in such relaxation techniques may contribute to lowering the blood pressure coincidental with synchronizing EEG patterns,[41] and a reversal of adrenal tone.[42] This function of yoga may contribute to a beneficial role in the treatment of hypertension and a reduction in drug dosage. Unfortunately, however, many of these reports have not been replicated or adequately controlled.

3.4 ASTHMA

The typical symptoms of asthma are wheezing, coughing, and breathlessness. Extreme hyperresponsiveness of the air passages to various kinds of stimuli, (e.g., immunological, infective, psychic, physical and chemical agents) characterize the disease.[43,44] Both the incidence of asthma and associated mortality in asthmatics are increasing. Therefore, any factor contributing to the amelioration of asthma will be clinically important.

3.4.1. Pharmacologic Management of Asthma

There are several drugs available for the treatment of asthma. These include antihistamines, theophylline, sympathomimetics, antimuscarinics, and corticosteroids. Most of the drugs used today act symptomatically as bronchodilators or antiinflammatories to relieve bronchospasms and inflammation. Studies have been reported that yoga may be effective in contributing to the management of asthma.[44-46]

3.4.2. Role of Yoga in Managing Asthma

Numerous reports suggest that yogic practices can be used effectively to prevent as well as control asthma attacks.[44-53] Table 3 (References 54–60) presents the reported effects of yoga on a number of pulmonary function tests, frequency and severity of attacks, as well as drug taking while Table 4 (References 61–64) presents the reported effects of yoga exercises on lung function per se.

The results of Tables 3 and 4 are summarized as follows: (1) lung function parameters such as forced volume capacity (FVC), forced expiratory volume (FEV), peak expiratory flow rates (PEFR), maximal midexpiratory flow rate (MMFR), chest expansion, resting respiratory rate (RR), breath-holding time, timed vital capacity, and air velocity index have been improved; (2) improve-

TABLE 3
Effect of Yoga Exercise in Controlling Asthma

Type of Yoga	No. of Subjects	Duration		Effect on Blood Pressure (mmHg)	Ref.
Yogasanas pranayamas, kriyas meditation and other types of yoga practices	177	6 months	↑	Improvement in peak flow rate respiratory rate pulse rate chest expansion breath holding time endurance stamina	Nagarathna et al.[54]
			↓	Asthmatic attacks and severity	
			↓	Duration of attacks per week	
			↓	Airway obstruction	
Pranayama yogasana suryanamasker and meditation	53	65 min/day 2 weeks	↓	Asthmatic attacks	Nagarathna and Nagendra[55]
			↓	In medication	
			↑	In peak flow rate	
Yogasana pranayama meditation kriyas	570	75–150 min/day 3–54 month	↑	In peak expiratory flow rate	Nagarathna and Nagendra[45]
			↓	In severity and number of attacks	
			↓	Duration of attack	
			↓	Intake parenteral drugs 72%	
			↓	Intake oral drugs 69%	
			↓	Intake cortison drug 66%	
Pranayama	30	30 min per day 75 days	↑	Improvement in sympton score and airway obstruction (male 15 days and females 30–75 days)	Murthy et al.[56]
			↓	In drug dose	
Pranayama	26	30 min/day	↑	Improvement in airway obstruction. Better improvement in males than females	Kumar et al.[57]
Pranayama 1:2 Inspiration: Expiration ratio	18	15 min twice per day for 2 weeks	↑	Improvement in lung function	Singh et al.[58]
			↓	In medication	
Vastra dhauti	27	4 weeks	↑	In timed vital capacity air velocity index	Gore and Bhole[59]
Kriyas Asana Pranayama	46	90 min morning 60 min	↑	Expiratory volume, maximal voluntary ventilation; expiratory flow rate	Jain et al.[53]
		evening 2 years	↑	Physical fitness index	
			↓	Exercise-induced	

TABLE 3 (CONTINUED)

Type of Yoga	No. of Subjects	Duration	Effect on Blood Pressure (mmHg)		Ref.
			bronchial constriction		
			↑ Exercise tolerance		
Yoga practice	25	3 months	Initial	3rd Month	Bose et al.[60]
			FVC(L) 3.23	3.42	
			FEV$_1$(L) 2.96	3.36*	
			FEV$_1$ 91.6	98.2*	
			FVC		
			PEFR 504	560*	
			(l/min)		

Note: FVC = forced volume capacity, FEV = forced expiratory volume, PEFR = peak expiratory flow rates. * = p <0.02, <0.001, <0.01.

TABLE 4
Influence of Yoga Exercises on Lung Function

Parameters	Control/ Non Yoga	Yoga	Significance/ Improvement	Ref.
Minute ventilation	7.07 l/min	5.53 l/min	p <0.001	Stanescu et al.[61]
Tidal volume	0.56	1.03 l/min	p <0.001	
Rate of breathing	13.4 times/min	5.5 times/min	p <0.001	
End tidal PCO$_2$	35.03 Torr	39 Torr	p <0.05	
Ventilatory response to CO$_2$ in asthmatics			p <0.01	
Air wave resistance (RAW, m/H20/1/sec)	5.63 (1.40)	2.90 (0.57)	p <0.05	Wilson et al.[62]
Forced expiratory volume	2.09 (0.20)	2.33 (0.19)	p <0.05	
Peaked expiratory Flow rate	377 (28)	423 (29)	p <0.05	
Vital Capacity L/M2BSA (BTPS)	2.18 (.32)	2.54 (.51)	p <0.01	Nayar et al.[63]
FEV	1.79 (.52)	1.77 (.51)	p <0.05	
Breath holding time	59 (8.3)	79 (7.1) sec	p <0.01	
Max. breath capacity	70.8 (7.8)	71.7 (7.0)		
FVC (ml)	348	483	Improvement	Prakasamma and
FEV (ml)	249	233	in all the	Bhaduri[64]
MVV (l/min)	12.5	8.72	variables	
PEFR (l/s)	86	113		
Chest expansion (cm)	1.4	3.3		

Note: In parentheses is standard deviation.

ment in exercise tolerance (distance in meters walked in 12 min) (12 MD), physical fitness index (PFI), and exercise induced bronchial liability index (ELI); and (3) reduction in medication, severity, and number of attacks per week.

Of particular significance are the reports indicating a reduction in drug dosage required to control asthma attacks.[55,56,58] This is especially important in chronic, severe asthma in children who may require treatment with corticosteroids. Why yoga could be of benefit in managing asthma is subject to conjecture but may involve a psychogenic component of asthma. Phillip et al.[65] have reported that anxiety in asthmatics may provoke, aggravate, and prolong an attack. The authors suggest that relaxation training helps break the vicious cycle of anxiety and bronchospasm in asthmatics. This view is supported by others[66,67] who believe that localized muscle tension creates psychosomatic imbalances in asthmatics.

As mentioned above, a minimal degree of stimuli may generate severe bronchoconstriction in asthmatics.[68] Yoga-stretching seems to improve cardiorespiratory fitness along with total physical fitness in asthmatics.[53,69] Therefore, physical stimuli, such as exercise-induced bronchoconstriction, may be reduced with yoga by improving exercise tolerance.[53,71]

3.5. PSYCHOLOGICAL DISORDERS

Research studies have shown that relaxation treatment procedures can significantly reduce the intensity of anxiety neurosis.[72-75,82] A summary of a number of yoga types on psychosomatic disorders is presented in Table 5 (References 72, 76, 78-82). These data suggest that yoga can be an essential intervention technique in the treatment of anxiety neurosis and associated disorders. They also suggest that yogic exercises, designed as nonpharmacological methods of treatment, can be important in managing anxiety (cognitive and somatic), neurotic illness, schizophrenia, depression, and various personality disorders. In all these cases, yoga emphasizes the principles of relaxation, self-awareness, and/or an altered state of consciousness. Unfortunately, the psychosomatic disorders considered in these reports are extremely diffuse and poorly defined. Therefore, serious attempts to assess the effectiveness of yoga is hampered by poor quantification.

Yoga-relaxation reportedly achieves physiological changes by "integrating" body–mind responses[82] which, in turn, can affect physiological parameters such as oxygen consumption, heart rate, respiratory rate, blood pressure, serum lactic acid, and resistance and blood flow.[75,84] Reduction of these peripheral physiological changes may serve to decrease the internal arousal state of the individual.[85] EEG studies have been reported to show increasing formation of alpha and beta waves which, in turn, indicate a more relaxed state of brain centers.[86]

3.6. OTHER AILMENTS

Recently, Wood[86] has studied the effects of three different procedures; relaxation, visualization, and yogic breathing (pranayama) and stretch on

TABLE 5
Effect of Yoga Exercise in Controlling Psychosomatic Disorders

Yoga Type	No. of Subjects	Duration	Effect of Yoga Psychosomatic Disorders		Ref.
Asana, pranayama, and others	30	4–6 weeks	↑	75% Improvement	Vahia et al.[77]
Mantra yoga and Zen	10	30 min/day for 10 weeks	↑	Improvement in self-concept personality variables	Blanz[78]
Meditation		3–4 times/week for 4 months	↑	Improvement in psychological and physical illness improvement in mood	Gersten[79]
Meditation	3	2 weeks	↑	Improvement in controlling disorder	Walsh and Roche[80]
Agni yoga progressive relaxation	40	45 min/day for 3 weeks	↓	In different anxiety types	Norton and Johnson[72]
Astanga yoga	—	3 months	↑	Improvement in neurotic illness	Sharma and Singh[81]
Yoga relaxation, Savasana, meditation, and others	—	—	↑	Benefits — neurosis and personality, schizophrenia, depression	Nespor[76]
			↓	Sexual offense, alcohol and drug abuse	

	MR GG		90 children with mental retardation		Uma et al.[82]
Pranayama, kapalabhati, yogasanas, suryanamaskar, and meditation	Mild 12 12 Moderate 17 17 Severe 16 16	5 hr/week for 1 year	Change in IQ score		
				Yoga	Control
			Mild$_{avg}$	+8.09	−1.71
			range	(−6 to 14)	(−12 to 14)
			Moderate$_{avg}$	12.58	4.60
			range	(−4 to 25)	(−5 to 25)
			Severe$_{avg}$	6.0	3.42
			range	(1 to 11)	(−5 to 11)

Note: ≠, Reduction; Ø, reduction; IQ, intelligence quotient; MR, mentally retarded; CG, control group.

perceptions of physical and mental energy and on mood changes. Yogic pranayama practice was reported to increase perceptions of physical as well as mental energy and also feelings of alertness and enthusiasm. Hedstrom[87] has reported that hatha yoga exercises (eye movements and visual mechanisms) also induces relaxation and reduces anxiety. However, Rice and Allen[88] have reported that regular practice of yoga exercises, especially inverted-posture, increases the intraocular pressure on the eye and may be a factor in the development of early glaucomatous optic disk changes and visual field loss.

TABLE 6
Influence of Yoga Exercises on Blood Parameters

Parameters	Control/Non-Yoga	Yoga	p Level	Ref.
Blood glucose (mg%)	74.00 (2.80)	69.00 (2.50)	<0.05	Selvamurthy[91]
Blood cholesterol	170 (5.20)	154 (4.20)	<0.001	
Total protein	7.60 (.20)	7.90 (.25)	<0.05	
Lactic dehydrogenase	52.00 (4.0)	63.00 (2.90)	<0.05	
Dopamine-hydroxylase	10.60 (1.10)	6.40 (.34)	<0.05	
Plasma cholinesterase	4.90 (.12)	5.10 (.13)	<0.01	
17 Ketosteroid-urine (mg/24 h)	9.8 (.72)	13.40 (1.18)	<0.01	
17 Hydroxy steroid-urine	10.60 (.80)	11.40 (.84)	<0.01	
Monoamine oxidase (IU)	39.00 (2.70)	73.00 (7.30)	<0.01	
Blood cholesterol (mg%)				Karambelkar et al.[21]
Male (above normal)	271.66	205.33	<0.01	
Female (above normal)	272.5	255.8	<0.05	
Blood cholesterol (mg%)				Karambelkar et al.[22]
Females	293.29	233.75	<0.01	
Plasma catecholamine		↑		Udupa et al.[92,103]
Histaminase	60 Units	85 Units		
Plasma cortisol		↓		
Urinary 17-hydroxyl steroid		↓		
Urinary 17-ketosteroid		↑		
Acetylcholine		↓		
Cholinesterase		↓		
Uropepsin	22.2	13		Karambelkar and Bhole[93]
Thyroxine secretion	4–8 mg%	↑	<0.05	Dhanaraj[94]

Note: The values in parentheses are standard deviation.

Therefore, daily inverted posture exercises may be inadvisable to glaucoma patients and may require an increase in dosage of drugs taken to reduce intraocular pressure (e.g., pilocarpine).

Recently, Haslock et al.[89] have studied the effect of yoga in rheumatoid arthritis and reported that asanas and pranayamas performed by the patients 2-h sessions daily 5 days per week for 3 weeks followed by weekly 2-h sessions for 3 months showed no change in levels of depression between yoga and the control group. However, left hand grip strength increased significantly whereas right hand grip strength increased slightly in the yoga group. The yoga group of patients also improved compared to controls on the basis of a health assessment questionnaire as well as left hand ring sizes. This clinical study supports the benefits of yoga exercises in the management or treatment of rheumatoid arthritis and suggests the possibility that pharmacological management might be reduced. Unfortunately, this parameter has not been investigated. Nespor[90] has reviewed the general use of yoga in the control of pain.

The influence of yoga exercises on various blood parameters is shown in Table 6. The effect of yoga exercises on physical fitness parameters such as

TABLE 7
Effect of Yoga Exercises on Physical Fitness

Parameters	Control/Non-Yoga	Yoga	Significance/Improvement	Ref.
Static motor performance (in terms of error committed by Ss)	217.8 (Errors)	183.3 (Errors)	$p < 0.01$	Telles et al.[95]
Balance Index	1.87 points	2.19 points	27.8% Improvement	Dhume and Dhume[96]
EMG activity in some yogic exercises	High	Low	$p < 0.01$	Karambelkar et al.[102]
EMG activity in some yogic exercises	High	Low		Gopal et al.[97]
Muscular relaxation	No change	Quick	$p < 0.05$	Bhatnagar and Anantharaman[98]
Neuromuscular excitability (Threshold)	No change	Increase	$p < 0.05$	
Cardiovascular efficiency (Index)	78.6	82.6	$p < 0.05$	Ganguly and Gharote[99]
Lean body mass				Madhavi et al.[100]
Male	43.31 (7.04)	45.22 (7.34)	$p < 0.05$	
Female	35.10 (5.03)	36.83 (5.14)	$p < 0.05$	
Fat %	No change	Decrease	$p < 0.05$	
EMG (biceps)	4.62 (.50)	2.47 (.19)	$p < 0.001$	Selvamurthy[91]
Body density	1.07	1.09	$p < 0.01$	Bera et al.[19]
Body fat (%)	10.05	3.71	$p < 0.01$	
Absolute fat weight	4.02	1.59	$p < 0.01$	
Ideal body weight (Fat Free)	40.28	49.81	$p < 0.01$	
Cardiovascular endurance (Pts)	60.74	72.53	$p < 0.01$	Bera and Rajapurkar[33]
Anaerobic power (kg/m/sec)	133.60	141.20	$p < 0.01$	
Motor function				Bera et al.[101]
Cardiorespiratory function	9.58	7.36	$p < 0.026$	
Body fat %	13.56	8.50	$p < 0.001$	
Abdominal muscular strength/endurance	34.12	37.25	$p < 0.005$	
Flexibility	30.18	35.99	$p < 0.001$	
Balance	36.11	40.15	$p < 0.001$	
Grip strength	19.50	24.23	$p < 0.001$	

Note: EMG = electromyography, ( ) = standard deviation.

static motor performance, balance index, electromyography (EMG), motor function, muscular relaxation, lean body mass are summarized in Table 7.

4. FUTURE PERSPECTIVES

Yoga research has resulted in the publication of numerous reports with potential pharmacological implications. Many physiologic and pharmacologic concepts have been proposed but, unfortunately, there is no supporting data resulting from basic science, because animal models cannot be developed in yoga research. Positron emission tomography (PET scans) might be a useful technique that could be applied to study the time course of yoga exercises. This imaging technology could conceivably pinpoint alterations in brain regions due to yoga practices. Recently, there has been great interest in basic research pertaining to the effect of exercise on enzymatic systems in various organs and at the subcellular and molecular levels. These basic aspects of exercise and the interactions with antioxidant system, adrenergic system (catecholamine), cholinergic markers (acetylcholinesterase, choline acetyltransferase and acetylcholine), hormonal changes, immunological changes and receptor alterations have been discussed in this monograph. Some of these aspects can be applied to yoga research in humans. Knowledge and concepts derived from this basic research would be expected to provide a basis for greater understanding of potential health benefits of yoga with obvious implications to drug management.

ACKNOWLEDGMENTS

Satu M. Somani wishes to acknowledge the Council of Scientific and Industrial Research-TOKTEN (Transfer of Knowledge Through Expatriate National) for their support to SMS during his visit to India under the United Nations Development Program. Yoga was one of the projects which he discussed and demonstrated the techniques to study the possible role of the antioxidant system in exercise (Chapter 3), and also the role of adenosine in exercise (Chapter 7).

The authors also wish to acknowledge the Chairman (Swami Maheshanandaji), the Secretary (Shri O. P. Tiwari), and the Director of Research (Dr. M.V. Bhole), Kaivalyadhama S.M.Y.M. Samiti (Lonavla, India) for their encouragement.

REFERENCES

1. **Kirschner, M. J.,** *Yoga All Your Life.* Schocken Books, New York, 1977.
2. **Kuvalayananda, S.,** *Asanas, Kaivalyadhama,* 7th Ed., Lonavala, India. 1982.
3. **Kuvalayananda, S.,** *Pranayamas, Kalvalyadhama,* 7th Ed., Lonavala, India, 1983.
4. **Feuerstein, G. and Bodian, S.,** *Living Yoga: A Comprehensive Guide for Daily Life,* Jeremy P. Tarcer/Perigee Books, Putnam Publishing Groups, New York, 1993.
5. **Feuerstein, G.,** *Encyclopedic Dictionary of Yoga,* Paragon House, New York, 1990.
6. **Siddhantalankar, S.,** *Heritage of Yogic Culture,* Taraporevala & Sons, Bombay, 1969.
7. **Worthington, V.,** *History of Yoga,* Routledge & Kegan, Paul, London, 1982.
8. **Gharote, M. L.,** Guidelines for yogic practices, *Kaivalyadhama,* Medha Publications, Lonavala, India, 1982.
9. **Anand, B. K.,** Yoga and medical sciences, *Ind. J. Physiol. Pharmacol.,* 35, 84, 1993.
10. **Udupa, K. N.,** *Stress and its Management by Yoga,* Motilal Banarasidass, Delhi, 1985.
11. **Gore, M. M.,** Yogic treatment for diabetes, *Yoga-Mimamsa,* 26, 130, 1988.

12. **Jain, S. C. et al.,** A study of response pattern of non-insulin dependent diabetics to yoga therapy, *Diabetes Res. Clin. Prac.,* 19, 69, 1993.
13. **Sahay, B. K. et al.,** Effect of yoga in diabetes, in *Diabetes Mellitus in Developing Countries,* Bajaj, J. S., Ed., Interprint, New Delhi, India, 379, 1984.
14. **Divakar, M. V. et al.,** Effect of yoga therapy in diabetes and obesity, *J. Diab. Assoc. India,* 18, 75, 1978.
15. **Shembekar, A. G. and Kate, S. K.,** Yogic exercises in the management of diabetes mellitus, *J. Diab. Assoc., India,* 20, 167, 1980.
16. **Rugmini, P. S. and Sinha, R. N.,** Effect of yoga therapy in diabetes mellitus, *Semin. Yoga, Sci. Man,* C.C.R.1.M.H., 1976, 175.
17. **Digambarji, S.,** *Hathapradipika of Svatmarama,* KSMYM Samiti, Kaivalyadhama, India, 1970.
18. **Digambarji, S. and Gharote, M. L.,** *Gheranda Samhita,* KSMYM Samiti, Kaivalyadhama, India, 1978.
19. **Bera, T. K., Ganguly, S. K., and Rajapurkar, M. V.,** Effect of yoga training on body density in school going boys, *NIS Sci. J.,* 13, 23, 1990.
20. **Gharote, M. L.,** An evaluation of the effects of yogic treatment on obesity: a report, *Yoga-Mimamsa,* 19, 13, 1977.
21. **Karambelkar, P. V., Gharote, M. L., Ganguly, S. K., and Moorthy, A. M.,** Effect of short-term yogic training on serum cholesterol, *Yoga-Mimamsa,* 19, 1, 1977.
22. **Karambelkar, P. V., Ganguly, S. K., and Moorthy, A. M.,** Effect of yogic practices on cholesterol level in females, *Yoga-Mimamsa* 20, 1, 1981.
23. **Moorthy, A. M., Ganguly, S. K., Gharote, M. L., and Karambelkar, P. V.,** Cholesterol level and yogic training programs, *J. Res. Ind. Med. Yoga Homoeo.,* 13(4), 1, 1978.
24. **Holmes, D. M.,** Diabetes in its psycho-social context, in *Joslin's Diabetes Mellitus,* 12th ed., Marbie, A., et al., Eds., K. M. Varghese Co., Bombay, India, 1985.
25. **Tiwari, O. P. and Bhole, M. V.,** Rehabilitation of patients of acute myocardial infraction and mild arterial hypertension through yoga — a report, *Yoga-Mimamsa,* 26, 1, 1987.
26. **Tulpule, T. H. and Tulpule, A. T.,** Yoga — a method of relaxation or rehabilitation after myocardial infraction, *Ind. Heart J.,* 32, 1, 1980.
27. **Ornish, D.,** *Dr. Dean Ornish's Program for Reversing Heart Disease,* Ballantine Books, New York, 1991.
28. **McNamara, D. J.,** Dietary fatty acids, lipoproteins, and cardiovascular disease, *Adv. Food Nutr. Res.,* 36, 253, 1993.
29. **Blackwell, B. et al.,** Transcendental meditation in hypertension, *Lancet,* 7959, 223, 1976.
30. **Baride, J. P. and Sancheti, S. S.,** Yoga: a boon for health? [letter], *World Health Forum,* 15, 61, 1994.
31. **Ornish, D., Brown, S. E., Scherwitz, L. W., Billings, J. H., Armstrong, W. T., Porta, T. A., McLanahan, S. M., Kirkeeide, R. L., Brand, R. J., and Gould, K. L.,** Can lifestyle changes reverse coronary heart disease? The Lifestyle Heart Trial, *Lancet,* 336, 129, 1990.
32. **Patel, C.,** 12-month follow-up of yoga and biofeedback in the management of hypertension, *Lancet,* January 11, 62, 1975.
33. **Bera, T. K. and Rajapurkar, M. V.,** Body composition, cardiovascular endurance and anaerobic power of yogic practitioner, *Ind. J. Physiol. Pharmacol.,* 37, 225, 1993.
34. **Stancak, A., Jr., Kuna, M., Srinivasan, M. A., Dostalek, C., and Vishnudevanada, S.,** Kapalabhati-yogic cleansing exercise. II. EEG topography analysis, *Homeostasis Health Dis.,* 33, 182, 1991.
35. **Stancak, A., Jr., Kuna, M., Srinivasan, M. A., Vishnudevananda, S., and Dostalck, C.,** Kapalabhati-yogic cleansing exercise. I. Cardiovascular and respiratory changes, *Homeostasis Health Dis.,* 33, 126, 1991.
36. **Bhole, M. V. and Desai, B. P.,** Theoretical considerations of diet for yogic practicant, *Yoga-Mimansa,* 21(1 & 2), 97, 1982.
37. **Sunder, S., Agrawal, S. K., Singh, V. P., Bhattacharyya, S. K., Udupa, K. N., and Vaish, S. K.,** Role of yoga in management of essential hypertension, *Acta Cardiol.,* 39, 203, 1984.

38. **Patel, C. and North, W.R.S.,** Randomized control trial of yoga and biofeedback in management of hypertension, *Lancet,* July 19, 93, 1975.
39. **Gharote, M. L.,** Effect of yogic exercises on strength and endurance of the abdominal muscles of the females, *Vyayam Vidnyan,* 4, 11, 1970.
40. **Frumkin, K., Nathan, R. J., Prout, M., and Cohen, M. C.,** Nonpharmacological control of essential hypertension in man: a critical review of the experimental literautre, *Psychosom. Med.,* 40, 294, 1978.
41. **Anand, B. K. and Chinna, G. S.,** Investigation of yogis to stop their heart beats, *Ind. J. Med. Res.,* 49, 82, 1961.
42. **Patel, C.,** [letter] TM and hypertension, *Lancet,* 1, 539, 1976.
43. **Guyton, A. C.,** *Text Book of Medical Physiology,* 7th ed., W. B. Saunders, Philadelphia, 1986.
44. **Mohan, S. M.,** Scientific evidence in support of yoga treatment for asthma, in *Yoga Therapy in Bronchial Asthma,* Vol. 1, Sharma, S. K. and Rai, L., Eds., Central Research Institute for Yoga, New Delhi, India, 1994.
45. **Nagendra, H. R. and Nagarathna, R.,** An integrated approach of yoga therapy of bronchial asthma: a 3–54 month prospective study, *J. Asthma,* 23, 123, 1986.
46. **Nagendra, H. R. and Nagarathna, R.,** *A New Light for Asthmatics,* Vivekananda Kendra Yoga Research Foundation, Bangalore, India, 1986.
47. **Wilankar, G. N., Patel, P. M., and Bapat, S. T.,** Yogic management of bronchial asthma, in *Yoga Therapy in Bronchial Asthma,* Vol. 1, Sharma, S. K. and Rai, L., Eds., Central Research Institute for Yoga, New Delhi, India, 1994.
48. **Dave, A. S. and Dave, S. S.,** Serum transaminase levels in asthmatic subjects, in *Yoga Therapy in Bronchial Asthma,* Vol. 1, Sharma, S. K. and Rai, L., Eds., Central Research Institute for Yoga, New Delhi, India, 1994, 48.
49. **Gitananda, Y. S.,** Prana — the cosmic catalyst, in *Yoga Therapy in Bronchial Asthma,* Sharma, S. K. and Rai, L., Eds., Central Research Institute for Yoga, New Delhi, India, 1994, 148.
50. **Telles, S., Nagarathna, R., and Nagendra, H. R.,** Shifts in the autonomic balance as an explanation for the beneficial effects of an integrated yoga therapy in bronchial asthma, in *Yoga Therapy in Bronchial Asthma,* Vol. 1, Sharma, S. K. and Rai, L., Eds., Central Research Institute for Yoga, New Delhi, India, 1994.
51. **Rai, L., Ram, K., Kant, U., Sahni, S., and Sharma, S. K.,** A multidimensional evaluation of the effectiveness of an integrated set of yogic technology of subjective symtomatology on asthma, in *Yoga Therapy in Bronchial Asthma,* Sharma, S. K. and Rai, L., Eds., Central Research Institute for Yoga, New Delhi, India, 1994.
52. **Oak, J. P. and Bhole, M. V.,** Direction of change in the order of values of asthmatics by yogic treatment, *Yoga-Mimamsa,* 20, 25, 1982.
53. **Jain, S. C., Rai, L., Valecha, A., Jha, U. K., Shatnagar, S. O. D., and Ram, K.,** Effect of yoga training on exercise tolerance in adolescents with childhood asthma, *J. Asthma,* 28, 437, 1991.
54. **Nagarathna, R., Nagendra, H. R., and Uma, R.,** Studies on bronchial asthma. An integrated approach of yogic practices in the treatment and rehabilitation of bronchial asthma, in *A New Light for Asthmatics,* Vivekananda Kendra, YOCTAS, Bangalore, India, 1986.
55. **Nagarathna, R. and Nagendra, H. R.,** Yoga for bronchial asthma: a controlled study, *Br. Med. J.,* 291, 1077, 1985.
56. **Murthy, K. R. J. et al.,** Effect of pranayama (rechaka, puraka, and kumbhaka) on bronchial asthma — an open study, *Lung India,* 2, 187, 1984.
57. **Kumar, A. et al.,** Immediate effect of pranayama in airway obstruction, *Lung India,* 3, 77, 1985.
58. **Singh, V., Wisniewski, A., Britton, J. L., and Tattersfield, A.,** Effect of yoga breathing exercises (pranayama) on airway reactivity in subjects with asthma, *Lancet,* 335, 1381, 1990.

59. **Gore, M. M. and Bhole, M. V.,** Respiratory responses to vastra dhauti in asthmatics, *Yoga-Mimamsa,* 22, 47, 1983.
60. **Bose, S., Belapurkar, N., and Mishra, U.,** Specific chiroglyphic, bronchial asthma and yoga [letter], *J. Assoc. Phys. India,* 40, 279, 1992.
61. **Stanescu, D. C., Nemery, H., Veriter, C., and Marenchal, C.,** Pattern of breathing and ventilatory response to CO_2 in subjects practicing hatha-yoga, *J. Appl. Physiol. Resp., Environ. Exer. Physiol.,* 51, 1625, 1981.
62. **Wilson, A. F., Honsberger, R., Chiu, J. T., and Novey, H. S.,** Transcendental meditation and asthma, *Respiration,* 32, 74, 1975.
63. **Nayar, H. S., Mathur, R. M., and Kumar, R. G.,** Effects of yogic exercises on human physical efficiency, *Ind. J. Med. Res.,* 63, 1369, 1975.
64. **Prakasamma, M. and Bhaduri, A.,** A study of yoga as a nursing intervention in the care of patients with pleural effusion, *J. Adv. Nursing,* 9, 127, 1984.
65. **Phillip, R. L., Wilde, G. J. S., and Day, J. H.,** Suggestion and relaxation in asthmatic, *J. Psychom. pbs,* 16, 193, 1972.
66. **Goysche, J. R. M., Abo, Y., and Jkemi, Y.,** The yoga perspective. II. Yoga therapy in the treatment of asthma, *J. Asthma,* 19, 189, 1982.
67. **Jain, S. C. and Talukdar, B.,** Evaluation of yoga therapy programme for patients of bronchial asthma, *Singapore Med. J.,* 34, 306, 1993.
68. **McFadden, E. R.,** Pathogenesis of asthma, *J. Allergy Clin. Immunol.,* 73, 413, 1984.
69. **Ganguly, S. K.,** Cardiovascular responses to yogic treatment of asthmatic patients, *Yoga-Mimamsa,* 20, 35, 1982.
70. **Desai, B. P. and Bhole, M. V.,** Study of yoga treatment in relation to serum protein in asthmatics: a preliminary study, *Yoga-Mimamsa,* 22(1,2), 40, 1983.
71. **Desai, B. P. and Bhole, M. V.,** Gastric responses to different lengths of vastra dhauti, *Yoga Rev.,* 2, 101, 1982.
72. **Norton, G. R. and Johnson, W. E.,** A comparison of two relaxation procedures for reducing cognitive and somatic anxiety, *J. Behav. Ther. Exp. Psychiat.,* 14, 209, 1983.
73. **Ost, L. G., Jerramalm, A., and Johansson, J.,** Individual response patterns and the effects of different behavioural methods in treatment of social phobia, *Behav. Res. Ther.,* 19, 1, 1981.
74. **Ost, L. G., Johansson, J., and Jerramalm, A.,** Individual response patterns and the effect of behavioural methods in the treatment of claustrophobia, *Behav. Res. Ther.,* 20, 445, 1982.
75. **Davidson, R. J. and Schwartz, G. E.,** The psychology of relaxation and related states: a multi-process theory, in *Behavioural Control and Modification of Physiological Activity,* Mostofsky, D. I., Ed., Prentice-Hall, Englewood Cliffs, NJ, 1976.
76. **Nespor, K.,** Twelve years experience with yoga in psychiatry, *Int. J. Psychosom.,* 40, 105, 1993.
77. **Vahia, N. S., Vinekar, S. L., and Doongaji, D. R.,** Ancient Indian concepts in the treatment of psychiatric disorders, *Br. J. Psychiat.,* 112, 1089, 1966.
78. **Blanz, L. J.,** Personality changes as a function of two different mediative techniques, *Diss. Abst. Int.,* 34, 7035, 1974.
79. **Gersten, D. J.,** Meditation as an adjunct to medical and psychiatric treatment, *Am. J. Psych.,* 135, 598, 1978.
80. **Walsh, R. and Roche, L.,** Precipitation of acute psychotic episodes by intensive meditation in individuals with a history of schizophrenia, *Am. J. Psych.,* 136, 1085, 1979.
81. **Sharma, L. and Singh, P.,** Treatment of neurotic illness by yogic techniques. Bulletin, *Ind. J. Med. Soc.,* 43, 3, 1989.
82. **Uma, K., Nagendra, H. R., Nagaranthna, R., Vaidehi, S., and Seethalakshmi, R.,** The integrated approach of yoga: a therapeutic tool for mentally retarded children: a one-year controlled study, *J. Mental Def. Res.,* 33, 415, 1989.
83. **Benson, H., Beary, J. F., and Carol, M. P.,** The relaxation response, *Psychiatry,* 37, 37, 1974.

84. **Davidson, J. M.,** The physiology of meditative and mystical states of consciousness, *Perspect. Biol. Med.,* 19, 345, 1976.

85. **Kutz, I., Borysendo, J. Z., and Benson, H.,** Meditation and psychotherapy: a rationale for the integration of dynamic psychotherapy, the relaxation response, and mindfulness meditation, *Am. J. Psych.,* 142, 1, 1985.

86. **Wood, C.,** Mood change and perceptions of vitality: a comparison of the effects of relaxation, visualization and yoga, *J. R. Soc. Med.,* 86, 254, 1993.

87. **Hedstrom, J.,** A note on eye movements and relaxation, *J. Behav. Ther. Exp. Psychiat.,* 22, 37, 1991.

88. **Rice, R. and Allen, R. C.,** Yoga in glaucoma, *Am J. Ophthalmol.,* 100, 738, 1987.

89. **Haslock, I., Monroe, R., Nagarathna, R., Nagendra, H. R., and Raghuram, N. V.,** Measuring the effects of yoga in rheumatoid arthritis [letter], *Br. J. Rheumatol.,* 33, 787, 1994.

90. **Nespor, K.,** Pain management and yoga. [Review], *Int. J. Psychosom.,* 38, 76, 1991.

91. **Selvamurthy, W.,** Yoga for every one — a physiologist's view, *2nd Congr. Asian Oceanian Physiol. Soc.,* New Delhi, India, 1990, 10.

92. **Udupa, K. N., Singh, R. H., Settiwar, R. M., and Singh, M. B.,** Physiological and biochemical changes following the practice of some yogic and non-yogic exercises, *J. Res. Ind. Med.,* 10, 91, 1975.

93. **Karambelkar, P.V. and Bhole, M. V.,** Effect of yogic asanas on uropepsin excretion, *Ind. J. Med. Res.,* 57(5), 944, 1969.

94. **Dhanaraj, V. H.,** The effect of yoga and the 5BX fitness plan on selected physiological parameters, Ph.D. dissertation, University of Alberta, Edmonton, 1974.

95. **Telles, S., Manumanthalah, B., Nagarathna, R., and Nagendra, H. R.,** Improvement in static motor performance following yogic training of school children, *Perceptual Motor Skills,* 76, 1264, 1993.

96. **Dhume, R. R. and Dhume, R. A.,** A comparative study of driving effect of dextro-amphetamine and yogic meditation on muscle control for the performance of balance on balance board, *Ind. J. Physiol. Pharmacol.,* 35, 191, 1991.

97. **Gopal, K. S., Anantharaman, V., Nishith, S. D., and Bhatnagar, G. F.,** The effect of yogosanas on muscular tone and cardiorespiratory adjustments, *Yoga Life,* 6, 3, 1975.

98. **Bhatnagar, D. P. and Anantharaman, V.,** The effect of yoga training on neuromuscular excitability and muscular relaxation, *Neurology India,* 25, 230, 1977.

99. **Ganguly, S. K. and Gharote, M. L.,** Cardiovascular efficiency before and after yogic training, *Yoga Mimamsa,* 17, 89, 1974.

100. **Madhavi, S., Raiu, P. S., Reddy, M. V., Annapurna, N., Sahay, B. K., Kumari, D. G., and Murthy, K. J. R.,** Effect of yogic exercises on lean body mass, *J. Assoc. Phys. India,* 33, 465, 1985.

101. **Bera, T. K., Jolly, S., Ganguly, S. K., and Gharote, M. L.,** Effect of three-year yogic exercise program on motor functions in school boys, (unpublished manuscript), Scientific Research Dept., KSMYM Samiti, Lonavla, India, 1995.

102. **Karambelkar, P. V., Bhole, M. V., and Gore, M. L.,** Muscle activity in some asanas, *Yoga-Mimamosa,* 12, 1, 1969.

103. **Udupa, K. N., Singh, R. N., Dwiredi, K. N., Pandey, M. P., and Rai, V.,** Comparative biochemical studies on meditation, *Ind. J. Med. Res.,* 63, 1676, 1975.

INDEX

347

348

Pharmacology In Exercise and Sports

Pharmacology In Exercise and Sports

effect of exercise on tissue blood flow,
6–7
Exercise, pharmacodynamics of drugs and,
39–55
ergogenic drugs and exercise, 45–49
amphetamines, 46–47
caffeine, 47–48
erythropoietin, 48
sodium bicarbonate, 48–49
sodium phosphate, 49
ergolytic drugs and exercise, 49–51
alcohol, 49–50
cocaine, 50
marijuana, 51
nicotine, 50–51
medicinal drugs and exercise, 41–45
acute anti-inflammatory drugs, 44–45
metabolic disease/therapeutic drugs,
42–44
pulmonary disease drugs, 41–42
Extensor digitorum longus (EDL), 271, 274
Extraction ratio (ER), 5, 11, 20
Eye lens, 100

F

Fast twitch muscles, 271
Fatty acid oxidation, 48
Fentanyl, 14
Ferric uptake regulation (Fur), 132–133
FEV, see Forced expiratory volume
Fibrinogen, 212, 213, 226
Fibronectin, 213, 216
First-order kinetics, 4
Fitness boom, 2
Flosequinan, 250
Flucytosine, 14
Flunitrazepam, 14
Fluorescein, 30
Fluorouracil, 14
Fnr, see Fumarate nitrate reductase
Forced expiratory volume (FEV), 335
Forced volume capacity (FVC), 335
Free fatty acids, 225, 298
Free radicals, 60
cytotoxic, 299
formation of, 223
generation of, 170
Fumarate nitrate reductase (Fnr), 132
Fur, see Ferric uptake regulation
Furosemide, 15
FVC, see Forced volume capacity

G

Galactose elimination, 27
Gastrointestinal tract, drug metabolism in, 18
Gene expression
changes in, 129
heat-responsive, 156
Gentamycin, 320, 321
GFR, see Glomerular filtration rate
GH, see Growth hormone
Glomerular filtration rate (GFR), 29, 30
Glucagon response, inhibited, 107
Glucocorticoids, 101, 297
Glucose
intolerance, 211
uptake, 43
Glucuronidation, 32
Glucuronosyl transferases, 137–138
Glutamate, 175
γ-Glutamyl cycle, 112, 118
γ-Glutamylcysteine synthase, 115
γ-Glutamyltranspeptidase, 98, 111, 114
Glutathione (GSH), 26, 27, 63, 68, 89, 136
consumption, hepatic, 106
depletion, 112–114
homeostasis, 108, 113
interorgan transport of, 102
oxidized (GSSG), 26, 27, 61, 63
peroxidase (GPX; GSH-Px), 60, 89, 99,
177
activity, 111
induction, 110
reductase (GR), 60, 99, 177, 179
supplementation, 299
synthase, 111
synthesis, 101, 140
system, 64–65, 67, 127
training adaptation of, 110
transferase, 139
S-transferase (GST), 137
transport of, 118
utilization, 109
Glutathione, exercise and, 97–123
biochemistry of glutathione, 98–103
functions of glutathione, 98–100
glutathione homeostasis, 100–103
glutathione deficiency and exercise,
111–115
glutathione response to acute exercise,
103–108
intracellular glutathione redox status,
103–106

production of prostacyclin and
thromboxane, 221–222
PLC, see Phospholipase C
PNA, see *p*-Nitroanisole
Polycyclic aromatic hydrocarbons, 88
Polyenoic acids, 228
Polymerase, bad, 154
Polyunsaturated fatty acids, 66
Positron emission tomography (PET), 342
Postexercise recovery stage, 161
Pralidoxime, 23
Prazosin, 15
Prednisolone, 15
Prednisone, 14
Pregnancy, exercise during, 236
Primidone, 14
PRL, see Prolactin
Probenecid, 15
Procainamide, 14, 23
Progesterones, 298
Prolactin (PRL), 296, 306, 309
Propranolol, 9, 13, 14, 16, 17, 21, 23, 247
Prostacyclin, 219, 221
Protein
    binding drugs, 32
    kinase C (PKC), 136, 182
Protriptyline, 15
Psychosomatic disorders, 40, 339
Pulmonary disease drugs, 42
Pulmonary disorders, 40
Pulmonary toxicity, 88
Pyridostigmine, 14, 308
Pyridoxamine oxidase, 127

Q

Quinapril, 244
Quinidine, 9, 15
Quinine, 14, 30
Quinones, 88

R

Ranitidine, 14
Reactive oxygen species (ROS), 60, 68, 77,
    125, 159
    formation, 127
    production of, 79
Reactive oxygen species, detoxification of,
    125–146
    antioxidant defenses, 127–128
    Bcl-2 in antioxidant defense, 140–141
    DNA regulatory elements, 137–138

hydrogen peroxide inducible *oxyR*
    system, 133
metal binding transcription factors in
    antioxidant defense, 140
oxidative stress regulons, 130
oxygen tension inducible OREs in
    humans, 138–139
oxygen toxicity, 125–127
physical exercise induced oxidative stress,
    128–130
phytoalexin-induced oxidative stress,
    139–140
ROS responsive transcription factors,
    134–136
superoxide inducible *sox* and *mar*
    systems, 130–133
thiol redox status and transcription
    factors, 136–137
Receptor
    alterations, 342
    binding capacity, muscarinic, 282
    blockage of, 309
    sensitivity, 284
Redox-cycling compounds, 131
Renin release, 174, 176
Respiratory disorders, treatment of, 174
Respiratory infections, susceptibility to, 301
Respiratory rate (RR), 335
Respiratory system, 174
Rheumatic fever, 317
RNA polymerase
    activity, 43
    redistribution of, 151
ROS, see Reactive oxygen species
RR, see Respiratory rate
Running, 49, 242

S

SAH, see S-Adenosyl homocysteine
Salicylate, 9, 18, 30
Salicylic acid, 10
Schizophrenia, 338
SDS-PAGE, see Sodium dodecyl sulfate-
    polyacrylamide gels
Second messenger molecule, 40
Sedentary vs. ambulatory status on
    pharmacokinetics and
    pharmacodynamic effects of drugs,
    317–327
    effect of sedentary status on specific
        drugs, 320–324
        acetaminophen, 323